Child Abuse and Neglect

Guidelines for Identification, Assessment, and Case Management

Marilyn Strachan Peterson, M.S.W., M.P.A.

Michael Durfee, M.D.

Co-editors

Kevin Coulter, M.D.

Medical Editor

VOLCANO
· PRESS ·

Child Abuse and Neglect: Guidelines for Identification, Assessment, and Case Management

Copyright © 2003 by Marilyn Strachan Peterson and Michael Durfee

All Rights Reserved. No part of this book may be copied or reproduced by any means, electronic or mechanical, including photocopying, recording, or by any information storage and retrieval system, without prior permission in writing by the publisher.

Permission to reproduce Figure 1 on page 25 is granted by Michael Young, © 1990 Elsevier Science.
Permission to reproduce Figure 4 on page 27 is granted by Kempe Center Slides, Dr. Barton Schmitt Series, ©1978.
Permission to reproduce Figure 8B on page 30 is granted by Kempe Center Slides, Dr. Barton Schmitt Series, ©1978.

Library of Congress Cataloging-in-Publication Data

Child abuse and neglect : guidelines for identification, assessment, and case management / editors, Marilyn Strachan Peterson & Michael Durfee ; medical editor, Kevin Coulter.
     p.   cm.
  ISBN 1-884244-21-1
    1. Child abuse—Diagnosis. 2. Child abuse—Prevention. 3. Abused children—Services for. 4. Parent and child (Law) I. Peterson, Marilyn Strachan. II. Durfee, Michael. III. Coulter, Kevin.
    [DNTM: 1. Child Abuse—diagnosis. 2. Child Welfare. 3. Government Programs. 4. Parents—education.
5. Professional Rolse. 6. Risk Factors. WA 320 C534018 2002]
  RC569.5C55 C445 2002
  616.85'82223–dc21

                                                      2002033162

Interior page design by Jeff Brandenburg/image-comp.com

Volcano Press, Inc.
P.O. Box 270
Volcano, CA 95689

First printing, Volcano Press, Inc. 2003
Printed in the United States of America

CONTENTS

Co-editors' Biographies

Marilyn Strachan Peterson, M.S.W., M.P.A.

Marilyn Peterson is the Director of the CAARE Diagnostic and Treatment Center and California Medical Training Center (CMTC), Department of Pediatrics, UC Davis Children's Hospital in Sacramento, California. The CAARE Center's medical services include sexual and physical abuse medical/evidentiary exams, foster care clearance and comprehensive exams, and child abduction clearance exams for over 260 children per month. Mental health services for abused and neglected children include individual, group, family therapy, and Parent-Child Interaction Therapy (PCIT) for over 400 children per month. The PCIT training program for mental health professionals delivers training in California, nationally, and internationally.

The CMTC, established in state statute, provides training for healthcare providers on how to perform quality medical forensic exams for victims of sexual assault, domestic violence, child abuse, and elder/dependent adult abuse. Ms. Peterson initiated the concept of a statewide training center and worked with State Senator Mike Thompson (now Congressman Thompson) to introduce legislation establishing the Center. The Center is funded through the Governor's Office of Criminal Justice Planning (OCJP) and provides multi-day skill based training courses.

Ms. Peterson initiated the legislation establishing minimum forensic medical exam standards in state law for victims of sexual assault and child abuse, domestic violence, and elder abuse. She was responsible for drafting and coordinating the production of the California Medical Protocol for Examination of Sexual Assault and Child Sexual Abuse Victims and four medical forensic report forms for OCJP in conjunction with a multi-disciplinary committee. The medical forensic report forms include the OCJP 923 for adult/adolescent sexual assault victims; OCJP 930 for acute child sexual abuse victims; the OCJP 925 for nonacute child sexual abuse victims; the OCJP 950 for suspect exams; the OCJP 502 for domestic violence victims, the OCJP 602 for elder/dependent adult victims of abuse and neglect, and the OCJP 900 for child physical abuse and neglect victims, and guidelines. In addition, she authored the California SART (Sexual Assault Response Team) Manual for CALCASA (California Coalition Against Sexual Assault), a project funded by OCJP and published in 2001.

Michael Durfee, M.D.

Dr. Durfee, Child Psychiatrist, has worked over 26 years with children. His work has included the role of child psychiatrist and physician for multiple high risk populations, always with some focus on intervention for issues of pregnancy for the very young. His training highlighted the need to work with infants, toddlers, and high risk pregnancies so that children can arrive at school age psychologically, neurologically, socially intact, and competent to learn and relate to others. Dr. Durfee has been involved with numerous programs and committees, both legal and community based, focusing on infants, toddlers, and pregnancy. He has served as Assistant Clinical Professor in Child Psychiatry and Pediatrics; Medical Director, Child Abuse Prevention Program; Founder, national Center on Child Fatality Review, and Chairperson, California Child Death Review Council. Dr. Durfee has been the inspiration and the pioneer for the development of the child death review teams throughout California and the nation.

Kevin Coulter, M.D.

Dr. Coulter is the Section Chief and Medical Director of the CAARE Diagnostic and Treatment Center, Department of Pediatrics, UC Davis Children's Hospital, and the Director of the Child Physical Abuse and Neglect domain for the California Medical Training Center at UC Davis Children's Hospital.

Dr. Coulter completed medical school at Georgetown University in Washington, D.C. He completed his internship and residency at Children's Hospital in San Francisco, and was Chief Resident prior to completing a fellowship in Adolescent Medicine at San Francisco General Hospital. Dr. Coulter had been on the clinical faculty at the University of California, San Francisco, since completing his residency, where he was a Clinical Professor in the Department of Pediatrics. At San Francisco General Hospital he was the Medical Director of the Child and Adolescent Sexual Abuse Referral Center since 1984, the Medical Director of the Child Protection Center since 1989, and the Medical Director of the Children's Health Center since 1994.

He is well known in the field of child abuse and neglect for his clinical and administrative work. Dr. Coulter is an exceptional clinician and a dedicated advocate for children.

Acknowledgments

The editors wish to express profound thanks to the 95 authors who made this publication possible by sharing their knowledge and expertise. Identification and effective intervention to protect children from all forms of maltreatment and its sequelae requires a shared depth and breadth of knowledge. Each one of you brings unparalleled dedication and commitment to children and to this field of knowledge. This publication honors and celebrates your contribution to improving the lives of children.

Contributing Authors Updates Online

The contributing authors of this book may periodically update and share new developments in their respective fields. Please visit the Volcano Press website: www.volcanopress.com/booksupplements

---

Deborah S. Ablin, M.D.
Pediatric Radiologist and Professor, Emeritus
Clinical Radiology
UC Davis Medical Center
Sacramento, California

Carol Wildes Adolph, L.C.S.W.
Clinical Social Work Consultant
Los Angeles County Department of Health Services
Maternal, Child, and Adolescent Health
Comprehensive Perinatal Services Program
Los Angeles, California

Kerby T. Alvy, Ph.D.
Executive Director
Center for the Improvement of Child Caring
Studio City, California

Kristen Alexander, Ph.D.
Assistant Professor
California State University, Sacramento
Sacramento, California

Brooke Allison, M.A.
Consultant
Loomis, California

Sheila Anderson, M.A.
President and Chief Executive Officer
Child Abuse Prevention Council
Sacramento, California

Seth Asser, M.D.
Medical Consultant
Children's Healthcare Is a Legal Duty (CHILD) Inc.
Providence, Rhode Island

Sandra K. Baker, L.C.S.W.
Executive Director
Child and Family Institute
Sacramento, California

Nora J. Baladerian, Ph.D.
Director
Disability, Abuse and Personal Rights Project
Los Angeles, California

Michael F. Balash
Captain
Sacramento Fire Department
Sacramento, California

Karen Wellman Banker
Founding Director
Mustard Seed School
Sacramento, California

Linda Berger
Executive Director
Statewide California Coalition for Battered Women
Long Beach, California

Carol Berkowitz, M.D.
Executive Vice Chair and Professor
Department of Pediatrics
Harbor-UCLA Medical Center
Torrance, California

Lisa Bertaccini, L.C.S.W.
Chief
Child and Family Mental Health
Sacramento County Division of Mental Health
Sacramento, California

Stephen M. Blain, D.D.S., M.S.
Clinical Professor
Pediatric Dentistry
UCLA School of Dentistry
Westwood, California

Melanie Bobbitt, P.H.N.
Supervising Public Health Nurse
Sacramento County Department of Health and Human
Services
South City Health Center
Sacramento, California

Sue Bonk
Director
Sacramento Crisis Nursery
Sacramento Children's Home
Sacramento, California

Stephen C. Boos, M.D.
Lieutenant Colonel, United States Air Force, Medical
Corps
Armed Forces Center for Child Protection
Uniformed Services University of the Health Sciences
North Potomac, Maryland

Joaquin Borrego, Jr, Ph.D.
Assistant Professor
Department of Psychology
Texas Tech University
Lubbock, Texas

Linda Bowen
Chief
Sexual Assault Branch
Governor's Office of Criminal Justice Planning
Sacramento, California

Linda Boyers, L.C.S.W.
Licensed Clinical Social Worker
Child Development Section
UC Davis Children's Hospital
Sacramento, California

Cathy Boyle, P.N.P.
CAARE Team Coordinator
CAARE Diagnostic and Treatment Center
UC Davis Children's Hospital
Sacramento, California

Barbara Bradstock, M.A., R.N.
Director, Health Services (Retired)
Sacramento City Unified School District
Point Roberts, Washington

Marcia C. Britton, M.D.
Director
Child Health and Disability Prevention Program
Sacramento County Department of Health and Human
Services
Sacramento, California

Kay Buck
Director
Rape Prevention Resource Center
California Coalition Against Sexual Assault (CALCASA)
Sacramento, California

Marybeth Carter
Executive Director
California Coalition Against Sexual Assault (CALCASA)
Sacramento, California

Toni Cavanagh Johnson, Ph.D.
Private Practice Psychology
South Pasadena, California

Paula Christian, M.S.W.
Program Planner
Sacramento County Child Protective Services
Sacramento, California

John "Jack" J. Corbett, III, P.T.
Pediatric Clinical Specialist
Department of Physical Medicine and Rehabilitation
UC Davis Medical Center
Sacramento, California

Dianna Costa, R.N., F.N.P.
Gold River, California

Kevin Coulter, M.D.
Clinical Professor
Medical Director and Section Chief
CAARE Diagnostic and Treatment Center
UC Davis Children's Hospital
Sacramento, California

Laura Coulthard, M.S.W.
Division Manager
Sacramento County Child Protective Services
Sacramento County Department of Health and Human
Services
Sacramento, California

Rebecca A. Craig, R.N., M.P.A.
Director
Standards and Correctional Health Care Programs
Institute For Medical Quality
San Francisco, California

Cheryl Davis
Director
Sacramento County department of Human Assistance
Sacramento, California

Faye Diskin, O.T.R.
Pediatric Clinical Specialist in Occupational Therapy
Department of Physical Medicine and Rehabilitation
UC Davis Medical Center
Sacramento, California

Michael Durfee, M.D.
Director
Child Abuse Prevention Program
Los Angeles County Health Department
Los Angeles, California

Maria Annette Enrione, M.D.
Inova Fairfax Hospital for Children
Pediatric Intensive Care Unit
Falls Church, Virginia

Agnes Feliciano, F.N.P.
Gold River Pediatric Group
Rancho Cordova, CA

Linda Garcia, MA, C.C.L.S.
Manager
Child Development Services
Children's Hospital, Los Angeles
Los Angeles, California

Nancy Gadsby, P.H.N.
Child Protective Services
Sacramento County department of Health and Human
Services
Sacramento, California

Gail S. Goodman, Ph.D.
Professor
Department of Psychology
University of California, Davis
Davis, California

Joann Grayson, Ph.D.
Professor of Psychology
James Madison University
Harrisonburg, Virginia

William Green, M.D.
Clinical Professor of Emergency Medicine
UC Davis Medical Center
Sacramento, California

Rachel Garcia guerrero, L.C.S.W.
Chief
Office of Multicultural Services
California State Department of Mental Health
Sacramento, California

Sandra J. Guine, L.C.S.W., A.C.S.W.
Program Manager
Child Abuse Prevention Program
Los Angeles County Health Department
Los Angeles, California

Kevin Gutfeld, L.C.S.W.
Private Practice
Ukiah, California
Robin Lee Hansen, M.D.
Associate Professor and Chief
Child Development Section
UC Davis Children's Hospital
Sacramento, California

Emily Harris, M.D.
Associate Professor of Psychiatry
CAARE Diagnostic and Treatment Center
UC Davis Children's Hospital
Sacramento, California

Geoffrey M. Hash, J.D.
Oakland, California

Nancy C. Hayes, L.C.S.W.
SCAN Team Coordinator
UCLA Medical Center
Culver City, California

Philip W. Hyden, M.D., J.D.
Chief, Division of Child Protection
Department of Pediatrics
New York Presbyterian Hospital
Joan & Sanford Weill Medical College of Cornell
University
New York, New York

Carol A. Johnson Schroetlin, Psy.D.
Mental Health Clinician
San Benito County Mental Health Department
Hollister, California

Nancy Joye, M.D.
Co-Director and Clinical Professor
Foster Care Health Program
CAARE Diagnostic and Treatment Center
UC Davis Children's Hospital
Sacramento, California

Jayanthi M. Kasiraj, Ph.D.
Clinical Psychologist / Program Manager
CAARE Diagnostic and Treatment Center
UC Davis Children's Hospital
Sacramento, California

Diamond Kassam, M.D., M.P.H.
Medical Director
Juvenile Court
Sacramento County Juvenile Hall
Sacramento, California

Fleurette Kersey, P.H.N.
Sacramento County Department of Health and Human
Services
Public Health Education and Promotion Division
North Area Field Nursing Unit
Sacramento, California

Linda Kimura, M.A.
Babies Can't Wait National Training Center
Woodland, California

Susan Kreston, J.D.
Deputy Director
National Center for Prosecution of Child Abuse
Alexandria, Virginia

Lynn Loar, Ph.D., L.C.S.W.
President
Pryor Foundation
El Granada, California

David D. Love, M.F.T.
Executive Director
Valley Community Counseling Services, Inc.
Stockton, California

Gary Lowe, L.C.S.W.
Consultant and Trainer
Retired-California Youth and Adult Corrections Agency
Sacramento, California

James Malouf, D-ABMDI
Chief Deputy Coroner
Kern County Sheriff/Coroner's Office
Bakersfield, California

John McCann, M.D.
Medical Director Emeritus
CAARE Diagnostic and Treatment Center
UC Davis Children's Hospital
Sacramento, California

Marilyn McCartney, M.D., M.P.H.
Medical Director
Berkeley Women's Health Center
Berkeley, California

Jean McGrath, Ph.D.
Psychologist
CAARE Diagnostic and Treatment Center
UC Davis Children's Hospital
Sacramento, California

Mary Beth Metcalf, M.D.
Co-Director and Clinical Professor
Foster Care Health Program
CAARE Diagnostic and Treatment Center
UC Davis Children's Hospital
Sacramento, California

Connie Mitchell, M.D.
Director, Domestic Violence Education
California Medical Training Center
UC Davis Medical Center
Sacramento, California

Marilyn Peterson, M.S.W., M.P.A.
Director
CAARE Diagnostic and Treatment Center and
California Medical Training Center
UC Davis Children's Hospital
Sacramento, California

Allison Redlich, Ph.D.
Senior Research Associate
Policy Research Associates
Delmar, New York

Angela Rosas, M.D.
Assistant Professor of Clinical Pediatrics
Associate Medical Director
CAARE Diagnostic and Treatment Center
UC Davis Children's Hospital
Sacramento, California

Terry L. Rudolph, Ph.D.
FBI (Retired)
Stafford, Virginia

Herbert Schreier, M.D.
Chief of Psychiatry
Oakland Children's Hospital
Oakland, California

Elliot Schulman, M.D.
Health Officer / Medical Director
Santa Barbara County Health Department
Santa Barbara, California

Kathleen A. Shanel-Hogan, D.D.S., M.A.
Consultant
California Dental Association
Sacramento, California

Michael Siegal, J.D.
Law Offices of Michael Siegel
Loomis, California

Theresa F. Spear
Supervising Criminalist
California Department of Justice
Bureau of Forensic Services
California Ciminalistics Institute
Sacramento, California

Norman 'Skip' Sperber, D.D.S.
Diplomat, American Board of Forensic Odontology
Chief Forensic Dentist of San Diego and Imperial
Counties
San Diego, California

Marv Stern, J.D.
Supervising Deputy District Attorney
Child Abuse Unit
Sacramento County District Attorney's Office
Sacramento, California

Patricia Stock, M.F.T.
Clinical Specialist
CAARE Diagnostic and Treatment Center
UC Davis Children's Hospital
Sacramento, California

Sara Stratton, M.S.W.
Adult Protective Services
City and County of San Francisco
Department of Aging and Adult Services
Sacramento, California

Sherri Y. Terao
Research Associate/Psychologist
Chapin Hall Center for Children
University of Chicago
Chicago, Illinois

Margaret Thompson, R.N., W.H.N.P., M.S.
OB/GYN Nurse Practitioner
Sacramento County Juvenile Hall
Walnut Grove, California

Captain R.P. "Toby" Tyler
San Bernardino County Sheriff's Department
Barstow, California

Anthony J. Urquiza, Ph.D.
Director, Mental Health Services
CAARE Diagnostic and Treatment Center
UC Davis Children's Hospital
Sacramento California

Sylvia Villarreal, M.D.
Private Practice
Taos Clinic for Children and Youth
Taos, New Mexico

Jonaas Walton, L.C.S.W.
Los Angeles County Department of Health Services
los angeles, California

James Williams, M.D.
Medical Director
Child Advocacy Center
San Joaquin General Hospital
Stockton, California

Cynthia Anne Winn, L.C.S.W.
MIND Institute
UC Davis Children's Hospital
Sacramento, California

Stephen J. Wirtz, Ph.D.
Research Scientist, Program Manager
Child Maltreatment Surveillance / FCANS Program
Epidemiology and Prevention for Injury Control (EPIC)
Branch
California Department of Health Services
Sacramento, California

Celeste Wiser, M.D.
Child, Adolescent, and Adult Psychiatrist
Chief of Professional Education
Napa State Hospital
Napa. California

Theresa Witt, Ph.D.
Clinical Psychologist
MIND Institute
UC Davis Children's Hospital
Sacramento, California

Mindy Yamasaki, M.S.W., M.B.A.
Sacramento County Department of Health and Human
Services
Sacramento, California

Matt Young, M.D., M.P.H., F.A.A.P.
Director of Pediatrics
Grossman Burn Center
Sherman Oaks Hospital and Health Center
Sherman Oaks, California

Ruth Marie Young, J.D.
Deputy District Attorney
Child Abuse Unit
Sacramento County District Attorney's Office
Sacramento, California

Nancy Zebell, Ph.D.
Clinical Psychologist
CAARE Diagnostic and Treatment Center
UC Davis Children's Hospital
Sacramento, California

This project was supported, in part, by a grant awarded to the Los Angeles County Department of Health Services' Child Abuse Prevention Program by the California Department of Health Services, Maternal and Child Health Branch; and, in part, by a grant awarded by the Governor's Office of Criminal Justice Planning, Grant Award Number EMO2061141, to the CAARE Diagnostic and Treatment Center, California Medical Training Center, within the Department of Pediatrics, UC Davis Children's Hospital, to provide guidelines for the identification, assessment, and case management of child abuse and neglect. The grants covered part of the development of this publication.

The opinions or points of view expressed in this book are a consensus of the authors of the individual chapters. These views are not necessarily the views of the organization with which the authors are employed (or otherwise associated), nor the views of the authors of other chapters.

From the Publisher

It is with pride that Volcano Press is publishing *CHILD ABUSE AND NEGLECT: Guidelines for Identification, Assessment, and Case Management.*

We are an independent press, publishing about the life span of abuse, from prenatal to old age. We have been involved in the movement against all forms of domestic violence and abuse since 1976, when we published BATTERED WIVES, the first book in the U.S. on the subject.

Today, we continue to participate in the great progress that has been made by so many professionals, organizations and legislation since those early days.

When Marilyn Peterson and Michael Durfee first contacted us to publish *CHILD ABUSE AND NEGLECT*, we recognized that this compendium from nearly 100 contributing authors represented enormous, multi-disciplinary advances in the prevention of child abuse.

We also released the book as quickly as possible. Our mantra became "Move fast on printing—each day might save the life of a child."

What you will read is the result of a team effort. We wish to thank Marilyn Peterson, Michael Durfee, Kevin Coulter, April Tang, Jeff Brandenburg, and last but not least—Adam Gottstein of Volcano Press.

We are fortunate to live in times in which both the printed word and online technology can augment each other. Therefore, we have created a special web page on the Volcano Press website, by which the contributing authors may update and share new developments in the fields of medicine, law, technology, forensic and investigative techniques.

To visit this page, log on to: www.volcanopress.com and click on "Book Supplements."

Ruth Gottstein, Publisher
Volcano Press
April, 2003

Introduction

Our goal is to provide information to enable professionals from various disciplines to establish a basic standardized approach for identification, assessment, and case management of suspected child abuse and neglect. The primary focus is to provide information fundamental to effective intervention. Professionals in the fields of medicine, nursing, social work, and law enforcement will find this information useful. The guidelines focus on the broad range of types of child abuse and neglect, risk factors, intervention, child fatalities, prevention, and administrative issues.

The philosophy in the development of these guidelines is based upon five tenets:

- to be inclusive in the development of these guidelines;

- to educate professionals on the scope and impact of child abuse and neglect;

- to inform professionals about intervention needed to effectively address this problem for the individual child and to identify broad systems issues;

- to provide information on related issues such as family violence, drug and alcohol abuse, disabilities, physical rehabilitation, sibling loss, etc.

- to direct professionals to cutting edge resources;

- to reach the maximum number of professionals employed in various capacities related to children and families; and,

- to adopt a systematic approach to the dissemination of this information.

Michael Durfee, M.D.
Director, Child Abuse Prevention Program
Los Angeles County Health Department
Los Angeles, California

Marilyn Strachan Peterson, M.S.W., M.P.A.
Director, CAARE Diagnostic and Treatment Center and
the California Medical Training Center
Department of Pediatrics
UC Davis Children's Hospital
Sacramento, California

PART 1

Red Flags: Caretaker History, Family History, Caretaker, and Child Behavior

Red Flags: Caretaker History, Family History, Caretaker, and Child Behavior

Linda Boyers, L.C.S.W. and Kevin Gutfeld, L.C.S.W.

Case Vignette

A 7-month old child is admitted to the pediatric inpatient unit with an initial diagnosis of pneumonia. Upon physical examination, the child is noted to have bruises of different coloration and size on his buttocks, abdomen, and fore-head. Developmentally, the child is able to sit alone, hold a bottle, but he does not crawl or pull to a standing position. The psychosocial interview reveals that the parents have been married one year, the mother is mildly mentally retarded and the father is minimally delayed. The mother attends a special education community college program and the father is employed part time in school-yard maintenance. The parents are the child's primary caretakers. The maternal grandmother has cared for the child in the past, although not for several weeks. The pregnancy was planned, the mother received prenatal care and the child has been followed by a pediatrician for routine care. The mother has bruises on her arms and explains that she was recently assaulted at school. The parents are interviewed separately and both adamantly deny a history of domestic violence or knowledge as to the cause of the child's bruises. The father becomes angry during the interview, slamming hist fist on the table, raising his voice, and eventually leaving the room. The parents are clients of the Regional Center and public health. They both receive SSI and live in an apartment.

Questions

1. What are the risk factors for child abuse in this case?

2. What psychosocial factors are consistent with child abuse?

3. What psychosocial factors are inconsistent with child abuse?

4. Does this history warrant a referral for a comprehensive child abuse evaluation?

Signs and symptoms of child abuse must be evaluated when children are seen by a school nurse, public health nurse, in a clinic, emergency room, or admitted to a hospital for any reason. An unexplained injury or one consistent with child abuse needs to be referred for a comprehensive medical examination. If the following psychosocial risk factors are present and the child presents with bruises or injuries that are possibly consistent with child abuse, an abuse work-up needs to be initiated.

General Risk Factors for Child Abuse in the Context of Injuries

History of Injuries

- Caretaker is unable to provide an adequate explanation for the injuries.

- History is inconsistent with the injuries or there are gaps in the history.

- Caretakers delay seeking treatment for the injuries.

- Caretakers give conflicting histories.

- Caretakers are vague or unclear.

- Caretakers change the history during subsequent interviews.

- Caretakers refuse to be interviewed.

- Caretakers do not accompany the child to the hospital.

- Injury was reportedly unwitnessed.

- Caretaker blames a third party for the injury.

- Caretaker claims to have "found the child this way" or received the child this way, e.g. "he was this way when I got him."

- Child or sibling has a history of previous injuries.

Family History

- Substance abuse in the home.
- Single parent.
- Unrelated caretakers in the home.
- Limited financial resources.
- Social isolation.
- Unwanted pregnancy.
- Emotionally immature parents.
- Mentally disabled or developmentally disabled parents.
- Domestic violence in the home.
- Prior child protective services history.
- Limited parenting skills.
- Caretakers have unrealistic expectations of child and have limited understanding of normal child development.
- Caretakers were victims of abuse and/or neglect as children.
- Parents are involved in custody dispute.
- Children are left with an unrelated caretaker who has a criminal history, drug or alcohol abuse history, or is mentally disabled.
- Boyfriend or live-in partner lives in the home and has a past criminal history.

Caretaker Behavior

- Caretaker is hostile, defensive, refuses to cooperate, and/or unwilling to be interviewed.
- Caretaker appears to be under the influence of drugs/alcohol.
- Caretaker is unable to respond to questions due to psychiatric or developmental disability.

Child Behavior

- Child is placid, does not respond to painful procedures, and is not fearful of the hospital setting.
- Child carefully answers questions about injuries.
- Child clings to strangers, wanting attention, close contact.
- Child is agitated, difficult to calm.
- Child does not seek reassurance from caretaker, seems fearful, avoids contact.

Case Resolution

Among the risk factors in the above-cited case are the locations and varying ages of the child's injuries, especially considering the child's developmental level. The bruises to his buttocks and abdomen were most likely caused by intentional trauma, although the bruise to his forehead could have occurred as a result of falling into an object while sitting. Of concern were the injuries on the mother's arms which appeared to be of varying ages and about which she seemed embarrassed and tried to hide once they were noted. She also had failed to report the "assault" to her school campus police. The parents appeared to have a limited understanding of the child's developmental abilities and unrealistic expectations of his behavior. They commented that the child needed to learn how to behave appropriately and love his parents. The father's poor impulse control eventually led to the father threatening to remove the child from the hospital and barricading himself and his wife in the family room on the pediatric ward. The X-rays of the child's long bones revealed multiple rib fractures of varying ages, all of which were consistent with child physical abuse. Photographs were take of the child's injuries. A report to Child Protective Services was made, the child was placed in protective custody and foster care. The mother made multiple telephone calls to the pediatric ward threatening to harm staff if the child was removed from her care. Both parents maintained throughout the child's hospitalization that they were not responsible for the injuries.

Resources

Besharov, D. *Recognizing Child Abuse.* The Free Press, New York, 1990.

Briere, J. et al. *The APSAC Handbook on Child Maltreatment.* Sage Publications, Thousand Oaks, 1996.

Crime Prevention Center. *Child Abuse Prevention Handbook.* California Department of Justice, Office of the Attorney General, 1993.

Kessler, D. et al. *Clinica Symposia. Physical, Sexual, and Emotional Abuse of Children.* Ciba-Geigy, Summit, 1991.

Myers, J. *Legal Issues in Child Abuse and Neglect Practice.* Sage Publications, Thousand Oaks, 1998.

PART 2

Abuse Detection and Screening

Abuse Detection and Screening

Stephen C. Boos, M.D.

Case Vignette #1

A two-year-old child from your practice is brought in by an unfamiliar adult. The child has not been to visit you since you raised questions of failure to thrive at a nine-month visit. The adult identifies herself as the foster mother and she is seeking a placement examination on this child recently placed into her care. She is unsure as to the reason for placement, but was told that she needed to get the child seen by his regular physician within one week.

Questions

1. What sort of examination do you need to do to evaluate this child?

2. What might you find of importance, and how can you communicate this to the appropriate authorities?

Case Vignette #2

A four-month-old comes in for a well baby check. Earlier checks have been on time and appropriate. You have cared for this child and her two-year-old sibling from birth. The family is intact, with the mother providing most of the care, and presenting for all medical appointments. A pair of faint linear bruises is noted on the child's cheek, and another set of three parallel faint bruises is seen on the lateral thigh.

Questions

1. How can a busy practitioner be alert to the possibility of child abuse in their practice?

2. What standards for reporting govern this contact?

3. What sort of laboratory and imaging studies would you consider ordering on this child?

Many practitioners see the possibility of abuse as remote, and associated with social conditions not applicable to their practice. This chapter provides a basic approach that can help physicians and nurses be alert to the possibility of child abuse and neglect, and better serve the children in their care.

Step One: Acknowledge the Possibility of Abuse

Over 600,000 reports of child abuse and neglect are made every year in California. Over 100 child deaths due to child abuse and neglect are confirmed every year. Child abuse and neglect pose a significant public health problem. Much of what we read on child abuse, however, is about data and demographics.

When dealing with any individual patient, the demographic data must be set aside. A health practitioner must be willing to consider child abuse in any of their patients when the history and medical circumstances suggest it. Adherence to a well-grounded system for recognizing medical evidence of child abuse is a recommended standard of practice for healthcare providers.

1999 California Emergency Response Statistics	
Physical Abuse	140,156
Sexual Abuse	73,153
Severe Neglect	16,384
General Neglect	216,139
Emotional Abuse	49,581
Exploitation	1,615
At Risk, Sibling Abuse	80,441
Other	44,841
Total	**622,310**

Step Two: Recognize a Patient History that Does Not Match Findings

Patient History Patterns Suggestive of Possible Child Maltreatment

- No explanatory history for significant trauma or trauma in a highly supervised age

- Inconsistent history
  - History that fails to explain the nature, severity, or pattern of the injury
  - History of the logistics or mechanics of the injury do not match the injury
  - History of minor or common trauma to explain severe or unusual injuries
  - History that reports child actions inconsistent with developmental abilities
  - History that blames or suggests a third party
  - Injuries are indicative of an object, e.g. belt buckle not included in history

- History that changes with retelling or provider probing

- History that blames the child for injuring himself or herself

- History that blames another child for causing the injury

- History that suggests neglect and/or lack of supervision

Care providers falsify histories to protect themselves and others from culpability associated with the true events. When health practitioners point out the inconsistency of the given or absent history, care providers may alter their story in an attempt to satisfy the practitioner. When detailed histories are taken from two historians, or at different times, discrepancies may appear as on-the-spot falsification of events occurs. Discrepancies that cannot be resolved are a strong indication of falsification and the culpability it implies.

Step Three: Recognize Medical Evidence of Possible Abuse

Cutaneous Patterns Suggestive of Possible Child Maltreatment

- Bruises or burns shaped like recognizable objects

- Repeated but un-recognizable patterned bruises or burns

- Bruises in children who are not pulling themselves up, and walking along furniture

- Buttock bruises in children wearing diapers

- Two or more facial bruises without clear explanation

- "High tide mark" burn distribution

- Symmetrical lesions

- Burns with no evidence of motion effect

Cutaneous Injuries

The skin is the most common site of abusive injury. Skin surfaces are usually injured by blows, or by application of heat. In both situations the object causing the injury often leaves an impression of itself. Experienced examiners have often seen the shape of a hand, belt, loop of cord or other object in a bruise. A recognizable pattern of bruising makes it clear what injured the skin. The remaining question is how. Active children have at times fallen against objects creating a patterned injury. The identification of a hand, belt, or loop of cord imprint, however, speaks for itself. Children with bleeding disorders typically present with excess but un-patterned bruises, but a non-abusive spanking of such a child may leave a hand print. Studies of suspected abusive injuries in such patients, however, have found the greater portion to be truly abusive. Some skin injuries may have a repeated pattern that can be recognized, but not identified. At times these injuries are symmetrically distributed, ruling out the typical random distribution of accidental injuries. These patterns too, often indicate abusive injury.

Abusive bruises are not always patterned. A few rules will help the practitioner recognize excessive bruising. Children who are not pulling themselves up, and walking along furniture are not usually bruised. Buttock bruises should not occur in children in diapers. Two or more facial bruises require special explanation. Common areas for accidental bruising in infants and toddlers are the scalp, shin, and forehead. Pre-schoolers may also have bruises on the thigh, chest, back, forearms, and occasionally the face. Virtually all of these accidental bruises overlie a bony prominence.

Most abusive burns are caused by hot liquid. Certain findings have been shown to be associated with abusive hot water burns[8]. A sharp burn edge consistent with a static water surface parallel to the ground, sometimes referred to as a high tide mark, is perhaps the most distinctive characteristic of abusive immersion burns. Sparing of flexural creases is often noted, as the child retracts in pain, or is tightly restrained by the abuser. Symmetry of burns such that they appear as two gloves or two socks is often noted with inflicted injury. A helpful guideline is that accidental burns show evidence of motion, from a falling hot object or fleeing child. Inflicted burns typically lack this evidence of motion because an abusive adult held the child in contact with the hot object.

Skeletal Injuries

Skeletal Injuries Suggestive of Possible Child Maltreatment

- Rib fractures in young children, particularly when posterior

- Metaphyseal corner fractures

- Fractures in infants other than simple skull and clavicle fractures

- High energy fractures without serious accidents (i.e. long distance fall, MVA)

- Multiple fracture sites without serious accidents (i.e. long distance fall, MVA)

- Evidence of untreated healing fractures

- New fractures on old

After the skin, the skeleton is probably the most common site of abusive injury. By some estimates 50% of abused children have skeletal injuries, and 45% of these injuries are clinically unsuspected by evaluating examiners. Two particular injuries are so pathognomonic of abuse, that they should be regarded as abuse until proven otherwise. Posterior rib fractures, adjacent to the spinal column result when young children are squeezed forcefully about the chest[9]. Any rib fracture in a young child is suspicious for abuse. Breaks through the metaphysis of long bones result in the appearance of chips, or arcs of bone adjacent to the growth plate[10]. These are almost invariably inflicted. The most common accidental fractures of early childhood are simple skull fractures and clavicle fractures from short falls. Once children can walk, simple fractures of the tibia and femur, distal radius and ulna, and supra-condylar humerus may occur. All other fractures in children under three should be considered reason for suspicion. This is particularly true in children under one-year-old in whom accidental fractures are very uncommon, and usually associated with major verifiable events such as motor vehicle accidents.

Two other patterns should alert the medical examiner to abusive fracturing, the presence of multiple or untreated healing fractures, as 89% of accidental fractures involve only one site. In contrast, more than one site is involved in up to 75% of abusive injuries. The presence of multiple fracture sites are extremely suspicious. Multiple fracture times is further evidence of abuse. Fractures are generally very painful at the time of injury and for days afterward. The finding of a fracture with evidence of healing, demonstrates that the care provider has been ignoring or hiding pain and disability for at least one to two weeks. Finding multiple fractures in different stages of healing is strong evidence of abuse. Once again occult injury, like occult history, suggests abuse or at a minimum significant neglect.

Syndromes of Abuse

Syndromes of Possible Child Maltreatment

- "Battered Child Syndrome"
  - Multiple distinct injuries, separated by time or cause
  - Inadequate explanation by disease, accident, or typical childhood injury

- "Shaken Baby Syndrome" also called Abusive Head Trauma
  - Intra-cranial injury
  - Absence of verified severe trauma (MVA, long distance fall)
  - Additional findings of rib fracture, metaphyseal fractures, other injuries
  - Retinal hemorrhages

Syndromes are patterns of associated findings, which suggest an etiology. Two syndromes have become well established in the abuse literature. The "battered child syndrome" can be defined as the presence of multiple separate injuries with inadequate explanation. The injuries must be distinct enough in age, location and mechanism, so that they were separately caused. Explanation by disease state, adequate history of accidental injury, and typical events of childhood, must be excluded. Once these conditions are met, inflicted injury is the most likely cause. The concept of multiple injuries in time and space is included in discussions of many of the specific abuse entities, and is a basic principle with high predictive value in child abuse. Once the whole story is known, this theme is seen again in abuser's tendency to use violence on multiple family members, and even family pets. For many abusers, violence or "losing it" is a habit that we see in child abuse.

The other major syndrome of child abuse is the Shaken Baby Syndrome. Originally described as the co-occurrence of long bone fractures and sub-dural hematoma, it is now known that fractures of the ribs or metaphyses are present about half of the time, and retinal hemorrhages are present about eighty percent of the time. The finding of retinal hemorrhages has been particularly well studied, and almost always signifies child abuse. Due to controversies in understanding the basic mechanism of injury, many authors now simply refer to "abusive head trauma". Identifying abusive head trauma rests on another basic principle of child abuse. The presence of intra-cranial traumatic injury, without a history of severe trauma identifies probable abuse. This principle of severe injury with trivial history has been noted in fractures, and is also found in abdominal and other internal injuries.

Sexual Abuse

Sexual Findings Suggestive of Possible Child Maltreatment

- Sexually obsessive, aggressive or coercive behavior
- Venereal diseases
- Acute anogenital injuries without clear accidental cause
- Absence or interruption of the posterior hymen
- Child discloses sexual abuse

The idea that adults perform sexual acts upon children has been discovered and forgotten throughout history. It is very hard for professionals and the public to accept even today. This is perhaps reinforced by the fact that most abused children never tell, and never have physical signs of their abuse. Many of the signs of sexual abuse are nonspecific, such as behavior problems, masturbation, urinary tract infection, and genital irritation. In these situations medical practitioners can, at best, introduce the possibility and create a comfortable place for discussing it.

Occasionally practitioners must recognize and evaluate more specific indicators of sexual abuse. The range of normal sexual behavior is only beginning to be delineated[13]. When sexual behaviors become obsessive, aggressive or coercive, sexual abuse must be considered. Sexually transmitted diseases are rarely found in sexually abused children. When found, however, it must be recognized that diseases such as gonorrhea, syphilis, chlamydia, genital herpes and genital warts usually have the same implication in children as in adults. Sexually transmitted diseases require an evaluation for sexual abuse.

Detecting the physical findings of sexual abuse has become a specialty practice. Routine examination of the genitals and familiarity with the anatomy should be a general practice. Common acute accidental genital injuries are labia minora injuries sustained in straddles, penile bruises from falling toilet lids, and ventral penis lacerations from zipper injuries. Other acute anogenital injuries without a clearly consistent history may be evidence of acute sexual abuse. Absence or interruption of the posterior hymen is widely accepted as evidence of healed trauma and should be considered evidence of sexual abuse. Extreme narrowing of the hymen may also indicate abuse. Other changes to the anogenital region may occur in abuse, but experience with normal variation is necessary in making the determination.

False claims by children of sexual abuse are very rare. False denials of sexual abuse, however, are common and all children's claims of sexual abuse should be taken seriously. Children's involvement in sexual abuse is characterized by fear, secrecy and guilt. Revealing these secrets is scary and embarrassing. Many children never tell. Those that do often make unconvincing disclosures to "safe" people, disclose details over time to test potential reactions of support or disbelief, and generally are uncomfortable talking about it. The results of this disclosure are often upsetting to the child due to the family reaction and ensuing disruption. This often results in a recantation of the initial statement. No suspicion of child abuse should be dismissed simply because the child fails to disclose to the health practitioner or discloses details over time.

Other Issues

Other Findings Suggestive of Possible Child Maltreatment

- Child does not gain weight as expected
- Child's development and behavior is disturbed
- Child has too many accidents
- Illnesses are more severe or prolonged than expected
- Illnesses defy diagnosis
- Medical treatments are not effective
- Illnesses are found to be due to poisoning or occult trauma
- Accidental or non-accidental illicit drug ingestion

Child maltreatment has affected children in various ways. Simple neglect may present with a physically healthy child developing below genetic potential. Disordered family function may result in babies not gaining weight. A large number of genuine accidents, may be due to poor management of the home environment. Children may present with non-traumatic medical problems that are fabricated or induced by their parents (Munchausen by Proxy). Medicine is a large and complicated field. When the healthcare practitioner cannot figure out a child's problems, it is easy to attribute the lack of understanding to lack of knowledge. In response to being puzzled, the trained response is to take more history, perform more detailed examinations, and order more tests. When things begin not to make sense; children do not grow, develop, or recover, as they should; and treatment does not progress as expected; the possibility of child maltreatment should be considered. The cause may be neglect, poisoning, fabricated illness, or occult trauma. Practitioners struggling for explanations of a child's medical problems must consider maltreatment as one major possibility.

Step Four: Evaluate the Child for Possible Abuse

Evaluation of the Possibly Abused Child

History
- Extensive probing history of explanatory events
  - do not accept absent history
  - challenge inadequate histories
  - note changes in history and when they occur
  - push for details consistent with the apparent mechanism of injury
- Review of systems
  - medical history suggesting alternate diagnoses
  - medical history of significant concurrent illness
  - immunization and developmental status

Physical Examination
- Height, weight, and head circumference plot against age based norms
- Developmental abilities, particularly speech
- Multisystem total body exam
- Special scrutiny of important abuse areas
  - scalp
  - behind ears, in folds of pinna, and along top edge of pinna
  - mouth, labial and lingual frenula, tonsilar pillars, posterior pharynx
  - palms of hand and soles of feet
- Genital exam
  - traction of labia majora
  - knee chest exam

Ancillary Evaluation
- Radiology
  - skeletal survey on children less than two
  - CT scan of the head for abused children with any neurologic signs
- Laboratory
  - CBC,PT, PTT, bleeding time for abusive bruises
  - urinalysis, amylase and transaminases for occult abdominal injury
- Consultative examinations
  - indirect ophthalmoscopy for any suspicion of Shaken Baby Syndrome

Obtain Caretaker History

When an injured child presents with the responsible care provider, the practitioner must take the opportunity to request an explanation of the injuries. Bruises on young infants, and patterned bruises on older children should not be bypassed without comment or question. In most cases of abuse, diagnosis rests with the lack of adequate explanatory history. Careful, persistent questioning, pursuing areas of apparent inconsistency, may produce a true abuse disclosure, or serve to further demonstrate the inconsistency. On the other hand, failure to accept the initial, inconsistent history may force the caretaker to reveal details of an unusual accident, which they were too embarrassed, upset, or confused to disclose at first asking. When the practitioner has a strong sense of how the injuries occurred, he or she may choose to reveal this in questioning. Before doing so, it is important to carefully note the caretaker's first response, as abusers may incorporate your suggestions into their defensive falsehoods. Documenting this changing history may become important in identifying child abuse. Similarly, the medical practitioner must take a history that probes for possible exonerating differential diagnoses. It is best that these questions be asked neutrally, and answers examined critically, so as to avoid providing an excuse for the guilty, or missing innocent explanations. The format of a traditional review of systems and family history is excellent in that it is familiar to practitioners, seeks all information pertinent to the care of the child, and reviews a wide range of information, the significance of which may only be grasped later.

Obtain Children's History

When the child is verbal the medical practitioner should take a separate history from the child. If possible this history should be taken alone. The child may be able to tell the practitioner the true history, or may have been coached to lie, but produce significant inconsistencies, which should be noted. Other reasons exist to speak with the child. Many children from abusive and neglectful homes are developmentally delayed. Careful listening to the child's speech, and general questioning about their life has led to diagnoses of delay, depression, anxiety, or even autism.

Screen for Developmental, Behavioral, Emotional, and Dental Problems

The physical examination of an abused or neglected child must evaluate all body systems. A high percentage of abused and neglected children have been found to have medical problems. A good well child examination serves as the basis for a good child maltreatment evaluation. Such an examination begins with a developmental assessment. The behavioral, mental, and physical development should be compared against age based norms. A Denver Developmental Screening Test (DDST) or similar developmental inventory will begin to screen for delays in language and motor development. An experienced practitioner will have a large experience with similar aged children, and should comment on important departures in the child's office behavior. Accurate height, weight, and head circumference must be obtained and plotted on appropriate growth charts. Small children may be further evaluated by having a body mass index, or weight for height checked. Single points in developmentally or growth delayed children are of limited value. When the initial assessment is concerning follow up evaluation and more in depth assessment will be necessary.

Perform Comprehensive Medical Examination

Perform a comprehensive "head to toe" medical examination. Certain elements of the examination take on particular importance in the setting of possible child abuse. As the most common target for abusive injury, all surfaces of the skin deserve special scrutiny. The scalp is often difficult to see due to long or dense hair. Contusions, lacerations, scars or even tattoos may be hidden by hair. The external ears are often overlooked. Looking behind the ears may reveal fingernail marks, battle sign or other injuries. Small subtle bruises may be found within the folds or along the top of the pinna, which are strong evidence of abusively striking or pulling the ears. Other less commonly seen surfaces of the skin, including the perineum and bottoms of the feet should be viewed, searching for injuries.

Areas of Injury

Special attention should be paid to areas of injury. Providers should carefully look at injuries for pattern or shape, evidence of healing or delayed care seeking, and possible alternate explanation. Red marks should be pressed or stretched to see if they blanche, in order to distinguish vascular markings from bruises. Follow up examination may be required to completely evaluate skin findings. Fresh bruises often become more prominent. Injuries such as bruises and lacerations are expected to heal over a predictable period of time. Following them through healing may help to distinguish trauma from other findings such as nevi, vascular lesions, and "mongolian" spots. All injuries should be measured, described, drawn, and, where possible, photographed with a size standard in the photo. Polaroid photos are often used for their convenience, but the quality of images produced with consumer Polaroid products is not adequate for this work.

The Head, Eyes, and Mouth

Other structures of the head should be examined more closely than in typical well child checks. Petechiae of the conjunctiva are seen both with direct trauma, and with strangulation or suffocation. Retinal hemorrhages are sometimes seen during direct ophthalmoscopy, and are significant both as signs of abuse, and probable neurologic injury. The mouth requires careful attention. Bruises, lacerations or impressions inside the lips may occur when a child is struck in the face. Tearing of the labial or lingual frenula may occur during blows to the mouth, or forced feeding. Lacerations of the posterior pharynx have also occurred during forced feeding, and may result in serious medical complication. The abdomen and head are the most common sites for severe and fatal injuries to children. The examiner must be certain that the belly is benign, and the child's neurological status is clear.

Musculoskeletal System

The musculoskeletal system, as another commonly injured system, also receives greater scrutiny than in typical general physical exams. Observe the child for deformity. See if a limb is favored, or seems painful. The chest and extremities should be palpated, feeling for tenderness, mass, or crepitance. Any signs of possible trauma require examination in greater detail, and radiological assessment.

A skeletal survey is recommended when evaluating possibly abused children below age two. Unfortunately, as suggested above, child abuse is an event that is likely to be repeated, with children held back from medical attention. Skeletal injuries may be clinically inapparent because they have begun to heal. Many fractures found in child abuse settings are clinically unexpected. Inexperienced facilities may obtain whole body views or "baby grams" when a skeletal survey is requested. This is inadequate. Properly posed and exposed views of the ribs, spine, head, upper extremities, lower extremities, hands and feet are required[17]. Two views of the ankles, knees, shoulders and elbow, will help to detect metaphyseal fractures. When rib fractures are suspected, oblique views may help to detect them.

Genitals and Anus

Putting the child on his or her knees, with the buttocks in the air, chest on the table, and back in a lordotic posture makes this examination much easier. Evaluation of the anus and genitals may require special techniques, which are easily learned by general medical examiners. Separation of the buttocks in this posture gives an excellent view of the anus. Lifting and separating the buttocks exposes the female genitalia giving the best view for evaluating the hymen. Female genitalia may also be evaluated with the child on her back with the legs abducted and externally rotated. Grasping and drawing outward on the labia majora will open the vestibule and vaginal orifice for better inspection.

Laboratory Testing

Laboratory testing is ordered based on the practitioner's assessment of the child. A complete blood count will screen for anemia, which is commonly found in neglected children. The platelet count will also help to rule out causes of easy bleeding. A prothrombin and partial thromboplastin time, and possibly a Von Willebrand's Panel will complete this screen in children with bruises. If there is suspicion of abdominal trauma, but the patient does not appear to require imaging or surgery, urinalysis, amylase and liver transaminases will increase the likelihood of detecting milder internal injuries. Children who have neurologic injury, and those with rib or metaphyseal fractures, should have a dilated indirect ophthalmoscopy exam. Direct ophthalmoscopy, even with dilation, is inadequate to completely rule out retinal hemorrhages. Any child with signs of abuse, such as facial bruises, and even mild neurologic signs, such as vomiting without diarrhea, irritability or somnolence deserves a CT scan of the head. Milder forms of abusive head injury have been overlooked, and children returned with complications of the delay, in similar situations.

Step Five: Reporting and Referring

Once the medical practitioner has completed the evaluation, the decision must be made if there is reasonable suspicion of child maltreatment. Many practitioners feel that they must prove abuse prior to reporting. This is not true. The legal statute for mandated reporters in the state of California requires a report for a reasonable suspicion of abuse or neglect. If the practitioner has a genuine concern for child maltreatment, and has not eliminated it through their own evaluation, an immediate telephone report must be made to the county children's protective services, or local law enforcement agency, and a written report filed within 36 hours. If a practitioner recognizes one of the medical findings detailed above, and fails to find a reasonable explanation, suspicion is reasonable regardless of the social circumstances and reporting should occur.

A report is not treated as proof of abuse. The appropriate agencies will investigate the family situation, often finding important information of which the practitioner is not aware. The investigation may request more medical information from the practitioner, or consult a medical child abuse expert. Sometimes cases are unsubstantiated, because the investigation finds other explanatory evidence, or cannot adequately establish that abuse has occurred.

Practitioners sometimes fail to report cases of child maltreatment. Usually, this is because they have failed to acknowledge the possibility, missed medical signs, or consciously chosen to set aside concerns of abuse. Child abuse experts at tertiary medical centers are usually willing to discuss cases by phone, or take direct referrals to help resolve these difficult cases. It is helpful to consider the legally required telephone and written report as a mandatory consultation.

Whether the practitioner makes a report of a suspicious situation themselves, or refers the patient to a medical expert, addressing the reporting issue is a central to providing adequate medical care for these children. Approximately 70% of children dying from abusive injuries have evidence of earlier abuse that could have been detected, possibly saving the child's life. By acknowledging the possibility of abuse, recognizing medical evidence, thoroughly evaluating, and then reporting suspicions, medical practitioners can fulfill their obligation to the state and the children they serve.

Reporting Forms

Submit written child abuse report form pursuant to state law to County Children's Protective Services or your local law enforcement agency.

References

Jenny, C., Hymel, K., Ritzen, A., Reinert, S.E., Hay, T.C. Analysis of missed cases of abusive head trauma. *JAMA*. 1999; 281: 621-626

U.S. Department of Health and Human Services, Children' Bureau. *Child Maltreatment 1996: Reports from the States to the National Child Abuse and Neglect Data System.* Washington, DC: U.S. Printing Office; 1998

Hammond, J., Perez-Stable, A., Ward, C.G. Predictive value of historical and physical characteristics for the diagnosis of child abuse. *South Med J.* 1991; 84: 166-168

McMahon, P., Grossman, W., Gaffney, M., Stanitski, C. Soft-tissue injury as an indication of child abuse. *J Bone and Joint Surg.* 1995; 77-A: 1179-1183

O'Hare, A.E., Eden, O.B. Bleeding disorders and non-accidental injury. *Arch Dis Child.* 1984; 59: 860-864

Johnson, C.F., Coury, D.L. Bruising and hemophilia: accident or child abuse? *Child Abuse and Neglect.* 1988; 12: 409-415

Sugar, N.F., Taylor, J.A., Feldman, K.W. Bruises in infants and toddlers: those who don't cruise rarely bruise. *Arch Pediatr Adolesc Med.* 1999; 153: 399-403

Purdue, G.F., Hunt, J.L., Prescott, P.R. Child abuse by burning – an index of suspicion. *J Trauma.* 1988; 28: 221-224

Kleinman, P.K., Schlesinger, A.E. Mechanical factors associated with posterior rib fractures: laboratory and case studies. *Pedatr Radiol* 1997; 27: 143-149

Kleinman, P.K., Marks, S.C. Relatiionship of the subperiosteal bone collar to metaphyseal lesions in abused infants. *J Bone and Joint Surg.* 1995; 77: 1471-1476

Kempe, C.H., Silverman, F.N., Steele, B.F., Droegmueller, W., Silver, H.K. The battered-child syndrome. JAMA. 1962; 181: 17-112

Caffey, J. On the theory and practice of shaking infants, its potential residual effects of permanent brain damage and mental retardation. *AJDC.* 1972; 124: 161

Friedrich, W.N., Fisher, J., Broughton, D., Houston, M., Shafran, C. Normative sexual behavior in children: a contemporary sample. *Pediatr.* 1998; 101: e9

Adams, J.A. Significance of medical findings in suspected sexual abuse: moving towards consensus. *J Child Sexual Abuse.* 1992; 1: 91-99

Hammond, J., Nebel-Gould, A., Brooks, J. The value of speech-language assessment in the diagnosis of child abuse. *J Trauma.* 1989; 29: 1258-1260

Gottbrath Flaherty, E., Weiss, H. Medical evaluation of abused and neglected children. *AJDC.* 1990; 144: 330-334

Belanger, P.L. Quality assurance and skeletal survey standards. pp. 418-424 In Kleinman PK Ed. *Diagnostic Imaging of Child Abuse.* St Louis: Mosby Inc; 1998

Note: The opinions and conclusions in this article are those of the author and not intended to represent the official position of the Department of Defense, USAF, or any other governmental agency.

PART 3

Interviewing Children

Interviewing Children

Kristen Alexander, Ph.D., Allison D. Redlich, Ph.D., Paula Christian, M.S.W., and Gail S. Goodman, Ph.D.

Case Vignette

Armed with a search warrant, police used force to enter a disabled man's apartment. Inside, they found two scantly clad girls, along with photographs and audiotapes indicating the girls had been sexually abused repeatedly. Medical examinations were consistent with penetration. The disabled man argued that the girls had been suggestively interviewed and fabricated the charges (Bidrose & Goodman, 2000). However, the children's testimony matched the photographic, audiotaped, and medical evidence, and he was convicted.

While a 4-year-old boy's temperature was being taken during a medical exam, he told a doctor's assistant, "That's what my teacher does to me at nap time at school." Over many days, the boy was asked highly leading questions in a coercive manner about suspected sexual abuse. In the end, the boy made explicit allegations of sexual assault. The accused was convicted but eventually released on appeal. The following excerpt is taken from the coercive interviews (Bruck & Ceci, 1995):

I: Do you think [the defendant] was not good when she was hurting you?

C: Wasn't hurting me. I like her.

I: I can't hear you, you got to look at me when you talk to me. Now when [the defendant] was bothering kids in the music room?

C: I got socks off.

I: Did [the defendant] make anybody else take their clothes off in the music room?

C: No.

I: Yes.

C: No.

I: Boy, I'd hate having to tell your friends that you didn't want to help them.

Questions

1. What feelings may children be experiencing in answering questions about possible abuse?

2. What special considerations should be given for children?

3. What is the difference between a medical interview and a specialized forensic interview?

The Feelings of Children

- Several factors influence the experience of talking to children about what happened to them:

- It may feel traumatic or embarrassing for children to describe what happened to them;

- Children may feel responsible for the abuse; and,

- Abuse is stressful, and this may influence how children remember and describe what happened to them.

Linguistic Capabilities of Children

- Children may not understand the vocabulary used by the interviewer. Use developmentally appropriate questions.

- Children may not understand questions if they are worded in a complex manner, e.g. use of compound sentences or double negatives. Use simply worded questions, e.g., "What happened to you" or "Tell me what happened."

Special Considerations for Interviewing Children

1. **Avoid multiple, lengthy interviews**
   Establish agreements with local law enforcement personnel, prosecutors, and child protective service workers to coordinate the number of interviews needed.

17

2. **Interview children alone**
   Children are often reluctant to talk about abuse in the presence of parents, especially if a parent is non-protective, in denial, colludes with the perpetrator, or is the perpetrator.

3. **Avoid having the child present during the adult's description of what occurred**
   The child may experience shame, which further deepens the experience; react to the shame by minimizing their own account; or, be influenced by the adult's description of events.

4. **Avoid encounters, interactions, or confrontations between the child and alleged perpetrator**
   Encountering the alleged perpetrator may frighten children and cause them to deny or minimize the description of events.

5. **Interview setting**
   - Interview children in a warm, friendly setting oriented to their needs.
   - Provide privacy with no or minimal interruptions.

6. **Qualifications of the interviewer**
   Medical personnel should be knowledgeable about the differences between supportive, sensitive questioning and asking inappropriate, leading, or suggestive questions. Consultation on this issue with local law enforcement agencies or the county prosecutor's office is recommended. Multi-disciplinary interview teams exist in many counties with specially trained interviewers who can provide training.

7. **Exhibit a warm, friendly, supportive style**
   - Convey a relaxed, unhurried attitude and express concern about the child's well-being. Children easily recognize adults who are anxious, uncomfortable, hurried, or ill at ease and are affected accordingly.
   - Avoid being intimidating, judgmental, or biased about information supplied by the child or projecting your own feelings or perceptions about the situation onto the child. Do not presuppose guilt or anger, as neither may be present. Do not presuppose the child found the sexual contact unpleasant.

8. **Conducting the interview**
   - Take time to establish rapport. Begin with a discussion of common, non-abuse topics to enable the child to become comfortable with the situation and to determine the child's general level of functioning. Avoid focusing on the topic of abuse prior to establishing rapport.
   - Use language appropriate to the developmental level and background of the child.
   - Determine the child's understanding of, and terminology for, body parts and functions. Be prepared to use the child's own terminology.
   - After use of open-ended questioning, if a nonverbal communication vehicle for child is necessary, use toys or anatomical drawings cautiously, especially with young children. Avoid a "play" atmosphere when gathering information about sensitive issues.
   - Begin by asking open-ended, "free recall" questions such as WHO, WHAT, and WHERE questions. WHAT HAPPENED TO YOU or TELL ME WHAT HAPPENED and WHAT DID HE DO or WHAT DID SHE DO are easiest for children to answer.
   - Avoid WHY questions or questions that require understanding abstract concepts.
   - Avoid inappropriate prompting, leading, or suggestive questions.
   - Do not dwell too heavily on the identity of the alleged perpetrator. Ask questions about all parties involved.
   - Ask WHEN questions in terms children can understand. Children to the age of about nine years often have a poorly developed concept of time and may be inconsistent or unrealistic while answering questions. Time is related to events such as birthdays, holidays, the name of their teacher at the time, or their grade in school.

9. **Documentation of the medical interview**
   Record direct quotes of the interview's questions and child's statements. Do not paraphrase, minimize, or characterize a child's response.

10. **Reassurance of the child**
    Children need to be told they are not to blame for what happened to them. Be prepared to reassure them during or at the conclusion of the interview and examination about:
    - The presence or absence of physical injury;
    - Fear of consequences or punishment because of disclosure or the child's role in the incident; and,
    - Concerns about teasing at school, further assault, or potential family separation.

11. Reassurance of the parents
Be prepared to reassure the parent during or at the conclusion of the interview and examination about the:

– Presence or absence of physical injury; and

– Possible psychological consequences of the abuse for the child.

12. Follow-up psychological care
Arrangements and/or referrals should be made for crisis intervention or short-term or long-term therapy.

Differences between Medical Interviews and Specialized Forensic Interviews

It is important to understand the difference between a medical history prior to performing an examination, and a forensic interview typically performed by law enforcement, investigative social workers, or MDITs (Multi-Disciplinary Interview Teams).

1. Purpose of a medical interview conducted by physicians and nurses:

– to determine the likelihood that a child's signs and symptoms are consistent or inconsistent with abuse;

– to establish the type of physical findings that may be present;

– to ascertain if a child needs treatment; and

– to provide information to law enforcement officers, investigative social workers, deputy district

attorneys, defense attorneys, and judges about the history and whether it is consistent with case findings.

2. Purpose of an investigative interview:

– to gain factual insight into the incident;

– to establish the child's ability to accurately relate a history;

– to enhance communication while reducing suggestibility;

– to obtain a detailed description of the events by asking who, when, what, where, how, how many times; and,

– to avoid unnecessary multiple interviews of the child.

Contact your county department of health and human services, district attorney's office, or child abuse prevention council to determine whether an MDIT or MDIC exists in your community.

Resources

California Medical Protocol for Examination of Sexual Assault and Child Sexual Abuse Victims. July, 2000. Published by the State Office of Criminal Justice Planning, 1130 K Street, Sacramento, CA 95814.

Poole, D. and Lamb, M. (1999). *Investigative Interviews of Children: A Guide for Helping Professionals.* Washington, DC: American Psychological Association.

PART 4

Bruises

The photographs in the chapter can be viewed online at the Volcano Press website: www.volcanopress.com/booksupplements

James Williams, M.D.

Case Vignette

A 6-month old infant is brought to the Emergency Department by his parents who state that the baby has a cough and fever. On physical examination, the infant appears irritable when touched. Several tan-colored, oval-shaped bruises, approximately 1.5cm in diameter, are noted on the upper portion of his chest and mid-back. He has nasal congestion and a loose cough. The tympanic membranes are normal. The physical examination is otherwise within normal limits. The chest x-ray shows two posterior rib fractures with callus formation. The father states that he was out of the room for a few minutes on one occasion two weeks ago when the baby fell down the stairs; but he seemed to be all right ever since.

History/Questions (Table 1)

1. What are types of bruises commonly seen in child abuse?

2. What are some of the presenting histories of physically abused children?

3. What risk factors should be considered in the evaluation of bruises in children? (Table 2)

The skin is commonly injured during childhood accidents and abuse. Cuts and bruises that result from falls and collisions are an expected and frequent finding in growing children. As an infant begins to move about and interact with the environment, injuries begin to occur on the exploring edges of the hands and feet and frontal surfaces of the body. Toddlers and children often have some bruises over frontal bony prominences, such as the forehead, nose, chin, elbows, and shins due to falls and collisions. As the child acquires increasing mobility and speed, the number and severity of injuries may increase. When evaluating an injured child, a major consideration becomes whether the injury was accidental or abusive.

History

Table 1. Questions for the Examiner to Evaluate in the Patient History

- What caused the injury?
- Could this injury occur as the care provider says?
- What was the child's state of health before the injury?
- Are there past injuries?
- What is the child's level of motor development?
- Is this particular injury developmentally possible for the child?
- Are there family medical conditions in which easy bruising is a feature?
- Who was present when the child was injured?
- Where was the child when injured?
- What was done when the child was injured?

Table 2. Risk Factors in the Injury

History

- Explanation incompatible with the type or severity of the injury
- No history or no mention made of the injury in the chief complaint
- Chief complaint focuses on issues that are peripheral to the injury, e.g. crying, coughing, etc.
- Contradictory or significant changes made in the history on retelling
- Multiple injuries of different ages while the history indicates one or fewer episodes
- Child gives a different account
- Prior "accidents"

Table 2. Risk Factors in the Injury, continued

Behavior of Care Provider

- Delay in seeking medical care
- Care provider(s) are more concerned about themselves and/or exculpation than about the child's injuries

Physical Examination

The evaluation of skin injuries must be part of a comprehensive physical examination. (*Table 3*) Bruises should be carefully described, measured, located on body diagrams, and photographed when possible. An estimated age of the injuries should be made. Injured areas should be carefully inspected and palpated for scars, unusual swelling, bone step-offs, and hair loss. The injuries may leave an imprint or distribution, indicating that a particular object was involved. A wide variety of attacking objects have been used. (*Figure 1*) Bilaterally symmetrical skin injuries and injuries to central and protected parts of the body, such as genitalia, rectum, buttocks, upper thighs, chest, abdomen, back, and inner arms, are more likely to be abusive. (*Table 4*)

Injuries located near the pubic area, genitalia, and rectum should alert the examiner to also consider the possibility of sexual abuse. (*Figure 2*) Bruises over the ears may result from pinches or blows. (*Figure 3*)

Table 3. Physical Findings

- Injuries of various ages while the history indicates only one or fewer episodes
- Skin injuries not the same age as the history indicates
- Child is developmentally incapable of the discovered injuries
- Neglected injuries
- Pattern or silhouette of a hitting object found on the skin
- Location of injury on the body is not expected for accidental trauma
- Location of injury is not compatible with the developmental level of the child

Table 4. Location of Cutaneous Injuries

POSSIBLY ACCIDENTAL	LESS LIKELY TO BE ACCIDENTAL
- Leading or exploring edge of a body surface (e.g. ventral surface of hand or foot)	- Non-exploring surfaces of body (e.g. tops of hands, inner thighs, buttocks) - Symmetrical/bilateral location of lesions or bruises - Silhouette or geometric shape imprinted on body - More than one type of injury
- Forehead and chin - Facial scratches in infant	- Cheeks, neck, ears
- Lower arms, elbows	- Inner aspects of upper arms
- Prominences of vertebral spine	- Anterior Chest
- Hips (Iliac crests)	- Abdomen
	- Buttocks
	- Inner aspects of thighs
	- Genitalia, perineum, rectum
- Shins and knees	

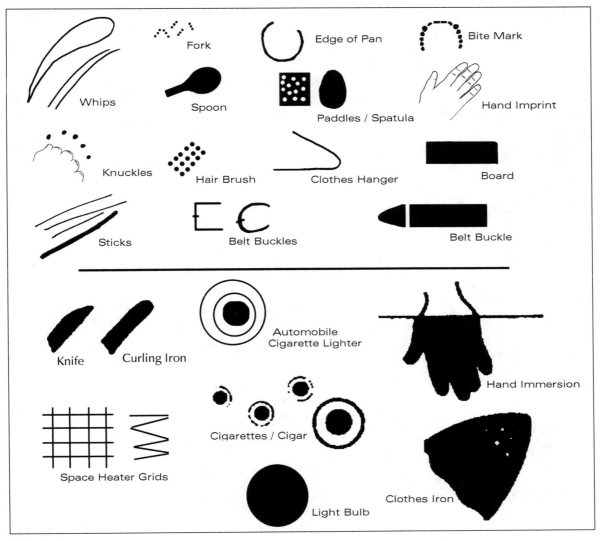

Figure 1
A variety of objects have been used to beat or burn children.

Developmental Assessment

The injury and its history should be evaluated within a developmental framework, in which the child's capabilities for rolling over, sitting up, arm extension ("parachute reaction"), crawling, walking, and running are compared with injuries that are possible at that age (*Tables 5 and 6*). Accidental injuries require that the child is capable of performing certain specific actions. Abusive injuries may be developmentally unlikely. Generally, infants who are not yet able to roll over neither fall from a bed nor present with extremity fractures as a result. Infants less than six months of age do not yet extend their arms in a protective manner when they are falling. When they fall, usually the heaviest body part, the head, strikes the ground first. The child with multiple bruises on more than one body surface should have a history that indicates multiple falls or tumbling, as in falling downstairs. Children, who are not yet able to cruise, rarely have leg bruises.

Table 5. Child Developmental Milestones

Age	Motor Skill or Reaction Observed
4 months	• Rolls over from front to back
5 months	• Rolls from back to front
6 months	• Sits alone 30 seconds or more
	• Automatically extends arms when falling forward ("parachute")
7-8 months	• Sits well
10-11 months	• Crawls
	• Walks by holding onto furniture ("cruises")
12 months	• Walks
18 months	• Runs
24 months	• Walks up and down stairs, one step at a time, holding on

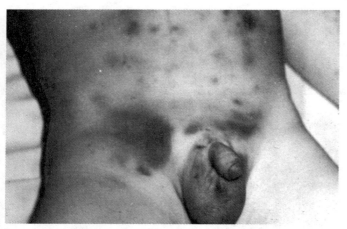

Figure 2 *Bruises on the lower abdomen, pubis or perineum should raise suspicion for possible sexual abuse.*

Table 6. Common Accidental Injuries by Age

Type of Injury Expected

Infants (0 to 12 months)	**Birth Trauma:** • skull fracture, cephalohematoma • clavicle, humerus, femur fracture • metaphyseal fracture **Falls/Being Dropped:** • simple skull fracture • soft tissue injury
Toddler (10 mo to 3yr)	**Collision and Fall Injuries:** • soft tissue injuries to bony prominences • superficial cuts • fractures of clavicle, distal radius/ulna, skull • toddler's fracture of tibia • splash burns to anterior body surface

Mechanisms of Injury

The postulated mechanism of injury is critical to determining its cause and validation of the history. Bruises and other cutaneous injuries develop as the result of force that imparts energy, in whole or part, to the skin. Considerations include the direction and velocity of the object, whether the injury is penetrating, and damage to underlying tissues. The velocity of the force may give rise to injuries that appear differently.

High velocity impacts tend to appear as a silhouette or outline of the object on the skin, while lower velocity strikes tend to appear as filled-in bruises. The forces in high velocity strikes are more concentrated at the periphery of

the object. The blow is sufficient to rupture capillaries in contact with the edges of the striking object. The forceful slap of an open hand, for instance, may leave an outline of parallel linear marks on the face or elsewhere. (*Figure 4*) Whip injuries, such as with an electrical cord, belt, or rope, leave linear bruises of uniform depth that wrap around curved body surfaces. (*Figure 5*) These injuries may be deeper at their distal end as well as at body curvatures. The injury caused by a looped wire appears to be oval or elliptical in shape. A belt or rope imparts a wider bruise. A belt is also suggested if the impression of eyelets and a buckle are seen at one end of the bruise. (*Figure 6A, 6B*) Permanent scarring, especially in children with dark skin, may result when the skin is broken in penetrating and deep whip-induced injuries. Ligature or restraint marks may appear on extremities, torso, and even the male penis as deep and narrow marks or broad rope burns. Unlike whip marks, ligature marks are often circumferential in appearance.

Low velocity skin injuries tend to result in forces that are more uniformly distributed beneath the impact area of the object. (*Figure 7A, 7B*) For example, oval-shaped bruises with central discoloration may be seen when fingertips grip and crush underlying tissues. Facial and scalp injuries are often the result of low velocity forces in accidents. Alone, they are not often diagnostic of abuse unless the pattern of a hand or other object can be discerned.

Bruises may suggest that more than superficial layers of the skin have been injured, in which case associated injuries need to be considered. For example, when chest or back bruises are present, underlying rib fractures should be considered in the evaluation. Bruises on an irritable infant's face, neck, or scalp suggest that possible injuries to the skull, brain, eyes, and ears should be considered. In abusive

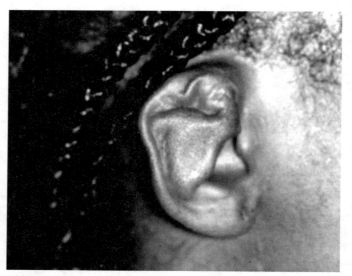

Figure 3 *Ear damage: this 12 year-old child was repeatedly beaten by her mother, who favored hitting her over across her right ear; shown is a close up view of the child's right ear.*

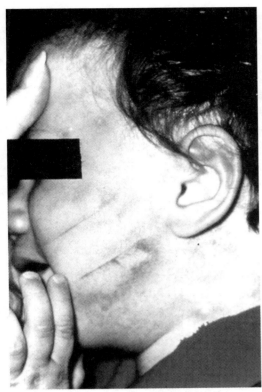

Figure 4 *Handprint injury: note the clear outline of the fifth digit on the child's cheek and the hematoma of the right auricle.*

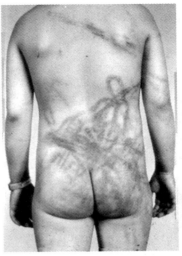

Figure 5 *Whip injury: this 10 year-old child was beaten with a braided rope.*

head trauma, the absence of bruises is common. Here, one must carefully search for retinal hemorrhages, since they may be the only sign of internal injury. Head CT and a dilated funduscopic exam are urgently required in suspected cases. Abusive eye injuries include orbital and lid ecchymoses, hyphema, anisocoria, subconjunctival hemorrhage, retinal hemorrhage, papilledema, and sixth nerve palsy. Bilateral periorbital hematomas indicate direct blows to the eyes, or seepage of blood from a nearby location, e.g., "raccoon's eyes." (*Figure 8A, 8B*) The visual fields and acuity should be included in an eye injury evaluation. Facial fractures are uncommon in abuse but involve the mandible when they occur. Damage to the external ears should alert the medical examiner to check the middle ear and the child's ability to hear.

Injuries in and around the mouth such as bruised lips, torn frenulum, or puncture of the hypopharynx occur when a bottle, finger, or other object is forced into the child's mouth. Gag marks appear at the corners of the mouth. Direct blows to the mouth may leave bruises to the lips, frenulum, gums, or fractures of the teeth. Linear and/or filled-in bruises around the neck should suggest choke injury. (*Figure 9A, 9B*)

Violent hair pulling can result in scalp and hair injury. Traumatic alopecia of the scalp, unlike alopecia areata, appears to be diffuse, non-discrete, incompletely bald, within which are broken hairs of various lengths and no loose hairs at the periphery. (*Figure 10*) If the traction is severe, the scalp may be lifted off the calvarium and result in a subgaleal hematoma. The examiner should palpate the scalp for evidence of new or old hematomas, since a subgaleal hematoma may not appear with an external bruise. An underlying skull fracture with spinal fluid leakage may be mistaken for a subgaleal hematoma. Computed tomography (CT) should be used to assess scalp swellings and hematomas in questionable cases. Abusive hair loss should be differentiated from self-induced hair pulling, or trichotillomania, and cosmetic practices.

Estimating the Age of Bruises

In cases of possible abuse, the medical examiner should give an opinion as to the age of the injuries. This is necessary to validate the history and may be helpful in legal hearings. **Such estimates however, should be cautious and within a general range. When the hemoglobin degrades, bruises undergo complex color changes. Until recently, medical examiners have assumed this to be a predictable and orderly process. However, this is not the case in most situations.** Color changes in bruises have been poorly studied. Available information indicates there is not an orderly process from one color to the next.[1, 4] Even within wounds of the same age, a great amount of overlap in color is possible. In addition to color change, an age estimate should also consider the physical characteristics of swelling, inflammation, tenderness, and the degree of skin penetration. Only then a general estimate within a range of time may be given. See Tables 7 and 8 on the next page.

Table 7. Estimated Age of Bruises*

AGE	APPEARANCE
0 – 1 day	Swollen, tender
0 – 2 days	Red, blue, purple
3 – 6 days	Blue, green
6 – 10 days	Green, brown
10 – 14 days	Tan, yellow
14 – 30 days	Faded to clear

*From: Wilson, E.F. Estimation of the age of cutaneous contusions in child abuse. Pediatrics, 1977;60:751-52. 0

- Bruises may be *fresh* if only red is present and older if yellow is present.
- Red may be seen as a color in the bruise for the first seven to nine days.

- Blue may be seen as a color in most bruises in the first seven days, but may persist in some bruises for much longer periods.
- The colors yellow and green may appear in the bruise as early as the end of the first day after the injury.
- Green and yellow may never appear as a color indicators
- Given the conditions of the injury and the amount of bleeding, bruises may be simultaneously red, blue and yellow in the same or different areas of the bruise.
- Bruises of the same age, in different parts of the body, may appear to be of different ages, if only their color is considered.
- Bruises in infants change usually color more rapidly than older age groups.
- Injuries with greater amounts of bleeding, deep bleeding, loculation of blood, or repetitive trauma at the same site may show delayed bruise appearance and/or healing.

Table 8. Color Changes in Bruises as They Age

Day	1	3	5	7	9	11	13	15	17	19	21
Red											
Blue											
Yellow											

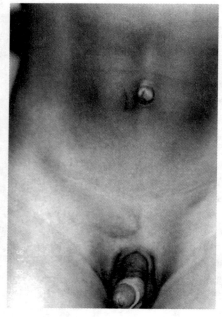

Figure 6A *Belt buckle injuries: this 4 year-old male was beaten with his mother's belt.*

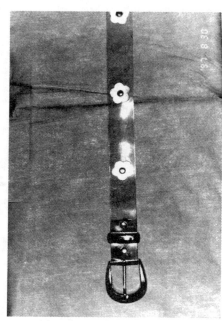

Figure 6B *Belt buckle injury: close up of the belt buckle used in the attack.*

- In child death cases, the "bruise" should not be mistaken for the post mortem pooling of blood.

- Deep bruises may not be noticed at all during life.

Differential Diagnosis

It is crucial to consider other possibilities in the evaluation of cutaneous injuries. A number of medical conditions may mimic traumatic injuries.[1] The list is long but most can be rapidly excluded with a few laboratory tests and the clinical history. Reporting of possible abuse to the authorities in the child protective system is required in cases when the medical examiner has *a reasonable suspicion* for abuse. Reasonable suspicion does not mean diagnostic certitude. It signifies that the possibility of abuse continues to exist in the differential as one of several points, or as the only possible consideration, after preliminary efforts have been made to exclude it.

Coagulation Disorder

Although accidental bruising is common in active children, an underlying bleeding disorder should be excluded in cases where abuse is being considered. At a minimum, the examiner should screen the child patient for bleeding disorders with a complete blood count, platelet count, prothrombin time, and a partial thromboplastin time. Evidence of a bleeding disorder and child abuse are not mutually exclusive.[1] Coagulation screens, bleeding time, and assays for Factor VII, VIII, IX should be performed in selected cases to exclude mild degrees of hemophilia and von Willenbrand's disease. By itself, the partial thromboplastin time is not a very sensitive screening test. Its prolongation

has occurred as an isolated finding after minor viral infections in children, brain tissue injury, and in cases of difficult venipuncture with blood clotting in the syringe.[1,2,3] Other systemic conditions, such as osteogenesis imperfecta, vitamin K deficiency, hypersensitivity vasculitis, erythema multiforme, and bleeding secondary to ingestion of salicylates, are known to contribute to easy bruising.[1,2,4,5,6,7,8]

Self-inflicted, Accidental, and Infectious Disease

Self-inflicted injury has occurred in mentally retarded and emotionally disturbed children. Self-injury has also been seen when sensation is lost. Certain congenital syndromes, and factitious illness should be considered.[1] Eczema, insect bites, and puncture wounds have been mistaken for abuse.

Folk Medical Customs

Customs and home remedies for minor ailments have been mistaken for child abuse. The Southeast Asian folk practice of dermabrasion, "Co ío" or "Qí Sa" (literally,"to scratch the wind"), produces bruises over the thorax and back.[1] Certain burns may be forms of folk medical treatments of Southeast Asian and East African people.[1] Small burns along the rectus abdominis have been used to treat jaundice and, sometimes, abdominal problems resulting from the "evil eye." Cupping and moxibustion produce superficial burns.[1] These lesions have been mistaken for abuse. Cultural sensitivity should be exercised at all times.

Other Skin Conditions

Mongolian spots are deep brown to blue-black dermal melanin deposits that have been mistaken for bruises. They are found in as many as 95% of African American infants,

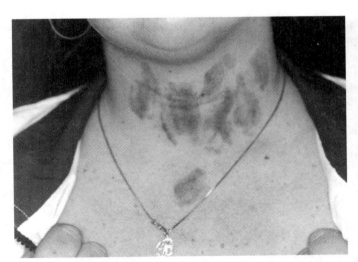

Figure 7A *Bruises of neck: known as "hickies," these bruises are caused by mouth suction force to the skin. This 13 year-old was drugged by her date and then raped.*

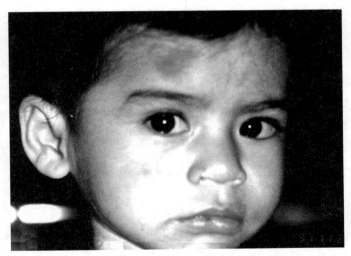

Figure 7B *Forehead bruise: typical of low velocity impact injuries is a bruise with a filled-in appearance; this 20 month-old had been beaten by her careprovider.*

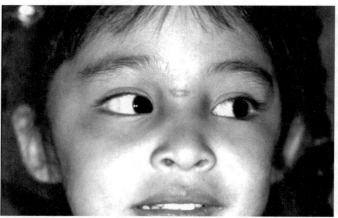

Figure 8A *"Racoon's eyes:" this 4 year-old accidentally fell and struck the bridge of her nose; several days later, seeping blood discolored the infraorbital areas of both eyes.*

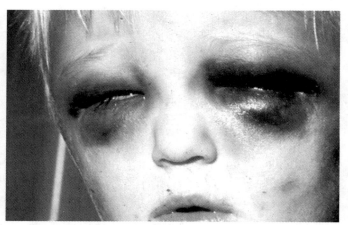

Figure 8B *Eye trauma: resulting from direct blows to the face.*

80% of Asians, 70% of Hispanic and American Indians, and 10% of Caucasian infants. They can be quite extensive, covering skin surfaces from the buttocks to the face. Mongolian spots are present at birth or shortly afterwards and usually fade completely by the first or second year but may persist into adolescence.

Differentiation of traumatic alopecia from tinea capitis, seborrhea, and atopic dermatitis is made by finding no evidence of scalp inflammation or scaling and a negative microscopic examination for hyphae and negative fungal culture. Trichotillomania, or self-induced traumatic hair loss, is a disorder seen in older children and young adults.[1] Traction alopecia is seen in certain hairstyles where tension and twisting weakens the hair shafts. Patchy bald spots, with areas of red skin and broken hairs adjoining the scalp patches, pimples, itching, and crusting of the face and scalp also can occur.

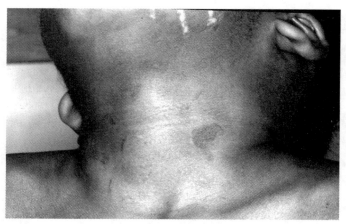

Figure 9A *Choke marks: this 4 year-old had two types of neck bruises—a filled-in type bruise, probably a thumb imprint, and linear semilunar marks near the midline, probably fingernail marks. The child also had numerous branding type burns on his body.*

Children whose skin is exposed to limes, lemons, figs, parsnips, celery, and herbal preparations may develop patchy areas of hyperpigmentation, erythematous plaques, and vesicles after sun exposure. This condition, known as phytophotodermatitis, can mimic scars or traumatic imprints. The child may have a well-demarcated hand print, for example, on the skin where someone with the toxin on their hand, had touched the child.

Brain tumors, such as neuroblastoma, may present with periorbital venous congestion and be mistaken for eye bruising. Leukemia and other blood dyscrasias may also present as bruising.

Case Resolution

The history of a 6-month-old child, who suffered rib fractures by falling down stairs, is inconsistent with the fact that children of this age are incapable of crawling. The pre-

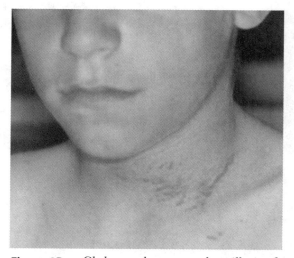

Figure 9B *Choke marks: ruptured capillaries form linearly around the front of this 10 year-old's neck.*

Table 9. Differential Diagnosis of Skin Lesions in Child Abuse

DIFFERENTIAL/CONDITION		STUDIES
BRUISES	Accidental trauma	History
	Hemophilia	History, CBC, PT, PTT, Factor VII, VII, & IX assays
	von Willebrand Disease	Bleeding time, ristocetin
	Hemorrhagic Disease of the Newborn (vit K deficiency)	History (home birth?)
	Cystic fibrosis (vit K deficiency)	History
	Salicylate ingestion	History, salicylate blood levels
	Osteogenesis Imperfecta	CBC, x-ray appearance, platelet count
	Idiopathic Thrombocytopenic Purpura	History, CBC, platelet count
	Hypersensitivity vasculitis	History
	Leukemia	History, CBC, platelet count
	Neuroblastoma w/ periorbital congestion	CT scan
	Meningococcemia	Blood culture
	Mongolian spots	History, observation over time
	"Çao Gio" or "Qi Sa"-coining	History (ethnicity?)
	Dyes or inks	History
	Sensitivity reaction, e.g. phyto-photodermatitis	History (contact w/ photo-sensitizing agents?)
	Allergic Ashiners'	History of nasal allergy
SCARS	Ehlers-Danlos Syndrome	History
	Congenital indifference to pain	History (mental retardation?)
	Varicella	History
BURNS	Accidental burn	History
	Staph impetigo	History gram stain, culture
	Cupping	History (ethnicity?)
	Moxibustion	History (ethnicity?)
	Infected atopic dermatitis	History
HAIR LOSS	Trichotillomania	History
	Tinea capitis	KOH, fungal culture
	Seborrhea	History, clinical appearance
	Atopic dermatitis	History, clinical appearance
	Syphilis	Serology

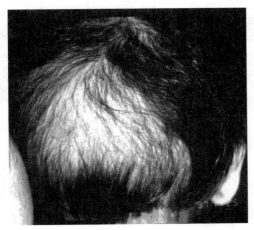

Figure 10 *Traumatic alopecia: seen on the occipital scalp (see Figures 7A, 7B).*

senting complaint of an upper respiratory infection, though present, did not have anything to do with the real problem of rib fractures and child abuse. The father did not volunteer any information about rib injury until confronted with the x-rays, and then only to repeat his belief that the baby had probably wiggled and squirmed on the floor to the edge of the stairs and then fell over. Children's Protective Services was called and the baby was immediately placed into emergency foster care.

Further Reading

Richardson, A. Cutaneous Manifestations of Abuse. In: Reece RM. (Ed) *Child Abuse: Medical Diagnosis and Management*. Philadelphia, PA: Lea & Febinger, 1994;167-84.

Johnson, C.F. Physical abuse: Accidental Versus Intentional Trauma in Children. In: Briere J, Berliner L, Bulkley, J.A., Jenny, C,. Reid, T. (Eds) *The APSAC Handbook on Child Maltreatment*. Thousand Oaks, CA: Sage Publications, 1996;206-26.

Monteleone, J.A, Brodeur, A.E. Identifying, Interpreting, and Reporting Injuries. In: Monteleone, J.A. (Ed) *Child Maltreatment: A Clinical Guide and Reference*, 2nd Ed. St. Louis, MO: GW Medical Publishing, 1998;7-22.

Williams, J.J. Child Physical Abuse. In: Reisdorff, E.J. *et al.*, (Eds) *Pediatric Emergency Medicine*. Philadelphia, PA: WB Saunders,1993;146-68.

References

1. Wedgwood J. Childhood bruising. *Practitioner* 1990; 234:598-601.

2. McDowell HP, Fielding DW. Traumatic perforation of the hypopharynx—an unusual form of abuse. *Arch Dis Child* 1984;59:888-89.

3. Wilson EF. Estimation of the age of cutaneous contusions in child abuse. *Pediatrics* 1977;60:751-52.

4. Schwartz A, Ricci L. How accurately can bruises be aged in Abused children? Literature review and synthesis. *Pediatrics* 1996;97 (2):254-56.

5. Stephenson T, Bialas Y. Estimation of the age of bruising. *Arch Dis Child* 1996;74:53-55.

6. Wardinsky TD, Vizcarrondo FE. The mistaken diagnosis of child abuse: A three-year USAF medical center analysis and literature review. Military Medicine 1995;160:15-20.

7. Johnson CF, Coury DL. Bruising and hemophilia: accident or child abuse? *Child Abuse Negl* 1988;12:409-15.

8. O'Hare AE, Eden OB. Bleeding disorders and non-accidental injury. *Arch Dis Child* 1984;59:860-64.

9. Sarnaik AP, Stringer KD, Jewell PF, et al. Disseminated intravascular coagulation with trauma: treatment with exchange transfusion. *Pediatrics* 1979;63:337-39.

10. Taylor GP. Severe bleeding disorders in children with normal coagulation tests. *Br Med J* 1982;284:1851-52.

11. O'Hare AE, Eden OB. Bleeding disorders and non-accidental injury. *Arch Dis Child* 1984;59:860-64.

12. Paterson CR. Osteogenesis imperfecta in the differential diagnosis of child abuse. *Child Abuse Negl* 1981;1:449-52.

13. Carpentieri U, Gustavson LP, Haggard ME. Misdiagnosis of neglect in a child with bleeding disorder and cystic fibrosis. *South Med J* 1978;71:854-55.

14. Waskerwitz S, Christoffel KK, Hauger S. Hypersensitivity vasculitis presenting as suspected child abuse: case report and literature review. *Pediatrics* 1981;67:283-84.

15. Owen SM, Durst RD. Ehlers-Danlos syndrome simulating child abuse. Arch Derm 1984;120:97-101.

16. Roberts DLL, Pope FM, Nicholls AC, Narcisi P. Ehlers-Danlos syndrome type IV mimicking accidental injury in a child. *Br J Derm* 1984;111:341-45.

17. Adler R, Kane-Nussen B. Erythema multiforme. Confusion with child battering syndrome. *Pediatrics* 1983;72:718-20.

18. Hurwitz A, Castells S. Misdiagnosed child abuse and metabolic disorders. Pediatr Nurs 1987;13:33-36.

19. Putnam N, Stein M. Self-inflicted injuries in childhood: a review and diagnostic approach. *Clin Pediatr* 1985;24:514-18.

20. Golden SM, Duster MC. Hazards of misdiagnosis due to Vietnamese folk medicine. *Clin Pediatr* 1977;16:949-50.

21. Feldman KW. Pseudoabusive burns in Asian refugees. *American Journal of Diseases ofChildren* 1984;138:768-769.

22. Feldman KW. Letter to the editor. *Child Abuse & Negl* 1995;19(5):657-58.

23. Asnes RS, Wisotsky DH. Cupping lesions simulating child abuse. *J Pediatr* 1981;99:267-71.

24. Muller SA, Winkelmann RK. Trichotillomania: a clinico-pathologic study of 24 cases. *Arch Dermatol* 1978;105:535-39.

Photo Credits

Figure	Source of photograph

1   Modified from: Johnson CF. Physical abuse: Accidental versus intentional trauma in children. In: Briere J, Berliner L, Bulkley JA, Jenny C, Reid T. (Eds) The APSAC Handbook on Child Maltreatment. Thousand Oaks, CA: Sage Publications, 1996;206-26.

2   J. Williams, MD

3   J. Williams, MD

4   Kempe Center Slides, Dr. Barton Schmitt series, 1978, slide #8 "slap marks on face of child"

Barton Schmitt, MD, Children's Hospital Denver, 1056 E 19th Ave, Denver, CO 80218, FAX 303-861-3992

5   J. Williams, MD

6A J. Williams, MD

6B J. Williams, MD

7A J. Williams, MD

7B J. Williams, MD

8A J. Williams, MD

8B Kempe Center Slides, Dr. Barton Schmitt series, 1978, slide #50 "black eyes"

9A J. Williams, MD

9B J. Williams, MD

10 J. Williams, MD

Abusive Head Injury and Shaken Baby Syndrome

Stephen C. Boos, M.D.

Case Vignette #1

A six-month old infant is brought to the clinic by her distraught mother. She picked up her sleeping baby from the day care provider late in the evening. In the morning she noticed two small oval bruises on the forehead, and many fine bright red dots within the curls of the ears. The baby was happy, and alert with a normal neurological exam.

Case Vignette #2

A ten-month old is brought to the emergency department due to vomiting and irritability. A prominent swelling is noted on the side of the head. Emergency CT scan shows bilateral branching skull fractures, an epidural hematoma, and a cephalhematoma. The mother says that the child fell off the couch landing on a toy telephone. When interviewed separately, the three-year old sibling reports that the father threw a heavy desk phone across the room striking the baby on the head.

Case Vignette #3

A four-month old who has been coming to the clinic for complaints of colic is brought by ambulance to the emergency department apneic and comatose. Emergency CT scan shows a thin subdural hematoma along the falx cerebri and over the surface of the right brain, swelling of the entire cerebrum, and a normal skull. The external exam is normal, but rib and metaphyseal fractures of the legs are found on x-ray, and the ophthalmologist reports extensive retinal hemorrhages and retinoschesis. The mother reports that her boyfriend called her from the home where he was watching the baby. He reported to her that the baby suddenly began shaking all over, and stopped breathing. She told him to call 911, which he hadn't yet done. She says the baby was fine and nursed normally in the morning when she left for work.

Questions

1. Each of these three infants was abused, what were the clues to this diagnosis?

2. What factors account for the wide variation in their presentation, and expected outcome?

3. What additional studies should be ordered in these infants to more thoroughly evaluate their conditions?

Recognizing Abusive Head Trauma

In 1996, the national child abuse and neglect data system reported that an estimated 1,077 deaths had occurred the previous year due to child abuse. Greater than 70% of such deaths result from head injury. This is even more striking considering that only 12% of the nation's 260,000 substantiated cases of child physical abuse involved head injury. Many abusive head injury cases are litigated and draw a great deal of media attention. High profile cases have generated both genuine and falsely orchestrated controversies in the assessment of head injury. Despite the anxiety that such controversy creates in medical personnel, the high mortality and morbidity of inflicted injury makes it essential that such cases be diagnosed.

After life and limb threatening conditions are addressed and patients are stabilized, the care provider's first job in pediatric head injury is to identify the possibility of abuse. Recognizable patterns in the patient's history and physical findings, can alert medical providers to most cases of child abuse. Once alerted, careful consideration of the epidemiology, biomechanics, pathophysiology and differential diagnosis of head trauma will allow providers to be more specific about the likelihood and nature of abuse.

Patterns

History

Three historical patterns recur in child abuse recognition: **absent history, changing history and inconsistent history.** Serious inflicted head injuries are a condition of young children. Most victims are under one year old, and nearly all are under three. Such young infants and children are closely supervised by their parent's and other care takers for all activities except sleep. For all but the most minor of injuries, the care provider should be aware of the originating trauma and its significance. Failure to provide this important information in time of medical need is evidence that it is being hidden, and thus suggests abusive injury.

When a historian who is hiding the truth is confronted with the inadequacy of their history, they may fabricate an innocent story, or give partial information from the history they are hiding. As the interviewer pursues more detail, or rejects historical postulates, further fabrication or disclosure may occur. The effect is a history, which changes during the interview. Totally fabricated histories may be remembered incompletely, resulting in inconsistencies upon re-telling. The histories of two historians may be inadequately coordinated and result in discrepancies. Serious trauma that results in serious injury to an infant can be expected to be memorable. Discrepancy within or between histories is again evidence that facts are being hidden. In the setting of childhood trauma changing history suggests abuse.

Historians who are fabricating histories often draw from their experiences, including the actual events of the abuse. The parent who strikes their baby's head, may report that the baby fell from the couch, a common parental worry which acknowledges the occurrence of trauma. In vignette #2, which involved a telephone, the telephone was incorporated into the given history, but the severity of the violence and the father's involvement was hidden. Such histories must be compared against the injuries found. Often a mismatch exists between the severity or nature of the traumatic event, and the injury found. Returning to vignette #2, short falls may indeed cause skull fracture, and rarely epidural hematoma. Striking one side of the head in a fall, however, cannot account for fractures on both sides of the head, and a two foot fall lacks the energy to cause complex, branching skull fractures. This inconsistency between the given history and the physical findings identifies the history as false, and once again suggest child abuse.

Syndromes

Syndromes are groups of individual findings which have special meaning when they co-occur. Identifying these patterns of findings often predicts a common cause, the presence of other unidentified findings, and ultimate outcome. In 1962 C. Henry Kempe et. al. reported the "battered-child syndrome".(1) Since that report, it has been widely recognized that children with multiple separate traumatic injuries, and inadequate explanatory history are often the victims of inflicted injury. The pattern of multiple unexplained injuries has retained the name battered child syndrome. Children presenting with unexplained head injuries will often have evidence of other, separate injury. In vignette #3, not only does the baby have unexplained head trauma, but fractures of the ribs, and the legs are also unexplained. This pattern meets the definition of the battered child syndrome, and identifies this child's injuries as inflicted.

The association of intracranial injury with multiple fractures had already been described in 1949 by Dr. John Caffey when the battered-child syndrome was identified.(2) The frequent lack of external injuries, and lack of easy neurological imaging at that time caused many to overlook the traumatic origin of this pattern In the early 1970's, Dr. Caffey, and independently A. N. Guthkelch, reported whiplash injury from shaking infants as the cause of this syndrome, which has since become known as the "shaken baby syndrome".(3,4) The term "shaken baby syndrome" has been widely applied to many babies who have serious intracranial injury, and no history of severe head trauma. Most, however, have additional findings, which may include rib fractures, metaphyseal corner fractures, other fractures, retinal hemorrhages, and external injuries such as bruises. Recent controversy over the adequacy of shaking alone to cause serious injury has lead to other names such as "shaken-impact syndrome" or simply "abusive head trauma", but the coexistence of individual findings which identify the common cause of inflicted injury still remains valid.

Individual physical findings

Certain individual findings are suggestive enough of abuse that they should be remembered, recognized, and considered patterns typical of abuse. While much attention is focused on the severe intracranial injuries of abused children, All layers of the head are involved in abusive injury. Areas of partial baldness containing short broken hairs mixed with stubble of re-emerging hairs may reflect traumatic allopecia from pulling the hair. When the scalp underlying the area of alopecia is bruised or swollen it is likely that large amounts of hair were forcefully yanked out. In general, children who are not able to walk along the edges of furniture should not have bruises. Once they achieve this milestone, they may get bruises of the forehead, and less commonly the scalp, but should not have bruises on their face.(5) These observations support the idea that infants and toddlers who have two unexplained bruises on the face should be evaluated for possible child abuse. In general, accidental bruises are oval, though they may reflect the shape of the edge of a coffee table. When facial bruises have other shapes, or wrap around the contours of the face, inflicted injury should be considered. A classic injury which illustrates this point is a slap mark, which often appears as diverging rays of confluent petechiae. "Black eyes" may result when the blood in a forehead bruise settles into the loose tissue around the eye. If direct trauma to the orbital rim accompanies the black eye, however, a direct blow such as a punch is the likely cause. Fine bright red petechia in clusters within the curls of the ear or along the upper rim of the pinna may occur when children's ears are struck and seldom occur otherwise.(6) Rarely these injuries have been associated with more severe injuries within the skull.(7)

Injury to the head is not always visible. Swelling of the scalp may be felt on exam or seen on CT scan with no apparent marks. Bleeding in the deep tissues, resulting in cephalhematoma or subgaleal hemorrhage, is as pathognomonic of blows to the head as are bruises on the surface, and should prompt the search for a traumatic explanation. Skull fractures are common and may result from relatively minor accidents, but complex, branching or multiple skull fractures require trauma energies far beyond typical household accidents.

Certain other injuries are typical enough of abuse that their presence should always raise concern. While not all subdural hematomas arise from abuse, the presence of such a bleed, especially along the falx, should raise the strong possibility of abuse unless a motor vehicle accident or long distance fall has occurred. Similarly, retinal hemorrhages, particularly if they are extensive, involve multiple layers of the eye, or involve retinal tears or folds, rarely occurs outside of abuse.(9) Even high speed motor vehicle accidents seldom cause this finding, and then the hemorrhages are typically less extensive.

Taken together, these historical patterns, syndromes and recognizable injuries will identify most cases where child abuse should be considered as a possibility. In many cases with these findings, child abuse will be the only reasonable possibility. When these patterns are seen, the provider should report to the appropriate child protective services or law enforcement agency. The agency investigation, along with consideration of the principles to follow will serve to make a determination in those cases which still remain unclear.

Epidemiology

During infancy, defined as age under one year of age, from 50 to 95% of children's serious head injuries may be due to abuse. (10,11) Among children under two years of age, who die from head injury, 80% may have been victims of inflicted injury. (10) The predominant accidental cause of serious and lethal head injuries is motor vehicle accidents. While falls are often cited as an explanation by parents hiding abuse, falls are an unusual cause of accidental head injury. Certain forms of serious head injury have shown a particular association with inflicted head trauma. Subdural hematomas not confined to a focal area under an impact site, and subdural hematomas lying along the falx cerebri are statistically associated with abusive etiology. (8, 11, 12)

Consistent with the concept of the battered child syndrome, the presence of additional unexplained injuries suggests that head injuries were inflicted. Thirty to fifty percent of children with abusive head injury have evidence of earlier head injury. (8, 11, 13, 14) The presence of prior intracranial injury in the form of atrophy, subdural hygroma, or subacute or chronic subdural hematoma, has been shown to be statistically associated with abusive etiology. (8, 11) Evidence of abusive injury beyond the head is found in up to 70% of children with abusive head injury. (13) This most commonly takes the form of fracture, with rib and metaphyseal fractures being the most typical types, but also may take the form of bruises, such as grip marks.

Retinal hemorrhages are a particularly important form of injury, that commonly accompanies abusive head trauma. From 70 to 90% of children with significant inflicted head injury will be found to have retinal hemorrhages. (10) The presence of retinal hemorrhages in association with traumatic head injury almost always indicates child abuse. (15, 16, 17, 18) Retinal hemorrhages are rarely found in association with severe automobile accidents and even more rarely in fall injuries. (16, 17, 18) When retinal hemorrhages are found in non-abuse settings, they typically involve a smaller extend and fewer layers of the retina. (19) Attempts to blame retinal hemorrhages on CPR, coagulopathy or seizures, each of which may follow head injury, have largely been discredited. (20, 21, 22)

As mentioned above, falls are an infrequent cause of serious head injury, and even rarer cause of retinal hemorrhages. The epidemiology of fall injury is very important in evaluating possible abusive head injury. A history of a short fall off of a bed or couch is often offered to explain the injuries of abused children. Three separate studies have looked at falls of young children from hospital beds, together reporting on 396 such falls. Three skull fractures occurred, but no serious or intracranial injury. (23, 24, 25) Higher indoor falls, such as from bunk beds or down stairs have also been reported on. Cerebral contusions, and subdural hematomas occurred in about one to two percent of cases, and concussion in 10 to 15 percent. (26, 27, 28) The few subdural hematomas seen were focal bleeds underlying a skull fracture. While by definition these are serious injuries, none of them was fatal. In fact falls less than ten feet, when the history can be independently corroborated are rarely if ever fatal. (29, 30, 31) This contrasts dramatically with reported but uncorroborated short falls involving young children, which appear to be more dangerous than even severe long distance falls. Based on this data, severe head injury in children with a history of a short indoor fall should usually be considered inflicted.

Biomechanics

The absence of external trauma in infants presenting with severe head injury, and occult skeletal injuries is perplexing. Based on confession evidence, it was postulated that shaking injury could cause these injuries without any impact. (3, 4) This postulate has become embodied in the term "shaken baby syndrome" and continues to be asserted by many experts in child abuse. Perpetrators of abuse, and their defenders have suggested that babies may be injured by mild or reasonable shaking, in an attempt to belie the violence implicit in the injuries. Biomechanical studies done on primates and human volunteers have established that head acceleration, without impact, is adequate to cause all of the injuries seen in shaken baby syndrome. (32) The degree of necessary acceleration, however, is quite severe, and beyond any concept of gentle or reasonable action. In fact the necessary acceleration is so severe, that some researchers have suggested that shaking alone is inadequate to cause the injuries and impact is necessary to inflict the injuries of the "shaken baby syndrome". (33) This argument relies on single event acceleration data from adult subhuman primates and ignores both the importance of immaturity and repetition through back and forth shaking. Clinically evidence of impact is found in about 50% of infants with "shaken baby syndrome" suggesting that shaking alone may be adequate to cause the injuries found in some babies. (34)

When faced with a case of head trauma, the injuries seen often imply the effects of impact or acceleration, and allow the examiner to postulate the mechanism of injury. (32) Contusions, abrasions and lacerations of the soft tissues and skull fracture come from impact, as one might expect. Linear skull fractures result from accidents as minor as a three foot fall, but much greater energy is required to produce multiple, branched, or stellate fractures. Epidural hematoma, local subdural hematoma, and brain contusion are also attributed to impact. Often these injuries lie beneath other evidence of impact, but at times evidence of overlying impact is absent. In general impact injuries are accidental, although exceptions exist such as case vignette #2.

Diffuse or perifalcine subdural hemorrhage, "shearing injury" to the brain and concussion require acceleration injury. Diffuse axonal injury is a pathological finding with the clinical correlate of immediate, prolonged loss of consciousness, and the imaging correlate of corpus callosum, gray/white interface and deep white matter hemorrhages. This condition also requires acceleration injury. Retinal hemorrhages are most likely also due to acceleration injury. (35) As might be expected from the shaking model, most intracranial injuries cited as evidence of abuse are due to acceleration. Only motor vehicle accidents rival child abuse as an etiology of these sorts of injuries in this age group. A few injuries such as contra-coup hemorrhages are of uncertain biomechanical origin, and many clinically important fidings such as edema and infarct may be secondary to various primary injuries.

Pathophysiology

The complexities of what happens to the brain and surrounding tissue during and after trauma is only beginning to be understood. Beyond the obvious tearing of tissues, intracellular changes take place which result in neuronal and vascular dysfunction that further the immediate damage. If the patient recovers, healing follows, with its own changes. Two particular phenomena have presented questions for the physician evaluating child abuse, delayed onset of symptoms, and re-bleeding of subdural hemorrhages.

Up to 15% of adults with cranial injury will deteriorate or die after a "lucid" interval. (36, 37, 38) Some have used this data to suggest that an injured child may be transferred to another caregiver during a normal, assymptomatic interval, and subsequently deteriorate or die. There is some data that children too may deteriorate after being "lucid". (39, 40) Emergency room experience, however, suggests that while infants who are not only "lucid" but assymptomatic may have skull fracture or even intracranial bleeding, they do not later develop serious or life threatening symptoms. (41) Three studies have specifically addressed the likelihood of late deterioration of children and found a lucid interval to be associated with epidural hemorrhage, and absent in classical shaken baby syndrome. (14, 42, 43,) Serious injuries typical of abusive head trauma can be assumed to be immediately symptomatic. These symptoms serve as the best clue to the time of injury.

While most subdural hemorrhages resolve spontaneously and completely, some form a "neo-membrane" which may contribute to the development of a chronic subdural hematoma. (44) The current prevailing theory in the maintenance of this collection is that repeated micro-hemorrhages, from the fragile capillaries in the neo-membrane, contribute to the fluid mass, which would otherwise be resorbed. It has been suggested by some that rebleeding into a previous subdural hematoma could occur after trivial trauma, and lead to catastrophic deterioration. The repeated hemorrhages demonstrated to occur from the delicate capillaries of neo-membranes are tiny, resulting in a slow accumulation of volume, and gradual onset of symptoms. While it is common for infants with abusive head trauma to have multiple intra-cranial injuries, (8, 11, 13, 14) the catastrophic deterioration typical of child abuse head trauma is unlikely to occur from the sort of re-bleeding demonstrated to occur from subdural neo-membranes.

Differential Diagnosis

When considered separately, several of the findings of abusive head injury have an extensive differential diagnosis. In combination, however, the picture is usually quite clear, with little question as to etiology. The most important diagnosis to exclude is accidental injury. In mild cases of head injury, especially those lacking ocular findings, the likelihood of accidental injury must be considered. When serious injury and classical findings occur, only the most severe of accidents pose a reasonable possibility, and these should be easily verifiable.

Severe disorders of blood coagulation may result in intracranial bleeding. In particular thrombocytopenia associated with leukemia may lead to sub-dural hemorrhage, cerebral involvement and retinal hemorrhage, creating a picture similar to shaken baby syndrome. Both hematologic studies and the clinical course should distinguish abusive head trauma from these conditions. It is important not to confuse the relatively minor prolongations of coagulation studies that are sometimes found in brain injury with the sort of severe clotting abnormalities that may cause intracranial bleeding. (45)

Recent neurosurgery, Alagille syndrome, glutaric aciduria type one, and arteriovenous malformations are all cited as conditions that may result in findings confused with inflicted head trauma. For the most part these conditions are rare and distinguishable through careful history and examination. The findings of isolated subarachnoid hemorrhage and limited retinal hemorrhage with no other evidence of trauma should provoke the search for a vascular abnormality. Fortunately both this clinical picture and this condition, also known as Terson's syndrome, are rare in infancy.

The mildest forms of intracranial injury may present with symptoms limited to vomiting or irritability. In these cases the only clue to the traumatic origin of the symptoms may be a bruise on the face, or non-clearing blood with xanthochromic supernate on an LP done to rule out menin-

gitis. (46, 47) Such a picture may lead to head trauma being missed in favor of diagnoses such as viral infection, accidental head injury or rule out sepsis. In a study of 54 cases of missed head trauma, nine percent of the cases died, 28 percent were re-injured, and 40 percent suffered medical complications due to delayed diagnosis. (47)

Plan

The traumatic origin of a child's condition may be obvious from the onset, such as the bruises in vignette #1, or require diagnostic testing, such as the CT in vignette #3. Once a child has been diagnosed with head trauma, the medical care provider must assess how that trauma occurred. In classic cases with subdural bleeding, retinal hemorrhages, rib fractures and metaphyseal fractures, the cause will be obviously apparent. When the head injury is severe, and involves clearly traumatic findings such as subdural hemorrhage, only the sort of verifiable events such as a long distance outdoor fall, or a motor vehicle accident present a reasonable alternative to inflicted injury. In lesser or atypical cases, however, the provider must recognize the possibility of abusive injury and pursue evidence of additional trauma, which will establish the cause of the patient's injuries. In a child with intracranial injury of uncertain cause, the provider should, examine all exterior surfaces for trauma, order a skeletal survey to rule out occult fractures, and obtain a dilated indirect ophthalmoscopy exam to identify retinal hemorrhages. When one part of the abusive head injury picture is found, such as metaphyseal or rib fractures, the other parts should be searched for using indirect ophthalmoscopy and CT or MRI scanning. A child with non-specific symptoms consistent with head injury and evidence of cutaneous or skeletal trauma should have a CT scan to look for intracranial injury.

All reasonable suspicion of inflicted head injury must be reported to the Children's Protective Service, or responsible law enforcement agency. The medical system can neither thoroughly assess nor fully treat abusive head injury by itself. Not only is reporting of suspicion legally mandated, it is necessary for the medical care of the child. Without the law enforcement and social welfare systems the medical provider can not expect to return the child to a safe environment. The subsequent abuse and neglect, which is likely to result, can be regarded as a poor medical outcome. Only through reporting can medical providers prevent this event.

Outcome

The poor prognosis for inflicted head injuries was recognized from the time of Caffey's original description. (48) The outcome of inflicted head injury is worse than that of accidental head injury, with 10 percent of children dying and 50 percent significantly handicapped. (11, 14, 49) Of the remaining patients most or all have visual handicaps or developmental disabilities.

Those patients who are returned, for whatever reason, to their abusive environments have the additional complication of repeated abuse. These children may be re-abused as often as 70% of the time, with a long term mortality of up to 40%. (50, 51, 52) This possibility makes reporting suspected abuse, and vigorous advocacy for protecting surviving children a compelling part of their medical therapy.

Prevention

Recently, programs have been initiated to prevent abusive head trauma by urging parents to "never never never sake a baby." Such programs rest on the assumption that these warnings will be remembered and heeded when the parent is alone with the baby and at their wits end. This warning also ignores the shaking versus impact controversy. While public education is appropriate, additional measures will probably be necessary to prevent this form of abuse. Most serious abuse of infants is precipitated by crying events. Medical providers should ask about and assist with the management of colicky and temperamentally difficult babies. Respite may be necessary if the family is severely stressed. Many abusers have a history of other violence preceding child abuse. Care providers are urged to screen for domestic violence in the homes of all children, and refer identified cases to appropriate authorities. Finally, it is clear that 30 percent of abusive head trauma is missed at first presentation. Care providers must be alert for subtle cases presenting with mild symptoms, such as vomiting or irritability, and evidence of trauma such as facial bruising. Detecting, reporting and protecting mild cases of abuse may effectively prevent subsequent serious or fatal abuse.

References

1. Kempe, C.H., Silverman, F.N., Steele, B.F., Droegemueller, W., Silver, H.K. The battered-child syndrome. *JAMA*. 1962; 181: 17-24

2. Caffey, J. Multiple fractures in the long bones of infants suffering from subdural hematoma. *Amer J Roentgen*. 1949; 56: 163

3. Caffey, J. On the theory and practice of shaking infants, its potential residual effects of permanent brain damage and mental retardation. *AJDC*. 1972; 124: 161

4. Guthkelch, A. Infantile subdural hematoma and its relationship to whiplash injuries. *BMJ*. 1971; 2: 430-431

5. Sugar, N.F., Taylor, J.A., Feldman, K.W. Bruises in infants and toddlers: those who don't cruise rarely bruise. *Arch Pediatr Adolesc Med*. 1999; 153: 399-403

6. Feldman, K.W. Patterned abusive bruises of the buttocks and the pinnae. *Pediatr*. 1992; 90: 633-636.

7. Hanigan, W.C., Peterson, R.A., Njus, G. Tin ear syndrome: roatational acceleration in pediatric head injuries. *Pedatr*. 1987; 80: 618-622

8. Hymel, K., et. al. Comparison of intracranial computed tomographic findings in pediatric abusive and accidental head trauma. *Pediatr Radiol*. 1997; 27: 743-747

9. Gilliland, M., Luckenbach, M., Chenier, T. Systemic and ocular findings in 169 prospectively studied child deaths: Retinal hemorrhages usually mean child abuse. *Forensic Sci Intnl*. 1994; 68: 117-132

10. AAP Committee on Child Abuse and Neglect. Shaken baby syndrome: Inflicted cerebral trauma. *Pediatr*. 1995; 92: 872-875

11. Ewing-Cobb, L., et.al. Neuroimaging, physical , and developmental findings after inflicted and non inflicted traumatic brain injury in young children. *Pediatr*. 1998; 102: 300-307

12. Tzioumi, D., Oates, R.K. Subdural hematomas in children under 2 years. Accidental or inflicted? A 10 year experience. *Child Abuse and Neglect* 1998; 22: 1105-1112

13. Alexander, R., et. al. Serial abuse in children who are shaken. *AJDC*. 1990; 144: 58-60.

14. Gilles, E., Nelson, M. Cerebral complications of nonaccidental head injury in childhood. *Pediatr neurol*. 1998; 19:119-128.

15. Buys, Y.M., et. al. Retinal findings after head trauma in infants and young children. *Ophthalmology*. 1992; 99: 1718-1723.

16. Duhaime, A.C., et. al. Head injury in very young children: mechanisms, injury types and ophthalmologic findings in 100 hospitalized patients younger than 2 years of age. *Pediatr*. 1992; 90: 179-185.

17. Johnson, D.L., Braum, D., Friendly, D. Accidental head trauma and retinal hemorrhage. *Neurosurgery*. 1993; 33: 231-234.

18. Gilliland, M.G.F., Luckenbach, M.W., Chenier, T.C. Systemic and ocular findings in 169 prospectively studied child deaths: retinal hemorrhages usually mean child abuse. *Forens. Sci Int*. 1994; 26: 117-132.

19. Betz, P., Puschel, K., Miltner, E., Lignitz, E., Eisenmenger, W. Morphometric analysis of retinal hemorrhages in the shaken baby syndrome. *Forens. Sci. Int*. 1996; 78: 71-80.

20. Odom, A. Prevalence of retinal hemorrhages in pediatric patients after in-hospital cardiopulmonary resuscitation: A prospective study. *Pediatr*. 1997; 99: e3.

21. Gilliland, M., Luckenbach, M. Are retinal hemorrhages found after resuscitation attempts? *Am J Forensic Med and Path.* 1993; 14: 187-192.

22. Tyagi, A.K., Scitcher, S., Kozeis, N., Willshaw, H.E. Can convulsions alone cause retinal haemorrhages in infants? *J Ophthalmol.* 1998; 82: 659-660.

23. Helfer, R., Slovis, T., Black, H. Injuries resulting when small children fall out of bed. *Pediatr.* 1977; 60: 533-535.

24. Nitmityongskul, P., Anderson, L. The likelihood of injuries when children fall out of bed. *J Pediatr Orthop.* 1987; 7: 184-186.

25. Lyons, T., Oates, R. Falling out of bed: A relatively benign occurrence. *Pediatr.* 1993; 92: 125-127.

26. Joffe, M., Ludwig, S. Stairway injuries in children. *Pediatr.* 1988; 82: 457-461.

27. Selbst, S., Baker, M., Shamas, M. Bunk bed injuries. *AJDC.* 1990; 144: 721-723.

28. Chiavello, C., Christoph, R., Bond, G. Staiway-related injuries in children. *Pediatr.* 1994; 95: 679-681.

29. Chadwick, D., et. al. Death from falls in children: How far is fatal. *J Trauma.* 1991; 31: 1353-1355.

30. Williams, R. Injuries in infants and small children resulting from witnessed and corroborated free falls. *J Trauma.* 1991; 31: 1350-1352.

31. Reiber, G. Fatal falls in childhood. *Am J Forensic Med and Path.* 1993; 14: 201-207.

32. Hymel, K.P., Bandak, F.A., Partington, M.D., Winston, K.R. Abusive head trauma? A bimechanics based approach. *Child Maltreatment.* 1998; 3: 116-128.

33. Duhaime, A.C., et al. The shaken baby syndrome. A clinical, pathological, and biomechanical study. *J Neurosurg.* 198; 66: 409-41.

34. Alexander, R., Sato, Y., Smith, W., Bennett, T. Incidence of impact trauma with cranial injuries ascribed to shaking. *AJDC.* 1990; 144: 724-726.

35. Green, M.A., Lieberman, G., Milroy, C.M., Parsons, M.A. Ocular and cerebral trauma in non-accidental injury in infancy: underlying mechanisms and implications for paediatric practice. *Br. J. Ophthalmol.* 196; 80: 282-287.

36. Marshall, L.F., Toole, B.M., Bowers, S.A. The national traumatic coma data bank part 2: patients who talk and deteriorate: implications for treatment. *J. Neurosurg.* 1983; 59: 285-288.

37. Lobato, R.D., et. al. Head injured patients who talk and deteriorate into coma. *J. Neurosurg.* 1991; 75: 256-261.

38. Rockswold, G.L., Pheley, P.J. Patients who talk and deteriorate. *Ann. Emerg. Med.* 1993; 22: 1004-1007.

39. Hendrick, E.B., Harwood-Hash, D.C.F., Hudson, A.R. Head injuries in children: a survey of 4465 consecutive cases at the Hospital for Sick Children, Toronto, Canada in *Clinical Neurosurgery. Proceedings of the Congress of Neurological Surgeons.* Williams and Wilkins 1964 Baltimore MD pp. 46-65.

40. Snoek, J.W., Minderhoud, J.M., Wilmink, J.T. Delayed deterioration following mild head injury in children. *Brain* 1984; 107: 15-36.

41. Greenes, D.S., Schutzman, S.A. Occult intracranial injury in infants. *Ann. Emerg. Med.* 1998; 32: 680-686.

42. Starling, S.P., Holden, J.R., Jenny, C. Abusive head trauma: the relationship of perpetrators to their victims. *Pediatr.* 1995; 95:259-262.

43. Willman, K.Y., Bank, D.E., Senac, M., Chadwick, D.L. Restricting the time of injury in fatal inflicted head injuries. *Child Abuse and Neglect.* 1997; 21: 929-940.

44. Lee, K.S., Bae, W.K., Doh, J.W., Bae, H.G., Yun, I.G. Origin of chronic subdural haematoma and relation to traumatic subdural lesions. *Brain Injury.* 1998; 12: 901-910.

45. Hymel, K.P., Abshire, T.C., Luckey, D.W., Jenny, C. Coagulopathy in pediatric abusive head trauma. *Pediatr.* 1997; 99: 371-375.

46. Spear, R.M., Chadwick, D., Peterson, B. Fatalities associated with misinterpretation of bloody cerebrospinal fluid in the "shaken baby syndrome". *AJDC.* 1992; 146: 1415-1417

47. Jenny, C., Hymel, K.P., Ritzen, A., Reinert, S.E., Hay, T.C. Analysis of missed cases of abusive head trauma. *JAMA.* 1999; 281: 621-626.

48. Caffey, J. The whiplash shaken infant syndrome: Manual shaking by the extremities with whiplash-induced intracranial and intraocular bleeding, linked with residual permanent brain damage and mental retardation. *Pediatr.* 1974; 54: 396-403.

49. Bonnier, C., Nassogne, M., Evrard, P. Outcome and prognosis of whiplash shaken infant syndrome: Late consequences after a symptom free interval. *Dev Med and Clin Neurol.* 1995; 37: 943-956.

50. Jackson, G. Child abuse syndrome: the cases we miss. *Br. Med. J.* 1972; 2: 756-757.

51. Smith, S.M., Hanson, R. 134 battered children: a medical and psychological study. *Br. Med. J.* 1974; 3: 666-670.

52. Friedman, S.B., Morse, C.W. Child abuse: a five year follow-up of early case findings in the emergency department. *Pediatr.* 1974; 54: 404-410.

Note: The opinions and conclusions in this article are those of the author and are not intended to represent the official position of the Department of Defense, USAF, or any other governmental agency.

Child Abuse by Burning

Matt Young, M.D., M.P.H., F.A.A.P. and Philip W. Hyden, M.D., J.D.

Case Vignette

A 9-year-old boy left his bike on the street. As punishment, his mother filled the bathtub with scalding water and held the child in the tub burning him from the waist down. He was held in the water for over 3 minutes until his skin was floating off in the water. After a delay, he was taken to the local emergency room and then transferred to the burn center. His mother stated that he had slipped on a bar of soap and fell into the bathtub. His burns were not compatible with this history and the case was reported as suspicious of child abuse. His burns were full-thickness and circumferential from the waist down to the toes. He had no splash marks on other parts of the body. He had non-burned areas in his inguinal crease and behind one knee. He was hospitalized in critical condition. He required multiple surgical procedures for debridement and skin grafting of his burns. His hospitalization lasted for 3 months. After one month of hospitalization, when he felt safe from further torture, he confided the history of being held in the tub and burned by his mother. He is permanently scarred from the waist down. On discharge from the burn center, he was able to walk using a walker, but required hospitalization in a rehabilitation facility for 4 additional months.

His mother was arrested and prosecuted for child abuse and torture. The child testified in the trial describing in detail his burning. His description of the event was consistent with the pattern of his burn, down to which direction he was leaning in the tub. Using the rational that his delay in telling the truth made his testimony questionable, his mother was not convicted. He is currently living with his father in a different state, although his mother is fighting for custody.

Child abuse by burning is a critical medical problem. It is often a more calculated injury than other forms of abuse. A multidisciplinary approach is required in the treatment of the burn, and the prosecution of the perpetrator.

Questions

1. Describe three ways of classifying burns.

2. Describe the most common causes of abuse burn injury.

3. Describe the most important factors in distinguishing abuse from accidental burns.

Burn Injuries to Children

Burns cause disease in all organ systems in proportion to the amount of body surface area burned. In order to understand burn child abuse, one must first have a basic understanding of the burn injury. Burns can be classified in three ways and all relate to the severity of the burn injury:

- the percentage of the body surface area burned;

- the depth of the burn; and

- the agent that causes the burn.

Body Surface Area

Children are different than adults in burn severity. Children have a larger body surface area in relation to body mass than adults. Therefore the same percentage burn in a child is more serious than in an adult. Also, children have thinner skin than adults, so that the same amount of heat will cause a deeper or the same degree of burn in less time in a child. Burns can be best categorized by the amount of body surface area involved. The Lund Browder Chart takes into consideration the differing surface area proportions for different ages.

Grossman Burn Center
Sherman Oaks Hospital — Patient s History

Lund and Browder chart

	0-1	1-4	5-9	10-15	Adult	% 2°	% 3°	% TOTAL
Head	19	17	13	10	7			
Neck	2	2	2	2	2			
Ant Trunk	13	13	13	13	13			
Post Trunk	13	13	13	13	13			
R. Buttock	2 1/2	2 1/2	2 1/2	2 1/2	2 1/2			
L. Buttock	2 1/2	2 1/2	2 1/2	2 1/2	2 1/2			
Genitalia	1	1	1	1	1			
R.U. Arm	4	4	4	4	4			
L.U. Arm	4	4	4	4	4			
R.L. Arm	3	3	3	3	3			
L.L. Arm	3	3	3	3	3			
R. Hand	2 1/2	2 1/2	2 1/2	2 1/2	2 1/2			
L. Hand	2 1/2	2 1/2	2 1/2	2 1/2	2 1/2			
R. Thigh	5 1/2	6 1/2	8	8 1/2	9 1/2			
L. Thigh	5 1/2	6 1/2	8	8 1/2	9 1/2			
R. Leg	5	5	5 1/2	6	7			
L. Leg	5	5	5 1/2	6	7			
R. Foot	3 1/2	3 1/2	3 1/2	3 1/2	3 1/2			
L. Foot	3 1/2	3 1/2	3 1/2	3 1/2	3 1/2			
					Total			

Admitted SOCH Burn Center

Date:_____ Hour_____ AM / PM

Age_____ Sex_____ Race_____

Date and Time Burned_____ AM / PM

Circumstances of Burn_____

_____

_____

_____

ETIOLOGY OF BURN (CIRCLE)

Flame   Indoors-outdoors   Flash

Hot Liquid Immersion   Splash

Contact   Chemical   Electrical

_____   Good Fair Poor

Informant   Reliability (circle)

Treatment Prior to arrival SOCH Burn Center:

_____ AM / PM

Date   Time

_____

Nature of RX

_____

_____

Weight (KG)_____ %Burn_____

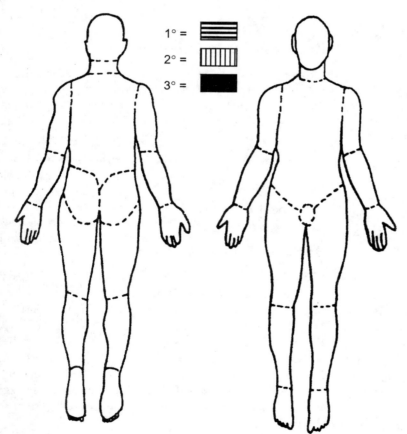

1° =
2° =
3° =

BURN INDEX

_____

(% 3* PLUS 1/4 2°)

IV FLUIDS GIVEN PRIOR TO ARRIVAL SHERMAN OAKS HOSPITAL

Type_____ Amt_____

Type_____ Amt_____

Type_____ Amt_____

Depth of Burn

Burns are classified as first, second, and third degree based on the depth of the skin involved. Burn depth is also categorized as full-thickness and partial thickness. The skin has epidermal and dermal layers that protect the body. A healthy dermal layer can produce new epidermis. When the dermis is destroyed, epidermis cannot regenerate.

First degree burns: involve only the epidermal layer and show redness of the skin, without blisters.
Second degree burns: involve loss of the epidermal layer, show blisters, and may involve injury to the dermal layer. Second-degree burns have some remaining healthy dermis. These are also designated as partial thickness burns.
Third degree burns: involve damage to both the epidermal and the entire dermal layer. These burns do not heal from the bottom up, and only scar in from the sides. They require surgery to remove the dead skin and skin grafting. When the dermis is non-viable, the burn is designated as full-thickness.

Burn Agent

Burns are classified by the agent that causes the burn:

- Scald
- Flame
- Contact
- Chemical
- Electrical

Scald burns are the most common burns of children. The most common accidental scald occurs to the toddler who pulls a cup of hot coffee, tea, soup, etc. off a table and onto themselves. This usually burns their face, arm, and chest. The liquid cools as it runs down the body, causing a less deep burn the farther it drips. It also causes an "arrow pattern" as the liquid comes to a point, as it drips down the body. The pattern of these burns can be differentiated from inflicted burns. It is important to note the developmental capabilities of the child and his measured "reach" potential (i.e. length including outstretched arm) in order to properly assess the history in relationship to the injury.

Flame burns occur more commonly in the older age child who plays with matches, lighters or firecrackers. Contact burns occur most often when a toddler reaches for a hot object such as an iron or curling iron. Chemical and electrical burns occur less frequently in children.

Abuse Burn Injuries

About 5 - 10% of pediatric patients admitted to a burn center are the result of child abuse. In determining the level of suspicion for an inflicted injury, it is most important that the history be consistent with the pattern of burn injury. The presence of other signs of abuse such as bruises, old fractures, or scars may also be present. Besides the pattern being consistent with the history, the history must also be compatible with the child's developmental age. Scald burns are the most predominant type of inflicted serious burn injury with tap water being the agent most commonly seen. These burns can be life threatening. Other agents of burn child abuse are contact burns from a hot object such as a curling iron, an iron, or cigarette burns. Contact burns often produce a brand on the skin from the hot object. In many cases, there are multiple burns from the same hot object.

Scald Burn Child Abuse

Scald burns produce a unique pattern usually characterized by a submersion type burn. Abuse burns are more likely to involve hands, feet, genitalia or buttocks as opposed to accidental burns, which commonly involve the face, chest or arm.

Immersion burns show several combinations of distinctive characteristics. Of classic significance is the involvement of both feet and/or both hands (mirror image burns). Submersion of hands or feet produces a stocking or glove like distribution, which is indicative of abuse. Other attributes of abuse burns from submersion are a sharp line of demarcation between the burn and unburned tissue, as well as sparing of flexion creases. The line of demarcation is produced when a part of the body is forcibly submerged showing the water level on the skin. In submersion burns, the children are held in the hot liquid, since no one will, without force, hold still with a part of their body in scalding water.

A child will try to protect sensitive skin surfaces, such as the popliteal fosse or the genitalia. To do this they will try to flex their body. This causes sparing of the flexion creases such as behind the knee and the groin area. These are spared because the skin is in contact with other skin, instead of hot liquid, sparing the area from a burn.

The classic donut sign on the buttocks is indicative of abuse. The donut sign is meaningful, if it is present, but its absence does not rule-out abuse. This donut sign represents the sitting area of the buttock being held against the cooler surface of the bottom of the tub; whereas, areas of the skin that are exposed to the scalding water form a circle around the unburned skin. If children are submerged in hot water with their clothes on, a zebra-like pattern can be seen. This results from burns to areas where the cloth is in contact with the skin, and sparing of areas where the cloth is not.

Another possible indication of burn child abuse is the lack of splash marks. When a child is burned accidentally, there is splashing of the water in an effort to escape from the scalding water. A child who is forcibly submerged may show no splash marks.

Depth of the burn in scald injuries is the consequence of two factors, temperature of the hot liquid and the time of exposure. Hot water for example, can cause a third degree burn in less than two seconds, if it is greater than 140° F degrees, which is a temperature that hot water heaters can produce. A longer period of time would be required to cause the same amount of burn if the water temperature is 130° F degrees. However, one can never exactly know the temperature of the hot water at the time of injury, because water is constantly cooling. Hot water temperature, the length of time that it takes for the water to get hot, and the temperature at differing time intervals are important information and should to be measured.

When immersion burns are present involving the genitalia, the question of sexual abuse must be investigated.

Patient History

The two most important aspects in evaluating the possibility of abuse are:

- Is the pattern of the burn consistent with the history of the burn?

- Is the burn consistent with the child's level of development?

Histories are commonly fabricated in instances of abuse. This can often be discerned by the conflicts between the burn pattern and the fabricated history. Suspicions should

Chart 1. Burn Temperatures: Developed by the Grossman Burn Center

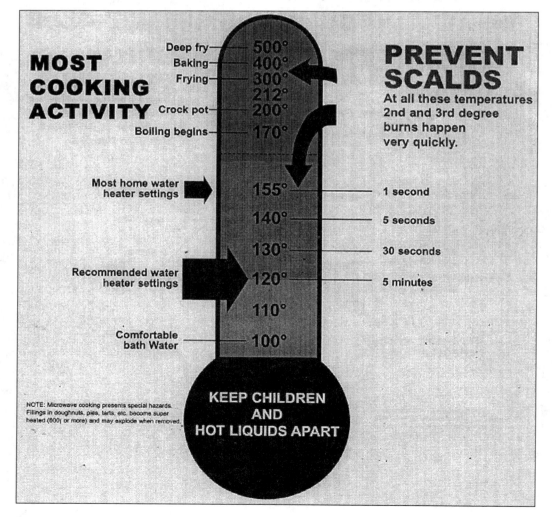

be raised by delay in seeking medical treatment or by having someone else bring the child to the doctor. A lack of appropriate emotional response to the child's injury manifests itself by blaming the child for the injury, whereas, parents of accidentally burned children will often blame themselves. The most common age for inflicted burns is 13–24 months. This is the time when children are very dependent. This dependence may be an increased stress on the parent. Family stability is often poor in abuse victims' homes.

Perpetrators

The Grossman Burn Center Scan Team studied 73 cases of burn abuse from North America. Of this group, 75% of the victims were between the ages of 12 – 36 months and 55% were males. Scald burns were inflicted in 69%, contact burns 17%, and flame burns 7%. The most common body area burned was buttocks, perineum, upper and lower extremity. Five of the victims died. Three of these victims had prior contact with Child Protective Services. The perpetrator was always someone that the child knew and was responsible for caring for the child. The perpetrator was most commonly the mother (46%), mother's boyfriend (17%), father (12%), babysitter (12%), extended family (11%), and day care worker (2%). The high incidence of abuse by the mother's boyfriend represents a situation where there are "two abusers", the boyfriend perpetrator and the passive mother. In these situations the mother will

allow the abuse of her child in order to not put her relationship with this man at risk.

Referral Criteria

Proper response to the child burn victim includes specialized care. A burn unit may treat adults or children or both. The American Burn Association has established the following criteria for referral to a Burn Center:

- Partial thickness burns greater than 10% total body surface area (TBSA);

- Burns that involve the face, hands, feet, genitalia, perineum, or major joints;

- Third-degree burns in any age group;

- Electrical burns, including lightening injury;

- Chemical burns; and

- Inhalation injury.

While burns are associated with prolonged hospitalization, abuse burns have longer hospital stays than accidental burns. It is critical that burns caused by abuse be identified, because inflicted burn injuries where children are returned to the perpetrator, carry a high risk of future more severe injury and death. Burn child abuse requires the coordinated efforts of multiple disciplines, including specialized burn medical teams, children's services, police, district attorneys

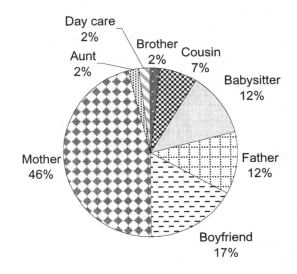

Chart 2. Perpetrators of Abuse

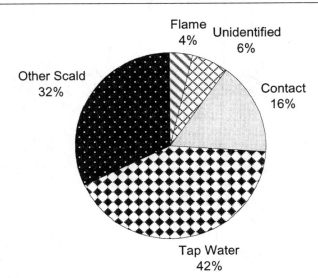

Chart 3. Abuse by Burn Type

Patterns of Abuse

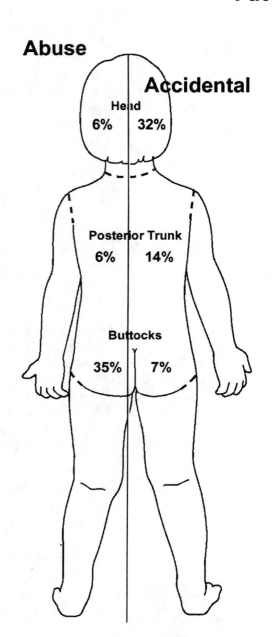

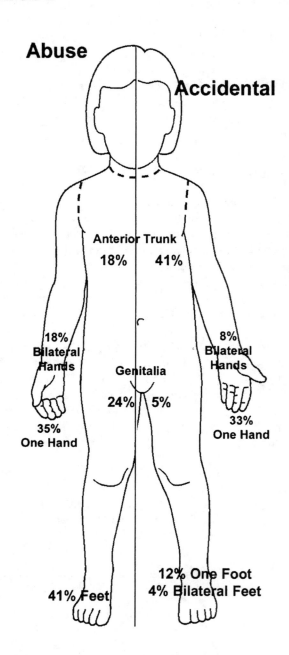

(all abuse cases of feet burns were bilateral)

and social service agencies. SCAN (Suspected Child Abuse and Neglect) Teams are vital in facilitating this coordination. It is vital that this coordinated effort be implemented to prevent further injury and death for these victims of violence.

Resources

American Burn Association
http://www.ameriburn.org

Grossman Burn Center
http://www.grossmanburncenter.com

Children's Burn Foundation
http://www.childburn.org

Shriner's Hospital for Children, Sacramento
http://www.shrinershq.org/Hospitals/index.html

References

Davis, H. W., and Zitelli, B. J. (1995). Childhood injuries: Accidental or inflicted? *Contemporary Pediatrics.* 94-112.

Fowler, J. Child Maltreatment by Burning. *Burns.* 83-85

Hight, D. W., Bakalar, H. R., & Lloyd, J. R. (1979, August 10). Inflicted Burns in Children, Recognition and Treatment. *JAMA* 517-520

Kumar, P., (1986). Child Abuse by Thermal Injury — A Retrospective Survey. *Burns.* 344-348

Rosenberg, N.M., and Marino, D. (1989). Frequency of Suspected Abuse/Neglect in Burn Patients. *Pediatric Emergency Care.* 219-221

Kessler, D. B., and Hyden, P. (1991). Physical, Sexual and Emotional Abuse of Children. *Clinical Symposia.* Novartis Pharmaceuticals Corp. 1-32

Brodeur, A. E., and Monteleone, J. A., (1994). *Burns and child maltreatment. Child Maltreatment, A Clinical Guide and Reference.* 89-104

Hobbs, C. J., (1986). When are Burns not Accidental? *Archives of Disease on Childhood.* 357-361

Diagnostic Imaging in Child Abuse

The photographs in the chapter can be viewed online at the Volcano Press website: www.volcanopress.com/booksupplements

Deborah S. Ablin, M.D.

Case Vignette

Tammy, a 19 year old mother, came home to find her 9-month-old baby favoring her right arm. Her 20 year old boyfriend had been baby-sitting the child. The baby was highly irritable. The boyfriend had said that the child rolled off the sofa onto the carpeted floor. The mother took the baby to her pediatrician. A radiograph of the right arm disclosed an acute spiral midshaft numeral fracture. The pediatrician became suspicious because the whole story was not clear, and the short height of the fall would not likely have caused a fracture. The pediatrician then ordered a skeletal survey. Through the skeletal survey, the pediatrician also found evidence of multiple healing rib fractures, a clear indication of abuse. There was no other history of trauma.

Questions

1. Describe the type of lesions with a high specificity for child physical abuse.

2. Describe the type of lesions with moderate specificity for child abuse.

3. Describe the type of lesions with low specificity for child abuse.

4. What is the most common cause of death from brain injury in children less than two years of age?

The concept of child abuse had its origins in the radiologic studies of the pediatric radiologist, Dr. John Caffey in the 1940's (1), and the term "battered child syndrome" was begun by Dr. Henry Kempe, a pediatrician in the 1960's (2). Approximately one million children were identified as victims of child abuse or neglect in the United States in 1996 (3). Of these children, approximately 229,300 (24%) suffered from physical abuse (3). Of physically abused children, approximately 33% will have injuries detectable by skeletal surveys; and the majority of these children (72%) will be under two years of age (4).

Recommendations for Imaging of Skeletal Injuries

1. Any child, age 2 or younger, seen for suspected physical abuse should have a skeletal survey (4,5).

2. In children, in the 2-5 year age range, skeletal findings are less common (22%), and the need for skeletal survey in this age group should be based on the specific clinical indicators of abuse (4,5).

3. A screening skeletal survey beyond 5 years of age is not recommended (4,5).

4. At any age, when clinical findings point to a specific site of injury, the customary protocol for imaging that region should be used.

A skeletal survey for suspected abuse should be performed by radiology technologists trained in dealing with children, and should be performed with high detail film-screen combinations (6-10). Each hospital should have a protocol for skeletal radiographs of children suspected of physical child abuse. A recommended protocol is shown on the next page.

Once the skeletal survey is obtained, the radiographs should be carefully reviewed by the radiologist prior to the child's departure from the radiology department, clinic, or hospital, whenever this is possible. This allows film quality to be checked, and additional repeat or coned views to be obtained to better image questioned areas of fractures or to better demonstrate subtle fractures, as necessary. Many of the fractures typical and diagnostic of child abuse may be subtle, especially metaphyseal corner fractures, bucket handle fractures, or rib fractures and may require additional views (6-8, 10-18). This requires careful attention to detail and excellent film quality (10). The same standard of film quality should be required for skeletal surveys on both live and dead children. Film quality should be maintained regardless of the legal jurisdiction of the child.

Skeletal radiographs for suspected child abuse should be interpreted by a radiologist trained in detecting child abuse. In some cases, when the films are initially interpreted by a radiologist lacking this expertise, a subsequent second opinion by a trained pediatric radiologist at a regional hospital or center may be necessary in the best interest of the child. Any positive findings of suspected physical abuse on the skeletal survey should be urgently called to the ordering physician or appropriate representative (9). Death or severe morbidity of a child could occur, if the child is inadvertently sent home with potentially abusive parents or caretakers by a physician unaware of the positive skeletal findings seen by the radiologist. Any findings suggestive of child abuse should be reported to appropriate child protective services by a physician or other appropriate qualified personnel.

Skeletal injuries of child abuse have been classified by Kleinman (6, 7, 19) into high, moderate, and low specificity lesions, especially in infants. The presence of these lesions should be searched for when evaluating a skeletal survey for suspected child abuse.

The lesions of high specificity for child abuse include[b]

- Metaphyseal corner fractures or bucket handle fractures (12-15)
- Rib fractures, especially posterior rib fractures (16-18)
- Scapular fractures
- Spinous process fractures
- Sternal fractures

The lesions of moderate specificity for child abuse include[b]

- Multiple fractures
- Multiple fractures of varying stages of healing/ages
- Vertebral body fractures and subluxations
- Digital fractures
- Complex skull fractures
- Epiphyseal-separation fractures

The recommended skeletal survey includes the following films[a]

Skull	anterior-posterior (AP) and lateral views
Cervical Spine	lateral view
Chest	AP and lateral views (show detail of the ribs and thoracic spine)
Abdomen to include pelvis	AP view (includes frontal view lumbar spine)
Lumbar spine	lateral view
Bilateral upper extremities*	
– Both humeri	AP and lateral views**
– Both forearms	AP and lateral views**
– Both hands	Posterior-anterior (PA) or oblique views
Bilateral lower extremities*	
– Both femurs	AP and lateral views**
– Both tibias and fibulas	AP and lateral views**
– Both feet	AP View

*Each side of the body and each portion of each extremity should be collimated to the region and filmed separately (not together). This is important to maintain good bony detail necessary for proper detection of fractures.

**Lateral films should be obtained if there are any positive findings on the AP views; or if the radiologist is not present to review the films when taken. If the radiologist is present to review the skeletal survey before the patient leaves, the lateral views may be optional, as determined by the radiologist.

[a.] Modification from reference 9, and modified and copyright permission from reference 10.

The lesions of low specificity for child abuse, although very common, include[b]

- Long bone shaft fractures
- Clavicular fractures
- Linear skull fractures

NOTE: The lesions in the moderate and/or low specificity categories may move into the high specificity category, when the history provided is inconsistent with the injuries, or when the history of trauma is absent (6,7).

[b.]Modified and copyright permission from reference 19.

Classic Metaphyseal Fracture

The classic metaphyseal fracture may be seen either as a "metaphyseal corner fracture" or as "bucket handle" fracture on the radiograph, depending on the radiographic projection at the fracture site when the film is exposed. When the peripheral fracture fragment is projected tangentially to the X-ray beam, the fracture fragment appears as a triangular fragment, and gives the appearance of a metaphyseal corner fracture, see Figure 1 and 2. When the peripheral fracture fragment is projected obliquely to the X-ray beam, the fracture fragment appears as a curvilinear fragment, and resembles a bucket handle or part of a bucket handle, depending on the severity of the fracture and degree of disruption, see Figure 3 (6-8, 12-15). As exquisitely demonstrated by Kleinman and colleagues (6, 8, 12-15), in all cases, these metaphyseal fractures, on histologic specimens, represent a planar injury through the weakest part of the bone, the primary spongiosa of the metaphysis of the long bone. The fracture line angles away from the growth plate toward the metaphysis as it extends toward the periphery of the bone. The fracture cuts under the subperiosteal bone collar (which remains attached), and results in a fracture fragment that is thicker peripherally (6, 8, 12-15). This causes the appearance of the metaphyseal corner fractures and the bucket handle fractures on the radiographs, as a visible triangular bony fragment or bony bucket handle fragment separated by a visible lucency from the rest of the bony metaphysis at the fracture site, see Figure 1-3. These fractures are highly specific and are strong indications of child abuse, especially in infants. These injuries are caused by violent shearing as the extremities are pulled, twisted, or torqued in a violent manner; or by violent shaking with acceleration—deceleration injuries as the extremities flail (6, 8, 12-15).

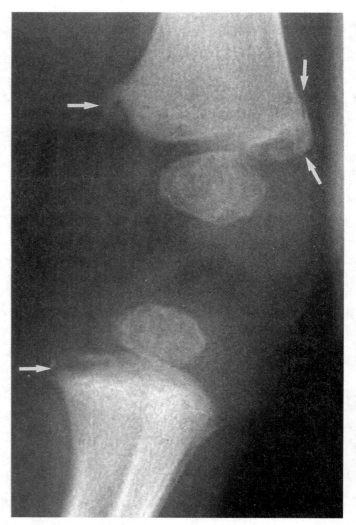

Figure 1 *Left knee, anteroposterior view, of a 1-month old abused infant girl, shows metaphyseal corner fractures of the distal femur and the proximal tibia (arrows).*

Posterior Rib Fractures

The posterior rib fractures, near the costotransverse process articulations (see Figure 4 and 5) result from excessive levering of the posterior ribs over the vertebral transverse processes, as the rib moves posteriorly with respect to the vertebral column during an attack (6, 8, 16-18). During abusive attacks, the abuser is usually facing the infant and holding the infant by the chest; while positioning the fingers in the back, palms at the side, and thumbs in the front. The abuser violently squeezes the infant, applying severe anteroposterior thoracic compression (6, 7, 16-18). At the same time, the infant may be shaken. Thus, posterior levering and fracturing of the posterior ribs occur during the anteroposterior thoracic compression. Similar type forces and mechanism could occur if an infant was violently slammed down face first onto a surface, or thrown face first onto a solid

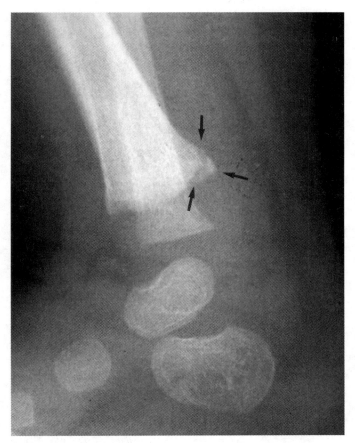

Figure 2 *Left ankle, lateral view, of a 2-month old abused infant boy shows a metaphyseal corner fracture of the posterior distal tibia (arrows).*

Skull Fractures

Skull fractures (Figure 7) are commonly seen in child abuse, but are again in the moderate and low specificity categories by themselves (6, 7, 19). Skull fractures need to be interpreted in the context of clinical history, severity, the presence or absence of intracranial injury and neurological signs, and the presence of retinal hemorrhages. Severe intracranial injuries resulting in mortality or severe morbidity may occur without the presence of a skull fracture or any external signs of trauma. Skull fractures rarely result from falls from short heights, and if they do result, they are not associated with intracranial injury (6, 7).

Dating of Skeletal Injuries

The dating of skeletal injuries is best provided by the radiologist (20). Dating is done by evaluating the appearance of the soft tissues, the amount of periosteal reaction, the amount of callus, the visibility of the fracture line, and the amount of bony remodeling (20). Correlation with the reported clinical history is also important in dating injuries. Limitations on the estimate of age depend on the date of imaging relative to the actual date of the discovered or reported injury, and many other factors. The accuracy of dating is best early after the injury. Often dating of injuries is at best an estimate of the age. The varied stages of healing of the bones, however, will give an estimate of the number of episodes of abusive trauma. The follow-up skeletal survey may provide assistance to the radiologist in dating of injuries (20).

Additional Studies

The need for additional studies such as bone scan, additional skeletal views, follow-up skeletal surveys, head CT or MRI, and other imaging modalities should be determined in consultation with the radiologist (5, 6, 7, 9).

Bone Scans

Bone scans should be used as a complement to the skeletal survey (5, 6). The bone scan is helpful to find occult fractures, confirm subtle suspected fractures, or to verify the presence of a fracture when poorly seen on skeletal radiographs. Bone scans may also be helpful when child abuse is suspected, and no fractures or only a single fracture is found on the skeletal survey. The finding of additional injuries on the bone scan may be crucial in making the diagnosis of abuse and protecting the child. Any positive areas discovered on the bone scan should be subsequently radiographed in at least two views (5, 6, 9). Although the bone scan is more sensitive than the skeletal survey, it is less specific (5, 6, 21).

object (17). In the absence of severe accidental forces with massive anteroposterior thoracic compression (such as a car accident), and in an otherwise normal infant, posterior rib fractures near the costovertebral junction are highly specific and strong indications of child abuse (17). However, rib fractures may occur in any location in abusive attacks.

Other Fractures

Scapular fractures (see Figure 6), spinous process fractures, and sternal fractures are highly specific for child abuse, but are uncommonly seen compared to the other fractures that occur in abuse (6, 7, 19). Multiple fractures and multiple fractures in different stages of healing (see Figures 1, and 3-6), are frequent hallmarks of abuse, but are in the moderate specificity group for child abuse. These injuries, as well as the other injuries in the moderate and low specificity group, as listed in the earlier section, must be combined with the clinical history and clinical exam to become high specificity lesions of abuse. The lesions in the moderate and low specificity groups may also become highly specific when seen in combination with other lesions in the high specificity categories (6, 7, 19).

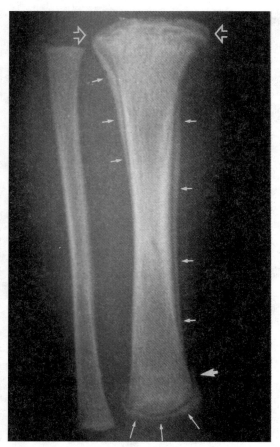

Figure 3 *Right tibia, anteroposterior view, of a 2-month old abused infant boy shows multiple fractures in different stages of healing. There is a bucket handle fracture of the distal tibia (long thin arrows) with associated small amount of adjacent periosteal reaction (closed arrowhead), indicating a subacute healing fracture. Mixed sclerosis and irregularity crossing the proximal tibial metaphysis (open arrowheads) indicates subacute healing metaphyseal corner fractures. The more extensive periosteal reaction along the medial and lateral tibial shaft (short thin arrows) indicated a more advanced stage of healing in the proximal fracture that in the distal tibial fracture. Vague curvilineal lucencies in the mid tibial shaft suggest the possibility of an old spiral tibial shaft fracture that may be healing, and difficult to see.*

Follow-up Skeletal Surveys

A follow-up skeletal survey may be helpful in selected cases to confirm subtle fractures; or to detect acute fractures, that may not have been apparent at the time of the initial skeletal survey. Fractures may not have been detectable on the initial skeletal survey because of lack of displacement at the fracture site, confluent shadows, overlapping structures, or lack of callus formation or periosteal reaction (5, 6, 11, 22). The follow-up skeletal survey is also helpful when the questions of abuse versus osteogenesis imperfecta arises as a cause of the fractures (22-27). Abusive fractures will cease to occur in a protected environment, and mineralization of

the bones may improve as the fractures heal. The follow-up skeletal survey may be helpful to show that there is no evidence of progressive bony deformity or bowing, continued fractures in a protected environment, or persistent osteopenia, that are common features in most cases of osteogenesis imperfecta (22-27).

Intracranial Injury

Intracranial injury from child abuse frequently results in death or severe morbidity, especially in infants and toddlers. Non-accidental or inflicted trauma is the most common cause of death from brain injury in children less than two year of age (33). All infants and children with suspected intracranial injury from abuse must be evaluated by cranial computed tomography (CT) and/or cranial magnetic resonance imaging (MRI). The initial evaluation of suspected acute intracranial injury is done to identify life threatening and acutely treatable conditions. Cranial CT, generally, is the first neuroimaging study of choice to be performed, and is well suited to diagnose acute hemorrhage. However, cranial MRI is significantly more sensitive than cranial CT in completely identifying, characterizing, and showing extent of intracranial injuries along with their complications due to child abuse (5, 33). Unfortunately, the critically injured and unstable child often cannot be transported to the MRI scanner, or there are other technical limitations, not allowing the performance of the MRI scan (33). Subdural hematomas and other subdural fluid collections, particularly over the cerebral convexities and along the falx; cortical contusions; cerebral hemorrage and/or edema; and white matter injuries are well documented with MRI (5, 33). Hyperacute and acute subarachnoid hemorrhage and some acute subdural hematomas are better demonstrated with cranial CT than MRI (33). MRI is more accurate in determining the characterization, extent, and age of subdural hematomas and other intracranial hemorrhages, when compared to cranial CT. MRI is more useful for trying to determine the age and number of intracranial injuries than CT. After a cranial CT shows positive findings of intracranial injury, cranial MRI is usually performed to more fully delineate the extent of intracranial injury and to help predict the clinical outcome. Cranial MRI should be performed as early as possible after the CT, when the clinical findings (neurological signs and symptoms) are not adequately explained by the abnormal findings on the CT; or the CT is normal and the child has unexplained neurological signs and symptoms. MRI should be performed in children with chronic neurological signs and symptoms; in infants with shaken baby syndrome without neurological signs and symptoms; or in children with non-specific clinical findings or no neurological signs or symptoms along

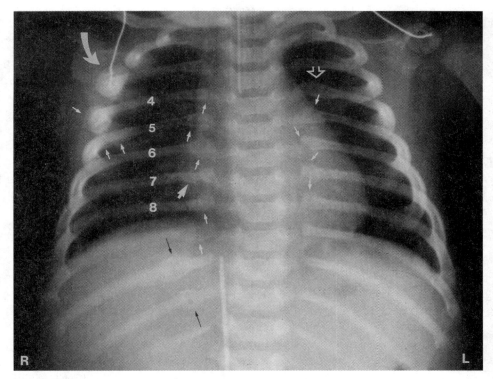

Figure 4a

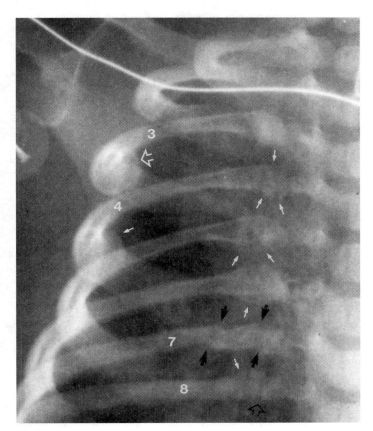

Figure 4b

Figures 4a and 4b *Chest radiograph, posterior-anterior view, 4a, and coned rib detail view, 4b, of a 10-week old abused infant boy shows multiple rib fractures in different stages of healing.*

In 4a, there is healed fracture of the left posterior medial 4th rib (open white arrowhead). In 4a, there are subacute healing fractures of the left 5-8th; right 4-6th; and right 8-11th posterior medial ribs; and right 4th lateral rib (closed thin black and short white arrows); with varying amounts of surrounding callus. Subtle periosteal reaction is present on the underside of the right posterior lateral 5th rib (two adjacent small white arrows). Fracture sites with fracture lines still visible along with the surrounding callus are best demonstrated in the right posterior medial 10th and 11th ribs (thin black arrows). The visibility of the fracture line in conjunction with the callus; as opposed to rib fractures with callus without a remaining visible fracture line, may indicate fractures of varying ages. However, they may also result from differences in radiographic projection at different fracture sites. Follow-up skeletal surveys or additional views may be helpful in further distinction.

The right posterior medial 7th rib is angulated in Figure 4a (white arrowhead), suggesting an occult fracture in this area, and detail of this rib is better seen in the coned rib view, 4b. In Figure 4b, there is a segmental fracture of the posterior medial 7th rib, near the costovertebral junction, with two step-offs (black arrowheads). There is absent or minimal surrounding callus, when compared to the ribs above and below, indicating that this fracture is more acute, and of a different age than some of the other fractures.

In 4a, an EKG lead (curved white arrow) is obscuring a right lateral 3rd rib fracture with callus; which is seen in 4b (open white arrowhead) after the EKG lead was removed. This points out the importance of removing these leads and any other overlying clothing or materials before imaging children for suspected abuse. Details of the other right rib fractures (except the lower ribs), seen in 4a, are also better seen in 4b; especially the posterior 8th rib, where the fracture line is now visible (open black arrowhead).

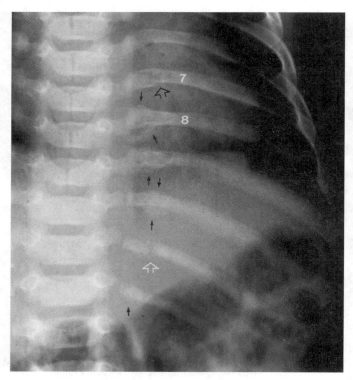

Figure 5 *Left rib coned anteroposterior detailed view, of a 4-month old abused infant boy, shows rib fractures in different stages of healing. There is an acute fracture of the left posterior medial 7th rib at the costovertebral junction (open black arrowhead) with no signs of healing. There are subacute healing fractures of the left posterior medial 8th through 12th ribs with surrounding varying small amounts of callus (closed black arrows and open white arrowhead). In the posterior medial 11th rib (open white arrowhead) a fracture line remains visible in the presence of surrounding callus. This suggests a rib fracture that is younger in age than the other healing rib fractures which contain more callus, but no longer have a visible fracture line.*

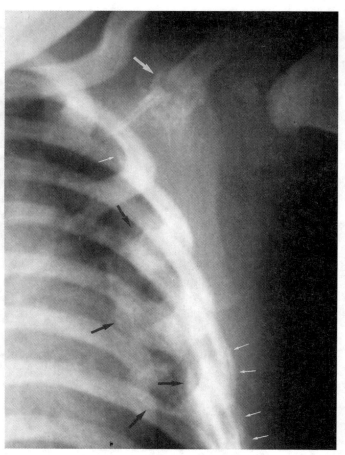

Figure 6 *Left shoulder, anteroposterior view, of a 3 and 1/2 month old abused infant girl shows a healing fracture of the left acromion (white large arrow) with surrounding callus. There are multiple overlapping fractures of the left lateral ribs with associated extensive sclerosis, periosteal reaction (small white arrows), and exuberant callus (black arrows).*

with the presence of other severe indications of severe physical abuse (5, 33).

In infants, although cranial ultrasound (US) may detect intracranial abnormalities, it does not replace cranial CT or MRI as the primary imaging modality in the evaluation of suspected intracranial injury in child abuse. US is not used to exclude subdural hematoma or intracranial injury in abuse. However, US may be useful in the acutely and critically ill infant in the intensive care unit, when the infant cannot be transported to CT or MRI. Under these circumstances it is helpful in identifying subdural hematomas or other fluid collections, frontoparietal white matter tears, and the presence of cerebral blood flow. US may be helpful in distinguishing convexity subdural fluid collections from enlargement of the subarachnoid spaces. In infants, US may be useful in the follow-up of subdural hematomas or other subdural fluid collections to evaluate their progression or resolution after treatment (33).

A complete discussion of neuroimaging in child abuse is beyond the scope of this article.

Thoracoabdominal Trauma

There are many potential approaches to the evaluation of the thoracoabdominal injuries in child abuse. The imaging of each child suspected of having thoracoadominal injuries is usually approached individually, depending on the clinical presentation; and is done in consultation with the radiologist. However, some general guidelines for imaging thoracoabdominal injuires from trauma due to suspected child abuse can be made. Major blunt and penetrating thoracoabdomial injury is uncommon in the infant, and more common and critical in the toddler and young child (5, 34).

Acute thoracoabdominal injuries from child abuse should be imaged like any other severe accidental trauma (5, 34). Initially, chest and lateral cervical spine plain films

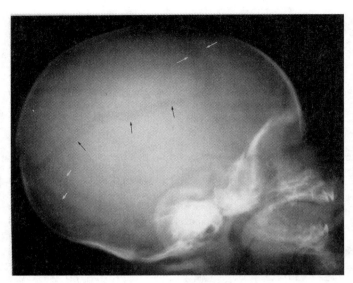

Figure 7 *Skull, lateral view, of a 6-week old abuse infant girl shows a diastatic linear parietal skull fracture (thin black arrows) extending from the lambdoid suture (short white arrows) to the coronal suture (thin white arrows). Both lambdoid sutures are visible in the posterior occiput due to the slight obliquity of the skull view, and do not represent fractures. There is associated widening of the coronal and lambdoid sutures. The diastasis at the fractures site and the widened sutures suggest increased intracranial pressure and intracranial injury. This indicates the need for a head CT and/or MRI.*

should be done to rapidly check for life threatening injuries. In the critically ill patient, if acute bowel perforation is suspected, plain films of the abdomen (supine and upright or decubitus views) should be done to detect free air. This will obviate the need for further imaging, as the child will go to the operating room (34). Severe injuries of the thorax (such as pneumothorax, pleural effusion, flail chest, or lung parenchymal injury) are rapidly imaged and easily diagnosed by chest radiographs, and then, chest computed tomography (CT) with intravenous contrast. Chest CT with intravenous contrast more completely diagnoses and evaluates the extent and severity of the lung parenchymal or pleural injury, mediastinal injury, fluid collections, lung/mediastinal abscess, and other intrathoracic injuries with their complications. Most life threatening intraabdominal injuries, such as bowel perforations; major lacerations of the liver, spleen, pancreas, or kidneys; are readily diagnosed by abdominal CT with intravenous contrast. Pancreatic injuries and pancreatic pseudocysts are well seen by abdominal CT and/or ultrasound. Hematomas of the duodenum or intestine are well detected by abdominal CT with oral contrast. However, small intestinal hematomas may be missed by CT, and only detected on upper gastrointestinal (UGI) or UGI with small-bowel-follow-through (UGI with SBFT) contrast studies. Of the gastrointestinal hematomas that occur in child abuse, duodenal hematoma is the most common. When duodenal hematoma or pancreatic pseudocyst are found in young children, they are often the result of physical child abuse, and the etiology of their presence should be investigated. Chest and abdominal CT can best evaluate the extent of injury and diagnose multiple thoracoabdominal injuries at once, potentially eliminating the need for other diagnostic imaging modalities. Although abdominal ultrasound may initially readily detect some intraabdominal injuries related to abuse, especially in infants under 1 year of age (5), abdominal CT is usually more efficient. CT and/or ultrasound may be helpful in follow-up studies, once initial injuries are fully identified and evaluated. To diagnose strictures of the esophagus and other parts of the gastrointestinal tract, or to diagnose occult perforation, contrast gastrointestinal (GI) studies may be required. Plain films of the neck and/or esophagrams/swallows with barium or non-ionic contrast are necessary to detect injuries of the pharynx, hypopharynx, or esophagus, including perforations. Abdomen, chest and/or neck CT are required to detect abscesses, and other complications that may result from abusive injuries. Rarely, angiography is needed when vascular injury is suspected (5, 34).

A complete discussion of thoracoabdominal imaging in child abuse is beyond the scope of this article.

Differential Diagnosis

The differential diagnosis of child abuse includes a large number of disorders: birth trauma, physiologic periosteal reaction of the newborn, congenital indifference to pain, myelodysplasia, neurologic disorders, osteogenesis imperfecta, osteomyelitis, congenital syphilis, rickets, scurvy, vitamin A intoxication, Caffey's disease, leukemia, prostaglandin E therapy, copper deficiency, methotrexate therapy, or Menkes' syndrome (23-27, 28-30). These disorders may present with metaphyseal irregularities, periosteal reaction, and/or fractures. Most of these conditions are easily recognized by radiographic features in conjunction with physical examination, clinical and family history, and laboratory parameters. The most common conditions that may be confused with child abuse are osteogenesis imperfecta, and metabolic or infectious bone diseases. The majority of these are not difficult to differentiate from child abuse by pediatric radiologist trained in their recognition with proper communication with the ordering physician or appropriate physician consults, such as a geneticist or orthopedist. Excellent reviews of the differential diagnosis of child abuse and the distinction of child abuse from osteogenesis imperfecta are already present in the literature

(23-27, 28-30). Only in selected cases, when the question of abuse versus osteogenesis imperfecta remains after a careful clinical and radiographic evaluation by experienced radiologists/physicians, may a skin biopsy for collagen analysis be helpful (23-27, 31, 32). In your community, clinic, or hospital, if difficulty arises in determining the proper diagnosis, referral to a regional center for expert consultation with a pediatric radiologist, pediatrician, or other physician specialist is recommended. The safety of the potentially abused child is of utmost importance.

Interpretation and Consultation

It is important that all diagnostic imaging be interpreted in consultation with the ordering physician along with the pertinent clinical history, physical examination, and laboratory parameters. Information on the presence of retinal hemorrhages, a summary of the birth history, whether or not the infant was a premature baby, a family history, scleral color, and the reported mechanism of injury are all important in the interpretation of the diagnostic imaging assessments.

References

1. Caffey, J. Multiple fractures in the long bones of infants suffering from chronic subdural hematoma. *Am J Roentgenology (AJR)*, 56:163-173, 1946.

2. Kemp, C.H., Silverman, F.N., Steele, B.F., Droegemueller, W., Silver, H.K. The battered-child syndrome. *JAMA*, 181:105-112, 1962.

3. U.S. Department of Health and Human Services, Children's Bureau. *Child Maltreatment 1996: Reports from the States to the National Child Abuse and Neglect Data System.* Washington, DC, U.S. Government Printing Office, 1998.

4. Merten, D.F., Radkowski, M.A., Leonidas, J.C. The abuse child: a radiological reappraisal. *Radiology*, 146:377-381, 1983.

5. Haller, J.O., Kleinman, P.K., Merten, D.F., Cohen, H.L., Cohen, M.D., Hayden, P.W., Keller, M., Towbin, R., Sane, S.M. Diagnostic Imaging of Child Abuse, Section on Radiology. American Academy of Pediatrics Policy Statement. *Pediatrics*, 87: 262-264, 1991.

6. Kleinman, P.K. *Diagnostic Imaging of Child Abuse.* Second edition. Mosby, Inc., St. Louis, 1998.

7. Kleinman, P.K. Diagnostic imaging in infant abuse. *AJR*, 155:703-712, 1990.

8. Kleinman, P.K., Marks, S.C. Jr, Richmond, J.M., Blackbourn, B.D. Inflicted skeletal injury: post- mortem radiologic-histopathologic study in 31 infants. *AJR*, 165:647-650, 1995.

9. American College of Radiology: ACR Standards 1999-2000. ACR standards for skeletal surveys in children. Res 22-1997, Reston, Va, 51-54, 1999.

10. Belanger, P.L. Chapter 23. Quality assurance and skeletal survey standards. In: Kleiman, P.K. Diagnostic Imaging of Child Abuse. Second edition. Mosby, Inc., St. Louis, 418-424, and Box 23-1, 422, 1998.

11. Kleinman, P.K., Marks, S.C. Jr, Adams, V.I., Blackbourne, B.D. Factors affecting visualization of posterior rib fractures in abused infants. *AJR*, 150:635-638, 1988.

12. Kleinman, P.K., Marks, S.C. Jr. A regional approach to the metaphyseal lesion in abused infants: proximal tibia. *AJR*, 166:421-426, 1996.

13. Kleinman, P.K., Marks, S.C. Jr. A regional approach to the metaphyseal lesion in abused infants: distal tibia. *AJR*, 166, 1207-1212, 1996.

14. Kleinman, P.K., Marks, S.C. Jr. A regional approach to the metaphyseal lesion in abused infants: proximal humerus. *AJR*, 167:1399-1403, 1996.

15. Kleinman, P.K., Marks, S.C. Jr. A regional approach to the classic metaphyseal lesion in abused infants: the distal femur. *AJR*, 170:43-47, 1998.

16. Kleinman, P.K., Marks, S.C. Jr, Nimkin, K., Rayder, S.M., Kessler, S.C. Rib fractures in 31 abused infants: post-mortem radiologic-histopathologic study. *Radiology*, 200:807-810, 1996.

17. Kleinman, P.K., Schlesinger, A.E. Mechanical factors associated with posterior rib fractures: laboratory and case studies. *Pediatr Radiol*, 27:87-91, 1997.

18. Kleinman, P.K., Marks, S.C. Jr, Spevak, M.R., Richmond, J.M. Fractures of the rib head in abused infants. *Radiology*, 185:119-123, 1992.

19. Kleinman, P.K. Chapter 2. Skeletal Trauma: General Considerations. In: Kleiman, P.K. Diagnostic Imaging of Child Abuse. Second edition. Mosby, Inc., St. Louis, pg. 9 and Box 2-1, 1998.

20. O'Connor, J.F., Cohen, J. Dating Fractures. In: Kleinman, P.K. *Diagnostic Imaging of Child Abuse.* Second Edition. Mosby, Inc., St. Louis, 1998, 168-177.

21. Sty, J., Starshak, R.J. The role of bone scintigraphy in the evaluation of the suspected abused child. Radiology, 146: 369-375, 1983.

22. Kleinman, P.K., Nimkin, K., Spevak, M.R., et al. Follow-up skeletal surveys in suspected child abuse. *AJR*, 167:893-896, 1996.

23. Ablin, D.S., Sane, S.M. Non-accidental injury: confusion with temporary brittle bone disease and mild osteogenesis imperfecta. *Pediatr Radiol*, 27:111-113, 1997.

24. Chapman, S., Hall, C.M. Non-accidental injury or brittle bones. *Pediatr Radiol*, 27:106-110, 1997.

25. Ablin, D.S. Osteogenesis Imperfecta: A review. *Can Assoc Radiol J*, 49:110-123, 1998.

26. Ablin, D.S., Greenspan, A., Reinhart, M., Grix, A. Differentiation of child abuse from osteogenesis imperfecta. *AJR*, 154:1035-1046, 1990.

27. Lachman, R.S., Krakow, D., Kleinman, P.K. Differential Diagnosis II: Osteogenesis Imperfecta. In: Kleinman, P.K. *Diagnostic Imaging of Child Abuse*. Second Edition. Mosby, Inc., St. Louis, 1998, 197-213.

28. Hilton, S. vW. Chapter 14. Differentiating the accidentally injured from the physically abused child. In: Hilton, S. vW; and Edwards, D.K. *Practical Pediatric Radiology*. Second edition. W.B. Saunders, Philadelphia, 1994, 389-436.

29. Brill, P.W., Winchester, P., Kleinman, P.K. Differential Diagnosis I: Diseases simulating abuse. In: Kleinman, P.K. *Diagnostic Imaging of Child Abuse*. Second Edition. Mosby, Inc., St. Louis, 178-196, 1998.

30. Kleinman, P.K. Differential Diagnosis III: Accidental and obstetric trauma. In: Kleinman, P.K. *Diagnostic Imaging of Child Abuse*. Second Edition. Mosby, Inc., St. Louis, 214-224, 1998.

31. Steiner, R.D., Pepin, M., Byers, P.H. Studies of collagen synthesis and structure in the differentiation of child abuse from osteogenesis imperfecta. *Journal of Pediatrics*, 128:542-547, 1996.

32. Wenstrup, R.J., Willing, M.C., Starman, B.J., Byers, P.H. Distinct biochemical phenotypes predict clinical severity in nonlethal variants of osteogenesis imperfecta. *Am J Hum Genet*, 46:975-982, 1990.

33. Kleinman, P.K., Barnes, P.D. Chapter 15. Head Trauma. In: Kleinman PK. Diagnostic Imaging of Child Abuse. Second edition. Mosby, Inc., St. Louis, 285-342, 1998.

34. Kleinman, P.K. Chapter 14. Visceral Trauma. In: Kleinman, P.K. Diagnostic Imaging of Child Abuse. Second edition., Mosby, Inc., St. Louis, 248-284, 1998.

Oral and Dental Aspects of Child Abuse and Neglect

Stephen M. Blain, D.D.S., M.S., Norman "Skip" Sperber, D.D.S. and Kathleen A. Shanel-Hogan, D.D.S., M.A.

Case Vignette

A healthy 3-year old male presented to the pediatric dental clinic with his mother with the complaint of "bad teeth". The clinical exam revealed a child with a missing maxillary incisor, multiple caries and poor oral hygiene. In addition, hematomas in different stages of healing were noted on the right eye, on the legs and right arm. Four weeks later, the patient again presented for treatment. A hematoma was noted on the child's left eye. Upon questioning the sister and the patient's mother, it was reported that the child had fallen on flat flag stones while trying to ride on top of a dog. The child was in the care of this sister at the time while she was visiting her boyfriend. The mother and sister also reported that the reason that the patient had so many bruises was because of his constant activity. It was also discovered that the child had a hip fracture at 6 months of age for some "unknown" reason. Contact with the Department of Social Services revealed that the mother canceled the following two appointments and failed to follow-up with any additional appointments for treatment.

Questions

1. Describe five types of oral injuries caused by physical abuse.

2. Describe considerations in sexual abuse cases for oral health.

3. What are the signs of dental neglect?

Physical Abuse

Craniofacial, head, face and neck injuries occur in 65% of the cases of child abuse. Careful intraoral and perioral examination is necessary in all cases of suspected abuse. The American Academy of Pediatrics and the American Academy of Pediatric Dentistry in their August, 1999 Joint Policy Statement reviewed the literature and reported that:

- Blunt trauma injuries are most commonly inflicted with an object, eating utensils, hands, or fingers; or, by scalding liquids or caustic substances. This may result in contusions; lacerations of the tongue, buccal mucosa, palate (soft and hard), gingiva alveolar mucosa or frenum; fractured, displaced, or avulsed teeth; facial bone and jaw fractures; burns; or other injuries. These injuries, including a lacerated frenulum, also can result from unintentional trauma.

- Discolored teeth, indicating pulpal necrosis, may result from previous injury.

- Gags applied to the mouth may leave bruises or scarring at the corners of the mouth.

- Multiple injuries, injuries in different stages of healing, injuries inappropriate for the child's stage of development, or, a discrepant history should arouse suspicion of abuse. Age-appropriate non-abusive injuries to the mouth are common and must be distinguished from abuse based on history, the circumstances of the injury and pattern of trauma, and, the history given and/or behavior of the child, caregiver, or both.

- The key factor in evaluating these cases is whether the observed injuries are consistent with the history supplied by the caretaker and/or the child. For example, if a child presents a fracture near the angle of the mandible, and there are no abrasions or lacerations of the soft tissues in that area, and history discloses that the child fell on a patch of concrete, there is an obvious inconsistency.

Sexual Abuse

The oral cavity is a frequent site of sexual abuse in children. The presence of oral and perioral gonorrhea or syphilis in prepubertal children is pathognomonic of sexual abuse. Pharyngeal gonorrhea is frequently asymptomatic. Unexplained erythema or petechiae of the palate, particularly at the junction of the hard and soft palate, may be evidence of forced oral sex. Although cases of syphilis are rare in the sexually abused child, oral lesions also should be sought and dark-field examinations performed. Oral or perioral condylomata acuminata, although probably most frequently caused by sexual contact, may be the result of contact with verruca vulgaris or self-innoculation.

Dental Neglect

Fifty per cent of 200 children evaluated at UC Davis Medical Center's Foster Care Health Program in 1999 showed evidence of dental neglect (Unpublished study, 2001). Dental neglect, as defined by the American Academy of Pediatric Dentistry is "the willful failure of parent or guardian to seek and follow through with treatment necessary to ensure a level of oral health essential for adequate function and freedom from pain and infection." Dental caries, periodontal diseases, and other oral conditions, if left untreated, can lead to pain, infection, and loss of function. Untreated dental infection can develop into system infection. These undesirable outcomes can adversely affect learning, communication, nutrition, and other activities necessary for normal growth and development.

Recommendations

1. When a child has oral injuries or dental neglect is suspected, consult with the child's dentist, a pediatric dentist or a dentist with formal training in forensic odontology.

2. Collaborations between pediatricians, child abuse medical experts, and pediatric dentists is recommended. The child's dentist may have important clinical history and observations that can provide collaboration to current observations.

3. Pediatric dentists and oral and maxillofacial surgeons, whose advanced education programs include a mandated child abuse curriculum, can provide valuable information and assistance to physicians about oral and dental aspects of child abuse and neglect.

4. Dentists, registered dental hygienists, and registered dental assistants are mandated reporters of child

abuse/neglect, domestic violence, and elder abuse/neglect. The California Dental Association's Abuse Detection and Education Program is continuing the work began by the P.A.N.D.A. Coalition in 1994 to educate dental professionals to recognize and report abuse and neglect. Collaboration between dental professionals and the community is encouraged to increase awareness of oral abuse and neglect and the legal responsibilities of the mandated reporter.

5. All children placed in foster care should be screened for dental problems during the required medical examination within 30 days of placement into foster care and referred for immediate dental care when outstanding problems are identified by a pediatrician. All children should be referred for routine dental examinations upon placement in foster care.

Resources

California Dental Association *Abuse Detection and Education Program* which incorporates the P.A.N.D.A. (Prevent Child Abuse and Neglect through Dental Awareness) Program.

California Medical Protocol for Examination of Sexual Assault and Child Sexual Abuse Victims published by the State Office of Criminal Justice Planning. http://www.ocjp.ca.gov/

References

Blain, S. Abuse and neglect as a compound of pediatric treatment planning. *CDA Journal*, 19(9):16-24, 1991.

Becker, D.B., Needleman, H.L., Kotelchuck, M. Child Abuse and dentistry: Orofacial trauma and its recognition by dentists. *Journal of the American Dental Association*. 97:24-28, 1978.

California Society of Pediatric Dentists. Dental neglect: When to report. *California Pediatrician*, Fall:31-32, 1989.

Chue, P.W. Gonorrhea: Its natural history, oral manifestations, diagnosis, treatment, and prevention. *Journal of the American Dental Association*. 90:1297-1301, 1975.

Donly, K.J., Nowak, A.J. Maxillofacial, neck, and dental lesions of child abuse. In: Reece, R.M., ed. *Child Abuse: Medical Diagnosis and Management*. Lea & Febiger, Philadelphia, 1994, chapter 7.

Folland, D.S., Burke, R.E., Hinman, A.R., Schaffner, W. Gonorrhea in preadolescent children: An inquiry into source of infection and mode of transmission. *Pediatrics*, 60:153-156, 1977.

Jessee, S.A. Child Abuse: Physical manifestations of child abuse to the head, face, and mouth: A hospital survey. *ASDC Journal of Dent Child*, 62:245-249, 1995.

Jessee, S.A., Rieger, M. A study of age-related variables among physically abused children. *ASDC Journal of Dent Child*, 63:275-280, 1996.

Kenney, J.P., Clark, D.H. Child Abuse. In Clark DH, ed. *Practical Forensic Odontology*. Wright, London, 1992.

Malecz, R.E. Child abuse, its relationship to pedodontics: A survey. *ASDC Journal of Dent Child*, 46:193-194, 1979.

Needleman, H.L. Orofacial trauma in child abuse: Types, prevalence, management, and the dental profession's involvement. *Pediatric Dentistry*, 8 (special issue):71-80, 1986.

Nelson, J.D., Mohs, E., Dajani, A.S., et al. Gonorrhea in preschool- and school-aged children: Report of the prepubertal gonorrhea cooperative study group. *JAMA*, 236:1359-1364, 1976.

Oral and Dental Aspects of Child Abuse and Neglect. Joint policy statement of the American Academy of Pediatrics and the American Academy of Pediatric Dentistry. *American Academy of Pediatrics*, 104 (2), 1999.

Sanger, R.G., Bross, D.C., eds. *Clinical Management of Child Abuse and Neglect: A Guide for the Dental Professional*. Quintessence Publishing Co, Inc., Chicago, 1984.

Schlesinger, S.L., Borbotsina, J., O'Neill, L. Petechial hemorrhages of the soft palate secondary to fellatio. *Oral Surgery, Oral Medicine, and Oral Pathology*. 40:376-378, 1975.

Schwartz, S., Woolridge, E., and Stege, D. The Oral Manifestation and Legal Aspects of Child Abuse. *JADA*, 95(3):586, September, 1977.

Seidel, J., Zonana, J., Totten, E. *Condylomata acuminata* as a sign of sexual abuse in children. *Journal of Pediatrics*, 95:553-554, 1979.

Shanel-Hogan, K.A., Jarrett, J.A. Reporting child abuse and neglect: Responding to a cry for help. *Journal of the California Dental Association*, 27:869-879, 1999.

Sognnaes, R.F., Blain, S.M. Child Abuse and Neglect, I: Diagnostic criteria of special interest to dentists, abstracted. *Journal of Dental Research*, 58:367, 1979.

Sperber, N.D. Bite marks, oral and facial injuries: Harbingers of severe child abuse? *Pediatrician*, 16:208-211, 1989.

Investigation of Human Bite Marks

The photographs in the chapter can be viewed online at the Volcano Press website: www.volcanopress.com/booksupplements

Norman "Skip" Sperber, D.D.S.

Case Vignette

A child is brought to a hospital for treatment of immersion burns seen on the legs and abdomen. Later radiographs reveal healing fracture of the right leg and left rib area. At the time of admission, physicians also noted purplish lesions on the left chest above the nipple and also on the right forearm. The lesions are described as approximately 30mm in diameter. The injury on the chest consists of two diffused arch-like areas, resembling two horseshoes with the ends pointing at each other. The bruise on the forearm is near the radius bone and consists of a diffused arch-like lesion on the ventral surface with eight dark lesions arranged in a half-circle approximately 35mm in breadth on the dorsal area.

Questions

1. Describe five examples of shapes of bite marks.

2. How can animal bites be differentiated from human bites?

3. What evidence documentation and collection procedures should be initiated?

Introduction

Bite marks are lesions that may indicate abuse. Human bite marks are a type of physical abuse sometimes seen on adults and children, who are victims of domestic violence, elder abuse, child abuse, sexual assault, and homicides. Individuals can be identified by the size and shape of their bite marks. Properly taken photographs of bite marks and bruises can assist in the identification of the person who inflicted the injury.

Differentiation Between Animal and Human Bite Marks

1. **Non-human bites**

   Animals such as dogs and large cats (i.e. pumas) will typically leave puncture marks in the skin. These marks will usually reflect the canine teeth (upper and lower) and will generally assume a pattern as below.

   Figure 1. The line of incision between the puncture marks represent the canine teeth on either side, leaving the wound as the upper and lower jaws come together.

2. **Human bites**

   Human bites may also reflect the canine teeth but they will usually include the incisors as well, due to the relative flatness of the edges of human teeth when compared to those of animals.

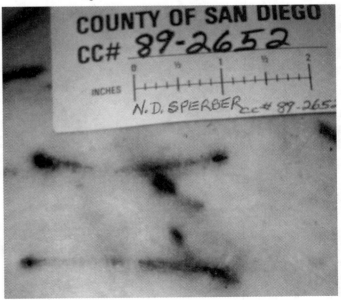

Figure 1

61

Recognition of Human Bite Marks

Bite marks should be suspected when ecchymoses, abrasions, or lacerations are found in an elliptical or ovoid pattern. Bite marks may have a central area of ecchymoses (contusion) caused by positive pressure from closing of the teeth with disruption of small vessels. The normal distance between the maxillary canine teeth in adult humans in 2.5 to 4.0 cm, and the canine marks in a bite will be the most prominent or deep parts of the bite. Bites produced by dogs and other carnivorous animals tend to tear flesh, whereas human bites compress flesh and can cause abrasions, contusions, lacerations, but rarely avulsions of tissue. If the intercanine distance is <2.5cm, the bite may have been caused by a child. If the intercanine distance is 2.5 to 3.0 cm, the bite was probably produced by a child or a small adult; if the distance is >3.0 cm, the bite was probably caused by an adult.

Recommended Consultations

The pattern, size, contour, and color(s) of the bite mark should be evaluated by a forensic odontologist. Since each person has a characteristic bite pattern, a forensic odontologist may be able to match dental models (casts) of a suspected abuser's teeth with impressions or photographs of the bite.

Since skin is not an ideal medium for the production of bite marks, these lesions often have different appearances, due to the distortion caused by manipulation, gravity, the flaccidity or lack of flaccidity of the underlying tissues and the effect of gravity. Physicians or investigators will usually

not see actual indentations in the skin but rather bruises or contusions below the skin, and above the adipose layer.

Bite marks may be recognized as:

- double horseshoe configurations (Figures 2a, 2b, 2c, 2d);
- doughnut shaped lesions;
- oval shaped lesions;
- individual teeth markings of either one or both jaws; and
- perforations or lacerations of the skin.

It should be noted that the darker the epithelial pigmentation of the individual who has been bitten, the more difficult it may be to detect bite marks.

Collection of Evidence

1. **Photograph bite marks.**

   Photographs should be taken as soon as possible after the bite mark is discovered. Ideally, color film with appropriate lighting should be used. In addition, alternate light sources are also recommended during photographic procedures. These light sources may include reflective ultraviolet and fluorescent photography. The camera (preferably a 35mm, or other non-distorting type) is placed at right angles to the various curves of the bite (see Figure 3). Orienting photographs are taken before cleaning or wiping the area. A scale or ruler should be placed near the bite mark in some of the photographs. A special photographic scale was developed by the American Board of Forensic Odontology (ABFO) for this purpose as well as for documenting other patterned injuries and can be obtained from the vendor. See the resource list on the next page for a reference.

2. **Swab bite mark areas for DNA and blood type evidence.**

   After taking the initial photographs, crime laboratory personnel or other forensic experts should swab the site with distilled, deionized, or sterile water. Collect a control swab from an unbitten atraumatic area adjacent to the suspected saliva stain. Label swabs, air dry in a swab drying box, and seal in a labeled envelope. All samples should be sent to the local crime laboratory for analysis. The chain of custody must be maintained on all samples sent for forensic analysis.

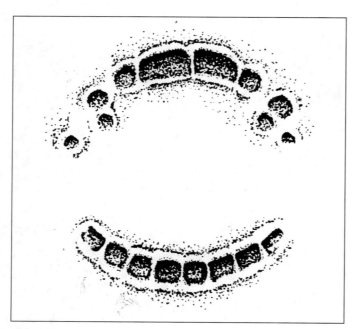

Figure 2a

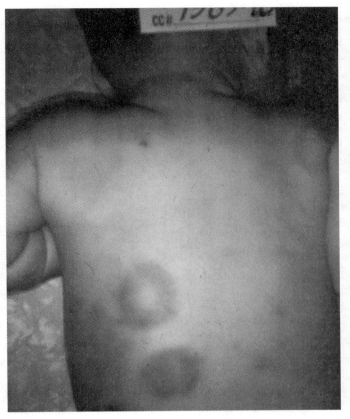

Figure 2b

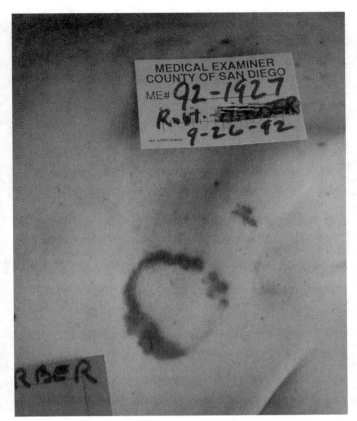

Figure 2c

3. Final photography.

After swabbing for salivary residue, the area is cleansed and an orienting photograph taken (an orienting photograph illustrates the relationship of the bite mark to the body). A ruler is placed as close to the bite mark as possible without obscuring it. Employing a flexible ruler or tape measure is not satisfactory for this procedure because distortion will occur on curved services. Close-up photography should be taken with the ruler in close proximity to the marks as in Figure 3. The ruler should be parallel to the camera lens to avoid distortion. This procedure is especially important if bite marks are discovered on round areas such as the shoulders, arms, legs, or breasts. Photographs should be repeated for at least three days at approximately 24-hour intervals on living and deceased victims together with written observations to document the evolution and age of the bite. When possible, an autopsy should not be performed before photographing. Incisions in the proximity of bite marks area are also to be avoided prior to taking photographs or collecting bite mark impressions.

4. Bite mark impressions.

Bite mark impressions should be taken by a forensic odontologist or a dentist using standard dental impression materials. This procedure should be undertaken if it is obvious that skin perforation has occurred.

Selected Readings

Manual of Forensic Odontology, 3rd Edition, 1997 (Printing Specialists, Montpelier, Vermont, 05602)

Bitemark Evidence in Crimes Against Persons, Norman D. Sperber, DDS, *FBI Law Enforcement Bulletin,* July 1981.

California Medical Protocol for Examination of Sexual Assault and Child Sexual Abuse Victims, July, 2002. Published by the State Office of Criminal Justice Planning, 1130 K Street, Sacramento, CA 95814. http://www.ocjp.ca.gov/

Oral and Dental Aspects of Child Abuse and Neglect. Joint policy statement of the American Academy of Pediatrics and the American Academy of Pediatric Dentistry. *American Academy of Pediatrics,* 104 (2), 1999.

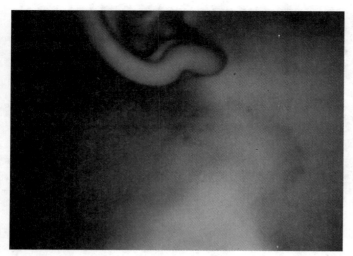

Figure 2d

Resources

American Board of Forensic Odontology (ABFO)
www.abfo.org

Lightning Powder Company, Jacksonville, Florida
http://www.redwop.com/technotes.asp

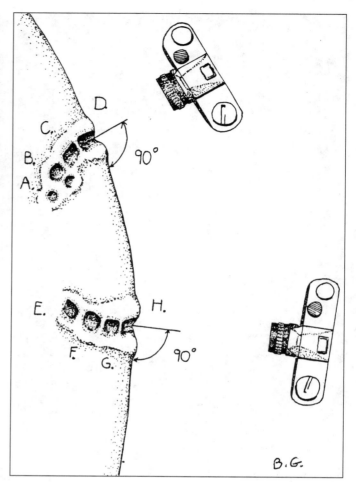

Figure 3

Conditions that Mimic Child Abuse

Stephen C. Boos, M.D.

Case Vignette

A two-year old boy is brought to the clinic by a daycare supervisor with a large purple hematoma over his left mandible. She says he slipped while drinking from the drinking fountain and struck his jaw on the rim. In addition to this index injury, there are multiple bruises of the face and forehead. When he is undressed, multiple bruises of the back, flanks, and buttocks are seen, as well as assorted bruises of the thighs, knees and shins. The daycare supervisor says she has not seen the other injuries before but the facial bruising was first noted this week.

Questions

1. Other than child abuse, what may be the cause of this extensive new onset bruising?

2. How should this child be evaluated?

3. What other medical conditions may present as possible child abuse?

Epidemiology

Approximately three million cases of child maltreatment are reported in the United States every year. Of those three million cases, one million are usually substantiated, with the others being dismissed. Many of these dismissed cases result from reports of false or misunderstood information. In others, the report is correct but the standard for defining abuse is not met. Some of these cases, however, have other medical conditions which were mistaken for abuse. What are these conditions? How often are they mistaken for abuse? How cautious must medical providers be to avoid such misdiagnosis?

Wardinsky et al (1995) analyzed 504 reports of suspected abuse. Two hundred and forty of the cases were substantiated. Of the 264 unsubstantiated cases, 18 were due to medical conditions mistaken for abuse. In this series 3.6% of reports were due to misdiagnosis. Thirteen of the eighteen, however, were readily diagnosed after evaluation by a pediatrician leaving five, or 1% of total reports, with conditions that were more difficult to distinguish. Wheeler and Hobbs reported another analysis of 50 children who were initially misdiagnosed with abuse. This cohort was gathered from a total of 2,628 reports for a rate of 1.9% (Wheeler et al, 1988). As in the Wardinsky study, the correct diagnosis was usually made without delay by the first pediatrician consulted. Based on these reports, we can expect about two percent of cases reported from the general population, including non-medical sources, to have medical conditions mistaken for abuse. Most of these cases can rapidly be excluded through evaluation by a cautious pediatrician.

A very wide variety of conditions have been mistaken for abuse at one time or another, but congenital variants, disorders of the skin, bone fragility, and disorders of coagulation are the most common. In addition, accidental injury is the most common differential diagnosis for non-accidental injury, and at times presents significant diagnostic difficulty. A less common problem which takes on greater significance in certain localities, is injuries inflicted during cultural medical practices.

Clinical Presentation

Congenital Variants

Variation affects nearly every system of the body. Variants of the skin, bones, and nervous system have proved both common, and possibly confused with abuse. Of these, skin variants are particularly common. Medical providers from multi-ethnic communities are quite familiar with the possible variety and extent of slate gray pigmentation, or mongolian spots, seen in dark skinned and Asian patients. Reporters without this experience have interpreted the presence of bluish blotches on the buttocks, back or proximal extremities as bruises. Similarly vascular markings of the skin are familiar to medical personnel, but may be interpreted by others as injury. This is particularly true of port wine stain, which often affects the face. Deeper vascular malformations may create a less distinct red-blue coloration, which can confuse even experienced medical providers. Occasionally other pigmented lesions may have an unusual pattern or location which invites diagnosis as a bruise or scar.

Skeletal variation has occasionally led to the mistaken diagnosis of abusive fracturing. Vascular markings in the skull, and the cortex of the long bones may give the appearance of a fracture, for which there is an inadequate explanation. Extremity films of a two-month-old will often show physiologic new bone formation, which may be interpreted as fracture healing. Beaks or spurs at the metaphyseal ends of long bones may sometimes give the impression of classical metaphyseal fractures. The suspected presence of fracture with inadequate history, fracture with evidence of healing, and classical abuse fractures such as metaphyseal corner chips would each lead to suspicion of child abuse.

Two of the five difficult cases reported by Wardinsky (1995) were due to "benign external hydrocephalus". This condition has been interpreted as chronic subdural hematoma especially on images from older generation CT scans. Symmetrical increase in the clear space between the brain and the skull over the frontal lobes is a relatively common variant in infants and young toddlers. When this is found in infants evaluated for overly large heads, subural hematoma is a reasonable explanation. Such a finding clearly suggests significant head trauma in the child's past, and thus abuse.

Skin Disorders

Disorders of the skin may alter the color or integrity of the skin, simulating bruises, burns, abrasions and scars. Because they develop in previously normal skin, one care provider may correctly identify a change while in the custody of another. Impetigo was the most frequent cause of misdiagnosis in the referenced series, accounting for 10 of the 68 combined cases (Wardinsky et al, 1995; Wheeler and Hobbs, 1988). Impetigo may appear like a cigarette burn, especially early. The author has seen both impetigo mistaken for a cigarette burn, and cigarette burns mistaken for impetigo, highlighting the possible similarity in the two conditions.

Other forms of skin inflammation may also simulate burning. Dermatitis from corrosive diarrhea may onset very rapidly. If confined in tight fitting diapers, it may result in a sharply demarcated denuded areas of skin similar in appearance to tub immersion burns. Contact dermatitis under a metal snap often creates a round crusted or ulcerated lesion possibly mistaken for a cigarette burn. Other sensitizing agents such as creams and vegetable juices may be applied in a pattern, reflected in the inflammatory lesion that follows, creating the impression of a patterned injury and abuse. A particularly interesting form of this phenomenon is phytodermatitis. In this entity, plant juices, notably citrus juices, act as photo sensitizers, resulting in erythema or ulceration. Parents handling citrus may touch their children resulting in a perfect hand print, hours or even days later, inviting accusations of abuse. Ten cases of this condition were reported in San Diego county, resulting in multiple false diagnoses, including child abuse (Goskowicz et al, 1994).

Bone Fragility

Many diagnoses of child abuse rest on distinguishing the trauma of maltreatment from the trauma of normal childhood. Children with fragile bones fracture from levels of trauma which would not injure a normal child. When these children present with a fracture and no history or history of a trivial fall, child abuse is a reasonable concern. Several causes of bone fragility may result in such a situation, and thus a misdiagnosis of child abuse.

Osteogenesis imperfecta is a genetic disorder of collagen synthesis that results in fragile bones. It is the prototypical brittle bone disease, resulting in easy fracturing. Though other features of the disease usually result in proper diagnosis, sub-type IVa has at times presented difficulty. This sub-type may lack the characteristic feature of blue sclerae, and the family history may be negative due to incomplete penetrance or new mutation. Unfortunately these difficulties have made this diagnosis a popular target for defense attorneys, creating a defensive response in many medical providers. Osteogenesis is best regarded as an unusual condition which can usually be diagnosed by a careful, open minded physician. Rarely, despite this caution, it will present genuine difficulty, inviting misdiagnosis of child abuse (Ablin et al., 1990)

Bone fragility may also arise from other chronic medical conditions. Children with complicated neuro-developmental disorders may have fragile bones due to immobility and seizure medications. Kidney problems from renal failure or complications of drugs, such as those used in transplantation, may result in low bone mineral content and fracture. Premature infants may have weak bones after prolonged intensive care unit stays. Many of these children are considered vulnerable to maltreatment due to their differences and disabilities. Fracturing may provoke significant concern leading to a misdiagnosis of abuse.

Disorders of Coagulation

Just as bone fragility results in confusion secondary to easy fracturing, coagulopathy results in confusion due to easy bruising. Because the hemophilias are hereditary and present from birth, there are often ready clues to diagnosis, preventing confusion with child abuse. Two common temporary conditions are more likely to cause confusion. Babies born outside the hospital, and occasionally other newborns, may not be given adequate vitamin K. Several weeks after birth these children may develop a profound bleeding problem. This may result not only in bruising, but in bleeding into the head or other body tissues, with catastrophic results. Such serious injury in a young infant will provoke concern for child abuse.

Later in childhood, usually following a mild viral illness, children may develop nearly spontaneous bruising due to an abrupt drop in their platelet count. This condition, termed ITP or idiopathic thrombocytopenic purpura, is usually transitory, lasting a few weeks to a few months. Many of these children are recognized clinically by the character and distribution of their bruising, but an atypical presentation may result in concern for child abuse until a blood count shows the true cause of their bruising. Another condition that is more likely to result in confusion is Von Willebrandt's disease. This entity is hereditary, like the hemophilias, but the severity of illness is quite variable. A child with severe disease may have a parent with disease mild enough to go undetected. In addition the laboratory tests used to diagnose this entity are sometimes difficult to interpret. Such a situation may create significant concern for child abuse.

Accidental Injury

Accidental injury is not typically discussed along with medical conditions that simulate child abuse, but is probably the most important alternative diagnosis to consider when diagnosing abusive trauma. Parents may hide or alter their history not only to hide deliberate misdeeds, but also to hide innocent accidents and actions of which they feel ashamed. Even when a correct history is given, physicians are not always able to predict a reasonable outcome, relying on statistical likelihood to give a best determination. Spiral fracture of the humerus is an injury that is strongly associated with abuse. Blaming another child for fracture is a historical pattern that is also suggestive of abuse. When an infant presents with a spiral fracture of the humerus, which reportedly occurred when his 3 year old sister rolled him over on the floor, child abuse is a natural diagnosis. Yet just such a case was serendipitously captured on video tape, providing a documented exception to the statistical rules (Hymel and Jenny, 1996). Limits in our knowledge of possible accidental outcomes can also result in the misdiagnosis of child abuse.

Cultural Practices

This last category does not so much create problems of misdiagnosis, but of communication and definition. Bruises, burns, and incisions have been created in efforts to relieve illness throughout medical history. Such practices as cao gio, moxibustion, quat sha, cupping and maquas are still practiced within populations of recent immigrants. When evaluated without history, these injuries may present difficulty in diagnosis. Once the history of "therapeutic" procedure is available, the difficult job of defining the limits of reasonable and abusive behavior must begin. This issue is distinct from that of misdiagnosis.

Evaluation

While some of the more common causes of confusion have been briefly outlined above, a full list of diseases possibly confused with abuse would be extensive. In both the Wardinsky and the Wheeler studies, evaluation by an experienced pediatrician usually resulted in rapid diagnosis of the confusing condition. In Wheeler's study, a large proportion of the 50 misdiagnoses were made in children with past history of abuse or significant social risk factors. It is imperative that the social setting not overwhelm the need to consider common and uncommon medical explanations for findings leading to the diagnosis of child abuse. In the end, a thorough assessment of child abuse must both fail to find a medical explanation for the child's injuries, and posit a reasonable traumatic cause. Caution must be used in determining the line between reasonable and unreasonable explanatory trauma. The certainty with which we can assert that household falls do not cause fracture is less than the certainty with which we can assert that it does not cause fatal head injury. When judging histories of accidental injury, we must distinguish between what is impossible, and what is merely unlikely. A few steps should be taken as a matter of routine to avoid misdiagnosis of abuse.

History

When a history can be obtained, it should be thorough, exploring innocent alternatives, as well as details which might explain abuse. The time course of any marks on the body should be evaluated. Bruises evolve and resolve over approximately two weeks, lesions which are evanescent, or persistent, may not be bruises. A past history and review of systems may uncover additional clues to alternative medical diagnoses such as phytodermatitis, contact allergy, diarrhea and others. Family history may provide clues to hereditary conditions such as osteogenesis imperfecta, and Von Willebrandt's disease which present the most diagnostic difficulty. Details of any accident should be probed, and apparent inconsistencies discussed. Such a discussion may uncover idiosyncrasies of the events, convincing detail, or uncomfortable facts, as well as the inconsistencies that come with abuse. When patterned marks are noted in ill children of recent immigrants, the nature of any home treatments should be explored. The many American families using non-traditional medicine are often embarrassed to divulge this information to physicians.

Physical Examination

The abuse physical must be a complete physical. As expected, the finding under suspicion must be thoroughly evaluated for details which might elucidate its cause, innocent or abusive. Additionally, the rest of the child must be thoroughly examined, to look for both additional findings that give evidence of abuse, and findings that support alternative explanations. Too often children with trivial injuries from suspected abuse are evaluated in busy emergency rooms without the time to adequately evaluate them. Social systems to protect children need access to other, more leisurely, avenues of assessment.

Tests and Procedures

The child with bruising or bleeding should have a laboratory evaluation for disorders of coagulation. Blood counts and coagulation times may be augmented by other studies as individual cases require. Young children with fracture should have a skeletal x-ray survey, which will present the opportunity not only to evaluate for additional abusive injury, but for skeletal changes suggestive of brittle bones. Additional studies of skeletal disorders are not recommended as routine, but may be obtained when history or physical examination suggests a diagnosis. When CT scans result in uncertain evidence of subdural hematoma, MRI scanning will often clarify the situation. Many other specific tests exist for the manifold alternative diagnoses, when careful history and physical examination suggest their existence.

Management

In the end a medical evaluation must answer two questions. First, does the child have evidence of physical or sexual abuse? Physical injuries with clear patterns or strong statistical evidence linking them to abuse are usually due to abuse regardless of the child' other medical conditions. Second, does the child have other medical conditions? Such conditions may fully explain the child's injuries, lessen the certainty with which abuse can be asserted, or exist separate and distinct from additional abuse. Children with chronic medical conditions may also be abused. Some data suggests they may have increased risk of being abused. Johnson and

Coury reported on two cases of children with hemophilia who presented with abusive bruising. O'Hare and Eden (1984) found evidence of coagulopathy in 16% of 50 children diagnosed with abusive injury. Clearly children can be both ill and abused (Johnson and Coury, 1988). To serve them best we must determine the existence of each, and the relationship between the two. Children taken into custody for abuse often have additional medical conditions requiring treatment.

Resolution

Abuse was suspected in the two-year-old due to the unusually large number of bruises. The bruises were not felt to be characteristic of any medical cause, but no pattern such as hand or loop marks were recognized either. A routine evaluation for coagulopathy was initiated and turned up a low platelet count of 4000. Past history uncovered a mild viral illness the preceding week. He was treated for his idiopathic thrombocytopenic purpura with intravenous immunoglobulin, and rapidly improved. A hospital social worker was involved in the case, but no report to county authorities was made due to alternative medical explanation.

References

Ablin, D.S., Greenspan, A., Reinhart, M., Grix, A. Differentiation of child abuse from osteogenesis imperfecta. AJR. 1990; 154: 1035-1046

Goskowicz, M.O., Friedlander, S.F., Eichenfeld, L.F. Endemic "lime" disease: phytodermatitis in San Diego County. Pediatr 1994; 93: 828-830

Hymel, K.P., Jenny, C. Abusive spiral fractures of the humerus: a videotaped exception. Arch Pediatr Adolesc Med. 1996; 150: 226-227

Johnson, C.F., Coury, D.L. Bruising and hemophilia: accident or child abuse? Child Abuse and Neglect. 1988; 12: 409-415

O'Hare, A.E., Eden, O.B. Bleeding disorders and non-accidental injury. Arch Dis Child. 1984; 59:860-864 Children taken into custody for abuse often have additional medical conditions requiring treatment.

Wardinsky, .TD., Vizcarrondo, F.E., Cruz, B.K. The mistaken diagnosis of child abuse: a three-year USAF medical center analysis and literature review. Military Med. 1995; 160: 15-20

Wheeler, D.M., Hobbs, C.J. Mistakes in diagnosing non-accidental injury: 10 years' experience. BMJ. 1988; 296: 1233-1236

Note: The opinions and conclusions in this article are those of the author and or not intended to represent the official position of the Department of Defense, USAF, or any other governmental agency.

Child Neglect

Carol Berkowitz, M.D.

Two Case Vignettes

- An 8-month old female infant is brought to the emergency department by her 16-year old mother because she has had a fever of 104°F for 3 days. The mother reports that the infant has had a decreased appetite and a runny nose. Review of the past medical history reveals that the infant has not been to the doctor since birth. She has not received any of her immunizations. She weighed 6 pounds 8 ounces at birth, currently weighs only 10 pounds 2 ounces, and is below the fifth percentile in height and weight. On physical examination, there is dry crusted mucous by both nares. Her hair is matted, and there is thick cerumen in both ears. Cleansing of the cerumen reveals bilateral otitis media. She has a brown bruise on her forehead which the mother relates to her falling off the couch. There is caked stool on her skin in the diaper area, and the area is red and inflamed.

- Three children are brought into the emergency department after a neighbor called the police because she heard persistent crying from across the hall. When the police arrived, they found the children, ages 7 years, 4 years and 15 months alone in an apartment. The 7-year old was trying to tend to the two younger children, but the 15-month old would not stop crying. The 7-year old was offering the infant a bottle filled with water. A search of the home revealed that there was no food in the refrigerator, the apartment was unkempt, and there was excrement on the floor. The 7-year old stated that his mother had gone out the night before and had told him to mind the other children until she got back, and not to open the door for anyone. He said she had done this before. On examination in the emergency department, the children were dirty and thin, and the 15-month old had a diaper rash. They had no acute medical problems. They were given food which they avidly consumed.

Questions

1. What are the different types of neglect?

2. What are the factors that contribute to child neglect?

3. What are the consequences of neglect?

4. What are some strategies to prevent neglect?

Neglect means the failure to provide for the essential needs of an individual. The term includes:

- the failure of a caregiver to provide food, shelter, clothing, health care, education, love and nurturance to a child in their care;

- the exposure of children to potentially harmful situations which can or do result in injury or harm;

- child abandonment including fatal or near-fatal abandonment, abandonment with physical needs provided by others, throwaways (adolescents whom no one wants), parental custody refusal, lack of supervision; and,

- emotional abandonment.

Epidemiology/Statistics

Data from the National Incidence Surveillance for 1996 reported 949,001 cases of neglect. There were 338,901 cases of physical neglect, 212,800 cases of emotional neglect, and 397,300 cases of educational neglect. Educational neglect can be subdivided into three main categories:

chronic truancy 216,900, failure to enroll in school 63,400, and failure to obtain remedial services 6,000.

Clinical Presentation of Neglect

General Neglect

Children who are neglected may come to medical attention for a variety of reasons. Sometimes they are brought to the physician for an unrelated infectious illness, and evidence of neglect is apparent on physical examination. For instance, the child may appear dirty, smell of urine or stool, and be underweight. Other times, neglect may result in children sustaining a serious injury, such as being burned or drowned because of inadequate supervision. Children who receive inadequate food may present with growth impairment. Children with emotional neglect may experience behavioral or conduct problems in school. Some children die as a result of neglect, and these cases are usually evaluated by the medical examiner's office.

THE DEFINITIONS GIVEN BELOW ARE USED IN THE NATIONAL INCIDENCE SURVEILLANCE STUDY.

Physical Neglect	
Refusal of Health Care	Failure to provide or allow needed care in accord with recommendations of a competent health care professional for a physical injury, illness, medical condition, or impairment.
Delay in Health Care	Failure to seek timely and appropriate medical care for a serious health problem which any reasonable layman would have recognized as needing professional medical attention.
Abandonment	Desertion of a child without arranging for reasonable care and supervision. This category includes cases in which children are not claimed within two days, and when children are left by parents/substitutes who give no (or false) information about their whereabouts.
Expulsion	Other blatant refusals of custody, such as permanent or indefinite expulsion of a child from the home without adequate arrangement for care by others, or refusal to accept custody of a returned runaway.
Other Custody Issues	Custody-related forms of inattention to the child's needs other than those covered by abandonment or expulsion. For example, repeated shuttling of a child from one household to another due to unwillingness to maintain custody, or chronically and repeatedly leaving a child with others for days/weeks at a time.
Other Physical Neglect	Conspicuous inattention to avoidable hazards in the home; inadequate nutrition, clothing, or hygiene; and, other forms of reckless disregard for the child's safety and welfare, such as driving with the child while under the influence of drugs or alcohol, or leaving a young child unattended in a motor vehicle.
Supervision	
Inadequate Supervision	Child left unsupervised or inadequately supervised for extended periods of time or allowed to remain away from home overnight without the parent/substitute knowing (or attempting to determine) the child's whereabouts.
Emotional Neglect	
Inadequate Nurturance/Affection	Marked inattention to the child's needs for affection, emotional support, attention, or competence.
Chronic/Extreme Abuse or Domestic Violence	Chronic or extreme spouse abuse or other domestic violence.
Permitted Drug/Alcohol Abuse	Encouraging or permitting drug or alcohol use by the child, or cases where parent/guardian was informed of the problem and did not attempt to intervene.

Refusal of Psychological Care	Refusal to allow needed and available treatment for a child's emotional or behavioral impairment or problem in accord with competent professional recommendation.
Delay in Psychological Care	Failure to seek or provide needed treatment for a child's emotional or behavioral impairment or problem which any reasonable layman would have recognized as needing professional psychological attention e.g., severe depression, suicide attempt.
Other Emotional Neglect	Other inattention to the child's developmental/emotional needs not classifiable under any of the above forms of emotional neglect (e.g., markedly overprotective restrictions which foster immaturity or emotional overdependence, chronically applying expectations clearly inappropriate in relation to the child's age or level of development, etc.)
Educational Neglect	
Permitted Chronic Truancy	Habitual truancy averaging at least 5 days a month is classifiable under this form of maltreatment, if the parent/guardian has been informed of the problem, and has not attempted to intervene.
Failure to Enroll/Other Truancy	Failure to register or enroll a child of mandatory school age, causing the school-aged child to remain at home for nonlegitimate reasons (e.g., to work, to care for siblings, etc.) an average of at least 3 days a month.
Inattention to Special Education Needs	Refusal to allow or failure to obtain recommended remedial educational services, or neglect in obtaining or following through with treatment for a child's diagnosed learning disorder, or other special educational needs without reasonable cause.

Additional Commentary on Incidence Study Definitions

Medical Neglect

Medical neglect may occur for acute problems, such as burns or injuries that are sustained accidentally; acute illnesses, such as gastroenteritis; or, for routine health maintenance. Some parents do access health care when their children have chronic problems, but then fail to follow the recommendations of the physician. For instance, a child with asthma may be prescribed several medications none of which are administered. As a result, the child may require repeated hospitalizations including admission to an intensive care unit.

Parents may utilize nontraditional medicine to treat their child's ailment. Examples of such practices include cao gio, or coining and moxibustion. Residual bruises from these practices may be mistaken for inflicted trauma. The use of non-traditional medicine is not condemned so long as it does not interfere with the child receiving appropriate medical care, and does not harm the child.

Child abandonment

Abandonment may involve frank abandonment, such as when a child is left in a trash dumpster, or, left alone,

unprotected in a house or apartment without any adult supervision. Abandonment also occurs when a parent leaves the child in the care of others and then fails to return at an appointed time. Inadequate supervision is another form of abandonment as well as cases where both parents renege on their responsibilities as parents. Adolescents who are expelled from the home because of "misbehavior" are abandoned. These adolescents are frequently referred to as "throwaways."

Delay in accessing medical care may be caused for various reasons:

- Parents may not have the financial means to pay for healthcare, and they delay seeking treatment in the hope that the illness will resolve on its own;

- Parents are unsophisticated and do not appreciate the seriousness of the illness;

- Parents are overtly negligent, and simply do not provide for their child's health care needs;

- Parents are mentally retarded or mentally ill and cannot properly care for their child; or,

- Parents whose child has been physically and/or sexually abused and they are trying to prevent this matter from coming to the attention of authorities.

Lack of supervision

Children who are left unsupervised may die as a result of such neglect. Common examples include children who die in house fires, from drowning, starvation or inadequate medical care.

Religious Beliefs

Some parents refuse medical care because of professed religious beliefs. Noteworthy among these individuals are those who are Jehovah's Witnesses or Christian Scientists. Such individuals may refuse traditional and well-established medical practices.

Pathophysiology

There are many factors which contribute to neglect. Parental factors include maternal depression, parental substance abuse, maternal developmental delay or retardation, and lack of education. There are also features in the child that put additional stress on the parent-child relationship. Children with chronic disabilities may strain the resources of a family. Similarly, infants who have been born prematurely are at increased risk of being neglected or abused. Bonding between a mother and her premature infant may be interrupted because of the separation between the two during the early period after birth. Sometimes the "goodness of fit" between the infant and mother is lacking, and the pair do not act as a reciprocal dyad.

Certain family features are also associated with neglect. These include absent or negative interactions between family members. Poor parenting skills may also be noted. There is frequently social isolation and a single parent struggling with stressors such as unemployment, illness (including mental illness), prison, and eviction. On a more global scale, community and societal factors also contribute to the risk of neglect. The lack of child care in a community means that single parents may leave young children inadequately supervised in order to go to work. The lack of convenient public transportation may impact access to medical care. Poverty, violence and substandard educational resources all contribute to neglect within certain populations. For instance, in neighborhoods perceived to be unsafe, children are frequently prohibited from playing outdoors and forming normal friendships because of safety concerns.

Differential Diagnosis

In any child who presents with a medical condition that may be related to neglect, one must explore other explanations that could account for the findings. Children who appear to be malnourished may suffer from a number of medical problems that affect their ability to grow and gain weight. Children who present with injuries need to be evaluated for the circumstances surrounding the injury. Did the parent's action contribute to the child being injured? Were these actions substandard, or would other parents have acted in a similar manner? For instance, if a child accidentally drowns in a bathtub, what reasons were given for leaving the child unattended?

The differential diagnosis of physical neglect depends on the presenting complaint. Children who are inadequately clothed may present with hypothermia. The differential diagnosis would include overwhelming sepsis, drug-exposure (COOLS—carbon monoxide, opiates, oral hypoglycemics [insulin], liquor, sedative-hypotics), or environmental exposure. Children with refractory medical conditions such as intractable asthma or unstable diabetes may be viewed as medically fragile, if the issue of non-compliance is not raised. Failure to obtain medical care in a timely manner may result in disease progression to a point where diagnosis and medical intervention are more difficult.

Evaluation

History

Obtain a complete medical history in children presenting with any condition suspected of being the result of neglect.

- Obtain the birth history and weight at birth.
- Ask whether the mother received prenatal care.
- What immunizations has the child had?
- Has the child received the appropriate health care over his/her lifetime?
- Does the child have a primary care provider?
- What is the baby's diet? Does the family have sufficient resources to meet everyone's nutritional needs? Do they receive food stamps? How often does the family skip a meal because of inadequate resources?
- Obtain a history of developmental milestones.
- Obtain information about schooling and school attendance. How often have children missed school during the previous 6 months? What school do they attend and what is their school performance?
- Where does the family live? Who else lives in the household?
- Obtain a social history, including economic resources, educational level of parents, substance abuse and incarceration.
- Who cares for the child when the parents are not available? Is extended family available?

Physical Examination

Perform a complete physical examination. Screen for developmental and dental problems.

- Weigh and measure the child, and plot measurements for gender and age on appropriate growth curves. When possible, review all prior growth parameters to determine whether growth impairment, if present, has been chronic or is of recent onset.

- Assess nutrition and hygiene. Evidence of substandard nutrition can be noted on physical examination in the form of diminished subcutaneous tissue.

- Assess bruises, scars, untreated injuries. Neglected children are at increased risk of physical abuse and for accidental injuries because of a general lack of supervision.

- Screen for sexual abuse. Neglected and homeless children are at risk for sexual victimization.

- Assess hygiene and absence of appropriate clothing, e.g. cleanliness, smelling of urine or stool, or lack of shoes and clothing.

- Assess healthcare history.

  - Has there been lack of care for accidental injuries?

  - If there is a chronic medical condition, has there been treatment?

  - What are physical findings relevant to the condition?

- Screen for dental problems. Unattended dental caries are frequently present in neglected children.

- Screen for developmental delay, especially for speech and language problems.

  - If developmental delay is suspected, a more formal evaluation can be done using the Denver II or the Bayley Infant Development Scales. Developmental delay can result from neglect if an infant is understimulated, or not given an opportunity to develop appropriate motor skills.

- Screen for mental health problem, e.g. withdrawal, clingy, aggressive, or overly-compliant when experiencing painful procedures.

- Review immunizations to ascertain whether the child is up to date. Depending upon the circumstances of the case, records may need to be obtained from schools, other hospitals and clinics, the local CHDP (Child Health, Disability, and Prevention Program), or the CWS/CMS system (a computerized database for managing information about children in the California child welfare system).

Laboratory Tests

Laboratory tests should be ordered to diagnose and evaluate untreated and/or chronic medical conditions and to ascertain whether there are conditions which may be mistaken for neglect. In general, a hemoglobin is an appropriate study to obtain to determine if the child is anemic. Lead levels are also appropriate in children under 6 years of age.

Imaging Studies

Skeletal trauma series are indicated in children under the age of 2 years who have signs of severe neglect. The purpose of these studies is to detect the presence of occult fractures.

Additional imaging studies are rarely needed in the assessment of the child who has been physically neglected unless there is some underlying medical condition that warrants such an evaluation. For instance, the child with recurrent urinary tract infections who has not been given the prophylactic antibiotics might need a renal scan to determine the extent of renal scarring that has developed.

Case Management

Assess whether the mother or caretaker will follow through to ensure that the medical problems will be addressed.

- Has the mother been reliable in the past on medical follow-up?

- Has anything new developed to prevent the mother from following up, e.g. alcohol or drug problems, domestic violence, abusive, controlling boyfriend, mental health problems?

- What resources does the family need to ensure compliance, e.g. transportation?

- Is the neglect representative of an isolated incident that occurred because of an unusual set of circumstances that has since been remedied? Or, are there risk factors which suggest that the child is at continued risk in their environment? Is the family in need of community resources that require the mobilization of social service agencies?

- Evaluate whether Children's Protective Services should be involved. Most cases of neglect require an evaluation not only by medical personnel, but also by social services because there are many factors which contribute to a child being neglected. An extensive medical and psychosocial evaluation is key to assuring a good outcome.

- Provide appropriate medical intervention.
- Consider and obtain authorization for in-patient treatment, if indicated, to assure compliance for treatment needs, e.g. burn injuries.

Prognosis

The prognosis in cases of neglect is quite variable. In some situations, children suffer irreversible damage as a result of a single neglectful act. In other cases, appropriate intervention and community assistance improve the health and nutrition of the neglected children. Family factors such as spousal abuse and substance abuse have a negative effect on the outcome.

The prognosis for physical neglect is dependent on the medical condition of the child and the willingness and ability of the parent to follow medical instructions and provide for the child's needs. Sometimes a referral to Child Protective Services serves to jolt the parents to the reality of the gravity of the situation. Parents who cannot care for themselves for reasons of alcohol/drug dependency or other psychosocial variables are in a poor position to care for their families, and need assistance from public social services to ensure the protection of the child.

Primary Prevention

- Home visiting services for parents of newborns
- Affordable, geographically accessible healthcare
- Good quality public education
- Parks and recreation programs for children
- After school programs

Secondary Prevention

- Job-training and employment opportunities
- Affordable, available child care
- Early childhood programs, e.g. Headstart, Early Headstart
- Home visiting services
- Family planning services
- Parent skills training
- Family Resource Centers (FRCs) in accessible locations

- Crisis Nurseries
- Parental Stress Lines
- Domestic violence counseling services

Tertiary Intervention

- Mental health services
- Drug/alcohol prevention and treatment
- Homeless shelters
- Domestic violence shelters
- Child abuse treatment programs for children and families

References

Dubowitz, H. and Black, M. Child neglect. In Reece, R.M., *Child Abuse: Medical Diagnosis and Management*. Lea & Febiger, Philadelphia, 1994, pp.279-290.

Gaudin, Jr. J.M. *Child Neglect: A Guide for Intervention*. National Center on Child Abuse and Neglect, U.S. Department of Health and Human Services, April, 1993.

Griest, K.J., Zumwalt, R.E. Child abuse by drowning. *Pediatrics* 83:41-46, 1989.

Helfer, R. The neglect of our children. *Pediatric Cl N Amer*, 37:923-942, 1990.

Kouno, A., Johnson, C.F. Child abuse and neglect in Japan: Coin-operated-locker babies. *Child Abuse & Neglect* 19(1):25-31, 1995.

Margolin, L. Fatal Child Neglect. *Child Welfare*, 64:309-319, 1990.

McHugh, M. Child abuse in a sea of neglect: The inner-city child. *Pediatr Ann*, 21:504-507, 1992.

Squires, T., Busuttil, A. Child fatalities in Scottish house fires 1980-1990: A case of child neglect? *Child Abuse & Neglect* 7:865-873, 1995.

Resources

Healthy Families America
http://www.preventchildabuse.org

Early Headstart
http://www.ehsnrc.org

Headstart
http://www.hdstart.org.uk

Failure to Thrive

Carol Berkowitz, M.D.

Case Vignette

A 4-month old infant is brought to the emergency department with a history of fever for 2 days. The infant has 3 older siblings, ages 4 years, 3 years, and 18 months. All have been ill with symptoms of an upper respiratory infection, specifically runny nose and cough. Review of the infant's past medical history reveals a normal pregnancy and delivery with a birth weight of 7 pounds and 8 ounces.

On physical examination, the infant is scrawny with decreased subcutaneous tissue. The infant has a fever of 102° F, and weighs 9 pounds and 3 ounces, which is less than the 5th percentile. The infant is irritable, has diaper dermatitis and evidence of an ear infection.

Questions

1. What is failure to thrive?

2. What are the common causes of growth impairment in children?

3. What family factors impact on children's growth?

4. What are nutritional interventions to improve a child's growth and weight gain?

Epidemiology/Statistics

Failure to thrive is a general term which refers to an impairment of growth. The term may be used non-specifically to cover all types of growth retardation, or it may be used more specifically to mean growth impairment that is associated with developmental delay and disorders of affect that are related to environmental deprivation.

Failure to thrive is frequently listed among the larger categories of child neglect, but the condition represents a distinct entity in which neglect may or may not be present.

If small stature is used as the definition of failure to thrive, then the statistics regarding the etiology of the growth impairment vary with the institution reporting their data. Failure to thrive has been characterized as organic or non-organic. Organic failure to thrive is the term used when growth impairment is secondary to a specific medical condition, such as cystic fibrosis or cerebral palsy. Non-organic failure to thrive occurs in children in whom the environment has not met their nutritional or emotional needs. These distinct divisions are somewhat artificial since children with organic medical conditions may also suffer from environmental inadequacies. In addition, some children may appear to be growth impaired, but they may be normal small individuals. Twenty percent of children referred to our Failure to Thrive Clinic have familial short stature, which means that they are short because their parents are short. Thirty percent of children we see are receiving grossly inadequate calories to assure adequate growth. National figures report that between 2–6% of children between 2 and 5 years of age demonstrate low weight-for-height.

While failure to thrive can affect children in any socio-economic group, poverty and inadequate access to food have negative impact on the growth of children. Thirteen percent of families living below poverty report food insecurity.

Clinical Presentation

Children with failure to thrive may present in a number of ways. Rarely do neglecting parents specifically bring their child to medical attention because of concern about the child's rate of growth. Such concern is more common among middle class families. Children may be referred for an evaluation when growth retardation is detected during a visit to a community agency such as WIC, or to an emergency department for an unrelated complaint.

The unifying finding is that the child is too small. Weight may be below that which is predicted based on the child's age or height. Similarly, height may be below that which is predicted by the patient's age. Another parameter that can be evaluated is the body mass index (BMI). The body mass index is the weight in kilogram divided by the height in meters squared. There are tables which correlate the age, gender and BMI of children and adults, and these numbers define thinness as well as obesity.

Pathophysiology

Failure to thrive (FTT) is related to inadequate nutritional intake to assure appropriate growth. In children with organic FTT, there may be decreased appetite secondary to the underlying medical condition, or to medications that the child is taking. Additionally, the child may experience increased loss of nutrients through the gastrointestinal tract, as occurs with diarrhea. Other children with organic conditions associated with FTT may have increased caloric needs, and the children are underweight because they are not receiving the added calories they need to support their growth.

In children with environmental FTT, growth impairment may be related to the fact that the children are simply not given enough to eat. Some children experience what is comparable to depression and appear apathetic and disinterested in eating. Food, when offered, may be rejected or regurgitated (rumination). Growth impairment with emotional withdrawal are findings of classic environmental or non-organic FTT.

Differential Diagnosis

The differential diagnosis of the growth-impaired infant is very long, but in our experience four major categories account for about 95% of children referred for an FTT evaluation.

The first category involves children who were small at birth. Premature infants normally catch up by about 2 years of age. Infants who do not demonstrate appropriate catch-up growth may have suffered some significant perinatal insult such as central nervous system damage or bronchopulmonary dysplasia. Infants who are small at birth but who are not premature have what is referred to as intra-uterine growth restriction or are small for gestational age. These infants may have been exposed to an infection in utero (such as congenital rubella syndrome), or to some drug or alcohol. Fetal alcohol syndrome is one of the most common reasons for a small infant who persists in becoming a small child.

The second category of children are those who are selectively underweight. Their height may or may not be abnormal. The underweight child is receiving inadequate calories. They may not be receiving appropriate calories because of environmental deprivation, increased caloric needs, or inadequate family resources. Certain medical conditions contribute to a child being underweight. For instance, children with HIV infection may fall into this category.

The third and fourth categories involve children who are short, but are not underweight given their height. These children may have familial short stature (they are short because their parents are short) or are suffering from constitutional delay (their rate of growth slowed down, and their rate of maturation is behind).

The list of medical conditions which can impact on growth is long and includes genetic, cardiac, endocrine, renal and neurologic disorders just to mention a few.

Evaluation

History

A full medical history should be obtained. It is important to assess the history of the birth including whether the pregnancy was planned and the infant was wanted. Prenatal care and the mother's nutritional status should be noted. It is important to determine whether the mother smoked, drank, or took any drugs during the pregnancy.

The past medical history should also be elicited, because the history may provide clues to some underlying medical condition. Within the family history, parental stature is important to obtain. Parents should be measured when possible. The child's developmental history will help the health care provider determine if the child is developmentally normal or not.

It is also key to obtain a nutritional history. This can be ascertained by having the mother relate the child's diet over the previous 24-hours. Additionally, the mother can record what the child eats for a 3-day period (3-day diet history).

A social history should be elicited. What are the family's resources? Who helps the mother with child care? What are the mother's strengths? Is she literate? Is there a history of spousal abuse?

Physical Examination

The key component of the physical examination is an assessment of the growth parameters, and a recording of these parameters on a growth chart. The child should be examined completely for any evidence of anomalies which suggest an underlying genetic condition or provide evidence of an underlying organic condition. Some abnormalities which may be detected on physical examination are cataracts, cleft lips/palates, heart murmurs, enlarged liver or spleen.

Laboratory Tests

There are no routine laboratory tests that should be included in the work-up of the FTT child. The only routine tests are those which are included in the health maintenance assessments of all children and these include a hemoglobin test to detect anemia and a routine urinalysis. All other studies should be determined on the basis of clues provided by the history or physical examination. Such studies include additional blood tests for electrolytes or chromosome analyses.

Imaging Studies

Imaging studies should be ordered if indicated by a relevant history or physical examination. Skeletal studies may be indicated if there is suspicion of inflicted trauma or skeletal dysplasia. A chest x-ray would be useful in a child with a heart murmur.

Health/Developmental Status

The health care provider should try to obtain as many of the prior growth measurements on the child as possible since the pattern of growth will also provide clues to the etiology of the growth impairment. For instance, children with environmental FTT will show a deceleration in their weight prior to any leveling off of their height. Children with familial short stature or constitutional delay show a leveling off in their height without a concomitant flattening of their weight curve. Children with neurologic disabilities may have a decreased head circumference.

As noted above, a developmental assessment should be done using both historical data as well as a standardized developmental test such as the Denver II or the Bayley Infant Development Scales. Immunization status should also be ascertained as part of the routine health care, and as a clue to prior health care.

Case Management

There are multiple components to the management of the infant with FTT. Any medical problem should be specifically addressed. Likewise, nutritional remedies should also be instituted. These include the use of special infant formulas (e.g., Nutramigen), concentrating regular infant formula, or supplemental nutritional agents such as Pediasure.

Community agencies may have to be mobilized to help access the needed resources. Food stamps and WIC referrals may serve to decrease food insecurity for a family. Parenting courses and counseling may also assist families where caretaker skills are inadequate.

Sometimes the management mandates that children be removed from their home and placed in a foster home to assure nutritional and medical care. Parents may need referral to specific programs such as parenting classes or drug rehabilitation units.

Prognosis

The prognosis with FTT is variable but can be good with the appropriate intervention. Children are quite resilient and, if adequate nutrition is given early, enough brain growth and development can proceed.

Case Resolution

The infant has significant growth impairment. The mother is depressed and overwhelmed with having to care for 4 small children. A review of the history reveals a non-supportive husband who is unemployed and drinks. The family does not receive food stamps and often goes without food. A decision is made to notify Department of Children and Family Services to help mobilize community resources to help the family.

References

Bithoney, W.B., Dubowitz, H., Egan, H. Failure to thrive/growth deficiency. *Pediatr Rev* 13:453-459, 1992.

Drotar, D. (ed.). *New Direction in Failure to Thrive: Research and Clinical Practice*. New York, Plenum Press, 1985.

Frank, D.A. and Drotar, D. Failure to thrive in child abuse: medical diagnosis and management. In: Reece RM (ed.). *Child Abuse: Medical Diagnosis and Management*. Philadelphia, Lea & Febiger, 1994, pp. 298-324.

Frank, D.A., Silva, M., Needlman, R. Failure to thrive: mystery, myth and method. *Comtemp Pediatr* 10:114-133, 1993.

Kessler, D.B., Dawson, P. (Eds). *Failure to Thrive and Pediatric Undernutrition: A Transdisciplinary Approach*. Paul H. Brookes Publishing Company, 1998.

Poisoning

Kevin Coulter, M.D.

Case Vignette

A 13-month old boy was seen in the emergency room because of convulsions. The mother and boyfriend both smelled of alcohol, and social services was notified. The child was found to have a blood glucose level of 15mg/100ml; the etiology of the convulsion was determined to be hypoglycemia, with alcohol-induced hypoglycemia suspected. A blood alcohol level was obtained and the child reported to the Division of Family services via the abuse hot line for suspected abuse, specifically alcohol poisoning. The blood alcohol level was determined to be elevated significantly. The mother initially denied any possibility of the child ingesting alcohol but later acknowledged that the boyfriend had convinced her to give the child vodka to "help him sleep."

Questions

1. List four common presentations of poisoning, by intent or neglect.

2. List five symptoms and signs following intentional poisoning.

3. List five presentations of Munchausen by Proxy poisonings.

Etiology

Poisoning is one of the most common medical emergencies faced by health care providers interacting with children. It accounts for numerous emergency room visits and is a significant cause of pediatric morbidity and mortality. The Center for Disease Control in 1986 reported 4,740 unintentional poisoning deaths, where 93 were children under 5 years old, 24 were between 5 and 9 years old, and 249 were adolescents (Olsen & Banner, 1991). A review of calls to 63 poison control centers participating in a national data collection program during 1987 disclosed 1.2 million ingested cases. In this study, 60% of the ingestion cases involved children under the age of 5 years, 22 children died, and 107,844 had symptoms of poisoning. Kempe was the first to propose poisoning as a part of the spectrum of injury in child abuse, stating, "In an occasional case the parent, or parent-substitute, may also have assaulted the child by administering an overdose of a drug or by exposing the child to natural gas or other toxic substances" (Kempe et al., 1962).

Cases of abuse are usually perpetrated by an individual with poor impulse control, a low tolerance for a child's upsetting behavior, and a tendency to act out violently against the child using a poison. While some of these cases undoubtedly represent a deranged individual attempting to directly harm a child, other cases can be viewed as a spectrum of parental dysfunction in attempting to cope with the stresses of caring for children. At one end of the spectrum are the young parents distressed by their fussy, colicky infant. The may try at times, with the direction of their physician, to sedate their infant with an antihistamine or paregoric. While this may not prove to be injurious, the parents may increase the dose to accomplish sedation without awareness of the potential ill effects that can be associated with these agents. In addition, with highly stressed and impulsive parents, the situation may escalate to include physical abuse, often by shaking, or possibly to chemical abuse with doses of potent sedatives such as alcohol or narcotics.

At the far end of this spectrum are adults or older children who deliberately introduce children to the effects of illicit drugs. A recent survey was conducted of adolescent females in a drug treatment program who had been babysitters. Nine girls (11%) state they had blown marijuana smoke into the faces or mouths of the children being cared for in an attempt to make them "high" (Schwartz et al., 1986). In a far more malicious setting, pedophiles may attempt to chemically sedate children before sexually abusing them.

Another context within which intentional poisoning occurs is Munchausen Syndrome by Proxy. Briefly, this syndrome is defined as an illness in a child that is caused or induced by a parent, usually the mother. Physical signs of illness promptly resolve when the child is separated from the perpetrator. In cases of MSBP where disease is actually produced, surreptitious poisoning of the child is a common mechanism. In a review of published cases of MSBP (Rosenberg, 1987), seven of the eight most common presentations of MSBP abuse were secondary to poisoning (Table 1, page 5). The abuse continued after the child was admitted to the hospital. The placement of intravenous lines or gastrostomy tubes while in the hospital in some cases afforded other routes of poisoning (Saulsbury et al., 1984).

Neglect is probably the most common reason for unintentional and intentional child poisonings. However, while all childhood poisonings represent some degree of improper supervision, it can be difficult to decide when a poisoning has resulted from true neglect. In an important study on the epidemiology of caustic ingestions, no difference was found in the number of safety hazards or safety precautions between homes where the ingestions occurred and control homes (Sobel, 1970). Similar factors appear in studies of homes of children who have experienced multiple ingestions. These studies consistently show that the common denominator in homes with accidental ingestions is not neglect but significant family stress. Where neglect is a factor, the poisoning brings to the attention of the health care provider the child whose basic needs are unmet. The child may appear dirty, malnourished, and lack immunizations. There may also be a delay in seeking medical care for the ingestions because the child is left unattended for long periods of time or the parents have been in a prolonged alcohol- or drug-induced stupor. At the point where neglect is suspected, child protective services must be contacted to save the child from further harm.

Children of parents abusing drugs and/or alcohol are at risk of injecting their parents' drugs or drug producing ingredients. Four routes of exposure are possible: (1) passive inhalation, (2) accidental ingestion, (3) accepting drugs from an older child or other nonparent adult, or, (4) deliberate poisoning (Schwartz et al., 1986).

As cocaine use grew into an epidemic, reports of cocaine intoxication in young children rapidly appeared. Much of this widespread use has been fueled by the ready availability of the relatively cheap form of freebase cocaine referred to as "crack," which is easily vaporized by heat and then smoked. Passive inhalation of these cocaine vapors was the presumed route of ingestion of four children who were seen at Harlem Hospital, two of whom had seizures and two of whom were lethargic (Bateman & Heagerty, 1989). Apnea and seizures have been reported in infants exposed to cocaine in breast milk (Chasnoff et al., 1987). Oral ingestion of cocaine was believed to have caused seizures reported in four children under 3 years old who were unex-

pectedly found to have cocaine on routine urine toxicologic screening (Ernst and Sanders, 1989). Upon further evaluation by social services, all children were found to have been in the company of cocaine-abusing adults. A 4-month old infant was believed to have been intentionally fed cocaine in an attempt to quiet her.

Children who have clinical evidence of acute cocaine poisoning are likely to be only a small portion of all children who actively or passively ingest cocaine. This was evident in a survey of children between 2 weeks and 5 years of age admitted to the emergency room at Boston City Hospital (Kharasch et al., 1991). In those children who did not have life-threatening emergencies or any history of suggestive cocaine exposure, the urine was screened for cocaine metabolites. Of 250 children whose urine was collected before discharge from the emergency room, six (2.4%) tested positive for cocaine. All the children testing positive were younger than 2 years of age, and four of the six were less than 1 year old. Only one of these children was being breast-fed at the time of the study.

The chemicals used in the conversion of cocaine hydrochloric acid to freebase cocaine ("crack") can be a serous hazard. A 20-month old child who sustained severe caustic esophageal burns requiring gastrostomy feedings and central hyperalimentation has been reported. The injury occurred after the ingestion of a lye solution, which was used in making freebase cocaine. The lye had been left in her home following a party. This child's urine was also positive for cocaine metabolites (Kharasch et al., 1990).

In recent years, methamphetamine (also know as meth, speed, crank, ice, zip, go-fast, chris, or "poor man's cocaine") has become the drug of choice over cocaine in the western United States. With the advent popularity of this drug, there arise new issues of child poisonings from exposure to illicit drugs. These include what chemical(s) the child has been exposed to, various routes of exposure, the concentration levels of the numerous methamphetamine-producing chemicals that the child has been around, and the possible long-term developmental effects after such exposure(s). Unlike cocaine, in which the final product is the possible poison in itself, most of the potential child poisonings occur during the manufacture of methamphetamine, with meth laboratories established in homes or garages in rural, mountainous areas. This, of course, makes it easier to avoid law enforcement detection.

"Thirty two chemicals can be cooked together to make methamphetamine, including anything from brake fluid to drain cleaner to red phosphorous, a highly flammable chemical that can easily combust when mixed with water or air and a nearby flame. Once mixed together, the chemicals create toxic fumes that can lead to liver and kidney failure, severe lung damage and cancer (Leonard, 1999)."

The apparent acute effect of children exposed to actual methamphetamine is the same as cocaine poisoning (Rosas, conversation 8/9/1999). However, there is almost no literature to statistically prove the degree of child poisoning from the drug itself. A protocol in California is being developed by the Governor's Office of Criminal Justice Planning, Drug-Endangered Children Division, to resolve the growing issues involved with child abuse, child poisoning, and child neglect from methamphetamine and its production.

Common Presentations of Poisoning by Intent or Neglect

In most incidents involving accidental poisoning the ingestion is either witnessed or is discovered soon after ingestion. The child still has the container in hand, with pills or solution in the mouth or nearby. Usually little has been ingested and the child has no symptoms, or very mild, transient symptoms. Death is an uncommon occurrence following accidental ingestion.

The child who has been poisoned by intent or neglect presents with a confusing or misleading history. One of four presentations commonly occurs (Meadow, 1989):

1. A parent brings the child to the hospital for treatment of an acute poisoning under the guise of an accidental poisoning.

2. A child presents with signs and symptoms of unknown etiology.

3. The child presents with recurrent unexplained illnesses (MSBP).

4. The child is found dead or near death because of significant time lapse since ingestion.

Given the confusing history, the physician must be alert to the myriad signs and symptoms children can manifest after an ingestion. Table 2, page 5 lists common presenting signs and symptoms reported in intentionally poisoned children with their respective etiologies.

Medical Examination

Various drug ingestions in children can rapidly lead to severe depression of the central nervous system and coma. The physical examination can differentiate drug induced encephalopathy from the other common causes of coma in children, such as mass lesions and seizures. Intact pupillary reflexes to light in the comatose patient indicate a functional midbrain. In most forms of metabolic coma, including drug-induced coma, pupillary reflexes remain intact.

The physical examination can also enable the physician to identify a specific toxicological syndrome accounting for the patient's unexplained symptoms (Table 3, page 5).

Laboratory data that can help in arriving at a diagnosis include serum osmolality, electrolytes, glucose, blood urea nitrogen (BUN), and creatine.

The routine toxicology screening test employed by most hospitals can be valuable in the identification of the poisoning agent if the child has been poisoned with a drug included in the screen. However, in many recorded cases of intentional poisoning, the drug was not part of the standard toxicology screen. It is important for the physician to consider which particular drugs may be responsible and ask the laboratory to perform specific assays for them. Also, the concentration of the drug or its metabolites may be below the detection range of the toxicology screen, so that a request for lower detection levels will be needed for the sample. It is advised that the urine sample for the screen be collected early to prevent possible elimination of the drug.

Examples of Poisoning Agents

Salt:

The literature contains several instances of infants intentionally poisoned with salt (Rogers et al., 1976; Meadow, 1977). The infants presented with multiple episodes of hypernatremia. They exhibited various findings, including seizures, lethargy, ataxia, coma, and dehydration. All had extreme elevations of serum and urine sodium levels. Normal renal function was demonstrated on recovery. Several authors have postulated that these infants would have been able to excrete the excess salt in the urine efficiently, but this mechanism failed because they were likely deprived of water. The clinical and biological findings in these salt-poisoned children are very similar to findings in children with hypernatremic dehydration secondary to intentional withholding of water (Pickel et al., 1970).

Pepper Aspiration:

Eight children dying of pepper aspiration have been reported (Cohle, et al., 1988). In each case the child was asphyxiated by forced pepper ingestion as punishment for some perceived wrongdoing. The children all died due to airway obstruction from pepper and mucosal edema. All but one of the victims was under 5 years old. Four of the children showed signs of chronic abuse.

Alcohols, Glycols, and Hydrocarbons:

Children intoxicated with ethanol may present to emergency departments with altered mental status, metabolic acidosis, and often hypoglycemia. The source may be half-consumed containers of alcohol (beer or wine coolers) or mixed drinks left after an adult party. Toddlers may access these beverages when there is inadequate supervision or neglect. Furthermore, parents have offered children alcohol to quiet them when the adults are frustrated by the child's "excessive" crying.

Alcohols, glycols, and hydrocarbons are three compounds that should be given special attention when investigating potential child abuse. These three agents are a unique group because they are common to most households and because their dangerous properties are not always realized. In addition, abusive forced ingestion can readily be passed off as an accidental injury if the investigator does not probe into this possibility. This is particularly true during "holiday" seasons.

There are several cases in the literature of intentional ethylene glycol (antifreeze) poisoning in small infants (Saldino & Shannon, 1991; Woolf et al., 1992). Ethylene glycol is sweet tasting and only a small amount is toxic, factors that may contribute to its ease of administration. In fact, cases of animal abuse or accidental poisoning have occurred as a result of these factors. Infants presenting with anion gap metabolic acidosis of unexplained etiology should be evaluated for infection; toxic overdose from agents such as ethylene glycol, ethanol, methanol, salicylates, and iron; and metabolic conditions such as diabetic ketoacidosis, uremia, and inborn errors of metabolism.

Hydrocarbons in various forms have been associated with intentional poisoning from practices such as lighter fluid administration in an intravenous line (Saulsbury et al, 1984) and recurrent pine oil intoxication in an infant (Hill et al, 1975). An unusual hydrocarbon-type odor and unexplained respiratory failure with pulmonary edema may be clues to this form of abuse.

Summary

The intentional poisoning of children is an uncommon but highly dangerous form of child abuse. It can occur in the context of extreme neglect, bizarre means of discipline, or MSBP. The physician must approach the family with as much understanding and compassion as possible. In some instances, what appears to be an attempt to harm a child may instead by the injudicious but well-intentioned use of a folk remedy the family felt too embarrassed to discuss. On the other hand, perpetrators of MSBP may be extremely sophisticated in their ability to conceal their intent. As always, the duty of the physician is to approach the ill child with sensitivity to the history and close attention to the physical findings and laboratory studies. When the latter is not explained by the former, child abuse must always be considered. The persistent search for an explanation of those findings, particularly in the intentionally poisoned child, may save that child from future harm and even death.

References

Bateman D and Heagerty M. Passive freebase cocaine ("crack") inhalation by infants and toddlers. *Am J Dis Child*, 143:25, 1989.

Chasnoff IF, Lewis DE, and Squires L. Cocaine intoxication in a breast-fed infant. *Pediatrics*, 80:836, 1987.

Cohle S, Trestail J, and Graham M. Fatal pepper aspiration. *Am J Dis Child*, 142:633, 1988.

Ernst A and Sanders W. Unexpected cocaine intoxication presenting as seizures in children. *Ann Emerg Med*, 18, 774, 1989.

Hill RM, Barer J, and Leighton H. An investigation of recurrent pine oil poisoning in an infant by the use of gas chromatographic-mass spectrometric methods. *J Pediatr*, 87:115, 1975.

Kempe CH, Silverman FN, Steel BF, et al. The battered child syndrome. *JAMA*, 181:17, 1962.

Kharasch S, Glotzer D, Vinci R, et al. Unsuspected cocaine exposure in young children. *Am J Dis Child*, 145:204, 1991.

Kharasch S, Vinci R, and Reece R. Esophagitis, epiglottitis, cocaine alkaloid ("crack"): "Accidental" poisoning or child abuse. *Pediatrics*, 86:117, 1990.

Leonard C. Meth: 'Killing Taxpayer' cleanup costs rise for poison at shut labs. *Arizona Republic*, August 5, 1999.

Meadow R. Munchausen Syndrome by Proxy: The hinterland of child abuse. *Lancet*, 2:343, 1977.

Meadow R. ABC of child abuse: Poisoning. *Br Med J*, 298:1445, 1989.

Olsen K and Banner W. "Emergency management of childhood poisoning" in *Pediatric Emergency Medicine*, edited by M Grossman and R Dieckmann. JB Lippincott, Philadelphia, 1991, pp. 332-339.

Rogers D, Tripp J, and Benovim A. Non-accidental poisoning: An extended syndrome of child abuse. *Br Med J*, 1:793, 1976.

Rosas A. Conversation on methamphetamine affects on children. August 9, 1999.

Rosenberg D. Web of deceit: A literature review of Munchausen Syndrome by Proxy. *Child Abuse Negl*, 11:547, 1987.

Saladino R and Shannon M. Accidental and intentional poisonings with ethylene glycol in infancy: Diagnostic clues and management. *Pediatr Emerg Care*, 7:93, 1991.

Saulsbury FT, Chobanian MC, and Wilson WG. Child abuse: Parenteral hydrocarbon administration. *Pediatrics*, 73:719, 1984.

Schwartz RH, Peary P and Mistretta D. Intoxication of young children with marijuana: A form of amusement for "pot"-smoking teenage girls. *Am J Dis Child*, 140:326, 1986.

Woolf AD, Wynshaw-Boris A, Rinaldo P, et al. Intentional infantile ethylene glycol poisoning presenting as an inherited metabolic disorder. *J Pediatr*, 120:421, 1992.

Child Sexual Abuse

Angela Rosas, M.D.

Case Vignette

An 8 year old girl who has been failing in school discloses to her mother that her stepfather has been sexually abusing her over the last year. The last contact was 2 weeks ago and there are no current anogenital complaints. The mother takes her to the emergency room where the child further discloses that she had some vaginal bleeding and pain with the first episodes of penile to vaginal contact.

Questions

1. What is meant by an acute or non-acute case of child sexual abuse?

2. What published procedures and standard state forms must be followed to perform acute and non-acute sexual abuse examinations?

3. What recommended methods should be used for the sexual abuse evaluation and why are these techniques important?

4. Will this child require screening for sexually transmitted diseases (STD)?

Epidemiology

Data from the 1996 National Incidence Surveillance Study found that more than 3 million children were reported as having been abused to child protective service agencies in the United States. Almost 1 million children were confirmed by child protective service agencies as victims of child maltreatment. According to the 1996 survey, physical abuse represented 23% of confirmed cases, sexual abuse 9%, neglect 60%, emotional maltreatment 4% and other forms of maltreatment 5%. Studies have suggested that approximately 1% of children experience some form of sexual abuse each year, resulting in the sexual victimization of 12-25% of girls and 8-10% of boys by age 18. 1999 California Department of Social Services data shows a total of 622,310 reports statewide and, of this number, 73,153 children or 12% were sexually abused.

Children are most commonly sexually abused by family members or acquaintances and are more frequently abused by males. It is estimated that 1 in 4 girls and 1 in 10 boys will be sexually abused by the age of 18. Boys are not as likely to disclose the abuse due to stereotypical expectations involving the socialization of boys. Adolescents are perpetrators in at least 20% of reported cases. Women may be perpetrators, however, men are the perpetrators in the majority of reported cases.

Clinical Presentation

Sexually abused children may present in a variety of circumstances which bring them to the attention of the health care system:

- the child may confide in a friend who, in turn, tells her mother, and the friend's mother notifies authorities;

- the child may disclose a history of abuse to a parent or relative who calls the regular doctor, on-call triage system, or brings the child into an urgent care facility;

- the child may be seen for a routine physical examination or for care of a medical illness, behavioral condition, or a physical finding (e.g. ano-genital laceration, ano-genital warts), or the parent reports concerns about sexualized behavior to the family pediatrician;

- the child discloses sexual abuse to a trusted adult such as a teacher, who is a mandated reporter, and the child is brought to the pediatrician by a social worker or law enforcement officer for a medical evaluation for possible sexual abuse as part of an investigation; or

- the child is brought to an emergency department after a suspected episode of sexual abuse for evaluation, evidence collection, and crisis management; and

- the child may be placed in foster care, brought by a foster parent for a placement examination, and the patient history indicates sexual abuse or the child is acting out sexually in the foster parent's home.

Signs and symptoms of sexual abuse

- Child discloses sexual abuse
- Acute anogenital injuries without clear accidental cause
- Rectal or genital bleeding
- Genital discharge or infection
- Anal or genital pain, itching, swelling, bruising
- Sexually transmitted disease
- Sexually obsessive, aggressive, or coercive behavior

Types of Sexual Abuse

- Inappropriate kissing, e.g. "french kissing"
- Fondling the genitals and/or breasts
- Genital exposure
- Fondling or masturbation of the child or requiring the child to fondle the perpetrator
- Oral genital contact or penetration
- "Dry intercourse", e.g. rubbing the penis against the child's legs, anal-genital area, inner thighs or buttocks
- Genital or vaginal contact or penetration
- Anal contact or penetration
- Child pornography or prostitution

General presenting symptoms which may indicate abuse or non-abuse-related stressors

- Sleep disturbances
- Sudden drop in school grades
- Chronic abdominal pain
- Enuresis
- Encopresis
- Phobias

Acute and Non Acute Examinations
Two types of forensic medical examinations

Acute Medical Forensic Examinations

If the child or adolescent discloses sexual abuse occurring within the past 72 hours, the patient receives a complete forensic examination for signs of injury, e.g. lacerations, bruising, erythema (redness); foreign materials, e.g. pubic hair, semen, saliva, secretions; and sexually transmitted diseases. These examinations must be conducted promptly to prevent the deterioration of evidence. An acute evidentiary exam may also be indicated in cases up to 7 days after a sexual assault when ejaculation may have occurred within the vagina.

Non acute Medical Forensic Examinations

The focus of the non-acute medical forensic examination is to look for signs of healed injury; irregularities in the genital structures due to chronic sexual abuse; and, sexually transmitted disease.

California Protocol for Examination of Sexual Assault and Child Sexual Abuse Victims

This protocol was developed in 1987 to standardize the performance of forensic medical examinations of sexual assault and child sexual abuse victims. The protocol and standard state forms were revised and re-issued July, 2002. These documents contain detailed procedures for the performance and documentation of acute and non acute child sexual abuse medical forensic examinations. The protocol and forms can be obtained from the Governor's Office of Criminal Justice Planning, Sacramento, California. http://www.ocjp.ca.gov/publications.htm.

SUGGESTED USE OF THE STANDARD STATE FORMS: FOLLOW LOCAL POLICY.	
OCJP 923	• History of **acute sexual assault** (<72 hours) • Examination of adults (age 18 and over) and adolescents (ages 12-17)
OCJP 925	• History of **nonacute sexual abuse** (>72 hours) • Examination of children and adolescents under age 18
OCJP 930	• History of acute **sexual abuse or assault** (<72 hours) • Examination of children under age 12
OCJP 930	• History of **chronic sexual abuse (incest) and recent incident** (<72 hours) • Examination of children and adolescents under age 18
OCJP 950	• Examination of person(s) suspected of sexual assault or sexual abuse
PC 11166 also called DOJ SS8576	• Written report required to report suspected child abuse within 72 hours in addition to the immediate telephone report • Submit to: County Children's Protective Services (CPS)

KEY TERMS FOR SEXUAL ASSAULT OR SEXUAL ABUSE EXAMS	
Acute	Less than 72 hours have passed since the incident (<72 hours)
Nonacute	More than 72 hours have passed since the incident (>72 hours)

Use of the Colposcope

Colposcopes revolutionized the field of child sexual abuse evidentiary exams. Pediatricians began to use the colposcope in the 1980's as a means of detecting subtle signs of child sexual abuse. The introduction of the colposcope established the concept of the non-acute sexual abuse examination. This was an important development for children because they are more likely to delay disclosure of sexual abuse than to report it immediately.

Colposcopes have magnifying lenses ranging from 4x to 30x power and can have 35mm camera or video camera attachments. In addition to a light source, colposcopes have a green filter which enhances the visualization of scars, unusual vascular patterns and genital warts.

The colposcope established a new standard of practice by enabling pediatric examiners to detect subtle injury and/or healed changes in the genital or rectal area. Its use facilitated the development of standards for evaluating normal and abnormal findings caused by sexual abuse. It is used for both acute and non-acute child sexual abuse forensic examinations.

Importance of the Multi-Method Approach for Prepubertal Adolescent Females

A multi-method approach for the female genital examination is currently the method of choice in many centers through the United States. It consists of a supine labial separation technique, a supine labial traction method, and a prone, knee-chest position. The multi-method approach allows for a complete evaluation of the anogenital structures for acute and healed injury without discomfort to the child victim.

• The labial separation in the supine position consists of a simple separation of the labia majora and provides an excellent view of the perineum. To apply supine labial traction, the examiner grasps the labia majora and applies an outward and downward traction. The hymenal edges separate approximately 90 per cent of the time with this approach, but the edges may still be folded and rolled.

- The prone, knee-chest position is the most successful technique for separating the edges of the hymen. In prone knee chest position, the child rests on her knees with upper chest on the examination table in a lordotic (swayback) posture. The examiner places her own thumbs under the patient's gluteal muscles and gently lifts upward, exposing the posterior hymen. The posterior hymen rim falls down and stretches out under its own weight. In this state, any unusual irregularity or defect in the hymen is easily visualized. Saline lavage in prone knee chest position may help further unfold a redundant hymen.

- Additional techniques such as manipulation with a moistened Q-tip or the use of a Foley catheter can also be used for adolescents.

Important Considerations in the Evaluation of Children

Tanner Stages

Tanner Stages describe the secondary sexual development of children. These developmental stages are relevant to the interpretation of physical findings in child and adolescent sexual abuse cases. There is a relationship between Tanner Stages and hymenal development. Physical findings must be evaluated in the context of hymenal development for an accurate interpretation of findings. See *California Protocol for Examination of Sexual Assault and Child Sexual Abuse Victims*.

Terms and Definitions for Genital Structures and Interpretation of Findings

The American Professional Society on the Abuse of Children (APSAC) has developed a handbook of standardized terms, definitions, and diagrams of genital structures and the interpretation of findings, the APSAC Glossary of Terms and the Interpretation of Findings for Child Sexual Abuse Evidentiary Examinations. Training on identifying genital structures and the interpretation of findings is provided by the California Medical Training Center at UC Davis. http://web.ucdmc.ucdavis.edu/medtrng/

Laboratory Tests

Consult the *California Medical Protocol on the Examination of Sexual Assault and Child Sexual Abuse Victims*, Chapter 12

Prophylaxis Against Sexually Transmitted Disease and Chapter 11 Possibility of Pregnancy.

- **Sexually Transmitted Disease**
  STD screening is usually not indicated in the prepubertal child victim unless there are symptoms of a sexually transmitted disease, or the perpetrator is at high risk for transmitting an STD. In acute adolescent cases, the victim is usually offered STD prophylactic antibiotics without anogential screening for STD's. Adolescents may need serology for syphilis and HIV depending on their risk for disease.

- **Pregnancy Screen**
  All adolescents who are at a puberty stage of Tanner III or beyond, menstruating, or previously sexually active are offered pregnancy prophylaxis following an acute sexual assault. There are a variety of effective hormonal regimens that provide effective prophylaxis. All regimens require confirmation of a negative pregnancy test and beginning the medication within 72 hours after the sexual assault.

- **Urine and Blood Toxicology**
  Urine and blood samples may be obtained for the sexual assault evidence collection kit whenever there is a suspicion that the victim was drugged or intoxicated during the assault. The sample may be assayed at the discretion of law enforcement at a later date. At the forensic lab, the blood can be assayed for alcohol and the urine can be tested for all common drugs of abuse as well as Rohypnol and Gammahydroxybutryic Acid (GHB). When there is a medical reason to identify the drugs or alcohol level of the victim at the time of the examination, an additional sample can be sent to the hospital laboratory. Most hospital labs cannot test for Rohypnol and GHB routinely. Since some of the drugs used during sexual assault are cleared rapidly in the body, it is important to collect the first urine specimen following the assault.

Classification of Examination Findings

Most forensic medical experts use the following criteria to classify findings of sexual abuse. This classification approach is contained on the standard state forensic medical exam forms listed on the next page.

OCJP 925 FORENSIC MEDICAL REPORT: NONACUTE (>72 HOURS) CHILD/ADOLESCENT SEXUAL ABUSE EXAMINATION	
Findings:	Examples:
• Normal exam: can neither confirm nor negate sexual abuse	• Normal findings and variations of normal
• Non-specific: may be caused by sexual abuse or other mechanisms	• Erythema (redness) of the anogenital tissues
• Sexual abuse is highly suspected	• Condyloma acuminata on a 9 year old without history of prior condylomata
• Definite evidence of sexual abuse and/or sexual contact	• Nonperinatal culture proven *Neisseria gonorrhea* • Pregnancy

OCJP 930 FORENSIC MEDICAL REPORT: ACUTE (<72 HOURS) CHILD/ADOLESCENT SEXUAL ABUSE EXAMINATION	
Findings:	Examples:
• Normal exam: can neither confirm nor negate sexual abuse	• Normal findings and variations of normal
• Non-specific: may be caused by sexual abuse or other mechanisms	• Labia minora contusion • Erythema (redness) of the anogenital tissues
• Sexual abuse is highly suspected	• Condyloma acuminata on a 9 year old without history of prior condylomata • Vestibular injuries with no labial trauma
• Definite evidence of sexual abuse and/or sexual contact	• Sperm • Bleeding hymenal tear/laceration with a history of acute genital penetration • Bleeding perianal laceration with a history of acute anal penetration.

Findings Indicating Medical Certainty of Sexual Abuse:

- Presence of semen or sperm
- Pregnancy
- Acute injury to the posterior hymen, fossa navicularis or posterior fourchette without a clear history of accidental injury
- Acute deep anal laceration
- Healed hymen transection
- Positive culture for Gonorrhea
- Positive serologic test for Syphilis or HIV

Findings Indicating Probable Evidence of Sexual Abuse:

- V-shaped or U-shaped deep cleft of the posterior hymen
- Very narrow hymen
- Positive culture for Chlamydia
- Trichomoniasis
- Condylomata accuminata presenting past 2 years of age

Findings Suggestive of Sexual Abuse:

- Anal dilation (immediate dilation, greater than 2 cm dilation with no stool in the ampulla)
- Gardnerella vaginalis vaginitis
- Herpes Type II infection
- Hepatitis B infection

Conditions That Mimic Sexual Abuse

- Congenital variations
- Capillary hemangiomas
- Congenital nevi
- Linea Vestibularis
- Fossa navicularis groove
- Lichen sclerosis
- Urethral prolapse
- Vulvovaginitis
- Labial Agglutination
- Prominent median raphe
- Perianal disease
- Midline anterior perianal projection

Frequency of Genital Injuries from Sexual Abuse

Significant anal/genital injuries are relatively uncommon in the sexually abused prepubertal girl and boy seen on a nonacute basis. It is estimated that only 30% of sexually abused prepubertal females have physical findings. The adolescent female is more likely to have abnormal physical findings following an acute sexual assault. These statistics are based upon various size sample studies.

Case management

RECOMMENDED FOLLOW-UP SCHEDULE	
Patients with evidence of acute trauma:	
• Schedule a short-term (1-4 days later) follow-up appointment	• To re-examine and document the development of visible findings, e.g., bruises; and • To photograph areas of potential injury, e.g., tenderness on the initial exam.
• Schedule a wellness exam and photographs (2-4 weeks later)	• To document resolution of findings or healing of injuries.
All patients:	
• Schedule a follow-up appointment 10 days to 2 weeks after the acute examination:	• To review lab test results with the patient, or child and family; and • For follow-up examination for sexually transmitted disease, i.e., cultures and wet mounts.
Long term follow up care can be performed by the patient's primary medical provider:	
• Schedule a follow-up appointment 6 weeks after the acute examination:	• For serologic tests, i.e., syphilis, HIV, second dose of Hepatitis B vaccine.
• Schedule a follow-up appointment 12 weeks after the acute examination:	• For an HIV test.
• Schedule a follow-up appointment 24 weeks after the acute examination:	• For a third dose of Hepatitis B vaccine if indicated; and • For a final HIV test.

Prognosis

The physical anogenital injuries heal very quickly. Small abrasions may disappear in days, while large lacerations may heal to a thin scar within weeks. Hymen transections and deep tears, however, usually persist as concavities on follow-up colposcope exam. These injuries will become more rounded off with time. The psychological effects of child sexual abuse or sexual assault require counseling to address acute and long standing issues related to Post-Traumatic Stress Disorder (PTSD).

Recommendations

- Children with history or signs and symptoms of sexual abuse should have a forensic medical examination by a trained health practitioner using a colposcope to conduct an assessment. Examination of siblings should be considered since there is often more than one victim in a family.

- Children with history or signs and symptoms of sexual abuse should be interviewed by a Multi-Disciplinary Interview Team with training in child development and forensic interviewing. See chapters on Interviewing Children and Specialized Multi-Disciplinary Interview Teams.

- Children who have been sexually abused should be referred to a mental health provider to assess the need for treatment and to evaluate the level of parental support.

- Children in foster care should receive comprehensive medical examinations during the first 30 days of placement which includes a screening assessment of the ano-genital area. Foster children with a previous history of sexual abuse and/or signs and symptoms on screening exam should have a complete forensic medical examination.

Important Cross References to Other Chapters Related to Child Sexual Abuse

Prophylaxis for Sexually Transmitted Disease

Interviewing Children

Specialized Multi-Disciplinary Interview Teams

Reimbursement for Services

CARE, SAFE, SANE Forensic Examination Teams

Training Resources for Physicians and Nurses

The American Academy of Pediatrics (January, 1999) issued the Policy Statement "Guidelines for the Evaluation of Sexual Abuse of Children: Subject Review" which contained these helpful charts:

TABLE 1. GUIDELINES FOR MAKING THE DECISION TO REPORT SEXUAL ABUSE OF PREPUBERTAL CHILDREN

Data Available			Response	
History	**Physical**	**Laboratory**	**Level of Concern About Sexual Abuse**	**Action**
None	Normal examination	None	None	None
Behavioral changes	Normal examination	None	Low (worry)	+/- Report*; follow closely (possible mental health referral)
None	Nonspecific findings	None	Low (worry)	+/- Report*; follow closely
Nonspecific history by child or history by parent only	Nonspecific findings	None	Possible (suspect)	+/- Report*; follow closely
None	Specific findings	None	Probable	Report
Clear statement	Normal examination	None	Probable	Report
Clear statement	Specific findings	None	Definite	Report
None	Normal examination, nonspecific or specific findings	Positive culture for gonorrhea; positive serologic test for syphilis; presence of semen, sperm, acid phosphatase	Definite	Report
Behavioral changes	Nonspecific changes	Other sexually transmitted disease	Probable	Report

* - A report may or may not be indicated. The decision to report should be based on discussion with local or regional experts and/or child protective services agencies.

It is helpful to think about reporting child abuse as a mandated consultation.

TABLE 2. IMPLICATIONS OF COMMONLY ENCOUNTERED SEXUALLY TRANSMITTED DISEASES (STDS) FOR THE DIAGNOSIS AND REPORTING OF SEXUAL ABUSE OF PREPUBERTAL INFANTS AND CHILDREN

STD Confirmed	Sexual Abuse	Suggested Action
Gonorrhea (*)	Certain	Report (**)
Syphilis (*)	Certain	Report
Chlamydia (*)	Probable (***)	Report
Condylomata acuminatum (*)	Probable	Report
Trichomonas vaginalis	Probable	Report
Herpes 1 (genital)	Possible	Report (^)
Herpes 2	Probable	Report
Bacterial vaginosis	Uncertain	Medical follow-up
Candida albicans	Unlikely	Medical follow-up

* If not perinatally acquired. ** To Children's Protective Services. *** Culture only reliable diagnostic method.
^ Unless there is a clear history of autoinoculation.

Resources

California Medical Protocol for Examination of Sexual Assault and Child Sexual Abuse Victims, July, 2002. Published by the Governor's Office of Criminal Justice Planning, 1130 K Street, Sacramento, California. http://www.ocjp.ca.gov/

Guidelines for the Evaluation of Sexual Abuse of Children: Subject Review (RE9819) published by the *American Academy of Pediatrics*, Volume 103, Number 1, January, 1999.

American Professional Society on the Abuse of Children, Chicago, Illinois

APSAC Glossary of Terms and the Interpretation of Findings for Child Sexual Abuse Evidentiary Examinations: APSAC at 407 Dearborn St., Suite 1300, Chicago, IL 60605 Phone: 312-554-0166 fax: 312-554-0919 E-mail: APSACPublis@aol.com

Kerns, D.L., Ritter, M.L., Thomas, R.G. (1992) Concave hymenal variations in suspected child sexual abuse victims. Pediatrics 90:2, 265-272.

California Medical Training Center

This state funded training center provides training and nurses on how to perform quality medical evidential exams for victims of child sexual abuse, child physical abuse and neglect, domestic violence, sexual assault, and elder/dependent adult abuse. Training on interpretation of findings is also provided for law enforcement officers, investigative social workers, and prosecutors. web.ucdmc.ucdavis.edu/medtrng

Sexually Transmitted Diseases

Angela Rosas, M.D.

Two Case Vignette

A 14-year old female presents one day after sexual assault at a party after drinking alcohol. She has little memory of the assault, but has evidence of acute genital trauma.

A 6-year old female presents with purulent vaginal discharge and discloses ongoing sexual abuse by her 17-year old stepbrother. She discloses repeated vaginal and anal penetration.

Questions

1. What STD testing if any should be done?
2. What STD treatment should be provided?
3. When should the patient have follow-up testing?

The following information has been adapted from the *2002 Guidelines for Treatment of Sexually Transmitted Diseases* by the U.S. Department of Health and Human Services, Centers for Disease Control and Prevention (CDC), Atlanta, Georgia and the *California Medical Protocol for Examinations of the Sexual Assault and Child Sexual Abuse Victim* published in July, 2002.

This treatment protocol promotes and encourages the highest quality medical and emotional care for all patients but does not purport to mandate or restrict medical decision making. Recommendations in the protocol regarding medical evaluation and treatment issues are included only as guidelines or suggestions to assist the examiner. The ultimate responsibility for medical management of the sexual assault patient rests with the clinician and is beyond the scope of the protocol.

Sexually Transmitted Disease Management in Adolescent Victims of Sexual Assault

- In sexually active adolescents, the issues of sexually transmitted disease (STD) risk and identification after sexual assault is more important for the medical and psychological management of the patient than for forensic purposes since the infection could have been present before the assault.

- No firm data or consensus have been developed to determine the risk of a victim contracting an STD following sexual assault.

- The most frequently diagnosed infections at the time of the sexual assault evaluation are trichomoniasis, bacterial vaginosis, chlamydia, and gonorrhea. Chlamydia and gonorrhea pose the added potential risk of ascending infection (PID or Pelvic Inflammatory Disease). Other significant STDs that are a potential complication of sexual assault include hepatitis B and C, syphilis, HIV (Human Immunodeficiency Virus), HSV (Herpes Simplex Virus), and HPV (Human Papilloma Virus).

1. **Standard STD testing**
   - The CDC recommends pre-treatment cultures for N. gonorrhoeae, C. Trachomatis, and a wet mount to evaluate for evidence of bacterial vaginosis and yeast. Wet mount and culture (if available) for *T. vaginalis* should be done.

   - This protocol does not require these tests, and leaves their use to the discretion of the clinician. For sexually active adolescents, these tests do not have forensic evidential value because they only show pre-existing health conditions.

   - If the patient chooses prophylaxis (see below) pre-treatment cultures are probably unnecessary.

91

2. Serologic STD testing

- The CDC recommends collection of a serum sample from the patient at the time of the examination for evaluation of hepatitis B, syphilis, and HIV.

- Post-exposure hepatitis B vaccinations (without HBIG) should adequately protect against infection from the hepatitis B virus. The protocol does not require hepatitis B testing but recommends prophylaxis (see next page). If the victim has a reliable history of complete hepatitis B vaccination, then hepatitis B prophylaxis is unnecessary.

- Incubating syphilis transmitted at the assault should be eradicated by the medication given to prophylax against gonorrhea and chlamydia. Syphilis testing at the time of the examination may uncover an unrecognized pre-existing infection. This infection is a personal and public health problem, but not a forensic issue. The protocol does not require syphilis serology and leaves the decision to the clinician.

- The issues related to HIV testing, counseling, prophylaxis, and follow-up are complex and controversial. This protocol recommends HIV risk assessment for all sexual assault patients but does not require testing as part of the forensic examination process. Patients should be expeditiously referred to local resources capable of comprehensive HIV services.

- Current California law allows alleged perpetrator testing, if requested by the victim; however, the suspect must be charged with the crime. The local county district attorney's office is responsible for handling these requests.

3. Prophylaxis

If the patient's clinical presentation suggests a pre-existing ascending STD infection, such as fever, abdominal or pelvic pain, and/or vaginal discharge, the patient should be evaluated and treated for the ascending infection. This may differ from recommended STD prophylaxis.

All patients should be strongly encouraged to accept routine preventive therapy after sexual assault. Adequate follow-up of sexual assault patients is very difficult; prophylaxis at the time of the forensic examination is prudent and cost effective. The enabling statute for the protocol does not require the law enforcement agency to pay for STD prophylaxis. Most medical facilities, however, have opted to dispense medication for STD (and pregnancy) prophylaxis directly to the patient at the time of the exam for the patient's well-being and for public health reasons.

See chart on for recommended STD treatment regimen for adolescents.

RECOMMENDED REGIMEN FOR ADOLESCENTS:			
• Gonorrhea	Suprax® (Cefixime)— 400mg orally once	OR	• Rocephin® (Ceftriaxone)— 125mg IM in single dose
		PLUS	
• Trichomoniasis	Flagyl® (Metronidazole)— 2gm in a single dose		
		PLUS	
• Chlamydia	Zithromax® (Azithromycin)— 1Gm. orally once	OR	• Doxycycline— 100mg orally 2x/day for 7 days
		PLUS	
• Hepatitis	Hepatitis B vaccination (without HBIG)		• First dose should be given at the time of the forensic medical examination. • The patient should be referred for follow-up to complete the immunization schedule

Many alternatives are available to address such factors as patient's age, pregnancy, or drug allergies. Consult the CDC guidelines for details.

4. CDC recommendations for approaching the risk of acquiring HIV infection from sexual assault
Although HIV-antibody seroconversion has been reported among persons whose only known risk factor was sexual assault or sexual abuse, the risk for acquiring HIV infection through sexual assault is low. The overall probability of HIV transmission from an HIV-infected person during a single act of intercourse depends on many factors. These factors may include the type of sexual intercourse (i.e., oral, vaginal, or anal); presence of oral, vaginal or anal trauma; site of exposure to ejaculate; viral load in ejaculate; and presence of STD in the patient.

In certain circumstances, the likelihood of HIV transmission also may be affected by postexposure therapy for HIV with antiretroviral agents. Postexposure therapy with zidovudine has been associated with a reduced risk for HIV infection in a study of health-care workers who had percutaneous exposures to HIV-infected blood. On the basis of these results and the biologic plausibility of the effectiveness of antiretroviral agents in preventing infection, postexposure therapy has been recommended for health-care workers who have percutaneous exposures to HIV. However, whether these findings can be extrapolated to other HIV-exposure situations, including sexual assault, is unknown. A recommendation cannot be made, on the basis of available information, regarding the appropriateness of postexposure antiretroviral therapy after sexual exposure to HIV. In children, even less information is available on post HIV-exposure prophylaxis.

Health-care providers who consider offering postexposure therapy should take into account the likelihood of exposure to HIV, the potential benefits and risks of such therapy, and the interval between the exposure and initiation of therapy. Because timely determination of the HIV-infection status of the assailant is not possible in many sexual assaults, the health-care provider should assess the nature of the assault, any available information about HIV-risk behaviors exhibited by persons who are sexual assailants (e.g., high-risk sexual practices and injecting-drug or crack cocaine use), and the local prevalence of HIV/AIDS.

If antiretroviral postexposure prophylaxis is offered, the following information should be discussed with the patient:

- critical need for frequent dosing of medications;

- the close follow-up that is necessary;

- the importance of strict compliance with the recommended therapy; and

- the necessity of immediate initiation of treatment for maximal likelihood of effectiveness.

Centers choosing to offer this prophylaxis should develop protocols for consent, treatment, and follow up.

5. Follow-up instructions and care
- Patients should be counseled about STD symptoms and the need for immediate evaluation if symptoms occur.

- Abstinence from sexual activity is recommended until STD prophylaxis is completed.

- The CDC recommends a follow-up visit two weeks after the forensic examination. At that time pregnancy and STD issues can be re-evaluated depending on the details of the case and in context with the initial management.

- Hepatitis B vaccinations should be given at current recommended intervals after the initial dose at the time of the exam.

- If the clinician has initiated syphilis and/or HIV serologic testing, follow-up sampling should be repeated at 6 and 12 weeks for HIV and at 6 weeks for syphilis.

Evaluation of Children for Sexually Transmitted Disease

STD testing has forensic evidential value for children and non-sexually active adolescents

- Perform procedures so as to minimize pain and trauma to the child.

- Make the decision to evaluate the child for STDs on an individual patient basis.

- Be familiar with the various STDs and their implication for evidence of child sexual abuse—see Table 2 in *Child Sexual Abuse*, of these Guidelines.

- Situations involving a high risk for STDs and a strong indication for testing include the following:

  – A suspected offender is known to have an STD or to be at high risk for STDs (e.g., has multiple sex partners or a history of STD);

– The child has symptoms or signs of an STD or of an infection that can be sexually transmitted; and/or

– The prevalence of STDs in the community is high.

1. **Standard STD Testing**

   • Cultures for *N. gonorrhoea* specimens collected from the pharynx and anus in both boys and girls, and the vagina in girls. Cervical specimens are not recommended for prepubertal girls. For boys, a urethral culture for *N. gonorrhea* should be obtained only if a urethral discharge is present. A meatal specimen of urethral discharge is an adequate substitute for an intraurethral swab specimen when discharge is present. Only standard culture systems for the isolation of *N. gonorrhoea* should be used. All presumptive isolates should be confirmed by at least two tests that involve different principles. Isolates should be preserved in case additional or repeated testing is needed.

   • Cultures for *C. trachomatis* from specimens collected from the anus in both boys and girls and from the vagina of girls. A urethral specimen should **only** be obtained if urethral discharge is present. Pharyngeal specimens for *C. trachomatis* are not recommended for either sex because the yield is low. Only standard culture systems for the isolation of *C. trachomatis* should be used. At present, non-culture tests do not have proven sensitivity and specificity in the prepubertal child to be used reliably as forensic evidence.

   • Wet mount of vaginal swab specimen for *T. vaginalis* infection. Obtain culture for *T. vaginalis* where available.

   • The presence of clue cells in the wet mount or other signs, such as positive whiff test, suggests Bacterial Vaginosis (BV) in girls who have vaginal discharge. The significance of clue cells or other indicators of BV as an indicator of sexual exposure is unclear.

   • Visual inspection of the genital and perianal areas for genital warts and ulcerative lesions. Conduct testing for herpes simplex if symptoms are present. Appropriate testing should include both HSV culture of a lesion and IgM and IgG serology for HSVI. HSV culture of a lesion is the only reliable method for distinguishing HSVI from HSVII infection.

2. **Serologic STD Testing**

   • Collect a serum sample to be evaluated immediately, preserved for subsequent analysis, and used as a baseline for comparison with follow-up serologic tests.

   • Sera should be tested immediately for antibodies to sexually transmitted agents such as *T. pallidum* (syphilis), HIV, and Hepatitis B. Hepatitis B serology is unnecessary in children with a reliable history of complete Hepatitis B vaccination.

3. **Presumptive Treatment**

The risk for a child's acquiring an STD as a result of sexual abuse has not been determined. The risk is believed to be low in most circumstances, although documentation to support this position is inadequate.

Presumptive treatment for children who have been sexually assaulted or abused is not widely recommended. However, some children, or their parents or guardians, may be concerned about the possibility of infection with an STD, even if the risk is perceived by the health care provider to be low.

If needed, the following are appropriate doses for treatment of uncomplicated STD's or STD prophylaxis. Adolescents, 12 years and older, may use the adult regimen.

Gonorrhea	Under 12 years old	Ceftriaxone	• 125mg IM single dose
Chlamydia	Under 9 years old	Erythromycin	• 50mg/kg/day divided 4x/day for 10-14 days. Maximum dose is 2g/day.
	Over 9 years old	Doxycycline	• 100mg orally 2x/day for 7 days
Trichomonas	Under 12 years old	Metronidazole	• 40mg/kg single dose or 15mg/kg/day divided 3x/day for 7 days. Maximum dose is 2g/day.

4. Follow-up care

Repeat tests should be conducted at the same intervals as adults.

Resources

California Medical Protocol for Examination of Sexual Assault and Child Sexual Abuse Victims, July, 2002. Published by the Governor's Office of Criminal Justice Planning, 1130 K Street, Sacramento, CA.
http://www.ocjp.ca.gov

2002 Guidelines for Treatment of Sexually Transmitted Diseases. Published by the U.S. Department of Health and Human Services, Centers for Disease Control and Prevention (CDC), Atlanta, GA. or
http://www.cdc.gov/mmwr/pdf/rr/rr5106.pdf.

Prenatal Drug and Alcohol Abuse

Sylvia Villarreal, M.D. and Robin Lee Hansen, M.D.

Case Vignette

Sharon was pregnant with her fourth child. She had a documented history of alcohol and cocaine use during her prior pregnancies. Her other children had been removed and placed in foster care because their newborn urine toxicology screens were positive for cocaine. She had made a few scheduled appointments to her prenatal visits this pregnancy and appeared ready and responsible to keep this child. Sharon arrived at Labor and Delivery at seven months gestation, in active labor after a crack binge. The infant was delivered blue and limp. His birth weight was 1500 grams; he was resuscitated and placed on a ventilator. His urine toxicology screen was positive for cocaine. His mother was vigilant and stayed with the infant in the NICU. After close consultation with the medical social worker, child protective services worker and the pediatrics health care team, the infant was discharged from the hospital with Sharon to a drug rehabilitation home.

Questions

1. Is identification and reporting of perinatal substance abuse beneficial to infant and mother?

2. What are the impacts on the legal and ethical rights/obligations of the mother, child and health care provider?

3. What are the impacts of prenatal drug exposure on the developing infant?

4. What are effective strategies for addressing this problem?

Epidemiology/Statistics

Estimates of the actual prevalence rates of prenatal substance abuse are central to the concerns raised about the impact of prenatal drug use on physical and developmental outcome. These estimates are also critical for public policy guidelines and adequate planning for allocation of needed resources. The prevalence of prenatal drug use is estimated to be as high as 10-20%, although the prevalence probably varies with ethnicity, socioeconomic status, and geographic location. Underreporting in self-identifying surveys is said to be a major bias in these studies (Gillogley, Evans, Hansen, Samuels and Batra, 1990; Frank, et al, 1988). Urine toxicology screening of pregnant women or their newborns may be standard practice in some hospitals, although this is only a reflection of the previous several days for most drugs of abuse, and is likely a low estimate of the prevalence of prenatal drug use. Hospitals have varying criteria for testing women or infants considered at risk for illegal drug use. The most frequently cited criteria for drug testing is maternal admission of drug/alcohol use, no prenatal care, health provider suspicion, risk factors for HIV, other sexually transmitted diseases and combinations of these problems. Hansen et al investigated the sensitivity and specificity of various risk factors related to positive urine toxicology screens and found that smoking was the most sensitive factor, although had insufficient specificity. In addition to cigarette use, women using illegal drugs during pregnancy also report significantly more alcohol use than non-drug users (Hansen et al, 1992).

Medical intervention, such as early prenatal care is an effective strategy in prenatal care delivery for women who use alcohol and abuse substances.

Policy and Legislation

The issue of identification of prenatal drug use is critical, since medical, drug treatment and social intervention resources are effective strategies in protecting the safety, health, and developmental outcomes of children with prenatal drug exposure. The threat of criminal prosecution for mothers using drugs prenatally has been a deterrent to seeking medical care and drug treatment services. Adirim and Gupta's survey concluded that in 1991, no state had enacted legislation regarding mandatory toxicology testing. Thirteen states had mandatory reporting policies, eleven required reporting to social service agencies, three states routinely reported to criminal justice agencies, and ten states required that reports be filed as child abuse or neglect.

California passed Senate Bill 2669 in 1990, which states that positive toxicology screen at the time of delivery of an infant is not, in and of itself, a sufficient basis for reporting child abuse or neglect. Amended with Section 11166 of the California Penal Code, it states that a report based on risk to the child related solely to the inability of the parent to provide the child with regular care due to the parent's substance abuse shall be made known only to county welfare departments and not to law enforcement agencies. The 1991 SB 2669 Model Needs Assessment Protocol was developed by a committee of representatives from the California Department of Alcohol and Drug Programs, Developmental Services, Health Services, and Social Services. The committee also had representation from the areas of hospital administration, public health, substance abuse prevention and treatment, and child welfare. It provided guidance in identifying needed services to assist the mother in caring for her child. It offered a framework for determining the level of risk to the newborn if released to the home and the corresponding needed levels of services and intervention to protect the infant's health and safety.

Impact of Prenatal Drug Exposure Upon the Developing Infant and Child and Relationship to Child Abuse and Neglect

All illicit drugs reach the fetal circulation by crossing the placenta and can cause direct toxic effects on the fetus, as well as fetal and maternal dependency. For example, the opiate-exposed fetus may experience withdrawal in utero when drugs are withdrawn from a dependent mother or, after delivery, when the mother's use no longer directly affects her newborn.

Isolating the effects of individual drugs on the infant and child is difficult because it is unusual for women to use only a single drug during pregnancy; and, many confounding variables exist that are known to have deleterious effects on outcomes, such as poor prenatal care, increased rates of infection and other medical problems, and poor nutrition. The effects of alcohol exposure on the developing fetus have been the most clearly described, and Fetal Alcohol Syndrome is felt to be the most common cause of preventable mental retardation internationally. Children with alcohol exposure prenatally that do not meet the diagnostic criteria for FAS may still have longterm effects on physical and developmental outcome which are frequently difficult to specifically relate to alcohol. Maternal alcohol use is frequently associated with other drug use, including cigarettes, cocaine, marijuana, amphetamines and opiates.

In the newborn period, the most consistent findings of multiple studies investigating the outcomes of drug exposed infants included increased rates of prematurity, lower birth weights and smaller head circumferences (Hansen & Ulrey, 1993). The majority of infants exposed to opiates prenatally do exhibit symptoms of opiate withdrawal which include hyper-irritability, jitteriness, increased muscle tone, gastrointestinal dysfunction, rapid breathing, increased temperature, poor feeding and seizures. These symptoms are often present at birth but may not reach a peak until 3 to 4 days or as late as 10 to 15 days after birth. Evidence of withdrawal from opiates can persist in subacute form for 4 to 6 months after birth, with persistent irritability, altered sleep patterns, and feeding difficulties. The existence of a true abstinence or withdrawal syndrome from cocaine or amphetamines has been questioned, as there are multiple studies with contrasting results (Neuspiel and Hamel, 1991) depending on the control for confounding variables such as the effect of alcohol use, obstetrical complications, blinded observers, etc. Some studies report increased rates of irritability and tremulousness, lethargy, inability to respond appropriately to stimulation, and abnormal cry patterns.

Perinatal cerebral infarctions have occurred in infants whose mothers have used cocaine during a few days before delivery (Chasnoff et al, 1986). These perinatal cerebral infarctions, although extremely rare, exemplify the severe morbidity that may be associated with intrauterine exposure to cocaine. Issues of increased risk of malformations have been raised but await analysis of data from large studies. Because most published studies of cocaine's effect on pregnancies and infants have focused on multiple high-risk, substance-abusing populations, little information is available regarding the effects of low doses of cocaine.

Longitudinal follow-up of drug-exposed infants has been limited by the same confounds noted in the studies of neonatal outcome, in addition to the variations in the postnatal environment that significantly affect outcome, such as high mobility, financial instability, inconsistent use of social support and medical services, high rates of familial violence and continued parental drug use. Several long-term studies have demonstrated that substance-exposed infants are at risk for developmental and learning problems, particularly behavioral, attentional and organizational problems. Struthers and Hansen (1992) found significant differences on a test of novelty preference, which has been shown to be more predictive of later cognitive outcomes than other developmental tests in infancy, between exposed and non-exposed infants. Developmental testing using the Bayley Scales of Infant Development has not shown consistent differences between groups of exposed and nonexposed infants when variables other than drug use are well controlled. Rodning, Beckwith and Howard (1989, 1990) found disorganized play and less secure attachment in exposed children, with poor attention, difficulty processing information and behavioral problems that interfere with their learning (Howard, Beckwith, Rodning & Kropenske, 1989). Griffith et al (1994) found no differences in cognitive outcome at three years of age, although Beckwith et al (1997) reported cognitive scores to be decreased in exposed preschoolers. Bentz, Hansen, Steward and Barton (1995) found no cognitive differences on cognitive measures at 4-6 years, but did find significant differences in two measures of executive functioning, which included a measure of impulse control and future planning. The exposed children had more difficulties with impulse control and future planning than their nonexposed controls.

The research to date indicates that most investigators now agree that there is no "typical profile" that holds true for children with prenatal drug exposure. The effects on outcome primarily related to prenatal drug exposure versus those related to environmental variables have not been adequately examined. The severity of problems within individual children and the percentage of exposed children with problems related to prenatal drug exposure remain unanswered.

Substance abuse in pregnant and parenting women is a disease which may lead to child abuse and neglect. Chronic substance abusers may have underlying mental illness, and may have complex socioeconomic problems such as homelessness, domestic violence, criminal justice issues, lack of education and job skills and little access to child care. Health care providers often face ethical dilemmas in providing medical care and supervision to an alcohol and/or substance abusing pregnant mother and her fetus or child. Issues of confidentiality, labeling and resource allocation are significant. If comprehensive identification of prenatal drug use is to be used primarily for criminalization and prosecution, little will be gained in our understanding or our treatment of drug abusing women and their children. Resources are needed to address issues of chemical dependency, housing, nutrition, employment, and potential chronic illness such as HIV disease as well as mental health services.

Recommended Model Programs

Comprehensive, culturally and linguistically appropriate rehabilitation treatment centers for women and their children are needed to address the multiple issues that face drug abusing, parenting women. SB 2669, Sections 10900-10902 to the Health and Safety Code, mandates that counties establish protocols among health and welfare departments and all county public and private hospitals to assess the need of all pregnant and birthing women and their infants for services related to substance-exposure and/or substance abuse problems. Incarcerated women who are pregnant or with young infants also need rehabilitative centers to aid in their recovery and potential release back into society

Chemical dependency is a disease, not a crime. Senate Bill 2669 Model Needs Assessment Protocol can be adopted by counties in its entirety or used as a blueprint for developing county specific protocols. There were no funds provided for the activities required by SB 2669. Many counties have filed claims for reimbursement for the development and dissemination of county specific protocols to the Commission on State Mandates.

Recommendations

Medical intervention, such as early prenatal care, rehabilitation services for pregnant women, and comprehensive pediatric care for the infant and child, planned and funded in a comprehensive manner can help pregnant and parenting women with chemical dependency cope with their addiction, support the health of the fetus/newborn, promote good infant and child outcome, and prevent child abuse and neglect.

1. A comprehensive medical and psychosocial history that includes specific information regarding maternal drug use needs to be part of every prenatal and newborn evaluation.

2. Maternal and newborn urine toxicologic analyses and newer drug tests of hair and meconium should be regarded only as potential adjuncts to a thorough maternal drug history and needs assessment.

3. The pediatrician should include maternal drug use in the differential diagnosis of any neonate with suggestive or otherwise unexplained symptomatology.

4. The pediatrician should evaluate the drug-exposed infant for other medical conditions associated with maternal drug use, including the possibility of concurrent sexually transmitted diseases in the mother and infant.

5. Because adverse effects of drug exposure may not be evident at birth, the pediatrician should be alert to potential long-term consequences that may become apparent during ongoing care.

6. In most circumstances, when a drug-exposed infant or drug-abusing mother is identified, the pediatrician should consider recruiting the assistance of local child protective services to provide multidisciplinary treatment and support for the affected mother, child and family.

7. The pediatrician should be knowledgeable about state and local child protection reporting requirements.

8. The development and evaluation of models of coordinated multidisciplinary prevention, intervention, and treatment services that improve access to early comprehensive care for all substance-abusing pregnant women and their children are needed. Evaluation of current and new treatment modalities is imperative to determine their effectiveness.

9. Pediatricians are encouraged to be involved in organizing community-based social service and child protection service systems designed to provide essential services for drug-abusing women and their children.

10. Funds for education, research, prevention, and treatment should be made available to address issued of drug-exposed infants.

Readings

MacMahon, J.R. Perinatal substance abuse: the impact of reporting infants to child protective services. *Pediatrics* 100(5): E1, 1997.

Capen, K. Mother's rights can't be infringed to protect fetus, Supreme Court's landmark ruling states. *CMAJ* 1,157(11): 586-7, 1997.

Chavkin, W., Breitbart, V. Reproductive health and blurred professional boundaries. *Women's Health Issues* 6(2): 89-96, 1996. The Center for Population and Family Health, Columbia University School of Public Health, New York, USA.

Birchfield, M., Scully, J., Handler, A. Perinatal screening for illicit drugs: policies in hospitals in large metropolitan areas. *J Perinatalogy* 15(3): 208-14, 1995 May-Jun.

Adirim, T.A., Sen Gupta, N. A national survey of state maternal and newborn drug testing and reporting policies. *Public Health Rep.* 106(3): 292-6, 1991.

Villarreal, S.F., McKinney, L.E., Quackenbush, M.J. *Handle with Care. Helping Children Prenatally Exposed to Drugs and Alcohol.* ETR Associates. Santa Cruz, California. 1992.

Chavkin, W., Breitbart, V., Elman, D., Wise, P.H. National survey of the states policies and practices regarding drug-using pregnant women. *AJPH* 88(1): 117-9, 1998.

Vega, W., Kolody, B., Hwang, J. Prevalence and magnitude of perinatal substance exposures in California. *NEJM* 329:850-4, 1993.

American Academy of Pediatrics Policy Statement. Vol. 96, No. 2, August, 1995.

Robins, L., Mills, J., eds. Effects of in utero exposure to street drugs. *Am J. Public Health*. 1993;83(suppl):2-32.

American Academy of Pediatrics, Committee on Drugs. The transfer of drugs and other chemicals into human milk. *Pediatrics.* 1994;93:137-150.

Chasnoff, I.J., Hatcher, R., Burns, W.J. Early growth patterns of methadone-addicted infants. *Am J Dis Child.* 1980;134:1049-1051

Finnegan, L.P. Neonatal abstinence syndrome: assessment and pharmacotherapy. In: Rubaltelli F.F., Granati, B., eds. Neonatal Therapy: An Update. New York: *Exerpta Medica;* 1986: 122-146.

Fried, P.A. Marihuana use by pregnant women: neurobehavioral effects in neonates. *Drug Alcohol Depend.* 1980;6:415-424.

MacGregor, S.N., Keith, L.G., Chasnoff, I.J., et al. Cocaine use during pregnancy: adverse perinatal outcome. *Am J Obstet Gynecol.* 1987;157:686-690.

Chasnoff, I.J., Burns, W.J., Schnoll, S.H., Burns, K.A. Cocaine use in pregnancy. *N Engl J Med.* 1985;313:666-669.

Chasnoff, I.J., Griffith, D.R., MacGregor, S., et al. Temporal patterns of cocaine use in pregnancy: perinatal outcome. *JAMA.* 1989;261:1741-1744.

Bingol, N., Fuchs, M., Diaz, V., Stone, R.K., Gromisch, D.S. Teratogenicity of cocaine in humans. *J Pediatr.* 1987;110:93-96.

Lester, B.M., Corwin, M.J., Sepkoski, C., et al. Neurobehavioral syndromes in cocaine-exposed newborn infants. *Child Dev.* 1991;62:694-705.

Chasnoff, I.J., Bussey, M.E., Savich, R., Stack, C.M. Perinatal cerebral infarction and maternal cocaine use. *J Pediatr.* 1986;108:456-459.

Chasnoff, I.J., Chisum, G.M., Kaplan, W.E. Maternal cocaine use and genitourinary tract malformations. *Teratology.* 1988;37:201-204.

Hoyme, H.E., Jones, K.L., Dixon, S.D., et al. Prenatal cocaine exposure and fetal vascular disruption. *Pediatrics.*1990;85:743-747.

Fried, P., Watkinson, B. 36- and 48-month neurobehavioral follow-up of children prenatally exposed to marijuana, cigarettes, and alcohol. *J Dev Behav Pediatr.* 1990;11:49-58.

Howard, J., Beckwith, L., Rodning, C., Kropenske, V. The development of young children of substance-abusing parents: insights from seven years of intervention and research. *Zero Three.* 1989;9:8-12.

Chasnoff, I.J., Griffith, D.R., Freier, C., Murray, J. Cocaine/polydrug use in pregnancy: two-year follow-up. *Pediatrics.* 1992;89:284-289.

Azuma, S.D., Chasnoff, I.J. Outcome of children prenatally exposed to cocaine and other drugs: a path analysis of three-year data. *Pediatrics.* 1993;92:396-402.

Benz, K., Hansen, R.L., Steward, M., Barton, K. Cognitive Development of Preschool Children Prenatally Exposed to Stimulant Drugs—A Neuropsychological Study. *CASP Today.* Summer 1995, 6–11.

Frank, D.A., Zuckerman, D.S., Amaro, H., Aboagye, K., Bauchner, H., Cabral, H., Fried, L., Hingson, R., Kayne, H., Leverson, S.M., Parker, S., Reece, H. and Vinci, R. Cocaine use during pregnancy: Prevalence and correlates. *Pediatrics*, 1988; 82, 888-895

Gillogley, K.M., Evans, A.T., Hansen, R.L., Samuels, S.J. and Batra, K.K. The perinatal impact of cocaine, amphetamine and opiate use detected by universal intrapartum screening. *American Journal of Obstetrics and Gynecology*, 1990;163: 1535-1542

Griffith, D.R. Developmental Follow-up of cocaine exposed infants to three years. Paper presented at the International Society for Infant Studies. Montreal, 1990

Hansen, R.L., Ulrey, G.L. Knowns and Unknowns in the Outcomes of Drug-Dependent Women. in *At-Risk Infants,* Anastasiow NJ and Harel S (eds), Paul Brookes Publishing Co. 1993; 115-125

Hansen, R.L,. Evans, A.T., Gillogley, K.M., Hughes, C.S., and Krener, P.G. Perinatal toxicology screening. *Journal of Perinatology.* 1992; 12(3):220–224

Neuspiel, D.R. and Hamel, S.C. Cocaine and infant behavior. *Journal of Developmental and Behavioral Pediatrics*, 1991; 12, 55-64

Rodning, C., Beckwith, L. and Howard, J. Prenatal exposure to drugs: Behavioral distortions reflecting CNS impairment? *Neurotoxicology*, 1989; 10, 629-634

Rodning, C., Beckwith, L. and Howard, J. Characteristics of attachment organization and play organization in prenatally drug exposed toddlers. *Development and Psychopathology*, 1990; 1, 277-289

Struthers, J.M. and Hansen, R.L. Visual recognition memory in drug-exposed infants. *Journal of Developmental and Behavioral Pediatrics*, 1992; 13, 108-111

Zuckerman, B. Drug-exposed infants: Understanding the medical risk. *The Future of Children*, 1991; 1, 26-35

Munchausen by Proxy (MBP)

Herbert Schreier, M.D.

Three Case Vignettes

- A mother was hospitalized for treatment of a chronic disorder and left her son with a family for care during her six-week hospital stay. The child had a rash on his buttocks and inner thighs and, after visiting a pediatrician, the mother accused the caretaking family of sexually abusing her son. After the police could find no basis for the charges, the child's mother filed a civil suit against the county and the foster family.

  Because it was a civil suit, prior records of both the child and the mother were made available. The mother had suffered from a chronic illness for twenty years. The illness had caused her to be wheelchair-bound for the previous five years. She was found to have falsified her own symptoms, which led to a suspicion of "psychosomatic illness," and she was referred to a psychiatrist. Her son had been hospitalized on several occasions with fever of unknown origin that happened only when the mother took his temperature. At one point, the mother was found holding the child's thermometer under hot water. However, the possibility of her falsifying his pediatric condition on her own was not raised.

- A child in the primary care of the mother was being treated at a major medical center for seizures, which only the mother had witnessed. A review of the chart led the neurologist to doubt that this was a genuine illness. The neurologist continued anti-convulsant medication partly because the mother told him that she was a nurse. This turned out not to be true.

The woman's estranged husband sued for custody of the child after the father learned that, on several occasions, after the boy had eaten lunch with his mother at school, the child fell into a deep, sleep from which he could not be aroused. On several occasions, the boy had been taken to the emergency room by ambulance. A court-appointed psychologist concluded that the mother had a "mild case of Munchausen's by Proxy." The father brought in a Munchausen by Proxy (MBP) expert who recommended a separation test in which the mother had only supervised visits.

For the next year, the boy was completely well. The mother's court-appointed treating psychiatrist, when asked by the court, says he doubted the diagnosis of MBP, but admits he did not know that the child was doing well outside the care of the mother. Despite the new knowledge, the psychiatrist stood by his report to the court.

- An eight year old girl was hospitalized with a serious illness of unknown origin in a local hospital. Her condition worsened and she was transferred to a major medical center's pediatric intensive care unit (PICU). At the PICU, the glass enclosed patient beds were visible from the nurse's station. The child's condition improved and she was transferred back to the local hospital. The child again became seriously ill and was returned to the medical center. The local hospital's pediatric beds were not easily visible by the nurses. The child's symptoms subsided and she was returned to the local hospital. Again she became seriously ill, and it was discovered that the mother had been injecting the child with pond water through intravenous tubes at the local hospital where she could not be observed. The mother was the daughter of a minister and was a highly believable, persuasive person.

Questions

1. What is Munchausen by Proxy and what is the origin of the term?

2. What new term is being introduced to clarify the various conditions illustrated by the case vignettes?

3. What is the potential for fatal outcomes for children with this disorder?

4. What is difficult about suspecting, diagnosing, and intervening in this condition that differentiates it from other forms of child endangerment?

Epidemiology

There is only one carefully done study and of only two conditions—poisoning and suffocation. Applying this British study [McClure et al 1996,] which used the most conservative clinical case finding standards, the numbers would translate into 1200 new cases of just these two conditions in the U.S. each year.

What is Munchausen by Proxy?

Munchausen by Proxy means the fabrication of a condition (usually medical, but sexual abuse, educational deficits, and psychiatric illnesses have also been reported) by a caretaker (most often a mother) to assume the sick role through a proxy (child). The motivation appears to be to gain attention and/or to manipulate powerful professionals. The professionals are usually physicians, but also social workers, school psychologists, police detectives, lawyers, and the media. Some suggest that a mother who produces factitious illness in her child experiences a deep emotional need to be the recipient of medical care and nurturing (Mehl, Cable, and Johnson, 1990). Up to 75% of mothers (overwhelmingly MBP is perpetrated by women) suffer or have suffered from somatization and/or Munchausen symptoms themselves (reported by Meadow at a Stockholm, Sweden presentation, 1998).

The origin of the term dates back to Baron Von Munchhausen (1720-97) who was a German soldier, adventurer, and teller of unbelievable tales. Munchausen is characterized by patients who fabricate illness and involve many physicians in diagnostic dilemmas and procedures. Munchausen by Proxy describes the involvement of a child and possibly siblings, whereby a child is brought to a physician with a factitious illness. The illness may be fabricated or induced by the mother, and occasionally involves the participation of the child. Many methods are used to pro-

duce factitious signs and symptoms (e.g. insulin administration, induced vomiting, urine contamination, laxative induced diarrhea, intentional poisoning, smothering). These symptoms are presented by parental fabrication of symptoms and/or signs; alteration of laboratory specimens, such as urine or blood; actual induction of illness or injury or a combination of the three (Schreier and Libow, 1993; Rosenberg, 1987).

An involved child may be harmed first as a direct result of the action of the mother, and second as a consequence of the physicians performing various diagnostic procedures and treatments (Bools, Neale, Meadow, 1994). The most immediately dangerous forms of the behavior are smothering (Meadow, 1990; Southall, Stebbins, Rees, Lang, Warner, & Shinebourne, 1987) or poisoning (Hvizdala & Gellady, 1978; Rogers, Tripp, Bentovim, Robinson, Berry & Goulding, 1976) to produce physical signs and/or to convince the physicians of a real illness. Children may die as a result of this behavior. Waller (1983) reviewed 23 previously reported cases and found 5 to be deceased. Most studies find a 9-10% death rate. Although these figures should be viewed with caution since they are based upon serious cases in published studies which may not be representative of all cases.

Current Definitional Thinking

Since Munchausen by Proxy is a confusing term, there is a growing consensus that Factitious Disorder by Proxy is a better, more easily understood description of the condition in the mother. This proposed change in terminology is expected to be helpful for problem conceptualization and intervention planning.

The American Professional Society on Abuse of Children (APSAC) has proposed definitional guidelines that have been accepted by several organizations. These guidelines propose that when there is a suspicion of what has been called Munchausen by Proxy, a diagnosis of Pediatric Condition Falsification (PCF) be demonstrated first. Then, when the primary motive of the caretaker is discerned, it should be decided whether Factitious Disorder by Proxy exists as well.

Using this paradigm, apnea (suspension of respiration) caused by suffocation would first be diagnosed as abuse using the terminology Pediatric Condition Falsification (PCF). The second step would be to assess the mother/caretaker and/or the child's history to determine whether the incident was caused by the mother/caretaker during an outburst of rage, a bout of depression or other mental health problems; an expression of revenge or retaliation toward another parent or caretaker; financial gain; or, other motives. The motive or condition of the mother determines or influences the course of action by law enforcement and Child Protective Services.

When these are the primary motives, the diagnosis remains Pediatric Condition Falsification (PCF)-Child Abuse. However, if the mother's motive is to seek the sick role through a proxy, or to involve herself in an intense and manipulative relationship with physicians or other powerful people, then an additional diagnosis of Factitious Disorder by Proxy in the mother is warranted. While the other motives (e.g., revenge at an abandoning spouse or monetary rewards) can be found in this latter group, these are not the *primary* driving forces in Factitious Disorder by Proxy (FDP). The motivational distinctions are important. The protection of the child and siblings hinges on parent/caregiver motivation and this should inform the disposition of the case, including visitation and possible termination of parental rights. MBP remains in use as the term overarching both conditions, PCF and FDP (Ayoob et al, 2002).

The dynamics that drive perpetrators of Factitious Disease by Proxy (FDP) or Munchausen by Proxy (MBP) are not fully elucidated or agreed upon. However, what is known needs to be considered and understood so that accurate and informed decisions about the mother's threat to the child are made (Schreier and Libow, 1993; Eminsen and Postlethwaite, 1999).

It is important to note that this discussion of psychiatric diagnosis is not intended to over-ride criminal justice or juvenile justice considerations involving homicide or an attempted murder, and the need to protect surviving siblings.

False Positive Diagnosis

Because the diagnosis of FDP depends upon a diagnosis of Pediatric Condition Falsification (PCF) and, at times, the diagnosis of the latter depends upon statistical improbabilities of the course of an illness, false positive diagnoses are a possibility that must be considered carefully. As the condition has become more widely understood in the general and medical community, pediatricians and others may be mislabeling other conditions as Pediatric Condition Falsification. An example of a false positive diagnosis is an infant with repeated bouts of diarrhea who may be suffering from an uncommon form of dehydration secondary to breast feeding. Similarly, positive lab findings may be misinterpreted as more specific or accurate than they are. For instance, substances in the stool that falsely suggest laxatives, may lead to a false diagnosis. Ipecac may cross-react with medications given during a "code" attempt to revive a child who has died. (There should be no ipecac in the child's blood if it was drawn prior to the code.) Potassium levels increase post-mortem.

Factitious Disorder by Proxy should not be diagnosed when a family with a chronically ill child is genuinely dis-satisfied with the care, seeks second opinions, or has suggestions that involve alternative medicine. Pediatricians are not trained to be detectives; but in cases where suspicions of Pediatric Condition Falsification arise, they must exercise the utmost care to avoid false positives and to collect accurate data to present their case.

Approaches to Diagnosis

Many hospitals have developed protocols for managing cases in the inpatient setting. An approach that has been found helpful is to use an interdisciplinary team of professionals with training in Factitious Disorder by Proxy that may be called by any member of the hospital community if there is a suspicion of a case. A high level of coordination and communication among team members and a systematic process of evaluation is essential. Approaches to diagnosis include:

1. Obtain and prepare a detailed summary of the history of the child's illnesses, symptoms, medical procedures, hospitalizations. Include the child's developmental history, school and social history.

2. Obtain medical histories for the siblings and parents as well.

3. Obtain all medical, mental health, social services, and school/daycare records on the child and, if possible, on the family.

4. Request that a professional (who is not part of the case) with medical expertise in the conditions involved and who is aware of the possibility of FDP, review the records.

5. Screen the reports for inconsistencies in the mother/caretaker's historical account of the child's illnesses and family medical and social history, as well as deviations from likely or typical presentations.

6. Contact treating physicians in person, if possible, and inquire whether their diagnoses and treatment were based on objective findings or mother's reports.

7. Identify independent witnesses to seizures and determine whether the witnesses were present before the episode started. This includes nursing reports.

8. Interview the child, separately from the parent/caretaker when developmentally appropriate, to gather data about his or her symptoms and care.

9. Observe the child under carefully controlled circumstances. If poisoning is suspected, consultations with toxicological/forensic experts should be requested.

10. Conduct psychological and psychiatric evaluations using only professionals familiar with FDP, as indicated.

11. If the child's life is at risk and/or suspicion of FDP is high, covert video surveillance at the hospital by law enforcement or hospital staff should be considered (Southall, 1997). It should be noted that in a series of 41 cases, a true medical diagnosis in four cases was arrived at through surveillance of what appeared to be FDP (Hall, Eubanks, Meyyazhagan, Kenny & Johnson, 2000).

Membership of an Interdisciplinary Team

Physicians involved in providing medical treatment for the presenting conditions, psychologist, psychiatrist, and medical social worker involved in the case; independent consultant (can be in-house) who is not involved in any way with the parent/caretaker and who is familiar with FDP; and a trained and experienced CPS social worker knowledgeable about FDP, detective, and prosecutor.

Case Disposition

The most difficult task for the treating medical team, Child Protective Services and the courts involves case disposition. Sometimes, the usual guidelines involving the severity of abuse cannot be relied upon. First, there often are siblings who have been harmed and sometimes killed, even though the current patient does not appear to be severely abused. Second, in the so-called milder cases, Davis et al (1998) found that 17% of the children were reabused. In cases involving suffocation or poisoning, evidence from siblings suggests that between 40 and 50% might experience abuse, some fatal.

FDP involves layers of complexity. First, experts have observed everything from subtle manipulation of professionals through exquisite lying, to *pseudo logica phantastica*, where repeated lying is difficult to miss [though it often is]. Second, this is a difficult to believe and elusive clinical problem. Third, the situation involves apparently well-intentioned mothers who appeal to the need of the doctor to be able to solve medical mysteries. This combination is likely to lead to cases where professionals are portrayed as overzealous in their responses. It is the job of the professional to evaluate and present to law enforcement officers, CPS investigators, prosecutors and judges the prevailing understanding of this condition and help guide them in their primary task of protecting the child. The reality must also be acknowledged that some abusive behavior toward a child (e.g., suffocation and poisoning) can be fatal and that murder or attempted murder are central to the issue.

Court-ordered separation of the mother and children may be critical to ensuring the safety of the children and to assess whether the child's disease symptoms decrease. Any gradual increase in visitation must be closely supervised. Every effort should be made to continue medical care with a stable group of providers, using regularly scheduled visits. Children under age 5 should be considered at increased risk due to limitations in language and communication. Infants and toddlers are at high risk for serious, rapidly deteriorating, and disabling conditions.

Fathers

Fathers may be completely uninvolved, subtly or actively collusive, or in a small percentage of cases, the only perpetrator. [Meadow, 1998]. This latter group tends to differ some from the mother perpetrators in being more openly aggressive [though some FDP mothers are as well], and much less involved with staff or the child's doctors.

Management

Much training needs to be done about the peculiar nature of this condition. It is often very difficult for most of us to believe that a seemingly caring and devoted mother would repeatedly harm or cause others to harm a helpless infant. Few hospitals can afford covert surveillance equipment. One California-based hospital mandates a review of cases by a board familiar with the disorder based upon suspicion by staff. Gathering the involved professionals for a case conference is potentially the singularly most effective approach. Soliciting help from a colleague who is not directly involved in the case can be also be helpful as they are likely to be more objective. There is a network of experienced professionals who have dealt with FDP and are available by telephone to discuss the details of a case. Several of their names can be found within the list of references.

The Child's or Family's Physician

Physicians are trained to rely upon the patient's or family's historical reports together with objective physical findings to guide their diagnostic search for the cause of illness. It is common medical practice to employ a battery of diagnostic tests to determine etiology in order to plan treatment. The presence of abnormalities encourages aggressive or invasive procedures to determine a diagnosis, no matter how rare the diagnosis might be.

The average pediatrician or family physician is typically not attuned to the bizarre motivation behind this form of child abuse. As a result of the complexity of the situation and the typical devoted mother, physicians can be caught up in the dynamics of the mother and become angry with those who raise or confirm their suspicions when they made the original referral.

Consultants themselves are not immune from the manipulations of FDP patients, and there are often disagreements among experts at the same or different medical centers. Such disagreements often lead to major confusion when these cases reach the court, and can complicate attempts to make decisions in the child's best interest. Face to face conferences with all treating physicians, though difficult to arrange, can obviate the problem of one or another physician receiving misrepresentations about the child's clinical history.

Conclusion

Factitious Disorder by Proxy will challenge all who work in programs involved in caring for the health, welfare, education and protection of children. Solving the complexities of these cases in the best interest of the children and parents will require sophisticated approaches in the ways that child physical and sexual abuse originally challenged the medical professions.

References

Ayoub, C. and Schreier, H. (2002). Munchausen by Proxy: Presentations in Special Education. Child Maltreatment.

Ayoub, C., Alexander, R., Beck, D., Bursch, B., Feldman, K., Libow, J., Sanders, M., Schreier, H., and Yorker, B. (2002). Position Paper: Definitional Issues in Munchausen by Proxy *Child Maltreatment* V. 7 #2 105-112.

Eminson, M.D. and Postlethwaite, R.J., *Munchausen Syndrome by Proxy Abuse: A Practical Approach*, London: Butterworth-Heinemann, 1999.

Parnell, Teresa and Day, Deborah, *Munchausen by Proxy Syndrome. Misunderstood child abuse.* Sage, Thousand Oaks, California, 1998.

Munchausen syndrome by proxy: Issues in diagnosis and treatment. A.V. Levin and M.S. Sheridan (Eds.). New York, NY: Lexington Books.

Hurting for love: Munchausen by proxy syndrome. H.A. Schreier and J.A. Libow. New York: Guildford Press, 1993a.

Hall, D.E., Eubanks, L., Meyyazhagan, S., Kenney, R.D., and Johnson, S.C. Evaluation of covert video surveillance in the diagnosis of Munchausen Syndrome by Proxy: Lessons from 41 cases, *Pediatrics* 105(6), 1305-1312, 2000.

Davis P., McClure R.J., Rolfe K., et al. Procedures, placement, and risks of further abuse after Munchausen syndrome by proxy, non-accidental poisoning, and non-accidental suffocation. Arch Dis Child. 1998;78:217-21.

Southall, D.P., Plunkett, B.M., Banks, M.W., Falkov, A.F., and Samuels, M.P. Covert Video Recordings of Life-threatening Child Abuse: Lessons for Child Protection, Pediatrics, Nov. 1997 v100 5:735-758.

Christopher Bools, Brenda Neale, Roy Meadow. Munchausen Syndrome by Proxy: A Study of Psychopathology. *Child Abuse and Neglect*, Vol. 18, No. 9, 773-788, 1994.

Munchausen syndrome by proxy: Another women's disorder? P.M. Robins, R. Sesan. *Professional Psychology: Research and Practice*, 22 (4), 285-290, 1991.

Albert L. Mehl, Larry Cobble, Scott Johnson. *Child Abuse and Neglect*, Vol. 14, 577-585, 1990. Munchausen Syndrome by Proxy: A Family Affair.

Meadow, R. (1990). Suffocation, recurrent apnea and sudden infant death. *The Journal of Pediatrics*, 117, 351-357.

Rosenberg, D.A. (1987). Web of deceit: A literature review of Munchausen syndrome by proxy. *Child Abuse & Neglect*, 11, 547-563.

Schreier, H. (2002). Forensic Issues in Munchausen by Proxy in Schetky, D. and Benedek, E. Principals and Practice of Child and Adolescent Forensic Psychiatry. APA Publishing, Washington D.C.

Waller, D.A. (1983). Obstacles to the treatment of Munchausen by proxy syndrome. *Journal of the American Academy of Child Psychiatry*, 22, 80-85.

Hvizdala, E.V., and Gellady, A.M. (1978). Intentional poisoning of two siblings by prescription drugs: An unusual form of child abuse. *Clinical Pediatrics*, 17, 480-482.

Rogers, D., Tripp, J., Bentovim, A., Robinson, A., Berry, D., and Goulding, R. (1976). Non-accidental poisoning: An extended syndrome of child abuse. *British Medical Journal*, i, 793-796.

Psychological Maltreatment

Marilyn Strachan Peterson, M.S.W., M.P.A., Joaquin Borrego, Jr., Ph.D.,
Sherri Y. Terao, and Anthony J. Urquiza, Ph.D.

Case Vignette

Jay is a 7-year old boy living with his biological mother, stepfather, and two stepbrothers. He has been the subject of constant ridicule by his stepfather who tells him that he is just like his father—a loser and worthless. Jay's teachers have noticed that his grades have declined since the second marriage and that he keeps to himself during recess and lunch.

Sara's mother erupts into rages and, for Sara, it seems to go on for days. Sometimes cumulative stress seems to set the rages off. During these periods of rage, Sara's mother often yells and screams and threatens them. Other times, another adult or Sara or her sister may say something that is misinterpreted and that sets her mother off.

Questions

1. What are the different types of emotional abuse?

2. What are the consequences of psychological maltreatment?

3. What type of treatment is recommended?

Epidemiology

In 1998, there were over 600,000 reports of child abuse in California. Of these reports, 49,581 were identified as psychological abuse. In review of the literature, little epidemiological research has been done in this area. Psychological maltreatment can exist on its own, or it can occur with other forms of maltreatment (e.g. physical abuse, sexual abuse, and neglect) or as a result of them (Hart, Brassard, & Karlson, 1996). Psychological maltreatment can have a profound impact on children as it serves as a strong predictor for negative developmental outcomes (Claussen & Crittenden, 1991). The term psychological abuse is synonymous with emotional abuse.

Behavioral Categories of Psychological Maltreatment

Hart and Brassard (1991) identify five subcategories of psychological maltreatment:

- **Spurning**
  Caregiver makes verbal statements that reject, degrade or humiliate the child.

- **Terrorizing**
  Caregiver makes threats such as harming a pet, sibling, or the other parent if the child does not comply with a request.

- **Raging**
  Yelling or screaming continuously on one or more topics in response to a precipitating event(s), e.g. cumulative stress or a chance remark that is perceived to be a put-down.

- **Isolating**
  Caregiver denies the child access to interactions and contact with other people.

- **Exploiting/Corrupting**
  Caregiver encourages the child to develop socially inappropriate behavior e.g. using the child as a runner for drugs.

- **Denying emotional responsiveness**
  Caregiver does not respond to the emotional needs of the child, e.g. ignoring the child when distressed, uninvolved, or detached.

Evans (1993) defined these categories of psychological abuse in her book:

- **Withholding**
  Caregiver withholds attention and verbal interaction for hours or days.

- **Criticism/ordering**
Caregiver constantly criticizes and finds fault, or orders the child.

- **Undermining**
Caregiver either covertly or subtley makes statements which undermine the confidence, motivation or interests of the child; or, withholds praise in response to positive behavior, e.g. a good report card.

- **Accusing/blaming**
Caregiver accuses or blames the child for everything that goes wrong.

- **Controlling by Defining Reality**
Caregiver denies reality with statements such as:
    "that's not what you said"
    "that's not what you did"
    "that's not what happened"
    "that's not what you saw"
    "that's not what you felt"

- **Controlling by Making Child Responsible**
"I wouldn't have gotten so angry if you hadn't done that."

Engle (1990) defined these categories of psychological abuse in her book:

- **Verbal assaults**
Berating, belittling, criticizing, name calling, screaming, threatening, blaming, and using sarcasm and humiliation.

- **Abusive expectations**
Abuser has unreasonable expectations or demands.

- **Emotional blackmail**
Abuser threatens to leave or give the child to someone else.

- **Unpredictable responses**
Drastic mood swings or sudden emotional outbursts for no apparent reason (often associated with drug/alcohol abuse).

- **Constant criticism**
Unrelenting criticism, constant fault finding, can never be pleased, always focuses on the "C" grade on a report card that has "A"s and "B"s.

- **Character Assassination**
Blows mistakes out of proportion, gossips about past failures and mistakes, makes fun of the child in front of others, and discounts achievements.

- **Constant chaos**
Continual upheavals, discord, and uproar over issues, conflicts.

- **Social abuse**
When parents directly or indirectly interfere with the child's access to peers or fail to teach their child essential social skills.

- **Intellectual abuse**
When a child's thinking is ridiculed or attacked and the child is not allowed to differ from the parent's point of view or alternate point of views are ridiculed.

Engle (1990) includes typologies of parental abuse which are found in all types of abusive situations, e.g., physical, sexual, and emotional abuse:

- **Possessive Parent**
This parent wants to control, own, and/or consume the child including restrictions on friendships and dating.

- **Overcontrolling Parent**
Domineering and overcontrolling, this parent believes strongly in rules and obedience and that parental authority should never be questioned. Sometimes this dynamic is found in fathers who sexually abuse their children and control all of the family dynamics.

- **Abandoning, Rejecting Parent**
These parents are emotionally unavailable to their children depriving them of necessary attention, affection, and encouragement. Parents who escape into alcohol, drugs, sleep, television, or books also abandon their children. This category also includes passivity and not being involved with the children, e.g. not talking to them or showing interest in them or their activity.

- **Hypocritical Parent**
The parent focuses a tremendous amount of negative attention on the child with little praise.

- **Alcoholic Parent**
The alcoholic parent is emotionally unavailable to the children. These parents tend to discipline out of irritation and rage about their own life. In addition to the primary alcoholic, there may be a non-alcoholic partner and parent who spends a good portion of his/her life trying to control the alcoholic with little energy left over for parenting.

- **Silent Partner**
  A silent partner is one who stands by and does nothing while the other parent sexually, physically, or emotionally abuses the child. Whenever a parent refuses to respond to his or her child's pleas for help or rescue from the tyranny or the abuse of the other parent, that parent is a passive participant in the injury. (Engle, 1990)

- **Mysogynistic Parent**
  This parent looks down upon and devalues females. Male mysogynist parents believe that males have the right to control females. Female mysogynist parents may show preferential treatment of male children and ignore female children to the extent of being neglectful or indifferent.

- **Sibling Abuse**
  Parents are indifferent to the overt abuse of one sibling by another, and the offensive behavior exceeds "rivalry" or normal sibling squabbles. Sibling abuse is a symptom of family dysfunction.

The U.S. Department of Health and Human Service's Centers for Disease Control's National Center for Injury Prevention and Control included psychological/emotional abuse in its' publication *Intimate Partner Violence Surveillance: Uniform Definitions and Recommended Data Elements* published in 1999. The emotional abuse categories include, but are not limited to:

- Humiliating the victim;

- Controlling what the victim can and cannot do;

- Withholding information from the victim;

- Getting annoyed if the victim disagrees;

- Deliberately doing something that makes the victim feel diminished (e.g., less smart, less attractive);

- Deliberately doing something that makes the victim fell embarrassed;

- Using the victim's money without permission or through intimidation or manipulation;

- Taking advantage of the victim;

- Disregarding what the victim wants;

- Isolating the victim from friends or family;

- Prohibiting access to transportation or telephone;

- Getting the victim to engage in illegal activities;

- Using the victim's children to control the victim's behavior;

- Threatening loss of custody of children;

- Smashing objects or destroying property;

- Denying the victim access to money or other basic resources; and

- Disclosing information that would tarnish the victim's reputation.

Consequences of Psychological Maltreatment

Psychological maltreatment can have numerous negative consequences at both the intrapersonal (e.g. depression) and interpersonal (e.g. aggression) levels. Research studies have linked psychological maltreatment to numerous emotional (e.g. depression, impaired relationships with parents) and behavioral (e.g. scholastic, competency, social skills) problems for children (Hart, Germain, & Brassard, 1987). Engle (1998) found a high rate of mental illness for infants and children experiencing emotional unavailability.

Intervention Modalities

Any intervention begins with a good assessment of the underlying factors contributing to the problem. Intervention examples include:

- **Social Support Intervention**
  If environmental stressors are a contributing factor, home visiting programs or other types of social interventions, e.g. housing, transportation, employment may be indicated.

- **Individual and/or Group Therapy for the Parent**
  Individual and group therapy provide avenues for the parent to discuss perceptions, experiences, and strategies for handling anger. Anger management groups are available in some communities.

- **Parent-Child Interaction Therapy**
  If the issues are child behavior management, this treatment modality provides structured sessions involving one-to-one coaching on how to interact and manage young children's behavior.

- **Al-Anon, Adult Children of Alcoholics, and Co-Dependency Groups**
  These groups operate at no charge throughout most communities and provide an outlet for persons struggling with alcohol, drug and other addictions. The themes discussed in these groups can help many people cope with issues that are beyond their control but which create frustration and feelings of rage in their lives.

Resources

Brassard M.R., S.N. Hart, and D.B. Hardy. *The Psychological Maltreatment Rating Scales*. Child Abuse and Neglect, 1993 Nov-Dec, 17(6):715-29.

Claussen AH; Crittenden PM. Physical and psychological maltreatment: relations among types of maltreatment. *Child Abuse and Neglect*, 1991, 15(1-2):5-18.

Engel, Beverly (1990). *The Emotionally Abused Woman*. Ballantine Books: New York.

Evans, Patricia (1993). *Verbal Abuse Survivors Speak Out*. Adams Media Corporation: Massachusetts.

Intimate Partner Violence Serveillance: Uniform Definitions and Recommended Data Elements. US Department of Health and Human Services Centers for Disease Control and Prevention, National Center for Injury Prevention and Control, 1999.

PART 5

Children (Under Twelve) Who Molest

Toni Cavanagh Johnson, Ph.D.

Case Vignette

John, who is ten years old, engages in oral-genital contact with his eight-year old brother, Freddie. Their mother walks in and sees them. She spanks them both and tells them that they are bad and disgusting. The boys promise they will never do it again. Two weeks later Freddie is engaging in oral-genital contact with his friend at his house when his mother walks in. The mother confides in Freddie's teacher who calls the hotline to make a suspected child abuse report.

Questions

1. Is sexual contact between children always due to one or more of the children having been sexually abused? Is it always abusive behavior by one child toward the other, if children are engaged in advanced sexual behaviors such as oral, anal, or vaginal sex?

2. Can children have problems with their sexual behavior and not be abusing other children?

3. How can we distinguish sexual offending from lesser but still important sexual problems?

4. Is the oldest always the perpetrator? Is the boy always the perpetrator? Is the tallest or heaviest always the perpetrator? Is it the age difference between the children that defines whether it is sexual abuse or sexual experimentation?

5. Have all children who sexually abuse others been victims of sexual abuse themselves?

6. How do the systems handle children who are sexually abusing children outside their homes?

7. What can the system do when siblings are involved in forced sibling incest?

Epidemiology

There are no current statistics on the number of children who sexually abuse other children because there are few police arrests of these children. Most child protective services' agencies do not have a place on their intake forms to indicate that a child is sexually abusing other children. The forms will indicate if the child is a victim. As a result, neither the criminal justice nor the dependency system statistics have accurate information about the incidence of children sexually abusing other children. Empirical evidence suggests that approximately 80% of children who sexually abuse others are boys.

Clinical Presentation

Children (under twelve) who are sexually abusing other children are generally oppositional defiant or conduct disordered; have attention deficit disorder and/or hyperactivity (or stress-related disorders which mimic ADHD). Their relationships with adults are characterized by distrust, anger and disappointment. They have poor peer relationships; poor problem solving skills; poor school progress; and are impulsive and destructive. Their sexual behavior is pervasive across situations and time. If they have been abused, it is generally in their past. A large number of these children have been emotionally and physically abused, as well as emotionally and physically neglected. In addition to a variety of types of abuse and neglect, virtually all of the children have lived in home environments marked by sexual confusion and lack of boundaries. They have also witnessed physical violence between their primary caretaker(s). The pairing of sex with aggression, hostility, and payback has been prevalent in the interactions of the adults and adolescents with whom the child has lived. Most parents of children in this group have sexual abuse in their family history, as well as emotional and physical abuse and, frequently, alcohol and/or drug problems.

113

Typical sexually abusive behavior of these children may include, but is not limited to, fondling, oral-genital contact, and vaginal or anal penetration of another child with fingers, sticks and/or other objects. Without intervention, these children's sexual behavior will continue and increase over time. They are typically part of a consistent pattern rather than an isolated incident. Even if their activities are discovered, they do not, and cannot stop without intensive and specialized treatment. Whereas some of these children plan the sexual abuse, others occur spontaneously or explosively. Some of the offensive behavior of these children can be seen in their sexually explosive and vulgar language, taunts, intrusive sneaky touching and hugging. Some of the physical feelings these children experience are associated with anger, fear, and residual trauma or stress-related sensations rather than sexual feelings. Sexual arousal is sometimes evident in the behaviors of these children and sometimes not. The closer the children are to puberty, the higher the probability that sexual arousal is involved. Their sexually abusive behavior may have the aim of alleviating negative feelings that overwhelm them. Sometimes the abuse is to retaliate against the victim. There is generally a chaining of feelings, sensations, and environmental cues which precipitate the sexual behaviors in these children. It is generally not solely for sexual satisfaction or pleasure. They have confused sex with hurt and use sex to find satisfactory ways to get along with others. They defend against their feelings of loss, hurt and abandonment by hurting others. These children hurt others in many ways; only one of them is sexual. This profile is characteristic of most of the boys and the girls. There are some girls whose behaviors appear less disturbed, particularly in the school setting, and some children who appear to be better socialized than previously described. This, however, is only an exterior presentation which, when scratched, allows the observer to see an angry, aggressive inner self which finds equilibrium when hurting others.

Is sexual contact between children always due to one or more of the children having been sexually abused? Is it always perpetration by one child to the other, if children are engaged in developmentally inappropriate sexual behaviors such as oral, anal, or vaginal sex?

Since at least 70% of children engage in sexual behaviors, it is not by definition a problem for children to be looking at and touching each other. A study of the sexual behaviors of sexually abused and nonsexually abused children found that children in both groups engaged in the same types of behaviors. Every sexual behavior had been observed by mothers of children in both groups. Yet, just because developmentally inappropriate sexual behaviors occur between young children without coercion does not mean that it is acceptable practice.

Can children have problems with their sexual behavior but not be sexually abusing?

There is a continuum of sexual behaviors in children from natural and healthy to children who sexually abuse other children. The vast majority of children's sexual behavior is natural and healthy, yet there are some young children with sexual behavior problems. Children who have sexual behavior problems can be divided into **three groups: "sexually-reactive," "children who engage in extensive, mutual sexual behaviors," and "children who sexually abuse other children."** It is of utmost importance to distinguish between children along this continuum. It can be devastating to the self-concept and developing sexuality of the child if his or her sexual behaviors are defined as abusive when this was not the child's intent. A thorough evaluation of the child by someone knowledgeable about sexual abuse, child development and child sexuality is very important to make a proper assessment. **The largest, by far, of these three groups is "sexually-reactive," the next largest is "children who engage in extensive, mutual sexual behaviors." There are relatively few children who sexually abuse other children.** When children are properly evaluated, it is generally difficult to find enough of these children in most medium size cities to have a treatment group. Residential facilities that have begun programs for children who sexually abuse find that they must admit other children because they cannot fill their beds with only children who abuse.

"Sexually-reactive" children engage in self-stimulating behaviors and also engage in sexual behaviors with other children and, sometimes, with adults. Generally, this type of sexual behavior is in response to environmental cues, which are overly stimulating or reminiscent of previous abuse, or feelings that reawaken traumatic or painful memories. The child may respond directly by masturbating or engaging in other sexual behaviors alone or with others. Hiding the sexual behaviors or finding friends to engage in the behaviors in private, may not be possible for these children as the sexual behavior is a way of coping with overwhelming feelings of which they can't make sense. This type of sexual behavior is often not within the full conscious control of the child. In some situations children are trying to make sense of something sexual done to them by doing it to someone else. These children do not coerce others into sexual behaviors but act out their confusion on them. Many of these children do not understand their own or others' rights to privacy. While there is no intent to hurt others, receiving sexual behaviors can be confusing for the other child and feel like a violation or abuse.

Often distrustful, chronically hurt and abandoned by adults, **"children who engage in extensive mutual sexual behaviors,"** relate best to other children. In the absence of close, supportive relationships to adults, the sexual behaviors become a way of making a connection to other children. They use sex as a way to cope with their feelings of abandonment, hurt, sadness, anxiety, and other despair. These children do not coerce other children into sexual behaviors but find other similarly lonely children who will engage with them. Almost all of these children have been sexually and emotionally abused and neglected. They look to other children to help meet their emotional needs and their need of physical contact.

How can we distinguish between children who are sexually abusing from children engaged in sexually-reactive behaviors or children engaged in mutual, but extensive sexual behaviors?

A thorough evaluation of the child by someone knowledgeable about sexual abuse, child development and child sexuality is very important to make a proper assessment. A complete evaluation to determine whether abuse has occurred, at a minimum, involves the following elements:

- a thorough assessment of each child involved in the behavior, their general functioning, and their current and past play/friend relationships;

- the children's current and past relationships as they relate to sexual behaviors;

- the history of sexual behaviors engaged in by each child separately from the other child;

- the context in which the sexual behaviors occurred;

- how the sexual behavior was discovered;

- the behavior and statements of each of the children when the behavior was discovered;

- whether there was use of force or coercion in this situation or in previous sexual interactions by either of the children; and,

- the history interpersonal dynamics in the family situation.

When it is determined that abuse has taken place, is the oldest always the perpetrator? Is the boy always the perpetrator? Is the tallest or heaviest always the perpetrator?

It is not always the older child who is the abuser when both are children under age twelve. In some cases, it is the younger child who is the abuser. It may also be a girl who abuses a boy, and the girl may be younger. Size is not the determinant. Children who sexually abuse generally abuse children who are vulnerable. Vulnerability is not accounted for by age, size, height or weight. Vulnerability may be due to developmental delays and/or the distressed emotional life of the child.

Is it the age difference between the children that defines whether it is sexual abuse or sexual experimentation?

While a wide age difference increases the probability it is abuse, this is not always true, as the children may be playmates or friends of different ages, and "exploring." Children engaged in sexually-reactive or mutual but extensive sexual behaviors may also be of different ages and sizes.

Have all children who abuse been victims of sexual abuse?

In the mid 1980's when this small group of children who abuse began to be studied, it was believed that for a prepubertal child to abuse, the child was most likely a victim of sexual abuse. This turns out not to be true. Approximately 60-70% of children who abuse have been sexually victimized in a "hands on" manner. Yet, virtually all children who abuse have been overexposed to adult sexuality. They have lived in chaotic environments that are pervaded by sexuality and aggression, and are characterized by sexual, physical and emotional boundary confusion.

How do the systems handle children who are sexually abusing outside their homes?

If a child is living in his or her home and abuses a child in the neighborhood or at school, it may be difficult to obtain help for this child particularly if the child is not a child abuse victim or witness to domestic violence. In many jurisdictions, the police do not intervene to get help for the child because of the child's young age and Child Protective Services may not intervene because there is no child protection issue in the home. The response of the systems varies between jurisdictions. If the school is not made aware of the situation, the child may continue to abuse children in the neighborhood or school setting.

What can Child Protective Services do when siblings are involved in forced sibling incest?

When there is forced sibling incest in the child's home, it generally means that the parents have been unable to provide a safe and sexually healthy environment in which the children could develop healthy sexual lives. It may be necessary to remove the child who abuses to a safe and structured environment with adults who model healthy sexual interactions free of aggression and the child can receive therapy. This will depend on the emotional resources of the parents, the stability of the home environment, and the health of the relationships between adults in the children's home. It will also depend on the level of force or coercion used by the child who abused, the behavioral characteristics of both children, the age and vulnerability of the victim and the ability of parents to quickly provide a structured and safe home environment.

Resolution of Case Vignette

Although it seems that John and/or Freddie may have been previous victim(s) of sexual abuse; they were not, at least, not in a "hands-on" way. Upon further questioning, it turns out that the boys are latch key kids and have been with their older brother and some of his teenage friends who have been watching pornographic videos. John and Freddie wanted to try it. After they were caught, they didn't do it again. Freddie's curiosity was satisfied, but another friend,

who had also watched the videos, asked him at a later time to engage in oral-genital contact at his house.

In this case, the boys need closer parental supervision of their after school activities. Neither boy is a perpetrator. An assessment of their general level of functioning and their feelings and thoughts about sexuality would be helpful to see if any mental health intervention is suggested. The children and parents will need some assistance in providing adequate child care. The boys may need some sex education.

Resources

Eliana, G. and Johnson, T. C. *Sexualized Children: Assessment and Treatment of Sexualized Children and Children Who Molest.* Launch Press: January, 1993.

Johnson, Toni, C. *Sexual, Physical, and Emotional Abuse in Out-of-Home Care: Prevention Skills for At-Risk Children.* The Haworth Press, Incorporated: April, 1997.

Johnson, Toni, C. *Understanding Your Child's Sexual Behavior: What's Natural and Healthy.* New Harbinger Publications: July, 1999.

Adolescents as Perpetrators

Sandra K. Baker, L.C.S.W. and Gary Lowe, L.C.S.W.

Two Case Vignettes

Case One

Mark was a 15-year-old boy, who engaged in mutual fondling, oral-genital contact and, on at least one occasion, sodomy with two neighborhood boys aged 7 and 8. The sexual abuse of the boys extenuated over a three-year period on the average of four times a week. It wasn't until one boy complained to his mother of anal bleeding that further questioning led to a criminal investigation and Mark was arrested.

Case Two

James, when 13 years old, was babysitting a 3 year old boy. He was playing a game with the child when he became sexually aroused. He pulled the boys pants off and began to orally copulate him and then had the child do the same to him. He then experienced a sudden realization of what he was doing and immediately became violently ill. Afterwards, he cleaned up his vomit and begged the child not to tell anyone what happened. However, the child disclosed within a few days, the abuse was reported and James was arrested.

It was only after his arrest that James learned that he had been sexually abused when he was 3 years old by his half brother, Stuart. Stuart was 13 when he was caught abusing James. Although that abuse was also reported, no legal action was taken against Stuart. At that time, the family was advised to make sure that Stuart was never alone with James (they did not live together) and that James would just forget about it if the family didn't make a big deal about it.

Questions

1. Is a perpetrator of sexual abuse as an adolescent likely to become an adult offender?
2. What is the extent of sexual abuse among the adolescent offender population?
3. With treatment intervention, is an adolescent less likely to become an adult offender?
4. What types of treatment interventions, in combination with supervision, have been found to be most successful with adolescent offenders?

History

Historically, the attention concerning treatment and prevention of sexual abuse has been on victims or potential victims. Adolescents who were involved in sexually offending behavior were not held accountable. Sexual behavior which was clearly exploitive and criminal was often dismissed as awkward experimentation of the adolescent's emerging sexuality, or adolescent adjustment reaction ("boys will be boys"). Part of the reason for this minimization, both by professionals in the field and the judicial system, was to protect the adolescent from being labeled and thus socially stigmatized. It has only been within the last twenty years that special attention has been paid to this problematic population of sexual abusers.

Epidemiology

There is no systematic data collection regarding adolescent sex offenders. Analysis of official child abuse reports in selected jurisdictions have shown that 30-50% of the child sexual abuse cases are perpetrated by adolescents. The scope of the problem may be under-reported because the most common form of adolescent sexual abuse is perpetrated within the family against siblings and step-siblings where it is kept a secret. In this setting, many victims are too young to report and family members are reluctant to stigmatize the young offender by involving the criminal justice system.

This early onset of sexual deviance can be carried into adult life. Studies of adult sex offenders have reported that 60-80% of adult offenders described offending as adolescents (Groth, et al., 1982, and Abel, et al., 1986). Adolescent offenders are reporting an average of just less than seven victims. Common types of sexual abuse beginning in adolescence include voyeurism, exhibitionism, pedophilia, and sadism.

Many adolescent offenders were themselves victims as children. There is considerable information to support the belief that many adolescent and adult sex offenders were themselves victims of sexual and/or physical abuse as children. If they were not sexually abused, many have a history of living in multi-problem families with a high degree of violence as a significant factor in their daily life. This latter factor is supported by the Widom and Ames (1994) study of arrest records of 908 children abused before age 11. The researchers found that children with a physical abuse history were two times more likely than the children with a sexual abuse history to be arrested as adults for violent sexual crimes (rape and/or sodomy). Children with a sexual abuse history are more likely to be involved in "nonviolent" sexual offenses. It is important to note that both non-violent and violent sexual abuse produces traumatized victims.

In recent years, an enormous body of clinical and judicial based statistics and knowledge have been generated in respect to the adolescent sex offender. It is erroneous to assume that an adolescent who engages in an inappropriate sexual act, even if the behavior is criminal in nature, will automatically continue this behavior and develop into a sexual psychopath as an adult. Intervention is crucial when the adolescent first begins to exhibit the symptoms of his pathology and before the abuse pattern is established and the adolescent is less responsive to treatment. Programs to treat this population have shown encouraging results.

Approaches to Treatment

Juvenile perpetrators are a heterogeneous population with a variety of types and levels of sexual offenses represented. Not all offenses or offenders present the same degree of threat to the victims and the community. As a result, there should be a continuum of system response as well as a variety of treatment services available to meet the varied needs of this population. Services to adolescent offenders needs to range from incarceration for the violent repeat offenders to specialized, court ordered out-patient treatment programs for the less violent offender who may be more amenable to changing the offending behavior.

It is important to be mindful that sex offenders, whether juvenile or adults, are largely unique from other types of mental health clients in that they typically do not self-identify or volunteer for treatment. To the contrary, they usually present for evaluation and treatment only at someone's (often their parent's) insistence after having been apprehended and confronted with their behavior and out of fear of the consequences of the legal system. If treatment (mandated long-term, abuse focused treatment in a structured program) is used as a way of avoiding the criminal justice system and the sanctions it can impose, it will most likely last only as long as the offender's fear of the legal system prevails. This is usually not a sufficient amount of time to effect meaningful or permanent change in the offending behavior.

For the outpatient adolescent population, it is the consensus of most clinicians working with adolescent sexual offenders that treatment needs to be **sanctioned** (court ordered) and **specialized** utilizing a variety of treatment modalities including group, family, and individual therapy as well as some educational components. Insight-oriented one-to-one psychotherapy between a therapist and the adolescent appears to have limited success, especially if it is used as the sole or major form of treatment modality.

Focused and Specialized Offender Treatment

Studies show that focused and specialized (offender specific) treatments are effective in reducing the risk of recidivism of adolescent offenders. (Becker, Kaplin, & Kavoussi, 1988; Shram, Milloy, & Rowe, 1991). Data shows that less than 15% of juveniles provided with specialized treatment programs re-offend, contrasted to recidivism rates as high as 75% in youth treated with more traditional methodologies. (Borduin, Henggeler, Blaske, & Stein, 1990). These studies create optimism that sexual acting out in juveniles need not be repeated in adulthood as a life-long pattern of behavior if appropriate intervention and specialized treatment programs are made available.

Family Therapy

Family therapy is an essential component of juvenile sex offender treatment. It is imperative that the family be involved in the youth's treatment, and that family systems and areas of dysfunction be addressed when the youth is to remain in the home or there is an expectation of reunification. This is critical in those situations where a sibling(s) was the victim and/or the offender was previously victimized by a family member. Each family member must be made to confront their individual role in the abuse (i.e. denial or enabling). In these situations, the physical safety and emotional needs of all victims must be the foremost consideration. If the family refuses to participate in the treatment of the adolescent offender, permanent out of home placement may be necessary.

Group Therapy

Group therapy in combination with individual therapy is typically the primary treatment of choice for most juvenile sexual offenders and generally is developed to include both a didactic as well as process format. Group therapy is not only an economical form of treatment but, when properly constructed, provides an emotionally supportive, and developmentally appropriate atmosphere wherein the adolescent can address the psychosexual problems with therapists and peers without embarrassment or fear. Youth treated in groups realize they are not alone in their problems and benefit from peer support and confrontation.

Treatment of the adolescent offender typically includes:

- accepting responsibility for the offending behavior;

- identifying and correcting distortions in their thinking that contributes to the tendency to minimize their behavior or to project blame onto others;

- addressing deficits in social and assertiveness skills which contribute to social isolation, low self-esteem, and the displacement of frustrations and anger onto others;

- sex education information that provides an understanding of normal sexual development;

- addressing issues of impulse control, poor interpersonal boundaries and impaired judgment;

- developing empathy for the victim which may include processing information and feelings regarding their own history of victimization;

- cognitive-behavioral methods to reduce the intensity of deviant sexual arousal and interests;

- identifying the elements of the cycle of abuse including behaviors and thinking patterns that place them at high risk for re-offending;

- learning coping strategies for high risk situations; and,

- relapse prevention training.

Resolution of the First Case Vignette

Mark was ultimately convicted of Lewd and Lascivious Acts with a Child under 14, and sentenced to the California Youth Authority (CYA) where he was assigned to a sex offender treatment program and spent two and one half years in treatment. Mark was a victim himself of early childhood sexual abuse at the hands of his maternal uncle. He was an only child. His mother was the sole provider for the family, having divorced Mark's father when Mark was two years old. The uncle was frequently called upon by Mark's mother to provide "fatherly support and male modeling."

Mark's abuse began with frequent "french kissing" when Mark was 5 years old. Mark recalled in treatment that the really big kisses came when his uncle was about to leave the house at which time he would arrange to be alone with Mark. Mark made attempts to tell his mother how his uncle made him feel "creepy", but she would pass it off by telling him that his uncle loved him and that he wouldn't do anything to hurt him. Mark also recalled that when he would attempt to hide from his uncle, his mother would come and find him and put him on his uncle's lap and tell him to give his uncle a big kiss good-bye. As Mark grew older, the abuse by his uncle increased and by the age of ten involved mutual masturbation, and oral-genital contact. It wasn't until he was ten years old when his mother found him and his uncle sexually involved in the back of his uncle's truck that the abuse was stopped and his uncle arrested. Interestingly, Mark received no treatment for his abuse after this discovery.

Like many victims of sexual abuse over time and with more victimization, Mark became increasingly vulnerable. At age 15, he was diagnosed with high levels of sexual arousal to young boys with distorted thinking which precluded empathy towards his victims and provided justification of his sexual behavior as just playing and normal.

Mark spent three years in intensive offense specific treatment in the CYA. The goals in treatment for Mark were to decrease his sexual arousal to young boys through participation in bio-feedback reconditioning; eliminate rationalizations for his sexual abusive behavior; replace rationalization with an understanding of the damage he was doing to his victims through participation in group therapy with other sexually abusive adolescents; address issues of his own victimization and participate in family counseling to increase communication and develop a positive support system.

Mark was a "model client", actively participating in treatment and successfully completing his treatment goals. He was released six months early from CYA with a report from the treatment staff that he had "successfully completed treatment." Parole staff considered him, therefore, a low risk and placed him on minimum supervision with no need of referral for continued treatment intervention.

Mark was in the community for three weeks before he reoffended. He and his mother were so confident of his ability to avoid further sexually abusive behavior that he was allowed to volunteer as a camp counselor for his church's youth group. Mark began experiencing sexual fantasies in respect to a particular 8 year old youth under his care. He then summarized that the years in treatment had not worked and that in fact he wasn't a success. With the temptation so near, he relapsed, sexually victimizing the boy.

By allowing or encouraging Mark to volunteer as a counselor for a youth group his mother "enabled" Mark to re-offend. This example illustrates the importance of treating the primary caretakers as well as the offender. It is also important for the mother to understand and confront her role in allowing Mark to be repeatedly abused by his uncle. A clear understanding of her role in "enabling" Mark's abuse by his uncle may have prevented her from repeating that role with Mark after his release.

It is vital for the offender and caretaker to understand that "low risk" to offend does not mean that the offender is "cured". There will always be a risk to re-offend. Relapse Prevention training should include an explicit safety plan for each offender. This safety plan should also be signed by the caretakers and the plan should include some type of follow up treatment for six months to a year after release or graduation from an outpatient treatment program to assist the offender and his caretakers in identifying high risk behavior (i.e. volunteering as a youth counselor for a church group).

Mark's case is an example where the perception that the adolescent has "completed" treatment inadvertently contributed to the denial that there is still an ongoing risk. An adolescent, who finishes a treatment program and returns to an environment lacking the structure and treatment supports that he has been accustomed to for months or years, may relapse. To be effective, aftercare should be an integral part of the rehabilitative process. In essence, aftercare is the transfer of the therapeutic message to daily life in the community. Although there is no guarantee that Mark would not have reoffended with aftercare elements in place, the programs that have shown the most success have in place a formal structured aftercare component of treatment and supervision.

Resolution of the Second Vignette

James participated in weekly outpatient JSO (Juvenile Sex Offender) group treatment as well as weekly individual or family therapy. Both of James' parents were in separate Parents' JSO groups, and participated in a combination of family, couples, and individual therapy. Darrell, the 11 year old younger brother of James, participated in family sessions on an as needed basis. Stuart was also asked to participate in treatment but declined to do so.

Treatment issues included those specific to all JSO client families: boundary setting, supervision needs, increase communication and assertiveness skills, empathy building, relapse prevention, etc. Issues specific to James were: addressing the abuse of himself for which he had no recollection, sexual identity issues and a debilitating degree of shame. A high degree of conflict existed within the family at the start of treatment and this was addressed first within the spousal relationship in couples therapy and then within the family as a whole in family session.

James was never able to remember his abuse as a 3 year old but did reach a workable resolution of related issues. The family, even the younger brother, exhibited a high level of commitment to therapy and to long-term follow through with safety measures. As a result James and his family graduated from the treatment program in only 17 months. Currently, James is a junior at New York University and Darrell is successfully pursuing his long-term dream of an acting degree. There has been no (known) reoccurrence of sexual abuse within the family.

Selected Readings

Gil, E. and Cavanaugh-Johnson, T. *Sexualized Children: Assessment and Treatment of Sexualized Children and Children Who Molest.* MD: Launch Press, 1993.

Knopp, F.H. *The Youthful Sex Offender: The Rationale & Goals of Early Intervention & Treatment.* New York: Safer Society Press, 1985.

Knopp, F.H. *Remedial Intervention in Adolescent Sex Offenses: Nine Program Descriptions.* New York: Safer Society Press, 1982.

Steen, C. and Monnette, B. *Treating Adolescent Sex Offenders in the Community.* Illinois: Charles C. Thomas Publisher, 1989.

The Revised Report from the National Task Force on Juvenile Sexual Offending, 1993 of the National Adolescent Perpetrator Network. University of Nevada: *Juvenile & Family Court Journal*, 44(4), 1993.

Child Pornography

Terry L. Rudolph, PhD, FBI (retired)

Case Vignette

The photo developing clerk at the local Wal-Mart notices that several pictures in a roll of 35mm film he is developing are of a nude little girl. He shows them to his supervisor who believes they are indecent and decides to call the police. An officer of the child abuse unit responds and believes the photos could constitute child pornography. Store records indicate that the film's overnight owner regularly develops one or two rolls of film at the store every month. Two rolls of film were submitted for processing. On one roll, five of thirty-six photos were of a nude little girl about six years of age, while eight of thirty-six photos in roll number two showed the nude little girl. The investigators decided to investigate.

Questions

1. What exactly constitutes child pornography?
2. Are all nude photographs of children child pornography?
3. What is child erotica and how does it differ from child pornography?

A Brief History of Child Pornography

Since the dawn of time adults have been sexually exploiting children. Children have been exploited under the guise of art in paintings, sketches, and other forms. However, it was with the advent of the camera in the mid 1800's, that child pornography was really born. From the mid 1800's to the 1900's, most child pornography produced remained in the hands of private individuals, few publishing their work. By the mid 1960's, several nudist magazines were being published that highlighted young children, often in very sexually explicit poses. The first commercial child pornography magazine, Bambino Sex, was published in 1970 and sold over 10,000 copies in the first week of the issue. Commercial child pornography saw its heyday from 1970 to around 1984. In 1984, the Dutch magazine, Lolita, one of the most popular child pornography magazines ever published, discontinued publication. Changes in the law both in the United States and abroad drove the child pornography industry completely underground. Today there is virtually no commercial child pornography sold or produced in the United States. It continues to be produced, traded and exchanged primarily on the Internet by private individuals which poses new problems for law enforcement officers.

Child Pornography Defined

What exactly is child pornography? Child pornography is a visual depiction of a minor engaged in sexually explicit conduct. Additionally child pornography is a permanent record of the sexual exploitation and abuse of a child.

First, to legally be child pornography, it must be a visual depiction, not the written word. The Internet contains hundreds, if not thousands, of writings by pedophiles[1] describing their sexual fantasies and/or alleged sexual adventures with children, but these writings are not prohibited child pornography in the United States.

Included in the definition of visual depiction are photographs, slides, movies, magazines, books, video tapes, even film negatives and undeveloped film. More recently, computer discs containing visual depictions have been added to the list.

Secondly, to be considered child pornography, the visual depiction must be of a child under the age of eighteen. In the United States, the Federal age of consent is 18, but in many countries of the world, it is lower, even as low as 12. It is possible that a picture which is legal in Denmark is illegal in the United States because the age of consent differs.

Occasionally in some child pornography investigations, the identity and age of a child in a photograph is unknown. Often a physician, usually a pediatrician, will assist investigators and make a determination of the approximate age of the child to assess whether the age element of the law can be met. This determination becomes difficult as the child reaches maturity or late adolescence.

Thirdly, to be unlawful child pornography, the child must be engaged in sexually explicit conduct. Davidson and Loker (1987) report Federal law has determined sexually explicit can be either actual or simulated and can be defined as:

- Sexual intercourse (oral, anal, or vaginal)

- Masturbation and sexual fondling

- Bestiality

- Sadistic or masochistic abuse

- Lascivious exhilaration of the genital or public area

Although most sexually explicit conduct is not difficult to determine and is usually quite obvious (i.e. intercourse with a child), that which constitutes lascivious exhibition of the genitals has not always been as clear. This issue will be addressed a little further in this work.

The last component of what constitutes child pornography is that it is a permanent record of the sexual exploitation and abuse of a child. Lanning (1992) states by its very nature, a photograph considered as child pornography is a permanent record of that sexual abuse of the child. It is a permanent record of sexual abuse which does harm to the child because the child is continually victimized every time the picture is viewed.

Scope Of Child Pornography

For many investigators, and many child advocates, the scope of what exactly constitutes child pornography is not broad enough. For some sex educators, sex therapists, artists, photographers, and pedophiles, the scope of what constitutes child pornography is too broad.

An issue that often arises in child pornography investigations is the question of when does the nude photograph of a child constitute child pornography. Common sense tells us that not all nude photographs of children are child pornography, but a line has to be drawn somewhere. That line is usually lascivious exhibition of the genitals. When is a simple photograph of a nude child playing or taking a bath child pornography?

Evaluating nude photographs of children

The courts through several different decisions have provided guidelines on what constitutes lascivious exhibition of the genitals. Some important factors are as follows:

- Was the focal point of the picture the child's pubic or anal area?

- Was the setting of the picture or the pose sexually suggestive?

- How was the child clothed?

- Was the picture was intended or designed to elicit a sexual response in the viewer?

Lanning (1992) offers guidelines on whether a picture might be child pornography:

- How were the pictures produced?

- How were they saved?

- How were they used?

Each picture that might be considered child pornography has to be determined on an individual basis. Many parents have taken pictures of their children in the nude, in the bath tub, playing in the sprinkler or getting their diaper changed. Rarely are these type of photographs considered child pornography because they fail to meet the court guidelines. The focal point of the picture is not the child's genitals nor is the child being posed in an overt sexual manner. Although the child may have been unclothed, the intent of the picture was to bring a laugh or a smile to the viewer or to document an event in the life of the child.

Lanning (1992) proposed guidelines asking first—how were the photographs produced? Were they taken surreptitiously? Did the child appear to be posing provocatively? Secondly, he asks how were the photographs saved? In a family photograph album among family pictures or as part of a collection of hundreds of nude children?

Whether or not a photograph of a nude child is child pornography has to be determined from the totality of the facts. Parents who take a few nude photographs of their young children have nothing to fear when the totality of the facts are considered. However, if the photograph in question shows close-ups of the child's genitals, the child is posing seductively in a bed, or the photograph is part of a very large collection of nude photographs—that picture might constitute child pornography.

Evaluating photographs of children who are clothed

Recently another dilemma has arisen in determining if a picture of a child is child pornography. Until 1993, various photographers and child pornographers considered photographs of children who were clothed and not engaged in any sexually explicit conduct as child erotica and legal. In 1992, a Court of Appeals decision known as the Knox Decision stated that photographs of children, where the focus of the picture is on the pubic area, can be child pornography even though they are clothed and engaged in harmless activities. These photographs which were actually videos of young girls ages ten to seventeen wearing clothing such as bathing suits and leotards had the camera zoom in on their pubic area. A new standard is now in place. Even though a child is clothed, if the photographer focuses on the pubic area and the intent of the picture is to pander to the pedophile, the picture could be child pornography.

The author is aware of a case where a roll of thirty-six pictures was intercepted at a local film developer. All thirty-six of the pictures were of a little seven year old girl watching a parade. Thirty-five of the thirty-six pictures showed the little girl sitting at the curb of the street with her panties exposed. These pictures were determined to be child pornography. Again the totality of the facts has to be taken into consideration before a judgment can be made. Ultimately the judgment of whether a picture is child pornography is made by a jury of the subject's peers.

Child Erotica

Another issue that arises when dealing with the topic of child pornography is "child erotica". What is child erotica and how does it differ from child pornography? The Manual of Child Abuse and Exploitation: Investigative Techniques (1995) defines child erotica as anything that may cause sexual arousal in a pedophile.

Child erotica unlike child pornography is legal and can include things that are not just visual depictions. Child erotica can include games, toys, books, writings, drawings, sex toys, children's underwear, diaries, as well as pictures, videos and even current movies and television shows featuring children. Usually if a person collects child pornography, it is not unlikely that he will also have a large collection of child erotica. Often collections of child erotica are larger than the child pornography collection because they are easier to obtain and are legal.

Lanning (1992) divides child erotica into five categories:

- Published material relating to children
- Unpublished material relating to children
- Picture, photographs, and video tapes of children
- Souvenirs and trophies
- Miscellaneous items

An important aspect for consideration when dealing with the issue of child erotica is that, although it is usually legal, it can be an indicator of an individual's behavior and interest in children. Possession of child erotica can be very strong circumstantial evidence that a person is a pedophile or at least has a proclivity toward a sexual interest in children.

Child Pornography and the Internet

With changes in the child pornography laws in the late 1970's and early 1980's, trafficking in child pornography worldwide was almost brought to a halt and was forced to go even deeper underground. However, with the accessibility of the home computer and the Internet, starting around the early 1990's, the child pornography industry was revitalized.

Advances in computer technology have totally changed how child pornography is distributed, exchanged, and traded. Now through the Internet, with virtual anonymity, anyone can both download and send child pornography anywhere in the world to thousands of users in a matter of seconds. The Internet has become the most popular medium of exchange of child pornography easily surpassing the mail which is more detectable.

Child pornography images found on the Internet pose the same problem as those found elsewhere. Do they meet legal standards of child pornography? Could they be legal child erotica? The standards previously discussed also have to be applied to the computer images. Are the victims children and are they engaged in sexually explicit conduct?

Many of the child pornography images found on the Internet are posted on a variety of news groups. The news groups allow easy access and permit the user to up and download images. Child pornography has also been traded in chat rooms and Internet Relay Chat channels. Both are places where users can go to communicate with people of similar interests.

Most of the images posted on the Internet, no matter what the source, were taken from the old child pornography magazines of the 1970's and 1980's like Lolita, Child Love and a variety of others. One private unpublished study from the mid 1990's showed that less than 10% of the images the researcher found on the Internet were current and home-made. Today, however, the trend is to post more and more current homemade pictures which are often made by the trafficker himself.

Some of the more recent advances that have greatly enabled the child pornographer using the Internet are scanners, digital cameras, and video capture boards just to name a few. Flatbed scanners which can be purchased inexpensively, allow the Polaroid and other photographs to be scanned into a file and readily posted onto the Internet. Digital cameras, also inexpensive, enable the photographer to go directly from the camera to the computer with no developing or risk. These photographs can be reproduced over and over with no loss of quality. Video capture boards, also relatively inexpensive, allow video clips to be converted to stills and then be placed in various files or interest to the trafficker. Inevitably when there is an advancement in computer technology, the child pornographers use it for their prurient interests.

Uses of Child Pornography

Lanning (1992) describes some of the uses of child pornography:

- Sexual arousal and gratification. Pedophiles use child pornography to feed their sexual fantasies, and to stimulate their sexual drive.

- To lower children's inhibitions. Child pornographic images are used to seduce children into having sex. Children are shown that it is normal; other children are doing it; and it's fun.

- For purposes of blackmail. Images of a victimized child can be used to perpetuate the sexual abuse and exploitation by using manipulation, fear, and shame that the photographs will be shown to others.

- A medium of exchange. Pedophiles and users of child pornography will exchange it to increase the volume of their collections. It is a medium of communication with fellow pedophiles.

- Profit. Years ago this was an important use of child pornography. Today, profit is rarely the motive.

Goldstein (1987) offers some other uses of child pornography often produced by the pedophile:

- Symbolically it keeps the child close to the pedophile. The photographs remind the abuser of the experiences he had with the child.

- Bragging or gaining of status. The offender will often use the photograph of the child he has victimized as a means of bragging or gaining status with like-minded offenders. This practice is common with some boy-lovers groups.

Healy (1996) offers yet another use:

- Validation and justification of pedophile behavior. These images are used to convince the pedophile that his behavior is not abnormal but is shared by hundreds of other sensitive, normal people.

Definitions

[1]Pedophile: As used herein, a pedophile refers to a person with a sexual preference for children.

Resources

Davidson, Howard A. and Loker, Gregory A. (1987). *Child Pornography and Prostitution*. National Center For Missing and Exploited Children.

Goldstein, Seth (1987). *The Sexual Exploitation of Children*. Elsevier Books; New York.

Healy, Pegy (1996). *Child Pornography: An International Perspective*. Presented to the World Congress Against The Commercial Exploitation of Children. Stockholm, Sweden. August 1996.

Lanning, Kenneth V. (1992). *Child Molesters: A Behavioral Analysis*. National Center For Missing and Exploited Children.

Shepard, Jack R., Downing, Bill, Farley, Robert Hugh, Fuss, Bradely J. and Fressler, Paul W. *Manual of Child Abuse and Exploitation: Investigative Techniques 1995*. The Office of Juvenile Justice and Delinquency Prevention, U.S. Department of Justice.

Prostituted Children

Susan Kreston, J.D.

Case Vignette

Police discover a child who appears to be about 14 giving a 40 year old businessman oral sex in the back seat of a car. Both the child and the man say it was "consensual." The child was given $25 by the man as a "gift." The police run rap sheets on both individuals. The man comes back with no prior arrests or convictions. The child is extremely uncooperative and has an extensive history of runaway behavior, petty theft and drug abuse. What should the police do?

Questions

1. Why isn't sexually exploiting a prostituted child routinely prosecuted as child sexual abuse?

2. What are the most prevalent myths surrounding prostituted children?

3. What is the average victim profile?

4. What are the best responses to this type of child sexual exploitation?

History and Statistics

There are estimated to be between 300,000 and 600,000 prostituted children in the United States. Child prostitution is defined as the act of engaging or offering the services of a child to perform sexual acts for money or other consideration. Most states and the federal government have laws against prostituting children. In most cases, these laws target the conduct of the economic exploiter/pimp, but ignore the culpability of the sexual molester/john. In identical factual scenarios involving an adult having sexual intercourse with an underage child, the penalty difference between the crime labeled "prostitution" and the crime labeled "child sexual abuse" is significant. "Patrons," as they are euphemistically referred to, are often specifically excluded from the coverage of child prostitution legislation. Even when included, the penalty generally pales in comparison to that of the molester prosecuted under traditional child sexual abuse laws. However, as the prostitution of children does not conform to traditional sexual abuse dynamics, the child's exploitation by a "patron" is generally not prosecuted under child abuse laws.

The infantilization of prostitution is a trend that will continue to grow. With the arrival of the potentially lethal sexually transmitted disease AIDS, the demand for younger and younger children has increased. Prostituted children seldom come to the life untouched. The reality is that prostituted children have usually been sexually abused and exploited by their parent(s), their pimp and/or others long before they were lured or forced into prostitution.

Prostituted children present special challenges to both the medical community and the criminal justice system. Often hostile toward law enforcement, social services and medical personnel, prostituted children believe no one has a genuine interest in helping them. The mistaken, yet prevalent, societal attitude that prostituted children are somehow responsible for their exploitation and, therefore, are unworthy of the protection the law affords to other victims of child sexual abuse, does nothing to alter this view. Attachment to their pimps, the children's belief that they know what's best for themselves, and the resulting non-cooperation from victimized children create untold difficulties.

Prostituted children are already marginalized, not to say alienated, from society. They begin with three strikes against them: they are children; they are designated as prostitutes; and they are often engaged in criminal activities such as drug usage, theft and related crimes. Many within society condemn or dismiss these children. Few ask what could have happened to a child to make him or her use sex to survive.

Victim Profile

Children become victims of prostitution in depressingly predictable ways. The vast majority are runaway, thrown-away or deserted children. Usually there was sexual abuse, physical abuse, emotional abuse and/or domestic violence present in the child's home prior to the child leaving. The average age of entry into prostitution is 14. Prostitution of children as young as 9 has been documented.

Most children become victims of prostitution in one of two ways. The first and most prevalent is deceit and manipulation. As with the preferential child molester, the pimp seduces these children. The pimp gains their trust and then exploits it. The pimp provides what is perceived to be comfort, affection, understanding and protection. The pimp makes the child feel loved and, initially, asks nothing in return. After gaining the child's trust, the tactic of completely separating the child from other friends or any remaining family contact begins. The child then becomes financially and emotionally dependent on the pimp.

Having isolated the child, the pimp begins the process of lowering the child's inhibitions. The child is shown pornography. The child is told the pimp needs money to be able to support them both. The pimp may begin with finding the child jobs in nude modeling or topless clubs. Out of the disastrously misplaced love and affection the child has for the pimp, the child is drawn into prostitution.

The child continues to be controlled by the pimp. Initially, this control is exerted by withholding the affection the child previously enjoyed. If this manipulation ceases to work, usually because the child comes to realize the pimp never had any genuine love for her, the pimp will resort to violence and fear. At this point, the child will suffer unimaginable physical and sexual brutality. The same dynamic of isolation and self-blame that is seen in domestic abuse victims, compounded by a fear of the police and juvenile prosecution, keeps the child from involving the authorities and escaping. Finally, when violence fails to work as a control mechanism, the pimp turns to involving the child in drugs or threatening to harm the child's former friends and family. If the child is pregnant or already has a baby, additional hold is exerted.

Coercion, the second recruitment mechanism, is practiced less often but with equally devastating efficiency. A child has only two choices to survive on the streets: petty crimes or survival sex. The pimp, learning of the child's presence on the street and recognizing the vulnerability of this situation, pressures the child into prostitution. Threats of physical violence or blackmail are the most prevalent means pimps use to compel the victim. The pimp may resort to outright violence to frighten the child into submission. Alternatively, threats may be made against the child's loved ones. The pimp makes these threats real by seizing the child's belongings, which usually contain the names and addresses of friends or family. Once in possession of that information, the pimp may also blackmail the child by threats of exposing her as a prostitute to people important to the child. The pimp may also threaten to alert the police to her presence on the street, thereby forcing her to return to an abusive home. Armed with this hold over the child, the pimp has now effectively trapped the child into a life of being prostituted.

Common denominators among prostituted children include: sexual, physical and/or emotional abuse in the home; dysfunctional parents or caretakers; low self-esteem; truancy/schooling difficulties; drug and/or alcohol abuse; multiple runaway episodes and; prior involvement in the juvenile justice system. Beyond these factors, there is little else the children share. Prostituted children come from all socio-economic backgrounds, all races and both genders.

Myths Surrounding Prostituted Children

At a recent World Congress Against Commercial Sexual Exploitation of Children, the link between the prostitution of adults and children was emphasized. Two main points were stressed. First, the vast majority of prostituted children in the United States are integrated into the mainstream of prostitution, rather than working in some isolated "market niche" which caters solely to the desires of pedophiles and preferential child molesters. Second, commonly accepted and widely endorsed myths about prostitution generally are used by those who prostitute children to justify their abuse. These myths allow abusers to distort reality and claim that as the child consented and, therefore, no harm has been done. Abusers are not alone in holding these views. Public acceptance of prostitution as a "legitimate" business or an unavoidable evil is widespread.

Myth 1: Prostitution is a necessity for inadequate sexual relationships.

Prostitution is the sexual and economic exploitation of those with little power. In the case of a child, the gap between the purchaser and the purchased is most pronounced. Prostitution is structured by the economic demands of the pimp and the sexual desires of the buyer. The person being bought and sold has no power in that dynamic. Prostitution is the dehumanization and objectification of an individual, who is redefined as a means to the end of the buyer's sexual gratification. Exploiting a powerless individual does not remedy inadequate sexual relationships; it exacerbates them.

Myth 2: Prostitution is a victimless crime.

When an adult uses a prostituted child for sexual gratification, it is child sexual abuse. The fact that the abuser gives the child money does not alter the fact that child abuse occurred. If the child is below the legally recognized age of consent, the fact that the child "consented" is equally irrelevant. The consent of the abused child is never a legally recognized defense in child sexual abuse cases, as the child cannot give meaningful consent. The presence of money merely allow perpetrators to engage in rationalizations that eradicate their personal responsibility for their own actions.

Immediate harm to the prostituted child is blatantly apparent and comes in many forms. Degrading and humiliating sexual encounters, muggings, severe beatings, rape and even death are the reality of prostituted children. Unwanted pregnancy, HIV/AIDS and other STDs are also constant facts of life for these children. Long term physical and psychological health problems are also to be expected.

Myth 3: Juveniles freely choose prostitution.

Juveniles are most frequently driven to prostitution in order to escape abusive and/or neglectful homes. These children are not running to prostitution; they are running from dysfunctional authority figures who emotionally, physically and/or sexually abused them. For many of the children the only way to escape the abuse is to run away. Unfortunately, they jump out of the frying pan and into the fire. Young, frightened, with limited or no skills, and unable to find shelter, the children are easy prey for pimps or johns. Once involved in prostitution, both pimps and customers replicate the abuse the children endured in their home-life. Eighty (80%) of all adult prostitutes started as prostituted children.

Myth 4: Prostitution can be an exciting and glamorous life.

Cultural mythology regarding prostitution is built on intentionally distorted misinformation. The typical depiction of the life style in movies, television, video and printed material is as far from the truth as it is possible to get. The movie *Pretty Woman* is an example of the worst offenders. *Leaving Las Vegas* is one of the few high profile films that offers a far more accurate portrayal of the bleak realities of the life. The truth is that juvenile prostitutes suffer both immediate harm, in the form of physical/sexual/emotional degradation and humiliation, and long term physical and psychological effects. There is nothing glamorous about the reality of prostitution.

Myth 5: Prostituted children have power and control within the system.

The reality is that prostituted children are controlled by their customers and/or their pimps. Once involved with a pimp, the child loses autonomy. The more involved the child becomes, the more difficult it is to get out. Pimps demand money from the children; shortfalls often result in punishment. If the child balks at performing the acts demanded by the abuser, this can also result in violence. Both the exploiter and the abuser choose children because children are easier to physically assault and intimidate into doing as they are told. These assaults are rarely reported to the police, further reinforcing the child's isolation and powerlessness.

Myth 6: Prostitution is a deterrent to sex crimes.

There is no methodologically sound evidence whatsoever that prostitution deters sex crimes. Rapists and child molesters commit their crimes out of a desire to control and exert power or to humiliate and degrade their victims. While sex offenders may use prostituted children as additional victims, this will only strengthen the offenders' belief that sexual violence and exploitation are acceptable. The fact that these crimes often go unreported allows the perpetrator to gain confidence and strike again. Prostitution does not deter sex crimes. It promotes them.

Best Practices/Model Programs

Effective responses to prostituting children must be initiated from the criminal justice community. There must be an orchestrated and coordinated response from law enforcement, prosecutors and the judiciary to this problem. All criminal justice professionals need to recognize that prostituting children is child sexual abuse. Sex with a child is sex with a child. Prostituted children should be treated as victims, not criminals. By arresting, prosecuting and sentencing the exploiter/pimp and child molester/john on child sexual abuse charges, the perpetrators begin to be held as accountable for their actions as other child molesters.

Specialized treatment and reintegration of the children by social services or not-for-profit organizations must also occur. There are three essential services that any program to assist prostituted children should have. First, prevention education should be made a priority. The dynamics that lead to children being lured or forced into prostitution and ways to neutralize or combat this dynamic must be stressed. Second, street-work outreach programs, with properly screened and trained staff, must be implemented. Coordination and collaboration with other community agencies is essential in this campaign. Third, a transitional living program must be created. The exact goals of such a program will vary with the age of the child. For the youngest victims, return to either the home or to members of the extended family may be one goal. If the child should not or cannot be returned, placement through local social services would be the other option. This option, however, may be very problematic as the child may have severe behavioral difficulties as a result of the exploitation.

For older children, group homes, family host homes, foster care or institutional placement may be appropriate. There are unique issues involved in assisting these children which must be addressed. If the child has left the street involuntarily (e.g., through police and social service intervention), the child may need to be segregated from other children in care to avoid putting the other children at risk of being recruited. Long-term, residential treatment centers may be the most appropriate transitional environment for some children, but the number of such facilities is low and the expense is high.

Regardless of whether the child is in transition voluntarily or not, it may be advisable to relocate the child away from the geographic area in which the victimization occurred, to deter the pimp attempting to reassert control. Intensive counseling to address the child's anxieties and to learn new behaviors must also be furnished. A successful transition to a safe and supportive environment cannot be accomplished overnight. Merely taking the child off the streets is not enough. It will take, at a minimum, months to effect any real and significant change. There is no quick fix for these children and the time and resources necessary to accomplish a meaningful, permanent transformation must be put in place. Two programs that may be contacted for assistance in instituting such treatment are:

Children of the Night
14530 Sylvan Street
Van Nuys, CA 91411
(818) 908-4474

Paul and Lisa Program
P.O. Box 348
Westbrook, CN
(860) 767-7660

What Health Care Professionals Should Remember about Prostituted Children

If a child comes into your care and you believe s/he may be a prostituted child, deal with this child as you would with any other child who you believe may be the victim of sexual and/or physical abuse. You are a mandatory reporter and this child's exploitation should be no less compelling nor dealt with differently than any other form of child abuse. Follow the protocols that are in place for dealing with children who you suspect to be abused. Medical personnel, social services, the police and the prosecutor's office should join forces and respond to this child's needs from a multidisciplinary perspective.

Case Resolution

The adult in the car should be arrested, charged and tried for child sexual abuse, child sexual exploitation or any other factually appropriate charge. The fact that he has never been caught harming children prior to this occasion will be taken into account at sentencing. It is not an excuse for failing to prosecute him now. The child should be taken for a medical examination and then placed with protective services. Prostituted children are victims, not criminals. The criminals are those who supply and those who demand the children. Criminal justice professionals and the medical community must take the lead in recognizing the prostitution of children as a form of child sexual abuse.

Selected Readings

Eva J. Klain, *Prostitution of Children and Child-Sex Tourism: An Analysis of Domestic and International Responses*, (National Center for Missing and Exploited Children, 1999).

Debra Whitcomb & Julie Eastin, *Joining Forces Against Child Sexual Exploitation: Models for a Multijurisdictional Team Approach* (OJJDP 1998).

Gwenn Lipka, Myth vs. Reality, RIISK (The Paul & Lisa Program, Inc. 1997).

Dr. Mark Belsey, World Health Organization, Commercial Sexual Exploitation of Children: The Health and Psychosocial Dimensions, World Congress Against Commercial Sexual Exploitation of Children (1996).

Dr. Julia O'Connell Davidson, Panel Report: The Sex Exploiter, World Congress Against Commercial Sexual Exploitation of Children (1996).

Byron Fassett & Bill Walsh, *Juvenile Prostitution: An Overlooked Form of Child Sexual Abuse*, 7 (1) The APSAC Advisor 9, 10 (APSAC 1994).

PART 6

Parental Substance Abuse and Its Relationship to Child Abuse

David D. Love, M.F.T.

Case Study

During a home visit a school nurse enters the home of an eight-year-old female student. The nurse observes that the home has a strong odor and appears not to have been cleaned for some time. The student and her younger siblings have lice and the mother has sores on her body and an agitated demeanor. The nurse calls local law enforcement and protective services. The mother is arrested for being under the influence of methamphetamine and the children are placed in the county children's shelter.

The mother is a single parent with a live-in boyfriend. They both have a history of substance abuse. The children are often absent from school. The eight-year-old has been diagnosed with Attention Deficit Hyperactive Disorder.

Questions

1. Does the case fit the legal definition of child abuse and/or neglect?

2. What course of action is available to assist the family?

3. Must the mother's substance abuse be addressed to protect the children?

4. Is permanent placement of the children in foster care a realistic option?

The relationship between parental substance abuse and child abuse has been well documented. The impairment of the parent is often significant enough to keep him or her from providing the basic functions of protection, shelter and nourishment. The experience of living in a home where the caretaker is handicapped by drug or alcohol abuse often leaves the child with severe damage.

In addition to the obvious elements of neglect, the child is at an elevated risk of both physical and sexual abuse. The first evidence of the dysfunctional household often appears in the school setting. Children become chronically truant, develop behavioral problems, exhibit learning handicaps or become involved in high-risk behaviors involving substance abuse and/or sexual activity.

Epidemiology

According to a study released in January of 1999 by the Center on Addiction and Substance Abuse at Columbia University, the number of abused and neglected children more than doubled between 1986 and 1997. This represents a growth from 1.4 million to more than 3 million.

The study reports that substance abuse causes or worsens seven out of ten cases of child abuse or neglect. It also states that children whose parents misuse alcohol or drugs are three times more likely to be abused.

The National Committee to Prevent Child Abuse further reports that every day at least three children die as a result of abuse and neglect. State child welfare records indicate that substance abuse is one of the top two problems exhibited by families in 81% of reported cases.

Joseph Colefano, a former secretary of Health, Education and Welfare who now heads the Center on Addiction and Substance Abuse at Columbia University, was quoted by *Reuters* in January of 1999 stating "a devastating tornado of substance abuse and addiction is tearing through the nation's child welfare and family court systems, leaving in it's path a wreckage of abused and neglected children."

Current Strategies

Two options are available for children living in homes where substance abuse is a major issue. The first is to remove the child from the home with a goal of permanent placement or adoption. This option faces both the issues of a shortage of foster placements and the fact that only one in four children available for adoption get adopted.

The second option is to develop a system of resources that could assist the family in effectively addressing the substance abuse and developing adequate skills to provide effective protection and care for the children in the family. This option requires a comprehensive system of resources, a coordinated effort by numerous social and welfare systems and a treatment strategy to address all the issues affecting both the adults and children in the family unit. Currently much of the needed effort to assist these families is either disjointed or completely absent.

Family Preservation: The Logical Goal

The U.S. Department of Health and Human Services prepared a series of goals for family preservation and support services in January of 1994. It would appear to be helpful to review these when developing a process to address the problems of substance abuse and child abuse.

The primary goals were to:

- Prevent the unnecessary separation of children from their families;

- Improve the quality of care and services to children and their families; and

- Ensure permanency for children by reunifying them with their parents or through adoption or another permanent living arrangement.

It was further suggested that the following steps would support these goals:

- Promote family strength and stability;

- Enhance parental functioning;

- Protect children and youth;

- Resolve crises and problems; and

- Prevent unnecessary out-of-home placement.

With this as the overall strategy it would then appear that a series of very specific steps could be outlined to assist substance-abusing caretakers who are placing children at risk. This then can be combined with a plan to both help the children and the family as a unit.

Assessment and Treatment

When a family presents with both substance abuse and child abuse issues it is unusual to find all the needed resources in a single agency. The first step must be to bring the needed resources to the table. Staff skilled in substance abuse assessment, assessment of potential underlying mental health issues along with staff prepared to provide long-term treatment, parenting education and family support must be a part of the team.

When parents have a substance abuse problem they normally are in denial about it's intensity and impact. There must be support from the court to require intensive substance abuse treatment as the first step in preparing the parent to learn to be an adequate caretaker. If the substance abuse treatment uncovers underlying mental health issues then those must be addressed as soon as progress in the substance abuse treatment permits.

Once the parent gets beyond the detoxification, withdrawal and stabilization phase of treatment then a plan to help them develop skills and resources to deal with parenting, housing and employment can be developed.

During the time the parent is in the first stages of treatment it is essential that the children be given an in-depth assessment to determine what impact their living environment has had on their lives and what services they will require. It is clear that they may have mental health issues, substance abuse problems and behavioral concerns that go beyond what any parent could address on their own let alone a parent facing their own recovery issues.

If the children can be made to feel safe, given a sense of mastery over their lives and the skills to cope with the world around them, they can be readied to work towards family reunification. Intensive individual and group therapy can provide this for children. Using resources from the Victims of Crime programs, community-based services and public agencies these children can be helped to gain an effective level of functioning.

The last stage of helping families with combined problems of substance abuse and child abuse is to develop a plan for long-term support. Substance abuse requires a lifetime of recovery. Using twelve-step programs, parent support networks and religious and community efforts, the parents and family can break the isolation that had previously supported their dysfunctional system.

The children will need support beyond the initial treatment services. Working with school staff is essential so that they have an advocate in the school setting to help them become involved in positive and supportive activities. This can often be linked with after-school opportunities such as Boys and Girls clubs, YMCA, YWCA, community recreation programs and religious community activities.

It is clear that if we view substance abuse and child abuse as elements of a family with inadequate resources, skills and support we can develop a course of action that helps them to become a caring and functioning system. This allows the parents to fulfill their roles as caretakers, allows the children to grow up in an environment that will assist them to become effective adults and it will reduce the cost to society in terms of dollars and social dysfunction.

Case Resolution

The opening case represents a situation that is all too common. By viewing this as a "protective" situation all the members of the family can receive the counseling, education, training and support necessary to help them become a safe and effective family unit. Without the assistance and support of the courts, protective services, substance abuse specialists, mental health therapists, child abuse counselors, parenting educators, employment counselors and community support systems it is very questionable that this family will be able to function. It is also very likely that one or more of the children will develop much more severe problems in the future.

Selected Readings

Eigen, L. (1991). Child Abuse Prevention with Substance Abusing Families. In DePanfilis, D. and Birch, T. (eds.), National Child Maltreatment Prevention Symposium. Washington, D.C.: National Center on Child Abuse and Neglect, U.S. Department of Health and Human Services.

Famularo, R.; Kinscherff, R.; and Fenton, T. (1992). Parental Substance Abuse and the Nature of Child Maltreatment. Child Abuse and Neglect, 16, 475-483.

Jones, L; Mitchel, L; and Ackatz, L. (1991). Substance Abuse and Child Abuse: Developing a Collaborative Action Plan. Proceedings of the Wingspread Conference, National Committee for Prevention of Child Abuse. Chicago, Illinois: National Committee for the Prevention of Child Abuse.

Murphy, J.; Jellinek, M.; Quinn, D.; Smith, G.; Poitrast, F.; and Goshko, M. (1991). Substance Abuse and Serious Child Maltreatment: Prevalence, Risk, and Outcome in a Sample. Child Abuse and Neglect, 15, 197-211.

Walker, C.; Zangrillo, P.; and Smith, J. (1991). Parental Substance Abuse and African American Children in Foster Care: Issues and Study Findings. Washington D.C.; National Black Child Development Institute.

Child Abuse and Teen Pregnancy: Relationship and Responses

David D. Love, M.FT.

Case Study

A fifteen-year-old young woman discloses in a school-based pregnancy prevention group that she is pregnant and the father is twenty-one years of age. She requests that the group counselor not discuss this with others outside the group. She is fearful of the reaction of her parents and explains she believes they will demand she leave the home as a bad influence on her siblings.

She has previously discussed in group her involvement with alcohol and marijuana. She appears depressed and has indicated that she has considered suicide in the past. She has been having academic problems and often is absent from school. She was referred to the group by a school counselor who was concerned about her poor social skills and behavioral problems.

Questions

1. Does this situation meet the requirements of a mandated child abuse report?

2. Do the presenting symptoms indicate the potential for child abuse issues preceding and/or underlying the sexual involvement with the 21-year-old?

3. Are pregnancy prevention programs offered in the public schools an appropriate and/or probable case-finding tool for potential child abuse?

4. Are there key elements that should be included in pregnancy prevention programs that would increase the probability of teen pregnancy reduction and simultaneously address potential co-existing child abuse issues?

Discussion

Child abuse therapists and child protective workers have witnessed the large number of young women survivors of child abuse who engage in high risk sexual behavior at a very young age. Early pregnancy, STD's, HIV and Hepatitis B/C present a real and present threat to these young women. Effective child abuse treatment programs can help young women address these threats by teaching risk reduction strategies. These include improving decision-making skills, problem-solving techniques, effective use of contraception, building improved support systems, and elevating self-esteem.

This learning process is enhanced by utilizing child abuse specialists with training on issues related to sexuality. In a child abuse treatment program, therapists have the opportunity to develop trust with their clients in areas often filled with anxiety and fear.

With the growing concern about teen pregnancy, school systems and other public and private entities have begun concentrated efforts to assist young people with early sexual activity and related issues. On the other hand, schools have faced obstacles that have not been a significant problem for the therapeutic community. Education codes and school district policies often limit the type of issues that can be addressed, the strategies that can be employed, the ability of students to participate without specific parental permission, and available time to address these issues at a level that could produce long-term change.

The question being, can the efforts of schools to address teen pregnancy and other related risks be combined and coordinated with the efforts of the child abuse prevention/intervention community? Are they working with the same young people? Can they support and reinforce each other's efforts by joint case finding, teaching concomitant skills, and reinforcing common goals.

Epidemiology

The Center for Disease Control and Prevention, in association with State Department of Education, conducts a Youth Risk Behavior Survey (YRBS). California data indicates that, in 1997, 5.4% of students indicated they had intercourse by age thirteen. Of the sexually active students, 43.5% indicated they had participated in intercourse and 11.9% had 4+ sexual partners.

Current research underway by the author and colleagues indicate that 37% of high-risk youth report intercourse by age thirteen. Preliminary findings indicate that over 80% of these students report they are sexually active and, of those who are active, over 40% report 4+ partners. High-risk students also report a high rate of other risk factors, e.g. alcohol use 88%, marijuana use 84% and methamphetamine use 44%.

Nearly one million teens give birth each year in the U.S., a rate five times higher than reported in any other developed country. California has the highest per capita rate of teen pregnancy in the U.S.

Studies show that adolescents who engage in high-risk sexual activity were more likely to have experienced either sexual or physical abuse. (Luster and Small, 1994) It has also been shown that early sexual behavior and conflicts with authority have been associated with sexual abuse in young teenage women. (Hibbard, Ingersoll & Orr, 1990)

Special Issues: Young Women, Older Men

Effective January 1, 1998 the child abuse reporting law [P.C.11166] was amended to include reporting unlawful intercourse for a minor under sixteen when the adult was twenty-one or over [P.C.261.5(d)]. This has had an impact on both child abuse treatment and pregnancy prevention programs. Staff in both types of programs now face the responsibility of understanding their obligation to report sexual activity if it fits the conditions described under the new mandate.

This has raised the concern about the loss of trust and rapport with young people served by these programs. Since the inception of mandated child abuse reporting laws, this issue has been a constant theme. It is important to understand that this type of "child abuse" is as serious as other issues covered by reporting laws.

When young women are involved with older men, research indicates that the younger the woman, the older the father is likely to be. When looking at twelve year old women who became pregnant, the father is likely to be twenty years of age or older. (Boyer & Fine, 1993) They also report that of the 535 pregnant teens interviewed, 62% reported prior history of sexual abuse.

A series of studies indicate that pregnant teens are more likely than their peers to have intercourse at a younger age, use drugs and alcohol together with sex, and be a survivor of physical abuse.

Effective Responses

Child abuse treatment programs have a positive impact on helping clients reduce their risk of early pregnancy by building self-esteem, and improving decision making and problem solving. It must be remembered, however, that treatment intervention programs can only reach a small number of the young people at risk. The best possibility of reaching a large number of young people is to address teen pregnancy in the schools. To be effective, prevention programs must have a strong research foundation to stimulate behavioral change leading to reduced risk.

In addition, there must be a widespread public and political consensus to address the underlying issues of poverty, social disorganization and family dysfunction. These elements are a major component of the lives of many young people participating in early sexual activity and other high-risk behaviors.

The benefit of school-based efforts is that large numbers of young people can be reached and young people can be identified before risk factors progress to the level of serious consequences. Secondary issues such as school attendance, substance use, and anger issues can help identify young people without disclosure about their sexual activity. In designing school-based programs to lower risk behaviors, these general guidelines are recommended:

- involve students in the planning process or focus groups to review the program design;

- plan and provide success for ideas and/or experiences that students value;

- be aware of student values versus adult values;

- develop student skills needed to conduct effective decision-making; and

- provide accurate and honest information on the real issues students face in daily life.

A number of studies have been conducted to examine effective programs. It has been shown that effective curricula show a number of common characteristics. (Frost & Forrest, 1995; Miller & Paikoff, 1992; Moore et al., 1995, Dusenburg & Falco, 1995; Kirby, D., 1997)

Characteristics of Effective Programs

- Focus clearly on reducing one or more of the sexual behaviors that lead to unwanted pregnancy.

- Develop behavioral goals, teaching methods and materials appropriate to the age, sexual experience and culture of the students.

- Use theoretical approaches found to be effective in influencing other health-related risky behaviors.

- Ensure sufficient duration of the program to complete important activities adequately.

- Employ a variety of teaching methods to engage the participants and to facilitate communication.

- Provide basic, accurate information about the risks of unprotected intercourse and methods of avoiding unprotected intercourse.

- Discuss social and peer pressure to engage in sexual activity and how to address it.

- Model and practice communication, negotiation and refusal skills.

- Select teachers, counselors, or peers who believed in the program and provide training for these individuals.

School-based efforts to reduce teen pregnancy are an important element in the total effort.

Research exists to provide guidance on how to develop programs with effective designs. The evidence is strong that many young people who are at high risk of early pregnancy are equally at risk for other problems such as substance abuse, HIV and STD's.

There are many life issues that increase a young person's vulnerability. Not the least of these is a previous history of child abuse. Knowledge about these relationships helps treatment programs, prevention programs, community-based agencies, schools and public agencies develop a comprehensive and coordinated response.

Recommendations

1. All child abuse treatment programs working with young people over the age of ten should have a strong component that addresses the potential of early pregnancy. This should include skill-based activities for young clients, specific staff training in the areas related to risk reduction activities, and coordination with other pregnancy reduction efforts in the local area.

2. All staff working in child abuse and pregnancy prevention program should be provided in-depth training on [P.C.11166] and the amendments which became effective January 1, 1998 related to unlawful intercourse.

3. Collaborate with schools to help them understand the breadth of issues that lead a young person to be at an elevated risk for early pregnancy. Help them

understand that by identifying survivors of child abuse, developing an effective reporting process, and making referrals for therapy directly impacts other issues such as pregnancy prevention and subsequent school drop out. Support for effective pregnancy prevention programs helps young people move beyond the trauma of child abuse and related issues.

4. Utilize the available research on effective pregnancy prevention programs to develop a strategic focus on activities that can effectively help students resist and/or reduce high-risk behaviors.

5. Child abuse treatment programs and pregnancy prevention programs should look at the research on contraception education and condom availability, and make a concerted effort to incorporate both into their programs.

Research by Mauldon and Luker (1996) indicates that adolescents who have received contraceptive education are 33% more likely to use some form of contraception than teens who have not received the education. Studies conducted in New York City and Philadelphia show that making condoms available in school does not lead to increases in sexual behavior but does increase condom use among sexually active students. (Guttmacher, Lieberman and Ward, et al., 1997)

Case Resolution

The case clearly requires a CPS report under [P.C. 11166]. The suicidal ideation, the substance use, the school attendance and behavioral problems all indicate a high-risk student. Assessment for potential PTSD (post traumatic stress disorder) issues is warranted and special consideration for child abuse issues is very appropriate. The investigation by Child Protective Services may provide sufficient evidence for referral to a child abuse treatment program. Whether the referral is made or the parent follows the treatment recommendations, the student can be assisted in a pregnancy prevention group. The key to the effectiveness of the assistance provided is dependent upon whether the therapeutic intervention design is based upon available research and has components consistent with the research.

References

Boyer, D., and Fine, D. (1992). Sexual Abuse as a Factor in Adolescent Pregnancy and Child Maltreatment. Family Planning Perspectives, 24, 4-11.

Dusenbury, L. and Falco, M. (1995). Eleven Components of Effective Drug Abuse Prevention Curricula. Journal of School Health 65 (10), 420-425.

Frost, J.J. and Forrest, J.D. (1995). Understanding the Impact of Effective Teenage Pregnancy Prevention Programs. Family Planning Perspectives, 27(5), 188-195.

Hibbard, R., Ingersoll, G., and Orr, D. (1990). Behavioral Risk, Emotional Risk, and Child Abuse Among Adolescents in a Nonclinical Setting. Pediatrics, 86, 896-901.

Kirby, D. (1997). No Easy Answers: Research Findings on Programs to Reduce Teen Pregnancy. Washington, D.C.: The National Campaign to Prevent Teen Pregnancy.

Luster, T. and Small, S.A. Factors Associated with Sexual Risk-Taking Behaviors Among Adolescents. Journal of Marriage and Family 1994; 56: 622-632.

Mauldon, J. and Luker, K. The Effects of Contraceptive Education on Method Use at First Intercourse. Family Planning Perspective 1996; 28: 19-24+.

Miller, B.C. and Paikoff, R.L. (1992). Comparing Adolescent Pregnancy Prevention Programs: Methods and Results. In B.C. Miller, J.J. Card, R.L. Paikoff, & J.L. Peterson (Eds.), Preventing Adolescent Pregnancy (p. 265-284). Newbury Park, CA: Sage Publications.

Moore, K.A., Sugland, B.W., Blumenthal, C., Glei, D., and Snyder, N. (1995). Adolescent Pregnancy Prevention Programs: Interventions and Evaluations. Washington, DC: Child Trends.

Is There a Link Between Child Maltreatment and Woman Battering?

Connie Mitchell, M.D.

Case Vignette

Bobby is an 8 year old boy with a fractured dislocated elbow from falling off his bike. After being asked what led to the fall, he said he had been standing astride his bike at the bottom of the porch stairs preparing to flee because his mom and dad were fighting. His mother wanted to leave the house and, as his parents were struggling over the keys on the front porch, his father pushed his mother and she fell down the steps onto Bobby causing him to fall and injure his elbow. Subsequent interviews revealed a long history of intermittent physical violence between the parents but no prior history or suspicion of child physical or sexual abuse.

Questions

1. Are children at risk for physical abuse in homes where domestic violence occurs?

2. What is the psychological impact of witnessing family violence?

3. Does California have mandatory screening and reporting laws for domestic violence?

4. What community collaborations are important to address this problem?

Epidemiology/Statistics

There are two types of data documenting the adverse effects of domestic violence upon children. The first group consists of children who witness family violence and who are also physically abused, neglected or endangered. The second group includes children who witness domestic violence, but are not physically abused.

Exposure to adult partner violence runs a gamut of scenarios. Ganley and Schecter (1996) have described the following: children being hit or threatened in their mother's arms, children taken hostage or threatened in order to coerce the mother's behavior, children forced to watch physical assault, a child used as a physical weapon, and a child used as a spy or interrogated regarding the mother's activities and whereabouts. Children are often involved in the aftermath of a violent episode trying to help or having to attend to injuries or contacting law enforcement.

Hangen (1984) studied all child protection cases in Massachusetts over a seven month period and found that 32% of the records documented adult domestic violence. The Walker (1984) study of 403 battered women in Colorado found that 53% of the women reported that their abuser also abused their children and that 28% of the women also disclosed that they abused their children. Stark and Flitcraft (1988) examined the mothers' medical records of 116 children referred to a hospital for suspected abuse, and found that 45% of the mothers' records showed evidence of a battering history. Suh and Abel (1990) questioned 258 women who had sought refuge in a battered women's shelter and found that 40% of the women reported that their spouse also physically abused their children. A national random survey of 6,000 American adults by Straus and Gelles (1990) through telephone interviews found that 50% of fathers who frequently beat their wives also frequently abused their children. The data appears to establish a clear link between woman battering and child abuse in many cases. Various studies using different samples and types of data show that 30-60% of battered mothers' children are maltreated. (National Research Council, 1993)

Children may not be directly abused but can be endangered or injured in the course of a violent episode in the home. Christian (1997) reviewed emergency department records of children identified as having been hurt during family violence. He reviewed the charts of 139 children, mean age 5 years, and found 29% were injured while held in the mother's arms and 24% of children were injured while intervening. The majority of those injured while intervening were adolescents.

Psychological Impact of Witnessing Family Violence

In 1999, Edleson reviewed 84 studies that specifically addressed children in homes with partner physical violence and, of these, 31 examined children who were witnesses to violence and had not been physically abused themselves. Studies using the Child Behavior Checklist (CBCL) and similar measures have found child witnesses of domestic violence to exhibit more aggressive and antisocial (often called "externalized" behaviors) as well as fearful and inhibited behaviors ("internalized" behaviors), and to show lower social competence than other children. Children who witnessed violence were also found to show more anxiety, self-esteem, depression, anger, and temperament problems than children who did not witness violence at home. Kilpatrick (1997) found that exposure to partner violence without direct victimization can lead to moderate to severe symptoms of posttraumatic stress disorder in 85% of children. Children from homes where their mothers were being abused show less skill in understanding how others feel and in examining situations from another's perspective compared to children from non-violent households.

Silvern et al.'s (1995) study also found long term developmental problems in children witnessing violence, depression, and low self-esteem. Other researchers have found higher levels of sensitivity/reactivity, anxiety, and lower social adjustment in adults who witnessed violence in their childhood. There is some support for the link between exposure to violence and subsequent violent behavior in the child. Singer, Miller, Guo, et al (1998) studied 2,245 children and found exposure to violence in the home to be a significant predictor of a child's violent behavior.

Impact of Abuse and Witnessing Familiy Violence

Child abuse victims who witness family violence experience a "double whammy" (Hughes, Parkinson, and Vargo (1989). They found that children who were both abused and witnessed family violence exhibited significantly more problem behaviors in a controlled study of abused children compared to children who witnessed violence only, and to children without abuse or family violence in their household. This same pattern has appeared in other studies. A summary chart of findings by age is provided below.

Pre-Natal	premature onset of labor
	increased rate of miscarriages
	increased alcohol, drug abuse and tobacco use in pregnancy
	increased rate of low birth weight infants (even when controlled for above)
Infants	increased crying and irritability
	sleep disturbances
	digestive problems
Toddlers/Preschool	more aggressive than other children
	more withdrawn than other children
	impaired cognitive abilities
	delays in verbal development
	poor motor abilities
	general fearfulness, anxiety
	stomachaches
	nightmares
	lack of bowel and bladder control over 3 years of age
	lack of confidence to begin new tasks

School Age	poor grades, or in special classes
	failure of one or more grades
	poor social skills
	low self-esteem
	general aggressiveness
	violent outbursts of anger
	bullying
	withdrawn, dependent
	bedwetting
	nightmares
	digestive problems, ulcers
	headaches (not related to eye strain or sinus)
Teenagers	poor grades, failure in school, quits school
	low self-esteem
	refuses to bring friends home or has few friends
	feels responsible to take care of the home and mother
	increased runaways
	violent outbursts of anger, destroying property
	poor judgment, irresponsible decision making
	withdrawn, unable to communicate feelings
	nightmares
	ulcers, digestive problems
	bedwetting
	headaches
	increased aggression with friends and dating partners
	increased health risk behaviors
	may join in on battery against mother

Some studies indicate that boys show more externalized behavior problems (hostility, aggression) and girls show more internalized problems (depression, somatization). Few studies have found any differences based on race and ethnicity. Modulating factors include the length of time that has passed since the violent event, and, the child's coping mechanisms, whether they express or utilize emotion-focused or problem-focused coping strategies.

Implications for Screening, Assessment, Reporting and Training

- All children should be screened for their experiences with abuse and violence including witnessing violence. The American Academy of Pediatrics Committee on Child Abuse and Neglect recognizes that intervention on behalf of battered women is an active form of child abuse prevention.

- Abused and neglected children should be screened for the possibility that their mother is being physically assaulted in the home.

- Battered women should be screened for the possibility that the children are being abused or neglected.

- Pregnant adolescents and women should be screened for the possibility of being in a battering relationship.

- Healthcare providers should consider whether medical problems may have a stress-related origin due to family violence.

- In the State of California, domestic violence screening by hospitals and clinics is required by state law.

- Many states, including California, have mandatory reporting laws requiring health care providers to report domestic violence, if the patient presents with injuries possibly caused by spousal or partner assault, to the local law enforcement agency. Health care providers must also report abused, neglected or endangered children to Children's Protective Services (CPS) and the local law enforcement agency.

General Screening Policy for Healthcare Providers

The Family Violence Prevention Fund, in partnership with the American Academy of Pediatrics, the American Academy of Family Physicians, the American College of Obstetricians and Gynecologists and the National Association of Pediatric Nurse Practitioners have produced "Identifying and Responding to Domestic Violence: Consensus Recommendations for Child and Adolescent Health". The following statements are based upon these recommendations.

Who should be screened routinely for domestic violence?

- Female caregivers/parents who accompany their children during new patient visits or well child visits or whenever a new intimate relationship is disclosed.

- All adolescents at new visits or health maintenance visits or whenever a new intimate relationship is disclosed.

- Pregnant teens at first pre-natal visit and at least once per trimester and in the postpartum visit.

Universal training should be provided to healthcare providers in patient care roles taking health histories.

- Dynamics of domestic violence and the need for safety plans.

- How to ask about family violence and how to respond when the patient answers affirmatively.

- How to access and refer to local shelters, counseling services, and advocacy programs.

- Issues pertaining to cultural competency.

How should screening occur?

- As part of a face-to-face health care encounter and part of the written health questionnaire.

- Using an empathetic, direct and nonjudgmental demeanor.

- Ensure patient privacy for responding to questions. No friends or relatives of the patients should be present during the screening.

- Preferably, no children over age three should be present during the screening. Although some believe that because older children are aware of the abuse, a frank discussion with the parent and older child can be helpful.

- Protect confidentiality. Patients should be assured of the confidential nature of the conversation but informed regarding the limits of that confidentiality due to mandatory reporting laws and the limits of confidentiality for medical records.

- Use professional interpreters when needed, rather than a patient's friend or family member.

How should a screening policy be implemented?

All health care providers who screen for domestic violence should receive appropriate training on how to ask about abuse, how to respond when it is identified, development of individual and organizational cultural competency, principles of increasing safety, and helpful and effective intervention methods with battered patients. Screening can be facilitated by the use of forms or other assessment tools such as the five-question Abuse Assessment Screen. Chart prompts are another effective tool to remind providers to screen and have been shown to increase screening rates.

When does child exposure to intimate partner violence become child maltreatment?

There is considerable evidence regarding the overlap of domestic violence and child abuse, the adverse psychological impact for children witnessing intimate partner violence and experiencing physical abuse in the context of this relationship. Some believe that a policy which automatically defines child exposure to partner violence as maltreatment or neglect, assumes all children are adversely affected by exposure to violence and assumes that the victimized adult is not making efforts to keep their children safe. Some states give discretion to healthcare providers so that the impact on the child, the current risk to the child, and the ability to access services can be evaluated. Other states do not allow discretion and mandate reporting in all cases of intimate partner violence. These states take the position that the aforementioned evaluation can only be performed by a social worker trained in the evaluation of children and families. In either case, assessment of the health and safety needs of both adult and child victims must be addressed and dual integrated interventions provided.

In California, health care providers are mandated to report child abuse and any patients with injuries related to domestic violence based on their knowledge or reasonable suspicion. Both oral and verbal reports to law enforcement and Children's Protective Services (CPS) are required.

Protocols and Collaboration

Collaboration between battered women shelters, Children's Protective Services, healthcare providers, and schools is needed and should include:

- Screening protocols and referrals;

- Strong risk and lethality assessment procedures;

- Collaboration and joint planning between domestic violence shelters, domestic violence counseling programs and CPS to resolve conflicts in mission, purpose, and case planning;

- Training for healthcare providers on the mandatory screening and reporting laws;

- Training for CPS social workers on the dynamics of domestic violence and needed services;

- Supportive intervention services for women and children; and,

- Effective intervention and support services for batterers in families that stay together.

RELEVANT CALIFORNIA PENAL CODE REPORTING LAW SECTIONS

Domestic Violence Screening Law	Penal Code 1259.5
Domestic Violence Mandated Reporting Law	Penal Code 11160 and 11161.9
Child Abuse and Neglect Reporting Law	Penal Code 11160
Crime Related Injury Reporting Law for Healthcare Providers	Penal Code 11161.2

Resources

California Medical Training Center at UC Davis
Domestic Violence Education Division
(916) 734-4143
web.ucdmc.ucdavis.edu/medtrng

California Alliance Against Domestic Violence
926 J Street, Suite 1000
Sacramento, California 95814
(916) 444-7163
http://www.caadv.org

Statewide California Coalition for Battered Women
P.O. Box 19005
Long Beach, California 90807-9005
http://www.sccbw.org

Family Violence Prevention Fund
San Francisco, California
(415) 252-8900
http://www.fvpf.org

References

Committee on Child Abuse and Neglect, American Academy of Pediatrics. "The Role of the Pediatrician in Recognizing and Intervening on Behalf of Abused Women". *Pediatrics*, Vol. 101 No. 6, June 1998, 1091-1092

Christian, C.W., Scribano, P., Seidl, T., Pinto-Martin, J.A. Pediatric injury resulting from family violence. *Pediatrics*. 99(2): E8, February 1997.

Edleson, J.L. Children's Witnessing of Adult Domestic Violence. *Journal of Interpersonal Violence*, Vol. 14 No. 8, 839-870, August 1999.

Ganley, A. and Schecter, S. Domestic Violence: A National Curriculum for Child Protective Services. San Francisco: Family Violence Prevention Fund, 1996.

Groves BM, Augustyn M, Lee D, Sawires P. "Identifying and Responding to Domestic Violence: Consensus Recommendations for Child and Adolescent Health". Family Violence Prevention Fund, September 2002.

Hangen, E. Department of Social Services Interagency Domestic Violence Team Pilot Project: Program Data Evaluation. Boston, Massachusetts Department of Social Services, 1994.

Hughes, H.M., Parkinson, D., and Vargo, M. Witnessing spouse abuse and experiencing physical abuse: A "double Whammy"? Journal of Family Violence, 4, 197-209, 1989.

Kilpatrick, KI, Litt M, and Williams L. "Post-traumatic stress disorder in child witnesses to domestic violence." American Journal of Orthopsychiatry, 67 (4), 639-644, 1997.

National Research Council. *Understanding Child Abuse and Neglect.* Washington DC: National Academy Press, 1993.

Silvern, L., Karyl, J., Waelde, L., et al. Retrospective reports of parental partner abuse: Relationships to depression, trauma symptoms and self-esteem among college students. Journal of Family Violence, 10, 177-202, 1995.

Singer, M.I., Miller, D.B., Guo, S., et al. The mental health consequences of children's exposure to violence. Cleveland, OH: Cayahoga County Community Mental Health Research Institute, Mandel School of Applied Social Sciences, Case Western Reserve University, 1998.

Stark, E. and Flitcraft, A.H. Women and Children at Risk: A Feminist Perspective on Child Abuse. International Journal of Health Services, 18(1), 97-118, 1988.

Strauss, M. Measuring intrafamily conflict and violence: The Conflict Tactics Scales. In M Strauss & R. Gelles (Eds) Physical Violence in American Families: risk factors and adaptions to violence in 8,145 families. New Brunswick, NF: Transaction Publishers, 29-41, 1990.

Suh, E.K., and Abel, E.M. The impact of spousal violence on the children of the abused. Journal of Independent Social Work, 4(4), 27-34, 1990.

Walker, L.E. *The battered woman syndrome.* New York; Springer Publishing, 1984.

Elder Abuse

Sara Stratton, M.S.W. and Mindy Yamasaki, M.S.W., M.B.A.

Case History

On Wednesday, a 78-year old woman was brought into the clinic by a neighbor after she was seen wandering up and down the street for a couple of hours. The neighbor states that the woman is a widow who lives alone with her three cats. The woman's daughter, who lives in the same city, visits her mother on weekends.

The woman's clothes are filthy and she is unkempt. Her hair is uncombed, her arms and legs are dirty, and her clothing is soiled. There is some blood on her right leg, below the knee. There is some bruising on the woman's arms. The woman is asking to return home, but is unsure of where she lives. She states her daughter will be angry if she is not home when she stops by. The woman is hungry and states she has not eaten or drank anything since lunchtime yesterday.

Questions

1. Is this elderly woman able to take care of herself with the assistance provided by her daughter?

2. What kind of care is being provided by the daughter to maintain her mother in an independent living situation?

3. Is there cause for concern that the woman may have been physically abused? Is clinic staff required to report their observations to local authorities?

4. What resources are in the community to assist this woman to remain in her home for as long as it is safe for her to do so?

Statistics

Approximately 44 million persons age 60 and older reside in the United States. The elderly are the most rapidly growing segment in the population. Those persons aged 85 or older are the fastest growing of the elderly population.

The majority of the elderly reside in community settings; thirty percent of these persons reside alone. With increasing age, vulnerability to abuse and neglect rises due to the onset of debilitating physical and/or mental impairments. A recent national incidence study of elder abuse in community settings found an estimated 451,000 elders who suffered elder abuse in 1996. The figure rises to 551,000 when self-neglecting elders are included. The study estimated that only 21% of cases of elder abuse are reported, leaving 79% unreported and untreated. The House Select Committee on Aging recently predicted that one out of every 20 elderly people will be a victim of neglect, physical, psychological, or financial abuse this year. In California, statistics for 1996 show that 225,000 incidences of elder abuse occurred. This is an increase of 1000% over the number incidences in 1986-87.

Elder abuse occurs in all socioeconomic, racial, and religious groups with victims varying in functional abilities and levels of dependency. The abuse is often concealed by the families and by the elderly person. The elderly are frequently fearful of admitting abuse, partially out of shame and embarrassment, and also due to fear of losing the small amount of independence they have. They may fear retaliation of family members or others on whom they have been dependent for care. Many elderly fear the consequences for an adult child or spouse if their reporting of abuse leads to involvement of their family in the criminal justice system. The signs of abuse can be subtle and go undetected by neighbors or infrequent visitors to the elderly person. A self-neglecting, isolated, elderly person may have no visitors, not recognize his or her own need for assistance, nor know how to access community services.

Historical Information

Although elder abuse is not a recent phenomena, it was not until 1975, that "granny battering" was discussed in medical literature. During the 1970's the U.S. Senate Committee on

Aging reported on the prevalence of elder abuse. In 1990, the Elder Abuse Task Force was created by the U.S. Department of Health and Human Services. These early efforts led to the establishment of an Adult Protective Services agency in every state.

Mandatory Reporting

Today, nearly every state has mandatory reporting laws. In California, as of January 1, 1999, the law requires that mandated reporters report suspected elder abuse including physical abuse, isolation, abandonment, financial abuse, neglect by others and self neglect. Psychological abuse remains optional reporting by mandated reporters. The penalty for not reporting is a sentence of up to six months in jail, or a fine of up to $1,000 or both. When the abuse results in death or great bodily harm to the elder, the penalty has been increased to a sentence of up to one year in jail or a fine of $5,000 or both.

Types of Abuse

The California Welfare and Institutions Code provides definitions for the types of elder and dependent adult abuse. These definitions are summarized as follows:

Physical Abuse

- Assault, battery, or force likely to produce injury
- Sexual assault
- Punitive or inappropriate physical or chemical restraint
- Intentional deprivation of food or water

Neglect of Another

- Failure of a person having care or custody of an elder to exercise a reasonable degree of care, e.g., not assisting the person in personal hygiene, not providing medical care, not preventing malnutrition.

Self-Neglect

- Failure of the elder to provide himself-herself with food, water, clothing, shelter, safety, and personal hygiene.

Abandonment

- Desertion of an elderly person by an individual who has assumed responsibility for providing care for an elder, or by a person with physical custody of an elder.

Isolation

- Intentionally isolating a person from social contacts such as telephone calls, visits, and receiving mail.

Financial Abuse

- The illegal or improper use of an elder's funds, property, or assets.

Psychological Abuse

- Infliction of anguish, pain, or distress through verbal or non-verbal acts.
- Includes verbal assaults, insults, threats, intimidation, humiliation, and harassment.

Reporting laws are considered to be less effective in the identification and treatment of elder abuse than professional awareness. Previously, elder abuse has been considered to be in the realm of social scientists. Healthcare professionals have been reluctant to intervene, in part, from the uncertainties of what will follow from reporting. Studies have shown that physicians have only reported 2% of the cases. Healthcare professionals can help in the prevention of elder abuse through an understanding of their ethical and legal obligations to report abuse. Reporting of suspected elder abuse cases is critical for the prevention of abuse which can have serious medical consequences as well as causing emotional harm to the victim.

Causes of Abuse

The causes of elder mistreatment are due to a number of factors. For many years, the stress of caring for a significantly physically and/or mentally impaired elder was thought to be a primary factor in the occurrence of abuse. Recent studies are suggesting that abuse is more keenly tied to the quality of the relationship between the caregiver and the elder. Abuse is more likely to occur in situations where the caregiver and the elder have a preexisting, problematic relationship. The caregiver may perceive the elder to be unappreciative and demanding. The caregiver may have feelings of guilt or powerlessness in coping with the care demands. Often the abuser is financially and/or emotionally dependent on the elder. Mental illness, addiction to alcohol or drugs, or characterological traits of the caregiver can also be factors leading to abuse. The aggressiveness of the elder toward the caregiver may trigger elder mistreatment. The cause of the abuse may be part of a cycle of long standing patterns of family violence. Some abusers were abused as children and/or witnessed abuse in the family. Studies have shown that the most frequent abusers are the adult children of the elderly person or the person's elderly spouse.

Identification of Abuse by the Healthcare Provider

Recognition is the first step toward the treatment and prevention of further abuse. Health professionals are in a unique position to recognize elder abuse and, in some cases, are the only service providers other than the person's caregiver who have contact with an elderly person. Patients may disclose or allow the healthcare practitioner to examine them as part of what is expected from a medical process.

Common indicators of abuse found from the physical examination include the following: the presence of bruises in various stages of healing; lacerations or abrasions to the mouth, lips or gums; burns in unusual locations or shapes, or marks on wrists and ankles. Other indicators are findings from the physical examination that are inconsistent with the explanation given by the patient or the caregiver. The demeanor of the elderly patient is also a key factor in detecting abuse. Abuse should be suspected if the patient appears fearful and apprehensive when the spouse, family member, or caregiver is present. The patient may exhibit a fear of touch, be withdrawn or have dramatic mood changes, or have little or no eye contact. The delay in seeking needed medical care can also be a sign of possible abuse. Such behaviors and injuries should arouse the suspicion of abuse for the health care practitioner.

Interviewing the patient regarding suspicions of abuse requires sensitivity to the elderly person's feelings and abilities. Care is required to arrange an environment that is conducive to disclosure of private, sensitive information. The patient should be privately interviewed in a safe environment apart from the possible abusers. The most effective approach is for the practitioner to ask the elderly patient simple, direct questions that the practitioner may have about the patient's injuries or condition. The patient should be allowed to express his or her feelings in a non-judgmental environment. The healthcare practitioner is encouraged to provide information to the patient regarding services in the community for the abused person. The development of protocols with other community service providers for care of abused elderly is desirable prior to encountering the abused patient.

Documentation of the physical findings from the examination and any statement that the patient or others who have brought the patient to the medical setting are crucial to prevention of elder abuse. The use of a body diagram for the physical findings in addition to a factual, narrative description can be helpful. The practitioner should also consider taking photographs of the injuries. Any statements or direct quotes from the patient or others should be identified with quotation marks.

Healthcare professionals frequently express concern regarding their therapeutic relationship with the patient once they make a report of suspected abuse of this patient. Although the name of the reporter of abuse is confidential information, the healthcare professional may want to discuss his or her suspicions of abuse with the elderly person. The elder should be advised that as a mandated reporter, the healthcare professional is required under the law to report the suspected abuse. Patient confidentiality does not apply in these circumstances. Mandated reporters have immunity from liability for reporting in good faith. The decision by the healthcare professional to notify the patient of his or her report of suspected abuse will likely depend on the situation at hand. Of primary concern is the elderly person's immediate health and safety.

Role of Adult Protectives Services

Upon identification of suspected elder abuse, healthcare practitioners must report their concern to Adult Protective Services (APS) or law enforcement. These agencies will cross report to one another. The verbal report is to be made immediately or as soon as possible by telephone. A written report must follow and be sent to Adult Protective Services or law enforcement within two working days of the suspicion of abuse. California uses the SOC341 form, "Report of Suspected Dependent Adult/Elder Abuse." These forms can be obtained from a local Adult Protective Services Agency.

When making the verbal report to APS, a social worker will ask questions about the suspected abuse and any knowledge the reporter may have about the patient's situation. Questions may be asked about the patient's physical and mental condition, family and support network, financial facts, and home environment. These questions are necessary in order for the APS social worker to determine how soon an APS response is required. The APS social worker will run a history check to determine if that agency has had any previous involvement with the patient. Collateral contacts may be warranted to obtain further facts about the person's situation. A response time will be designated. The response can be immediate if the situation appears to be life threatening or up to ten days if the patient appears to be at risk, but not in danger of immediate risk to life or limb. The referral will be cross-reported to law enforcement.

When APS investigates, it will refer any criminal elements to law enforcement. APS will stay involved to stabilize a situation, as long as the victim is willing to accept services. Adults have the right to self-determination. Unless the abused elder is mentally incompetent, he or she has the right to refuse any intervention in the abusive situation. APS services beyond the investigation may include: crisis intervention, assessment, and linkage with other services. APS should report back to the mandated reporter with a brief update of the situation.

As a rule of thumb, healthcare practitioners should err on the side of reporting suspected abuse, rather than waiting for something more concrete. The APS worker and healthcare practitioner must develop a multidisciplinary approach to bringing abused elders and dependent adults to the forefront of a community's interests. It is only then, that society can be assured that abuse of vulnerable elderly and dependent adult population will be reduced.

Case Resolution

The opening vignette describes a case of suspected elder physical abuse and self-neglect. The woman's physical condition and mental state alerted clinic staff to make their mandatory report to the local Adult Protective Services agency. APS conducted an investigation and determined that the daughter, who is married and has three small children, is overwhelmed with her mother's situation. According to the mother and daughter in two separate, individual interviews, the daughter has never physically hit her mother. Last weekend, however, the daughter grabbed her mother's arm to keep her from falling down the stairs. The clinic completed a medical work up and determined that the mother was taking a combination of prescribed medication that was causing her confusion. A change in medication has improved the mother's mental functioning. APS arranged for in-home care to relieve the daughter from being the only caretaker. In addition, the daughter is now attending counseling to deal with her frustrations about the changes she is experiencing as her mother ages.

Selected Readings

Quinn, M.J., and Tomita, S.K. *Elder Abuse and Neglect: Causes, Diagnosis, and Intervention Strategies, 2nd Edition.* Springer Publishing Company, Inc., 1997.

American Medical Association Diagnostic and Treatment Guidelines on Elder Abuse and Neglect (1992)

National Center on Elder Abuse. *The National Elder Abuse Incidence Study: Final Report.* September, 1998.

Baumhover, L.A., and Beall, S.C. *Abuse, Neglect, and Exploitation of Older Persons: Strategies for Assessment and Intervention.* Health Professions, 1996.

Ramsey-Klawsnik, H. Investigating Suspected Elder Maltreatment. *Journal of Elder Abuse and Neglect,* 7(1), 1995.

Dependent Adult Abuse

Nora J. Baladerian, Ph.D.

Case Vignette

Diane, a 30 year old developmentally disabled woman, resides at home with her parents. She was sexually assaulted on her way home from participating in a day treatment program. Diane was brought to the local hospital which has specialized forensic medical examination teams for both sexual assault and child sexual abuse victims. The law enforcement officer alerted the Emergency Department triage nurse about the circumstances in advance of their arrival at the hospital. Arrangements were quickly made to utilize a dual team approach with a nurse practitioner from the child sexual abuse team and a nurse practitioner from the adult sexual assault team working together to utilize examination techniques and procedures for the benefit of a non sexually active developmentally disabled victim of sexual assault.

Questions

1. What is meant by the term dependent adult?

2. What training is needed to effectively respond to victims with disabilities?

3. Describe best practices for interviewing and case management.

Statistics

Statistics on crime victims with disabilities are not collected systematically by federal, state or local agencies. This critical oversight makes it impossible to know the nature and extent of victimization of persons with disabilities. It is agreed that under reporting of dependent adult abuse is significant due to several factors:

- victims may be reluctant to tell anyone due to fear of reprisal or abandonment by the care provider who is the abuser;

- the dependent adults' lack of awareness of what constitutes abuse, and/or lack of knowledge about laws and their personal rights;

- possible fear of talking to authorities coupled with shame and embarrassment;

- fear of losing any independence they may have achieved;

- mandated reporters not filing reports;

- professionals, caretakers, and family members who minimize or ignore complaints of abuse; and

- law enforcement and social work investigators and prosecutors either underestimating the abilities of dependent adults, or unwilling to take the time involved in working with them.

Adults with serious disabilities comprise 12% of the population in the U.S., yet most would not qualify as "dependent adults". Dependent adults are those individuals who require the assistance of another person for activities of daily living (ADL) such as transferring (moving from bed to wheelchair, for example), mobility, eating, dressing, toileting, communication, and breathing among others. These adults include individuals with developmental disabilities, mental illnesses including dementia, both mental retardation and mental illness, or severe physical impairments requiring the presence of a personal care assistant. There may also be concurrent medical conditions such as cerebral palsy or diabetes, which should be made known to the investigator and interviewer.

Working with persons with disabilities creates a need for specialized training for professionals in:

- communication methods and techniques;

- sensitivity to the possible need for physical accommodations and supportive victim assistance arrangements;

- possible emotional reactions and behavioral responses to the victimization and case investigation procedures;

- screening for abuse, safety planning, and forms of abuse unique to the disabled population;

- specialized interview skills; and

- strong case management with follow through.

Effectively intervening in cases of dependent adult abuse requires training in the following areas:

- physical disabilities;

- mental retardation;

- developmental delay;

- mental illness;

- dual diagnosis (mental illness/mental retardation);

- Post-Traumatic Stress Disorder (PTSD) and its impact upon the population;

- cultural issues; and

- legal issues (Adults with Disabilities Act (ADA) compliance issues, conservatorship, interpreters, etc.).

It is important to recognize that most dependent adults' exposure to information about child abuse, interpersonal violence, social systems (e.g. child and adult protective systems, law enforcement agencies) may be absent or minimal. Even if explained, the role of the interviewer may be poorly understood. Dependent adults may have the following life-long perspectives:

- an experience of always having someone "in charge" of them resulting in an absence of the experience of autonomy in choice, privacy, and understanding of civil rights;

- an absence or reduction of body integrity due to having others bathe, clothe, and move their body for legitimate issues of therapy and assistance which, nonetheless, reduces the person's sense of "my body belongs to me";

- the use of unfamiliar vocabulary may be similar to the experience of learning a foreign language such as attorney, public defender, prosecutor, advocate, abuse, maltreatment, rape, assault, as well as more commonly used words such as decide, choose, request. Other words such as assailant, perpetrator, accuser, defendant, plaintiff may be unknowns. It is essential to use terms likely to be understood, or explained, then checked for understanding by asking the individual to explain what s/he understands of what's been said;

- an experience of disrespect, of being ignored or avoided, and stereotyped attitudes and beliefs about individuals with disabilities; and

- fear of being blamed for what happened and/or what happens to the alleged perpetrator.

Best Practices for Interviewing

1. Explain the reason for the interview and intervention.

2. Do not abruptly remove the victim from the home or workplace without explanation or reassurance, and a description of where you are going.

3. Victims or crime survivors should be transported to subsequent interviews by someone familiar.

4. Interviewers must have a comfort level and competence in working with individuals with a variety of disability factors including appearance, behavior and communication differences.

5. All services and facilities must be in compliance with all facets of ADA.

6. Interviews should be done within a MDIT (Multi Disciplinary Interview Team) including the representatives from Adult Protective Services, the District Attorney's Office and law enforcement agency.

7. Interview area should be roomy, uncluttered, and allow for the MDIT to have a full view of the interviewer and victim.

8. If an interpreter is required, this person should NEVER be a family member. A certified or qualified interpreter who does not know the victim is recommended. Otherwise, it could be a teacher, workplace counselor or job coach, unless these are suspected abusers.

9. If the victim requests to have someone present, this request should be carefully considered because that person may be the perpetrator or perceived agent of the perpetrator, in which case, the client may have been threatened and forced to request that person's presence

10. If the victim uses Facilitated Communication (FC), the "Baladerian Protocol for Interviews Using Facilitated Communication" should be implemented, to assure that the interview has the best chance of

being accepted for later prosecution evidence. See reference.

11. For questions about consent involving medical treatment or for a sexual assault forensic medical exam, follow the hospital facility protocol regarding consent.

12. If the victim states or behaves in a way that indicates further interviewing cannot be tolerated, the interview must be discontinued immediately. The next interview should be scheduled as soon as possible, but after the victim has had a chance to calm down. The victim should never be told "to calm down." Wait until an improved mental state can be observed.

Best Practices for Case Management

1. Individuals who are dependent adults often have a close and dependent relationship with their family. This can include individuals related through blood, marriage or adoption, domestic partnerships, communal living or chosen family relationships. Members of the individual's family will likely experience secondary trauma. Since they must help the victim, attention to their needs is critical. This includes a psycho-educational intervention and psychotherapy, if indicated.

2. If the individual is removed from her/his current dwelling, the trauma can be reduced if handled at the intellectual, emotional and developmental level of the victim. Whenever possible, it is best to move the suspected perpetrator from the dwelling. If the perpetrator is employed at the victim's workplace, the perpetrator should be placed on administrative leave until resolution of the case is completed. If the case does not end in a conviction of the perpetrator, consideration should be given to separation of the victim and alleged perpetrator through structural intervention, e.g., transfer of the alleged perpetrator, shift change, etc. If the resolution of the case indicates a false accusation, the perpetrator should be returned, and counseling should be implemented for both, separately.

3. Following the change in residential or vocational site, monitoring of this new situation is essential. For example, a 30 year old woman with moderate mental retardation was moved from her parent's home where her father had sexually abused her for years to a licensed group home where she was sexually assaulted by the licensed provider's paramour. Since the victim was in weekly therapy,

the abuse was reported relatively quickly. Had the victim not been seen weekly, the abusive conduct may have continued undiscovered for a long time.

4. There should be a close continuing communication among representatives of the agencies providing services to the victim including the CPS or APS worker, deputy district attorney, Victim Advocate, CASA, work supervisor, home provider and therapist. The therapist can prepare the individual for all legal activities in collaboration with the Victim Advocate from the Victim/Witness Assistance Center, as well as other activities that promote the victim's safety and healing such as medical appointments and additional interviews with law enforcement. The Victim/Witness Assistance Center can also assist the victim and family in filling a claim for unreimbursed medical expenses, job rehabilitation and mental health counseling with the State Victim Compensation Program.

5. It is not necessary to interview the victim with a disability any more than a victim who does not have a disability. Re-interviewing should only be done following the established protocol for any victim. It should be understood that after a period of time, two factors may effect the information initially provided. The first is the shock of the attack, which may have caused the victim to forget some important detail. The second is the impact of "Accommodation Syndrome" described by Roland Summit, M.D. This syndrome describes the emotional trauma resolution that includes initial cooperation in describing the incident, but misidentifying the perpetrator in order to assure the victim's safety, later retraction that anything occurred, followed by an accurate and enhanced report, including correct identification of the perpetrator.

6. There should be an assurance that representatives of the criminal justice system and others involved in case adjudication understand the victim's disability and do not dismiss the testimony as not being credible simply on the basis of the disability. It is critical to develop external evidence that can prove the case without the victim's statement (e.g. forensic medical examination and witness statements).

7. Sometimes perpetrators are fired without a complaint of maltreatment being filed. Investigations should consider the possibility of victims at other places of employment.

8. It is imperative throughout all interventions and interviewing that the victim's medication be

maintained and monitored. Stress can change metabolism and impact the effect of the medication; as a result, less or more medication may temporarily be indicated. Close ongoing monitoring of the individual's medical condition(s) is mandatory.

9. Follow up appointments to monitor the victim's physical conditions that may have resulted from the abuse are important such as pregnancy, STD's, wound healing, orthopedic and neurological implications.

10. The victim, if not in psychotherapy, should be evaluated for referral for psychotherapy. If nightmares, eating and sleeping patterns, behavioral or mood changes, social interest changes occur, a referral for an evaluation should be made.

11. Consultation with a professional skilled in the combined areas of disability and assault should be part of cases involving persons with disabilities.

Additional Readings and Resources

Baladerian, Nora J. Special Edition Survivor for People with Developmental Disabilities Who Have Been Sexually Assaulted: Booklet One: For Those who Read Best with Few Words, Pub. 1987.

Baladerian, Nora J. Special Edition Survivor for People with Developmental Disabilities Who Have Been Sexually Assaulted: Booklet Two: For Individuals with Learning Disabilities, Pub. 1987.

Baladerian, Nora J. Special Edition Survivor for People with Developmental Disabilities Who Have Been Sexually Assaulted: Booklet Three: For Family Members Advocates and Care Providers, Pub. 1987.

Bissada, Angela et al. Keeping our Children Safe: A booklet for Caregivers and Providers of Children with Developmental Disabilities to Reduce Risk of Abuse, Published by California State Council on Developmental Disabilities Program, 2000. http://www.scdd.ca.gov

Summit, Roland, M.D. 1983. Accommodation Syndrome, Child Abuse and Neglect. Vol. 7, pp. 177-173, Pergamon Press Ltd.

California SART Manual published by CALCASA (California Coalition Against Sexual Assault) http://www.calcasa.org

Child Abuse Prevention Handbook published by the Attorney General, California Department of Justice. http://caag.state.ca.us/cvpc/main_pub_videos.html

Crime Victims with Disabilities Training Curriculum published by California Medical Training Center through a contract with the State Department of Mental Health. http://web.ucdmc.ucdavis.edu/medtrng

Child Abuse and Children with Disabilities

Theresa Witt, Ph.D., Jayanthi M. Kasiraj, Ph.D., and Nora J. Baladerian, Ph.D.

Case Vignette

Madeline, a 13-year-old girl, with a diagnosis of mild mental retardation was mainstreamed in a 7th grade classroom with an aide to assist with academic skills at her functional level. She attended all nonacademic settings with same age peers, including lunch and gym. In the classroom her behavior became increasingly difficult and disruptive, with verbal aggression and outbursts of crying. Her parents experienced increasing difficulty getting Madeline to school in the morning, as she procrastinated and eventually threw tantrums. As a result of her behavior, the school placement was changed to a more self-contained class with a behavioral plan. Within this setting, Madeline's aggressive behavior improved, however, she demonstrated withdrawn behavior and avoided group activities. She did, however, seem to find another girl whom she was willing to work with on learning skills. Madeline eventually revealed to this girl, that in her old school setting, she had been verbally harassed by several boys during lunch. This harassment escalated to an incident in which Madeline was "hurt" (molested) by one of the boys in a school bathroom. The other boys laughed at her and teased her increasingly after this incident and threatened to "do it again" if Madeline told anyone. It was Madeline's classmate who informed the teacher of the abuse Madeline had experienced.

Questions

1. What is known about the extent of children with disabilities being abused?

2. What are the contributing risk factors for disabled children with abuse and neglect?

3. What are the therapeutic needs for children with disabilities who have experienced abuse?

Disabilities Caused By Abuse

The term "battered child syndrome" was identified by C. Henry Kempe in 1962 and focused on the physical abuse of children (Kempe, Silverman, Steele, et al., 1962). However, children were not spoken of as having acquired a permanent disability (e.g. head trauma resulting in mental retardation, sensory impairments including loss of vision or hearing, motor or mobility impairments such as cerebral palsy or paralysis). The picture in the minds of the public was one of temporary injuries, bone fractures that did not impact appearance, intelligence, and physical ability. Neglect has been an ignored area of child maltreatment and constitutes the majority of reports in every community. Neglect can result in speech and language delays, nutritional and growth deficits, and neurological damage due to drug and alcohol use during pregnancy that may have a lifetime effect upon the child's functioning.

Few studies exist that identify the percentage of children who become developmentally disabled due to abuse. A study by Jaudes and Diamond in 1983 implicated that 44% (8 of 18) of the developmentally disabled that were interviewed in an institution had histories of nonaccidental trauma. Nelson and Ellenberg (1979) indicated 12% of children who were diagnosed with cerebral palsy had acquired it through trauma that may have been abuse-related.

Disabilities include physical, developmental or sensory limitations. It is reported that 10–25% of children in the United States have some disability, ranging from profound developmental delays, to children with a variety of syndromes, to those with learning disabilities (Goldson, 1998). An estimated 1% of the U.S. population has a diagnosis of mental retardation, or about two million individuals. Within this population, 85% function in the range of mild mental retardation (IQs between 55 and 70); 10% function in the moderate range (IQs between 40 and 55); 3 to 4%

152

function in the severe range (IQs between 25 and 40); and 1-2% function in the profound range (IQ below 25). (American Psychiatric Association, 1987). Educational law makes provisions for children with disabilities, in an effort for them to benefit from the public education system. In contrast, relatively few other systems of care (e.g. mental health) provide planned and accessible intervention services for the disabled population.

Prevalence and Statistics of Abuse and Neglect of Disabled Children

Statistics on child abuse victims with disabilities have not been uniformly collected by any federal, state or local agency. The National Center on Child Abuse and Neglect (NCAAN), now the Office of Child Abuse and Neglect or OCAN, conducted the first and only national effort to determine the actual scope of maltreatment among children with disabilities in 1991. The reported incidence of abuse in the disabled population was 3.6% or 35.5/1,000 children with disabilities as compared to an incidence of 2.1% or 21.3/l,000 children without disabilities. Similarly, a nationally representative sample of children with disabilities was found to have a 1.8 times greater risk of sexual abuse, than nondisabled peers (Crosse, Kaye & Ratnofsy, 1993). A 1994 study of 949 children reported for suspected child maltreatment at the Child Advocacy and Protection Team at The Children's Hospital in Denver found that 21% of the children were found to be developmentally disabled or delayed before their abuse. Of the 949 children suspected of being abused, 51 were permanently disabled as a result of their abuse, and 15 (includes nondisabled and disabled children) of the physically abused children died (Goldson, 1998).

A Sullivan and Knutson (1994) study found that a significantly higher percentage of abused children had a diagnosis of mental retardation than a nonabused sample. Several previous studies support Sullivan and Knutson findings. In a study with 87 adolescent females with mental retardation, twenty-five percent had been sexually abused, with a higher incidence rate in the mild range (Chamberlain, Rauh, Passer, McGrath, & Burket, 1984). In another study of 500 multi-handicapped children, 53 or 10.6% had substantiated maltreatment reports filed with child protective services prior to the time of data collection. Of those reports, 34 or 64% were for abuse and 19 or 36% were for neglect. Of the 34 abuse reports, 31 children were physically abused and 3 were sexually abused (Benedict, White, Wulff, and Hall, 1990). In a 1993 study, 445 handicapped children in Spain were compared to a control group of subjects without any disabilities. The overall prevalence of maltreatment in the study group was 11.5% compared to 1.5% in the control

group. Of the abused children, 92% were physically neglected, 82% were emotionally neglected, and 65% were emotionally abused (Verdugo, Bermejo, and Fuertes, 1995).

In a 1998 study at an abuse treatment center, Mansell, Sobsey and Moskal found that the vast majority of developmentally disabled children in their sample had experienced more than one episode of abuse, similar to the nondisabled sample. The majority of characteristics of the two groups were very similar, although with greater frequencies for some behavioral problems. Vulnerability issues seemed to be present in their disabled sample, including "poor sense of personal safety, few friends, and is easily influenced."

Are mentally and physically disabled children more vulnerable to abuse and neglect?

Researchers have recently begun studies in an effort to determine if disabled children are at higher risk for abuse, and if so, what child, parent and environmental factors make them more vulnerable. While most information is based on studies of isolated factors, it is likely that more complex interactions need to be the focus of preventative interventions.

Ammerman, et al. (1994) studied a group of dually diagnosed children (those presenting with developmental/psychiatric and physical disabilities) to determine incidence rate of past or recent abuse. His concern involved the idea that "maltreatment impinges on psychiatric and medical intervention, in that treatment is likely to be unsuccessful if the child's home environment is compromised" by abuse or neglect. Child abuse ratings were obtained through structured interview with caregiver. Results indicated a high rate of maltreatment (61%). Physical abuse was found to be more common than neglect. Factors influencing the occurrence of abuse include the interaction of child and caregiver characteristics. Specifically, more severe disciplinary techniques were associated with children who were young, oppositional, and higher functioning (as reported by the mother during a parent interview measure), and with mothers who reported low levels of social support and increased anger reactivity.

The Verdugo, Bermejo, and Fuertes (1995) study suggested the following: (1) children who were less obviously disabled were at much more risk of maltreatment than the profoundly mentally retarded; (2) the less functionally impaired a child was, the more likely the child was to be abused; (3) the greater the speech defect, the greater the prevalence of maltreatment; and, (4) the worse the behavior of the child, the worse the maltreatment. In addition, the study reported that the abusive parents had the following risk factors: low socioeconomic status, problems with alcoholism, drugs, psychological disorders, mental retardation, marital conflict, or physical illness. In another research study, the parental characteristics were similar to abuse characteristics of the non-disabled abuse population (e.g. lower socioeconomic status, unmarried, little education, unstable employment). Contrary to the hypothesis of the study, the abused children were the higher functioning children, not the profoundly disabled population. It was theorized that parents of profoundly disabled children might have more resources and support due to governmental funding, community resources, and closer supervision. It was also suggested that parents of lower functioning children may have had lower expectations and are resigned to their situation. Whereas, parents of higher functioning children may have higher expectations of the children's abilities and were subsequently frustrated. (Benedict, White, Wulff, and Hall, 1990).

Rodriquez and Murphy (1997) explored the relationship between parenting stress, abuse potential and children's cognitive/adaptive functioning. High parenting stress was noted to be particularly prevalent in this sample of mothers with disabled children, particularly involving child-related characteristics. In addition, scores on a child-abuse potential inventory were significantly higher than norms matched for ethnic background and level of education. Rodriquez and Murphy report that single parenthood appears to "considerably increase the risk of maltreatment for children disabilities" based on child-abuse potential scores. Parent characteristics only partially capture the risks of abuse for this disabled population. This was highlighted in a study occurring in England, in which Turk & Brown (1993) reported that 14 percent of sexual abuse offenders against a developmentally disabled sample, were found to be agency staff or volunteers.

Gender Differences in Abused Children With and Without Disabilities

Sobsey, Randall, and Parrila (1997) found gender differences for some categories of abuse and children with disabilities. This study found that almost two-thirds (65%) of abused children with disabilities were boys. Research findings on the non-disabled population has consistently shown that a larger proportion of girls are victims of sexual abuse than boys (average figures reported are 80% girls and 20% boys). However, among the disabled population, several studies suggest that there are higher percentages of boys with disabilities sexually abused than in the general non-disabled population. Sobsey (1994) found that 76.9% of children 14 and younger who were sexually abused in an

institutional setting were males. This finding may relate to the disproportionately larger number of boys diagnosed with developmental disabilities.

Hypothesized Abuse Vulnerabilities for Disabled Children

Sexual Abuse

- Children and adults who are mentally retarded frequently are not taught about sexuality or sexual abuse/sexual assault prevention. Barriers exist for the provision of sexuality education and mature sexual knowledge and relationships, especially in institutionalized settings resulting in immature or inappropriate understanding/expectations of sexual interactions.

- Compliance with caregivers is emphasized at the expense of lessons in assertiveness or independence. They are vulnerable because they are dependent on others, and are relatively powerless in society.

- Overdependence and unquestioning compliance makes persons with mental retardation especially vulnerable to sexual abuse, as it places them in situations of unusual trust and enhances the possibility of coercion.

- If a child has severe developmental delays, coercion or physical force may not be necessary for abuse to occur.

- Children with no or limited verbal ability are prevented from reporting or describing what happened to them.

- If children have physical handicaps, they may not have the strength to fight back or the ability to run or to escape.

- For mildly retarded individuals, the quest for acceptance makes them especially vulnerable to coercion since some will do things to fit in with the normal population.

- Mentally retarded children are also reluctant to report because they are afraid that they won't be believed, they are not sure who to tell or whether they should tell (needing/wanting to be liked in the institution), they feel guilty and responsible, and they have a willingness to tolerate the abuse because they want to be liked, to fit in, or to receive rewards.

Physical Abuse

- Caretaking responsibilities for a physically disabled child create stress and abusive behavior.

- Parents/caretakers experience frustration over a child not reaching developmental milestones compared to other children.

- Parents/caretakers feel overburdened by the responsibilities of caring for disabled children.

Neglect

- Many caretakers do not have the financial resources to adequately care for the special needs of disabled children.

- Some caretakers have issues that prevent them from being adequate parents (e.g. alcohol/drug abuse, low income, employment problems, mental illness, mental retardation).

Ongoing Needs for Disabled Children Who Have Experienced Abuse/Neglect

Little systematic research has occurred to study the initial and long-term effects of sexual abuse on the emotional, psychological, and social development of mentally retarded victims. (Tharinger, Horton, Millea, 1990) There is ongoing controversy about the effects experienced by disabled persons, some reports emphasize the similarly of the sequelae as being similar to the general population, while others note the potential influences of developmental disabilities on the impact of abuse. Such compounding factors may include social isolation, pre-existing sense of stigma, dependency on others, self-esteem issues, fear of retaliation from "helpers", lack of comprehension about sexuality.

Diagnostic issues can be particularly complex with a developmentally disordered population. Symptomatology may not be expressed in a typical manner, or the person's limited capacity to communicate effectively may lead to misunderstanding the patient's experience. For example Razza (1997) has discussed the diagnosis of PTSD in persons diagnosed with mental retardation, noting that misdiagnosis of a psychotic disorder is prevalent. In addition, due to the cognitive or other developmental limitations in persons with mental retardation, some events may be traumatic for the disabled individual that would not necessarily be traumatic for others. Some researchers have noted that abuse of disabled individuals can result in greater emotional/behavioral difficulties than a nondisabled population. This has been hypothesized to be related to reduced ability to communicate distress effectively, decreased coping skills, greater vulnerability for psychiatric diagnosis, lack of resiliency-enhancing characteristics, limited social support.

Conversely, diagnostic overshadowing is a phenomenon to which clinicians working with this population are particularly susceptible. This is "a form of clinical bias in which professionals are less likely to diagnose psychopathology, or provide a diagnosis of lesser severity, when people are identified as having mental retardation, than when people demonstrate similar symptoms but do not have a diagnosis of mental retardation" (Levitan and Reiss, 1983). As a result, symptomatology that may be perceived as possibly related to abuse in a nondisabled population, may be overlooked in a disabled population.

Specialized Mental Health Services

While research continues to be equivocal as to the most appropriate form of psychotherapy to use with disabled persons who have been abused, a growing body of evidence exists from researchers documenting the implementation of treatments for sexually abused children who are developmentally disabled (Mansell, Sobsey & Moskal, 1998). A larger problem is the limited number of clinicians who are qualified to work with these individuals. Several approaches include adapting other therapeutic approaches to the developmental level of the client, or providing therapy in small groups with cotherapists, each of whom have expertise in one of the areas needed (e.g. developmental disorders and trauma related to abuse/neglect). Sullivan and Scanlon (1990) identified sexual abuse treatment goals for children with disabilities. These include relieving guilt, re-establishing trust, reducing depression, expressing anger, learning about sexuality, learning about self-protection/prevention, developing a "feelings" vocabulary to express oneself, and addressing secondary behavioral problems.

Role of the Regional Centers

The Regional Center was created by the State of California through the Lanterman Act to provide free advocacy and services for all individuals with developmental disabilities. The state defined five developmental disabilities that could qualify for regional center services: Mental Retardation, Autism, Epilepsy that is uncontrolled or disabling, Cerebral Palsy that is disabling, and any individual that requires treatment similar to Mental Retardation. Any family or professional can contact the regional center for more information and begin the eligibility process. There are 21 regional centers that cover various geographical areas. At Alta California Regional Center (which covers 10 Northern California counties including Sacramento) there are nearly 10,000 individuals (children and adults) who qualify for regional center services. Each Regional Center has a client rights advocate and referrals to various support services.

Conclusion of Case Vignette

Madeline's teacher approaches Madeline about the conversation with her classmate about being "hurt" (molested) and threatened by several boys at the school. Madeline repeats her story, but seems confused by the questioning. The teacher contacts Child Protection Service (CPS) and makes a child abuse report. CPS does open the case for investigation even though it involved boys the same chronological age as Madeline, since Madeline's developmental age and functioning is much younger than age 13. When the Emergency Response social worker from CPS questions Madeline about the abuse, Madeline presents confused, slow to respond, discrepant in the description of the boys and events, and giggling at times. The medical exam is inconclusive and the case is closed since Madeline does present with clear, consistent information. The teacher urges the family to take Madeline to a specialized therapist who works with children with developmental disabilities to address the sexual abuse and her reactive behaviors. The school agrees to change the Individualized Education Plan (IEP) from behavioral, seriously emotionally disturbed (SED) category to a more developmental focus that addresses sexual education, safety, and support. The family contacts the regional center for some assistance and guidance. The regional center agrees to provide referral for a therapist and to increase respite for the family to assist with the stress. The family was also encouraged to seek some therapy to address their feelings of guilt and anger.

Summary

Children with disabilities are more vulnerable to neglect and maltreatment than a nondisabled population. Based on the current research, children with the mild to moderate disabilities are at higher risk than the children with severe to profound delays or disabilities. Without educating and training families and professionals about the impact and risk factors related to abuse with special needs children, the child with a disability will continue to be vulnerable and at high risk for abuse.

Recommendations

1. Develop systematic data collection by Children's Protective Services regarding the incidence of abuse and disabled children. Plan placement of children contingent not only on safety factors, but with consideration of needs related to developmental and other disabilities to help reduce abuse from being repeated in out-of-home placements and to increase appropriate social and community support for these children.

2. Develop a community team approach to prevention and intervention. Establish multidisciplinary therapeutic intervention programs for disabled children who have been abused.

3. Develop specialized interview teams for the disabled population using established Multi-Disciplinary Centers (MDICs) or Multi-Disciplinary Interview Teams (MDITs).

4. Increase knowledge for medical, mental health, education and social services professions on child abuse in children with disabilities. Sensitize them to the vulnerabilities and incidence of abuse in the disabled population, and how to prevent and intervene.

5. Schools are the most common source of reporting child abuse of school age children with disabilities (based upon the national incidence study data), and the site where most needs related to disability will be addressed. Stronger training and collaboration between Children's Protective Services and schools is recommended.

6. Consideration should be given to routine screening of disabled children entering a medical, educational, or social institution for history of child abuse and neglect and current risk factors.

References

American Psychiatric Association (1987) *Diagnostic and Statistical Manual of Mental Disorders III-R.*

Ammerman, R.T., Hersen, M., Van Hasselt, V.B., Lubetsky, M.J., Sieck, W.R. (1994) Maltreatment in psychiatrically hospitalized children and adolescents with developmental disabilities: Prevalence and correlates. *Journal of the American Academy of Child and Adolescent Psychiatry,* 33 (4) 567-576.

Benedict, M.A.; White, R.B.; Wulff, L.M.; Hall, B.J. (1990) Reported maltreatment in children with multiple disabilities. *Child Abuse and Neglect,* 14, 207-217.

Crosse, S.B. Kaye, E. & Ratnofsky, A.C. (1993) A report on the maltreatment of children of disabilities (Contract#105-89-11639). Washington, DC: Westat Inc. National Center on Child Abuse and Neglect.

Goldson, E. (1998) Children with disabilities and child maltreatment. *Child Abuse and Neglect,* 22(7), 663-667,.

Kempe, C. H., Silverman, F.N., Steele, B.F., Droegemueller, W., Silver, H.K. (1962) The battered child syndrome. *Journal of the American Medical Association,* 181, 17-24.

Mansell, S., Sobsey, D., Moskal R. (1998) Clinical findings among sexually abused children with and without developmental disabilities. *Mental Retardation*, 36 (1), 12-22.

Nelson, K., & Ellenberg, J. (1978) Epidemiology of cerebral palsy. *Advances in Neurology*, 19, 419-432.

Razza, N (1997) Trauma and interpersonal violence in the lives of individuals with mental retardation: Understanding and diagnosing PTSD. *The Habilitative Mental Healthcare Newsletter*, 16, 53-55.

Rodriquez, C.M. and Murphy, L.E. (1997) Parenting stress and abuse potential in mothers of children with developmental disabilities. *Child Maltreatment*, 2(3), 245—251.

Sobsey, D; Randall, W; Parrila, R.K. (1997) Gender differences in abused children with and without disability. *Child Abuse and Neglect*, 21(8), 707-720.

Sullivan, P.M. & Knutson, J F (1994) The relationship between child abuse and neglect and disabilities: Implications for research and practice. Omaha, NE: Boys Town National Research Hospital.

Sullivan, P.M. and Scanlon, J.M. (1990) Psychotherapy with handicapped sexually abused children. *Developmental Disabilities Bulletin*, 18(2), 21-34.

Tharinger, D; Horton, C; Millea, S. (1990) Sexual abuse and exploitation of children and adults with mental retardation and other handicaps. *Child Abuse and Neglect*, 14, 301-312.

Turk, V, Brown, H (1993) The sexual abuse of adults with learning disabilities: Results of a two-year incidence survey. *Mental Handicap Research*, 6, 193-215.

Verdugo, M.A.; Bermejo, B.G.; Fuertes, J. (1995) The maltreatment of intellectually handicapped children and adolescents. *Child Abuse and Neglect*, 19(2), 205-215.

Additional References

Baladerian, Nora J. (1985) Survivor: For People with Developmental Disabilities who have been Sexually Assaulted, Three volumes: Volume One: For Those who Read Best with Few Words; Volume Two: For People with Developmental Disabilities; Volume Three: For Family Members, Advocates and Care Providers.

Baladerian, Nora J. (1993) *Abuse of Children and Adults with Disabilities: Risk Reduction and Intervention Guidebook for Parents and other Advocates*. Mental Health Consultants.

Baladerian, Nora J. (1998) *Recognizing Abuse and Neglect in People with Severe Cognitive and/or Communication Impairments, Understanding & Combating Elder Abuse in Minority Communities*, Archstone Foundation, 214-218.

Elvik, S.L.; Berkowitz, C.D.; Nicholas, E.; Lipman, J.L.; Inkelis, S.H. (1990) Sexual abuse in the developmentally disabled: Dilemmas of diagnosis. *Child Abuse and Neglect*, 14, 497-502.

Orelove, F.P.; Hollahan, D.J.; Myles, K.T. (2000) Maltreatment of children with disabilities: Training needs for a collaborative response. *Child Abuse and Neglect*, 24(2), 185-194.

Weinberg, L.A (1997) Problems in educating abused and neglected children with disabilities. *Child Abuse and Neglect*, 21(9), 889-905.

Jaudes, D.K. & Diamond, L.J. (1983). Child abuse in cerebral palsied population. *Developmental Medicine and Child Neurology*, 35, 169-174.

Chamberlain, Rauh, Passer, McGrath, & Burket (1984). Issues in fertility control for mentally retarded female adolescents I- Sexual activity, sexual abuse, and contraception. *Pediatrics*, 73, 445-450.

Sobsey (1994). *Violence and abuse in the lives of people with disabilities* (Toronto: Paul H. Brooks).

Levitan, G.W. & Reiss, S. (1983). Generality of diagnostic overshadowing across disciplines. *Applied Research in Mental Retardation*, 4, 59069.

Poverty and Homelessness

Karen Wellman Banker and Sandra K. Baker, L.C.S.W.

Case Vignette

The Brown family consisted of the mother, Jeanne, daughter, Sara, age 10, and son Justin, age 12. This was a chronically homeless family with a long history of methamphetamine drug use by the mother and clinical depression. Jeanne had been homeless beginning at age 15. She had been physically and sexually abused by her father. Her father also beat her mother and the other children in the family. At two years of age, she suffered a concussion from the beatings. Jeanne also remembered being force fed as a child until she gagged. Her drug use was self medication for depression and post-traumatic stress disorder symptoms. The children, Sara and Justin, had been sexually abused by Jeanne's boyfriend. Their school attendance was poor, and they had never finished a school year in the same school in which they started. The son needed special education, but was never in one school long enough to establish eligibility. Both children had chronic head lice and suffered from medical and dental neglect.

Questions

1. What are the characteristics of chronically homeless children and families?

2. What are the characteristics of crisis-based homeless children and families?

3. What are the emotional reactions observed in homeless and poverty children?

4. What role does parental mental illness and/or alcohol and drug addiction have in these circumstances?

A child in poverty lives at great risk for neglect, physical, emotional and sexual abuse. Likewise, a homeless child lives at an even greater risk. As a family's economic base spirals downward, stresses spiral upward. Children sleep in vehicles, camps, shelters, sleazy motels, abandoned buildings, doubled up with other families in shared rental space, and sometimes even on the street.

Chronically Homeless Children and Families

The chronically homeless child is usually in the care of an adult who is either mentally ill, drug or alcohol addicted, or an adult who is dependent upon another addicted or mentally ill adult. These families are typically either chronically homeless or have recurring episodes of homelessness.

These children may need the attention of Child Protective Services (CPS) for several reasons:

- No adult is consistently providing food.

- Children often have a total lack of supervision, even when the parent is present.

- Children are frequently left in unsafe places with strangers or alone.

- Children are dirty and wear filthy clothes even when facilities are available for washing.

- Children are exposed to drug paraphernalia and inappropriate sexual activities.

- Children (even very young children) may become the caretaker for the parent (role reversal).

- Addicted parents may keep the children in isolated situations, such as a motel or an apartment, and the children may not have opportunities for normal socialization.

- Children are often moved very frequently to meet the parent's needs and have no sense of stability or security. These parents do not function well in structured situations and cannot usually follow the rules in established shelters.

- Addicted parents often will teach children deceptive behaviors.

- Children may be used to steal or prostitute to provide money for drugs.

- Children in these families have often missed a great deal of school, have attended many different schools, and are often below grade level academically.

- Addicted parents are often noncompliant when offered assistance in obtaining medical or dental care for their children or when offered help in finding appropriate housing.

- Children may be exposed to dangerous drugs/drug paraphernalia including drug manufacturing in the home which carries health risks.

- Children may be exposed to or experience inter-personal violence such as physical and sexual assault.

- The children may be introduced to drugs by parents or adult acquaintances with impaired judgment thus establishing an early onset of dependency and addiction.

- Additional danger exists for these children because the child abuser is able to hide from authorities. Without an address, the family is hard to contact or can purposefully disappear to avoid detection. They may travel from city to city or state to state to avoid Children's Protective Services.

Two subtypes identified among chronically homeless parents are the Functionally Inadequate or Functionally Delayed Personality and the Abusive Controlling Adult.

Functionally Inadequate or Functionally Delayed Personality

This individual is chronically disorganized and lacks basic competencies. The Functionally Inadequate or Delayed Personality may be illiterate, has low functional ability, and typically has had no support system to teach or model daily living skills, decision-making, and planning. This is a pervasive character trait. With a combination of strong casework (characterized by duration and intensity), these individuals can be helped to acquire functional living skills to obtain housing and employment, and develop parenting skills. Recent literature suggests many of these individuals have a history of life-long foster care.

Other characteristics of these individuals may include:

- Personal and/or parental history of substance abuse and/or chronic mental illness;

- Lack of skills and resources necessary to provide a stable home;

- Impaired social skills and relationships;

- Low reading, math, and basic problem solving skills;

- Lack of skills and habits necessary to consistently hold a job;

- Inability to nurture or empathize with their children;

- Lack of ability to prioritize and focus on what is most important;

- Easily distracted;

- Impulsive—responding to the crisis of the moment, of which there are many;

- Easily manipulated, exploited and victimized;

- Inability to trust the right people and often put their trust in unworthy people;

- Often a hostile dependent personality; and

- Sometimes very over-controlling.

Abusive Controlling Adult

The Abusive Controlling Adult isolates and abuses his partner or his wife and children physically, sexually, and psychologically. Preferring the isolated life, the patriarchal head of these families moves from community to community and state to state. The family is totally under his control. The children in these families may endure significant abuse and deprivation. The father or father figure may terrorize the children for nonsensical reasons by torturing or killing their pets or imposing severe punishment. A very common trait found in these families is the need to keep the family isolated from the systems (e.g. health care, schools, homeless shelters) which may be the child's only resource for help and protection. Some of these men exploit their female partners sexually and, to obtain public assistance money, they may maintain relationships with several women for this purpose.

With an "abusive controlling" parent, the child may react in an exaggerated and fearful way if corrected for a behavior and may be overly sensitive about following directions precisely. Usually the child is secretive about any family business and is often withdrawn. The female partners of these controlling men are extremely passive and withdrawn. They are so emotionally dependent on these men that they will assist in the sexual abuse of their children by holding them down during the abusive episode(s) and also tolerate physical abuse of them. Some women may prostitute to obtain money for the male partner and family. The father's other motivation for isolation is to conceal his abusive treatment of the children and partner from authorities by preventing them from having opportunities for disclosure.

Crisis-based Homeless Children and Families

Families may become homeless due to gradual or sudden loss of financial resources. The crisis may be sudden, usually due to domestic violence, fire, natural disaster, housing being condemned, eviction, job loss, or work hours cut. The impact on the child may be noticeable, e.g. fearful and grief from the losses. The child in a crisis homeless family is usually very self-conscious about being homeless. The parent may be in a state of shock and not fully capable of assessing options. These families are probably the most receptive to helpful interventions and are more likely to have support from intact family and friends.

Children in families, who become suddenly homeless and are not successful in re-establishing their lives in a reasonable time, become increasingly susceptible to increased abuse. The parental stress level increases with each disappointment. Rapid deterioration in the mental health of the entire family can occur. Depression becomes obvious in the parent and this depression can be transferred to the children.

With parental depression, there is often less supervision and more apathy in providing appropriate parenting. The child may gradually take over the parenting role. The child becomes a worrier.

If a family has slipped into homelessness due to an eviction, this is usually an indication that the family has been financially struggling for some time. The children in these families have characteristically had several changes in schools and often missed a great deal of school. Generally, the parents in this situation are receptive to suggestions for finding resources for their children. The children in these families tend to be resilient and resourceful.

Indications of emotional abuse among children living in poverty or homelessness may include withdrawal, agitated depression, anger, low self-esteem, insecurity, and self-destructiveness. While some of these children show lack of attachment, others assume inappropriate levels of familiarity almost immediately.

Mental illness in a child's caretaker may contribute to neglect or abuse with children living in poverty, particularly if the family becomes homeless. Often the mental illness has not been diagnosed. Even if mental illness has been diagnosed, a parent in crisis of homelessness may not stay on needed medications. These families need extensive worker support to stabilize their living situation.

Children in homeless families frequently have medical, developmental and emotional issues that need to be addressed by professionals providing intervention services

Medical Issues to Evaluate:

- Malnutrition;

- Short stature and slow growth rate;

- Intestinal parasites from eating spoiled food and food from garbage cans;

- Undetected/untreated hearing, vision, and/or dental problems (serious cavities);

- Fungal infections;

- Other serious medical conditions that have been undiagnosed/untreated;

- Lack of immunizations for childhood diseases;

- Possible sexually transmitted disease from sexual abuse;

- Skin infection and head lice; and

- Pinworms.

Developmental and Educational Issues to Consider:

- Delayed language skills;

- Delayed or seriously impaired social skills;

- Delayed basic educational and social skills such as the inability to recognize colors, know the days of the week, the ability to tell time, or to know places such as the city they are presently located or were previously; and

- Appearance of retardation or developmental disability, however, these delays may be the result of excessive absences from school.

Emotional and Psychological Issues to Evaluate:

- Depression;

- Heightened levels of anxiety and fear;

- Sense of hopelessness and despair with heightened vigilance that bad things will happen;

- Post Traumatic Stress Disorder (PTSD) symptoms as a result of physical abuse, sexual abuse, neglect, and domestic violence;

- Sleep disorders;

- Eating disorders (hoarding food);

- Role reversal in which the child is the most responsible member of the family, protecting and parenting younger siblings as well as parents; and

- Noticeable over compliance.

Over-compliance is often misinterpreted by professionals from helping systems. Since the child is easy to care for they present no problems. Over-compliance may mask severe anxiety and fearfulness about the environment.

Resolution of Case Vignette

- Case management intervention and family support services to assist mother to:

  - find transitional housing;

  - obtain medical card and arrange medical and dental appointments;

  - facilitate mother's assessment by a psychiatrist and subsequent medication for depression;

  - support mother to find employment;

  - provide mental health treatment for the children;

  - assist the mother with learning parenting skills; and

  - accompany the mother to IEP (Individual Education Plan) school conferences to help son establish eligibility for special education services.

- This family situation was stabilized by locating housing and employment for the mother. The children completed the year in the same school that they enrolled in for the first time.

Recommendations

Professionals working with children in poverty must recognize the abuse and neglect risk factors present in caretakers who are crisis centered in their prioritizing or who are chaotically disorganized. It is very common to see parents who cannot focus on the child's needs when faced with urgent family needs for food and shelter, addiction prob-

lems, or other functional problems. It becomes necessary for child advocates to step-in to focus the parent and facilitate support services to take care of the children's medical, dental, and educational needs as well as to help the parent recognize the child's emotional needs. When help is offered and the parent is still unable to prioritize for the child's welfare, consideration must be given to bringing in Children's Protective Services and/or mental health workers.

Sound program development for homeless services should include planning for these factors:

- Focus on the needs of the children as well as the parents. Provision of crisis intervention, food, shelter, clothing, schooling, and medical/dental care are essential components of intervention in the lives of homeless children.

- Strongly emphasize skill building, preparation for self-sufficiency, and counseling for the parents including a focus on their possible histories of neglect, physical and sexual abuse.

- Focus intervention services on family support and case management services that are practical and easily available (on-site) keeping in mind Maslow's hierarchy of need (e.g. food and shelter). Attend to immediate basic needs and progress to higher needs based upon a building block process.

- Provide transitional care for adolescents raised in foster care or other out of home care (e.g. runaway shelters).

- Evaluate practical issues regarding access to resources such as the examples listed below:

  - Lack of transportation may prevent families from making or keeping appointments for medical or housing resources.

  - Long waits to get medical care, when stays at shelters are short, prevent access to health care. The family may move on before the appointment can be kept.

  - Schools refusing to enroll children without an address prevent access to education.

  - Lack of flexibility between agencies, lack of resources, and time constraints from high caseloads prevent good problem-solving for families.

- Unethical landlords may take advantage of families by taking them in and then increasing rent levels; or, by accepting the family's money even when the landlord knows the place is being condemned. These actions can force the family to return to the streets.

- The children of the mentally ill may need supported transitional housing with eventual monitored housing to maintain medication compliance.

- Overwhelming paperwork prevents parents already unable to understand the various "systems" from obtaining needed services.

• Staff training program which includes team building for the prevention of burn out.

• Anticipate and plan advocacy for system change to increase responsiveness to this challenging and complex population.

Reference

Maslow, Abraham H., *Toward a Psychology of Being*, D. Van Nostrand Company, 1968.

Resources

Mustard Seed School
1321 North C Street
Sacramento, California 95814

Child and Family Institute
4545 9th Avenue
Sacramento, California 95820

Parents with Serious Mental Illness (SMI): Risk Factor for Child Abuse?

Joann Grayson, Ph.D.

Vignette

Karen, age 11, lives with her grandmother. At age 6, she was removed from her mother who has a chronic, serious mental illness. Karen's mother refuses all treatment and manages with the help of her SSI disability check and public housing assistance. Prior to Karen's removal, she missed many days of school because her mother thought people were after them and took Karen and fled or drew the curtains and hid in the closets of their apartment. Karen still visits her mother who has "good days" and "bad days". "On a bad day she is hearing voices and talking to herself and I won't stay, " relates Karen. Karen's grandmother is in poor health. Karen worries that her grandmother will not live long enough to raise her. There are no other family members able to care for Karen. If her grandmother dies, Karen will need to go into foster care.

Questions

1. What are the prevalence rates of SMI and child abuse?

2. How common is dual diagnosis?

3. What problems are faced by the children?

Epidemiology

Serious Mental Illness (SMI) is a term that includes the most debilitating, persistent and long-term psychiatric diagnoses. These are conditions such as schizophrenia, schizoaffective disorder, major affective disorder (major depression), bipolar illness, and other psychotic conditions. The label SMI is also limited to conditions that last more than a year and result in serious dysfunction in one or more life areas.

Information in published literature concerning the parenting abilities of those with SMI appears to be limited. Even less is known about how children respond to a parent's mental illness. The research and literature examined has many problems because published studies are sometimes vague about diagnosis and frequently include a wide range of psychiatric conditions such as personality disorders or less serious psychiatric problems in the sample. Sometimes studies include persons who have difficulties but a psychiatric or psychological evaluation is not available or fails to include a definite diagnosis. Substance abuse may complicate the diagnostic picture. Rarely do the studies examine both the impaired parent and the children. Some studies contain very small sample sizes.

In early investigations, it was generally presented that parents with serious mental illness were a small minority of those who abused or neglected children. Spinetta & Rigler (1972) concluded that few abusing parents demonstrated severe psychotic symptoms. Evans (1981) also concluded that psychosis was rare in abusing parents, although his review suggested that "child abusers frequently show serious emotional disturbance and even mental illness..." (p.15).

Gradually, the assumption of "no diagnoseable pathology" was questioned. For example, a 1983 study of 76 parents referred for maltreatment and 38 matched non-abusive controls (Kaplan et al.) found a significantly greater number of diagnoseable conditions in the abusing population. Specifically, alcoholism, antisocial personality disorder and "labile personality" were prominent in the group of abusive and neglectful parents.

More recent studies also question the earlier assumption. Chafin, Kelleher & Hollenberg (1996) used data from the National Institute for Mental Health's Epidemiologic Catchment Area survey to follow 7,103 parents. These parents did not self-report physical abuse or neglect of their children when first interviewed. When interviewed a year later, .99 percent of parents without a disorder reported an onset of physical abuse and .71 percent reported an onset of neglect. In comparison, 4.3 percent of those with depression reported abusive behavior and, of those with substance abuse disorder, 3 percent became newly abusive and 3 percent became newly neglectful. The neglect rates for those diagnosed with depression were also high, but once those dually diagnosed with substance abuse were eliminated, the association was diminished. There were only 30 parents with schizophrenia. None self-reported new abuse and one self-reported new neglect. The authors note that abuse and neglect are likely under-reported since the study relied upon self-report.

A Boston study examined parents of 206 children (mean age 4.1) brought before the juvenile court for abuse or neglect. Of this sample, only 33 children had parents with no evidence of psychiatric disorder. A definite DSM-III diagnosis (made by a licensed professional) of intellectual impairment (low IQ) or emotional impairment was found for 104 records (51 percent) with another 23 records (11 percent) providing substantial evidence of a psychiatric disorder. When substance abuse was added, fully 75 percent of cases had at least one parent with a diagnosed disorder. Two specific disorders, severe depression and schizophrenia, accounted for 41.5 percent of the diagnosed disorders. Further, 28.7 percent of mothers and 17.4 percent of fathers had been hospitalized for psychiatric care in the past (Taylor et al., 1991).

A study by Famularo, Kinscherff, and Fenton (1992) confirms that mental illness and substance abuse can be associated with the worst outcomes in cases of child maltreatment. Fifty-four (54) mothers who maltreated their children and 37 controls were administered the Structured Clinical Interview for DSM III-R diagnoses. The maltreatment group showed a significantly greater incidence of both current and past diagnoses. Specifically, mood disorders were prominent in the maltreating group. Those with alcohol abuse were most likely to severely abuse children and the least likely to comply with court-ordered treatment.

These studies and others suggest that parent psychopathology can be an important factor in child maltreatment. Still, to date, there is little data about the types and extent of diagnoseable pathology in the general population of those who are known to have abused or seriously neglected their children (Taylor et al., 1991).

Dual Diagnosis

The combination of mental illness and substance abuse or substance dependence is termed dual diagnosis. Those with a dual diagnosis generally exhibit exacerbation of symptoms, more frequent relapses, greater treatment noncompliance and more violence. The range of both substance abuse and types of mental illness means that there can be complex interactions between these two long-term conditions (Dixon & DeVeau, 1999).

How common is dual diagnosis? Dixon and DeVeau (1999) cite findings from an epidemiologic study of 20,000 people. Findings were that persons with mental illness have a lifetime prevalence of 22.3 percent for an alcohol abuse disorder and a lifetime prevalence of 14.7 percent for a drug abuse disorder. In comparison, the lifetime prevalence rates for persons without mental illness are 13.5 percent and 6.1 percent, indicating that having a psychiatric disorder can double a person's risk for a substance abuse disorder.

Dual diagnosis might be an important factor in physical abuse of children. Untreated dually diagnosed persons are 12 times more likely to have a history of violence (Caffel et al., 1994, cited in Dixon and DeVeau, 1999). This corresponds with data indicating that substance use disorders, compared to other psychiatric problems, are most clearly associated with child maltreatment (Chaffin, Kelleher & Hollenberg, 1996).

Ways SMI Interferes with Parenting

The impact of SMI on parenting behaviors will vary according to both the diagnosis and the severity of the symptoms. The impact will also differ with the age of the child. The research reviewed shows many problems in parenting for those with SMI. Parenting by these individuals has been found to be less reciprocal (interactive), less responsive, and less involved. Parents with SMI in general display more negative affect towards their children and are less open in emotional expression.

Early studies of infants born to mothers with schizophrenia suggested that those in foster homes developed normally while those who remained with their schizophrenic mothers showed apathy, lack of smiling and laughter, irritability and delays in speech and motor development (Sobel, 1961 as cited in Yarden and Suranyi, 1968). This is similar to findings of Goodman & Brumley (1990) in which schizophrenic mothers of preschool children had a lower quality of parenting than depressed women or controls. The women diagnosed with schizophrenia were, in general, withdrawn and emotionally uninvolved with their children.

Compared to mothers suffering from medical conditions such as tuberculosis or mothers with post-partum depression, mothers with schizophrenia were more likely to maltreat or seriously neglect their infants during home visits. Further, less than 20 percent of children whose mothers had a schizophrenia diagnosis were able to return to their mothers, whereas most of the children whose mothers had medical problems or post-partum depression were returned (Yarden & Suranyi, 1968).

Many adults find it difficult to relate to and interact with untreated persons diagnosed with psychotic disorders such as schizophrenia. Thus, it is not surprising that children find a relationship with a psychotic parent to be characterized by confusion. Erroneous beliefs may cause the parent to behave in strange and unsettling ways. Disorganized thinking renders the parent inconsistent and unpredictable. For example, meals may be skipped or prepared at odd times, or suspiciousness and irritability may focus on the child and result in abuse (Famularo, Barnum, & Stone, 1986).

Persons with psychosis are often emotionally flat. It is not unusual for those with SMI to be withdrawn and interact with others only passively (Goodman & Brumley, 1990). Other disorders, such as major depression, exhibit this as well. Thus, persons with any of the SMI disorders are likely to have a reduced ability to notice, understand and respond to a child's behavior. The interaction needed for bonding and language development may be missing. Children who are ignored may misbehave or escalate behaviors in order to provoke a parental reaction. However, the parental reaction may be out-of-control and abusive as the child's misbehavior becomes more pronounced. This combination of emotional unavailability and maternal insensitivity can have serious negative effects.

A proportion of parents with SMI are overcritical and too harsh. They may lash out at their children, either in response to the child's behavior or in response to their own internal symptoms. Hallucinations (sensory experiences, such as voices which are not real) and delusions (false beliefs) could provoke a parent with SMI to harm a child. For example, a false belief that a strict diet is needed for religious reasons might result in an infant starving.

Abnormalities in physical activity (pacing, rocking, immobility) may interfere with starting or completing parenting tasks. A disturbed sleep pattern might mean that the parent with SMI is sleeping when children need care. Difficulty concentrating and focusing attention is a common problem for those with SMI. A reduced attention span may mean that appointments are missed, that children are not sent to school on time or on a regular basis, and that important information is lost.

According to the DSM IV (1994) most individuals with schizophrenia have relatively limited social contacts. Sometimes this is due to fears that others are dangerous. Sometimes it is due to apathy. Other times isolation is due to others avoiding the diagnosed individual. Regardless of the reason, children can suffer when their social contacts with others are meager or sparse. The isolation makes dependence upon the psychotic parent even more pronounced.

Children living with a parent with SMI are also adversely affected by the poverty that generally accompanies the disorder. Some persons with SMI have been unable to complete education and many are unable to hold a job for sustained time periods (DSM IV, 1994). Studies of parents with SMI confirm that these families are frequently living in poverty and less than one quarter have worked for pay in the last month.

In addition to poverty, parents with SMI often share other stressors, such as single parenthood, unstable residences, and frequent exposure to violence. Women with SMI appear especially vulnerable to being victims of violence (Apfel and Handel, 1993). Mowbray et al. (1998) found that one in seven mothers with SMI reported being physically or sexually assaulted within the year preceding the study.

A history of child abuse and neglect can place mothers with SMI at higher risk than the general population for potential child maltreatment. It is accepted by many that experiencing abuse or neglect as a child can increase the risk of adopting similar patterns of child rearing as a parent. One author who reviewed 15 studies of female psychiatric patients found that women admitted to psychiatric hospitals were approximately twice as likely as other women to have been abused as children (Read, 1997). This was similar to findings of Muenzemaier et al. (1993). The Muenzemaier study found that chronically mentally ill women experience higher rates of abuse, more types of abuse, and more severe abuse than the general population.

Children may respond to disturbed parents in various ways. Some may withdraw from social interactions, finding it unrewarding to relate or feeling safer not to risk an unpredictable response. Others may engage in coercive exchanges in an effort to elicit appropriate parental response (Goodman & Brumley, 1990). Some become self-critical and lack persistence.

From the child's standpoint, Dunn (1993) describes life with a psychotic parent as confusing and painful. In particular, the pervasive neglect and the fear of physical harm takes a toll. Dunn interviewed nine adults who had grown up with a psychotic parent. All nine spontaneously described experiences of abuse and neglect, ranging from withdrawal to excessive physical abuse to sexual abuse. The mothers' distorted sense of reality had a profound impact on their ability to consistently provide for their children's basic needs. The adults described serious lack of care by their parents and related that older children became the caregivers for younger siblings.

Guilt and loyalty were issues. One person expressed frustration that social workers expected her to "blow the whistle" on her mother. She feared hurting her mother who always asked, "Don't you love me? Why do you want to leave?" Guilt was also associated with going to college or leaving the home to establish an independent residence.

In a study by Caton et al. (1998), 39 offspring of schizophrenic parents (mostly mothers) were interviewed. They reported similar experiences to Dunn's study, with 43 percent mentioning violent or assaultive behaviors and 34 describing verbal abuse. Most related that the parent's behavior was embarrassing and/or that the parent's behavior was frightening.

Children who are embarrassed and distressed by their parent's disorder may be reluctant to be seen in public with their parents and may avoid inviting friends to their home. These children can fail to develop social skills and interests because of the social isolation they experience due to the parent being too uncomfortable to be able to make the necessary contacts to participate in community groups or activities.

Some blame their parent, feeling that if the parent cared about the children, the parent would put forth the effort to get better. This perception is strengthened if the parent is refusing medication and/or services. Some interpret their parent's continuing problems as proof that they (the children) are not worthwhile. The child believes if he or she were a better child, then the parent would improve. Self-blame and guilt can continue into adulthood, as many feel unable to help their parent.

There is general agreement that children of parents with SMI show greater behavioral problems compared to control children (Walker, Downey & Bergman, 1989). The association is, however, complex. Low socioeconomic status is, by itself, associated with a higher incidence of child behavior problems and many parents with SMI are poor. If parents with SMI also maltreat their children, the effects of maltreatment interact with the effects of exposure to the parent's pathology. Thus, parent and child live in a situation of accumulating stressors (children show negative effects that could be due to interactions between poverty, the maltreatment and exposure to parent pathology).

Results from a 4-year study by Rutter & Quinton (1984) comparing control children with children of psychiatric patients showed higher rates of persistent emotional and behavioral disturbances in children of psychiatric patients, with conduct disorders especially prevalent. Children were at greatest risk for problems when they were victims of aggressive acts or hostile behavior by the parent, were the target of parental delusions, were neglected for pathological reasons or were involved in parent symptomatology. About one-third of the children in this study showed no behavioral or emotional disturbances during the 4-year follow-up, another third showed only transient problems, and the remaining third exhibited serious and persistent psychiatric disorders.

Services for mothers with SMI and their children are not always readily available. Especially lacking are critically needed parenting skills training tailored to parents with SMI and assessment of the child's own needs for support and therapy. Mental health providers need to assess parenting skills as part of the psychosocial rehabilitation process rather than wait until the children are at risk for placement (Blanch, Nicholson & Purcell, 1994). Effective intervention must provide support, assistance and education to the parent while also providing stimulation, enrichment and therapy for children. Programs need to address 1) the mother's functioning and rehabilitation; 2) the cognitive, emotional and social development of the child; and 3) the

parent-child relationship (Rubovits, 1996). More training is needed to educate mental health clinicians about ways to address the needs of the both the child and the parent with SMI and to not let the parent's psychiatric needs overshadow the child's need for advocacy.

One important note is that many adults who grew up with a parent with SMI did not have anyone explain their parent's problems to them. Educating children about mental illness is not a single-time activity. As the child grows, he or she can appreciate and understand more about the disorder if given the proper support, therapy and information.

Finally, child welfare workers are generally not positioned well to deal with the complex needs presented in cases where the parent has SMI. CPS workers may not have had training in psychopathology and are likely unaccustomed to dealing with the challenges of SMI. CPS workers may have difficulty determining what symptoms are acute and which are long-standing problems. Assessing the parent's risk is complicated if the worker is not acquainted with the typical pattern for the diagnosis as well as the individual's history of adjustment and symptom control.

This article contains excerpts from "Parents with Serious Mental Illness" published in its entirety in Virginia Child Protection Newletter, *volume 56, Summer, 1999. Single copies of VCPN are available free of charge. Address requests to Joann Grayson, PhD, School of Psychology, MSC 7401, James Madison University, Harrisburg, VA, 22807 or can be ordered on the web at http://cep.jmu.edu/graysojh/vcpn_home.htm.*

Resources

Apfel, R.J., and Handel, M.H. *Madness and loss of motherhood.* American Psychiatric Association Press, Inc. Washington, DC, 1993, pp.99-118.

American Psychiatric Association. *Diagnostic and Statistical Manual of Mental Disorders* (4th Ed.). Washington, DC, 1994.

Blanch, A., Nicholson, J., and Purcell, J. Parents with Severe Mental Illness and Their Children: The need for human service integration. *Journal of Mental Health Administration,* 21(4):388-396, 1994.

Caton, C.M., Cournos, F.F., and Wyatt, R.J. Childhood experiences and current adjustment of the offspring of indigent patients with schizophrenia. *Psychiatric Services,* 49:86-90, 1998.

Chaffin, M., Kelleher, K., and Hollenberg, J. Onset of physical abuse and neglect: Psychiatric, substance abuse, and social risk factors from prospective community data. *Child Abuse and Neglect,* 20(3):191-203, March 1996.

Dixon, L.B., and DeVeau, J.M. Dual Diagnosis: The Double Challenge. *NAMI Advocate,* 20(5):16-17, April/May 1999.

Dunn, B. Growing up with a Psychotic Mother: A retrospective study. *American Journal of Orthopsychiatry,* 63(2):177-189, 1993.

Evans, A.L. Personal *Characteristics and Disciplinary Attitudes of Child Abusing Mothers*. Century Twenty-One Publishing, Saratoga, CA, 1981.

Famularo,R., Barnum, R., and Stone, K. Court-ordered removal in severe child maltreatment: An association to parental major affective disorder. *Child Abuse and Neglect*, 1986, 10(4):487-92.

Famularo, R., Kinscherff, R., and Fenton, T. Psychiatric diagnoses of abusive mothers. A preliminary report. *Journal of Nervous and Mental Disease*, 1992 Oct, 180(10):658-61.

Goodman, S.H., Brumley, H.E. Schizophrenic and depressed mothers: Relational deficits in parenting. *Developmental Psychology*, Jan, 1990, v26(1):31-39.

Kaplan, S.J., Pelcovitz, D., Salzinger, S., and Ganeles, D. Psychopathology of parents of abused and neglected children and adolescents. *Journal of the American Academy of Child Psychiatry*, 1983 May, 22(3):238-44.

Mowbray, C., Schwartz, S., Bybee, D., et al. *Mothers with a Mental Illness: Stressors and Resources for Parenting and Living*. Research funded by a grant from the National Institute of Mental Health, Nov 1998.

Muenzenmaier, K., Meyer, I., Struening, E., and Ferber, J. Childhood Abuse and Neglect Among Women Outpatients with Chronic Mental Illness. *Hospital and Community Psychiatry*, 44(7):666-670, 1993.

Read, J. Child Abuse and Psychosis: A Literature Review and Implications for Professional Practice. *Professional Psychology: Research and Practice*, 28(5):448-456, 1997.

Rubovits, P.C. Project CHILD: An intervention programme for psychotic mothers and their young children. In M. Gopfert, J. Webseter and MV Seeman (Eds), *Parental Psychiatric Disorder: Distressed Parents and Their Families*. Cambridge, UK, Cambridge University Press, 1996.

Rutter, M., and Quinton, D. Parental psychiatric disorder: Effects on children. *Psychological Medicine*, 14:853-880, 1984.

Spinetta, J.J., and Rigler, D. The child-abusing parent: A psychological review. *Psychological Bulletin*, 1972 Apr, 77(4):296-304.

Taylor, C.G., Norman, D.K., Murphy, J.M., Jellinek, M., Quinn, D., Poitrast, F.G., and Goshko, M. Diagnosed intellectual and emotional impairment among parents who seriously mistreat their children: Prevalence, type, and outcome in a court sample. *Child Abuse and Neglect*, 1991, 15(4):389-401.

Walker, E., Downey, G., and Bergman, A. The effects of parental psychopathology and maltreatment on child behavior: A test of the diathesis-stress model. *Child Development*, 1989 Feb, 60(1):15-24.

Yarden, P.E., and Suranyi, I. The early development of institutionalized children of schizophrenic mothers. *Diseases of the Nervous System*, 1968 Jun, 29(6):380-4.

Child and Animal Abuse: Recognizing Common Indicators of Risk and Designing Effective Interventions

Lynn Loar, Ph.D., L.C.S.W.

Vignette

In 1992, twelve-year-old Eric Smith killed a neighbor's cat. He was made to apologize and do some yard work for the wronged neighbor as restitution. The crime was not reported to a municipal animal control agency, the local humane society or SPCA, or to the police department. In 1993, Eric Smith killed a four-year-old boy. He was convicted of second degree murder for that offense the following year.

Questions

1. What are the common indicators of risk for child and animal abuse?

2. Why are animals often the first targets of violent behaviors?

3. What roles do animals play in cases of child abuse and neglect?

4. Why are animal-assisted therapy programs so useful in teaching gentleness and compassion to at-risk children and their families?

Significance of Animal Cruelty for Children, Elders, and Dependent Adults

Risk Assessment

Unfortunately, most parents spank their children as part of routine discipline, especially when their children are toddlers and pre-schoolers (Straus, 1994). What makes the "terrible twos" so terrible and so apt to elicit abusive behaviors is the confluence of a number of trying and seemingly contradictory factors:

- the child may be highly mobile, relentlessly energetic, and need constant supervision;

- the child may be noisy, crying or whining frequently, or banging things while playing;

- the child may be demanding, resistant, defiant or disobedient;

- the child may damage or break things, or make a mess;

- power struggles may develop over eating and other matters of self-care, and

- the child is not yet toilet trained.

This combination of energy (the child's mobility, demands, and resistance) and vulnerability (still in diapers and/or needing constant supervision) too often pushes parents beyond their limits. Throughout childhood, this mixture of active, oppositional, and/or messy behaviors puts children at risk of maltreatment by their parents and other providers of care.

Animal abuse tends to be triggered by many of the same behaviors as child abuse. A cute puppy is also a busy and energetic puppy needing supervision and activity. Animals bark and howl, especially when ignored or left alone too much. They may also be destructive, chewing, digging, and jumping on furniture or people. They eat food left on tables or counters and may turn away from their own rations. Housebreaking problems are common triggers of abuse.

Elder abuse and abuse of people with disabilities stem from some of the same provocations. Limited activity may lead to boredom, frustration, complaining and other irritating behaviors, and these may create emotional and physical stress for caregivers. Incontinence is often the last straw that brings on abuse.

Comparable behaviors can place children, elders, dependent adults and animals at risk: the need for care and supervision; the level of activity involved in their care; noise (crying, whining, barking, complaining); resistant, oppositional, defiant or irascible behavior; eating forbidden food, refusing to eat, or being a "picky" eater; damaging, breaking or chewing treasured objects; and, toileting accidents. These are normal, if trying, behaviors. Problems stem from the limitations of the parents or caregivers in meeting these demands and/or the stressful circumstances of their lives. Intervention needs to address the potential for neglect and/or abuse resulting from the limitations of the person in charge and/or environmental stressors.

The physical, behavioral and emotional indicators of physical abuse also tend to be the same for people and animals: inadequately explained injuries; withdrawn or aggressive behavior; self-destructive behavior (head-banging, creating sores, etc.); hypervigilance, extreme fear or anxiety; toileting accidents; wariness of physical contact; antisocial behavior; drastic behavioral change in the presence of the caregiver; and running away. Across ages and species, the emotional reactions are also consistent: fear, obsequiousness or cowering; depression; failure to grow or heal; hyperactivity; apathy, aggressive or bizarre behavior; unprovoked yelling, howling or crying; and self-defeating actions.

Neglect, the failure to provide minimally adequate food, shelter, clothing (for people), medical care, and supervision, poses a serious risk for all dependent living creatures. Unable to ensure their own safety, hygiene, or dietary needs, they suffer and are frightened when those they depend on fail them. Attempts to meet their own needs can create dangerous situations such as digging or climbing out of a fenced yard and getting run over by a passing car; eating poisonous substances when hungry and/or unsupervised; falling and injuring oneself in an attempt to find food, activity, companionship or to get to a bathroom.

The behavioral indicators evidenced by neglected animals, children, the disabled, and the elderly also have much in common: being dirty or hungry; lacking appropriate food, shelter, bedding and (for humans) clothes; being tired or despondent; having chronic untreated medical problems; showing fearfulness or learned helplessness; engaging in sucking, rocking, head banging and other regressive and self-destructive behaviors; begging for or stealing food.

All dependent living creatures have basic physical and affiliative needs, and the expression of these needs requires patience and protective responses by those providing care and supervision. Risks to potential victims increase when demands are high and/or resources and skills of the caregiver are low. Assessments must concentrate on the capabilities of and demands on the parent/caregiver, and consider attitudes that can indicate risk, e.g., disposability ("it's only a dog"), minimization ("she'll be all right, I had it much worse when I was a kid"), rationalization ("he won't learn any other way"), and justification ("she wet her pants because she is lazy"). Ignoring the cruelty or neglect of an animal by a pet owner not only allows the maltreatment of the animal, but additional animals the person may acquire, to continue unchecked. It also puts humans at risk who

exhibit comparable behaviors and make similar demands on the caregiver.

Effective Responses to Violent or Negligent Behaviors

Endangering behaviors can compromise the safety of all potential victims. Removing a victim may only cause the targets to rotate, thereby increasing the risk for other potential victims in the family or neighborhood. Abuse can be a combination of bad luck, bad timing, proximity, and availability, as well as individual characteristics that determine the hierarchy and likelihood of victimization.

The behavioral cues of the abusive or negligent caregiver are similar whether the one at risk is an animal, a child, an elder, or a person with a disability. These indicators include: a history of abuse or neglect in the caregiver's own childhood; the use of harsh discipline or rigid or inappropriate rules; lack of knowledge about developmentally appropriate norms and the need for flexibility as well as boundaries; judgmental interpretation and cruel treatment of problematic behaviors; abuse of alcohol or drugs; overuse or inappropriate use of medication or physical restraints to control or punish; and restricting access to the outside or to other people.

The emotional context in abusive families often includes harshness; blaming and belittling; being cold and rejecting; failing to support, encourage or express positive values; being inconsistent and unpredictable; being uninterested in or trivializing the problems; and failing to recognize the victim as a separate being with worthy wants, needs, and interests. In essence, the parent or caregiver fails to regard the other as separate, and fails to respond to his or her plight or vulnerability with compassion and empathy.

Negligent homes tend to be filthy, chaotic, unsanitary and unsafe. They may not contain nutritious food for any resident, regardless of age or species. The family is apt to be isolated from relatives and neighbors, and cut off from the environment, e.g., draping curtains or blankets over windows during the day or rarely venturing outside.

Roles Animals Play in Cases of Child Abuse and Neglect

The majority (75%) of families with children also own pets. Rates of ownership of animals are the same in healthy and dysfunctional families. The crucial difference is that there are rarely any pets over two or three years of age in troubled families. In these families, the parade of beloved yet disposable animals teaches children the risk of attaching and, because of their ready identification with the pet, makes them aware of their own precarious position in the family.

A fifth grader chronicled the inventory of pets in her family in the following poem:

FooFoo got hit by a car.
I cried.
Cream, my dog,
Born with a bad hip,
Got put to sleep.
I cried.
The rat's teeth overlapped.
She got put to sleep.
My ferret died.
All my animals die.
3 dogs, 7 cats, 10 fish, 1 bird.

A classmate wrote of the pain involved in losing so many pets:

I had too many pets that died.
I really don't want to write about it.
I can't tell you about them either.
I just don't want to.
It makes me too sad.
The door closed.
Don't ask me anymore.
I will cry into the ocean.

Children learn that there is little point in loving such transient creatures. Another one will always come and go... (Raphael, Colman & Loar, 1999).

Parents and caregivers may abuse or threaten to abuse an animal in order to control a child. Common examples include exacting compliance with a rule or goal by maltreating or threatening the welfare of an animal. Rooms get cleaned and noise is kept down because a child wants to spare a beloved pet. Children also report that parents threaten to kill or dispose of their pet if the child tells an outsider of the abuse in the home.

An animal may serve as a barometer for families needing help because its requirements are more straightforward than the subtleties of bonding between parent and child. The plight of the animal may also be more readily observed by neighbors if starvation and injuries are visible or if it howls and disrupts the quiet of the neighborhood when harmed or neglected. Moreover, people are more willing to report the maltreatment or neglect of an animal than of a child. With children, people tend to want to avoid interfering in some one else's family and may wonder what the child did to provoke the parent. Indeed, the role of the animal in troubled families may be to elicit intervention.

Best Practices and Model Programs

Collaborative Responses

Animal abuse is a problem of human behavior, and animal welfare workers are eager to cooperate with law enforcement, child protective and adult protective services in investigations and monitoring. In most states, animal control officers are mandated reporters of child abuse. In a number of states, people convicted of cruelty to or neglect of animals are required to participate in counseling as part of their probation or parole.

Collaborations between Battered Women's Shelters and Animal Shelters

Studies have shown that many women will not enter a shelter if they must leave their pet(s) behind (Jorgensen and Maloney, 1999; Adams, 1995; Ascione, 1997). Risk to the animal can increase if the batterer is faced with the departure of his partner. Throughout the country, "Safe Pets" programs provide gratis a few weeks of shelter for the animal to give the mother and her children time to come up with an alternative for the animal without having to worry about its immediate safety and care (Ascione, 2000).

Gentleness Programs

Humane organizations use gardening and animal care to teach gentleness and empathy to children and parents from violent homes and communities. Compassion and nurturance are better learned experientially and people enjoy caring for the animals. These activities are appropriate for people of all ages. Parents and their children can work enjoyably together without coercion or abuse. Both generations learn that kindness and positive rewards work better when teaching an animal to come when called than hitting in response to noncompliance. An animal attendant can explain how hitting only teaches the animal to fear the person's hand. This can be done without triggering the parents' defensive reaction that they were hit as children and it did not do them any harm.

These activities can become life-long hobbies that introduce otherwise isolated families to people with similar interests and greater personal resources. Through participation in an enjoyable activity, humane and altruistic values and actions are encouraged and reinforced, especially if they are shared by a nurturing community of fellow gardeners or dog walkers. These attributes, moreover, are introduced and incorporated into the fabric of people's lives in ways that do not put them at odds with their family or community (Ascione and Arkow, 1999; Rathmann, 1999; Ross, 1999).

The Humane Society of the United States (www.HSUS.org) publishes a directory of these therapeutic programs and information on the connection between animal abuse and human violence. The American Humane Association (www.americanhumane.org), having both child and animal protection divisions, is another resource. The Latham Foundation for the Promotion of Humane Education (www.Latham.org) publishes a quarterly newsletter, the Latham Letter. The Pryor Foundation (www.pryorfoundation.com) provides a web page devoted to promoting behavioral change exclusively through positive reinforcement.

Conclusion

Abusive or negligent people pose danger to others and should be the focus of interdisciplinary intervention. Assessment and protection should be available to children, elders, dependent adults, and animals. Risk assessments are most accurate when based on a survey of triggering behaviors and the potential abuser's ability to tolerate and respond appropriately to them. Collaborative responses involving child and adult protective services, animal control and state humane officers along with law enforcement are essential to ensure an appropriate and comprehensive array of protective measures and services.

Therapeutic and enrichment programs using gardens and animal care have the potential to break the cycle of abuse and deprivation. For people who have lived harsh lives, working with plants and animals introduces concepts of gentleness, nurturance and responsibility in fresh and appealing ways.

Selected Readings

Adams, C., "Woman-Battering and Harm to Animals," in Women and Animals, in C. Adams and J. Donovan, eds., Durham, NC: Duke University Press, 1995, pp. 55-84.

Ascione, F., "Battered Women's Reports of their Partners' and Their Cruelty to Animals," Journal of Emotional Abuse, 1, 1997, pp. 119-33.

Ascione, F., "Humane Education Research: Evaluating Efforts to Encourage Children's Kindness and Caring Toward Animals," Genetic, Social, and General Psychology Monographs, 1997, 123(1), pp. 57-77.

Ascione, F., Safe Havens for Pets: Guidelines for Programs Sheltering Pets for Women who are Battered, 2000, New Jersey: Geraldine R. Dodge Foundation.

Ascione, F.R. and P. Arkow, eds., Child abuse, domestic violence, and animal abuse: Linking the circles of compassion for pre-vention and intervention, W. Lafayette, Ind.: Purdue University Press. 1999.

Jorgensen, S. and L. Maloney, "Animal abuse and the victims of domestic violence," in Ascione, F.R. and P. Arkow, eds., Child abuse, domestic violence, and animal abuse: Linking the circles of compassion for prevention and intervention, W. Lafayette, Ind.: Purdue University Press. 1999. pp. 143-58.

Loar, L. "I liked the policeman who arrested that dog!" The Latham Letter, 1996, no. 1, pp. 1-8.

Loar, L. "'I'll Only Help You If You Have Two Legs,' or, Why Human Service Professionals Should Pay Attention to Cases Involving Cruelty to Animals," in Ascione, F.R. and P. Arkow, eds., Child abuse, domestic violence, and animal abuse: Linking the circles of compassion for prevention and intervention, W. Lafayette, Ind.: Purdue University Press. 1999. pp. 120-135.

Lockwood, R., "Training Key #392: Cruelty to Animals and Human Violence," Arlington, VA: International Association of Chiefs of Police, Inc., 1989.

Lockwood, R., and F. Ascione, eds., Cruelty to animals and inter-personal violence: Readings in research and application, W. Lafayette, Ind.: Purdue University Press. 1997.

Lockwood, R., and G. Hodge, "The tangled web of animal abuse: The links between cruelty to animals and human violence, Humane Society News, summer, 1986.

Miller, A., For Your Own Good: Hidden Cruelty in Childrearing and the Roots of Violence, New York: Farrar, Straus, Giroux, 1983.

Patronek, G. "Hoarding of animals: An under-recognized public health problem in a difficult-to-study population," Public Health Reports, Jan./Feb. 1999. vol. 114, pp. 81-7.

Pryor, K., Don't Shoot the Dog!, revised edition, New York: Bantam Press. 1999.

Raphael, P., L. Colman and L. Loar, Teaching compassion: A guide for humane educators, teachers, and parents, Alameda, CA: The Latham Foundation. 1999.

Rathmann, C., "Forget me not farm: Teaching gentleness with gardens and animals to children from violent homes and com-munities," in Ascione, F.R. and P. Arkow, eds., Child abuse, domestic violence, and animal abuse: Linking the circles of compassion for prevention and intervention, W. Lafayette, Ind.: Purdue University Press. 1999. pp. 393-409.

Ross, S., "Green chimneys: We give troubled children the gift of giving," in Ascione, F.R. and P. Arkow, eds., Child abuse, domestic violence, and animal abuse: Linking the circles of compassion for prevention and intervention, W. Lafayette, Ind.: Purdue University Press. 1999. pp. 367-79.

Straus, M. Beating the devil out of them: Corporal punishment in American families. New York: Lexington Books. 1994.

PART 7

Special Risk Factors Intensified by Social Isolation

Special Risk Factors Intensified by Social Isolation

Nancy Zebell, PhD and Marilyn Strachan Peterson, M.S.W., M.P.A.

Case Vignette

Judy, 9-year old Crystal's mother, was rarely seen in the neighborhood and seemed to have few friends and relatives. Crystal's teacher reported that Judy was pleasant but shy. Judy also had a serious weight problem. She rarely attended school functions or parent-teacher conferences. Crystal went to school most days, rarely spoke to anyone, went home after school, and never invited anyone over to her home. Judy only left the house to buy groceries and to run a few errands. Crystal's father went to work everyday but was rarely seen outdoors in the evenings and on weekends. Reportedly, there was a younger child in the family with medical problems, but she was never seen.

Questions

1. Describe special risk factors for children.

2. Describe special risk factors for parents.

3. Describe how social isolation can intensify these risk factors.

4. Describe parental tendencies toward social isolation.

Special Risk Factors in Children:

- Physical handicaps
- Developmental delay and mental retardation
- Cerebral palsy and other neuromuscular problems
- Hard-of-hearing or deaf children
- Visually handicapped children
- Mental slowness
- Down's Syndrome
- Children with mental illness
- Children with behavioral problems
- Attention Deficit Hyperactivity Disorder (ADHD)
- Drug exposed infants
- Colic and irregular eating/sleeping problems

Even the best of parents face challenges in coping with these situations. Successful coping requires personal strength, financial resources, ability to find and utilize community resources, and a strong support system from family, friends, and the community.

Special Risk Factors in Parents:

- Physical handicaps or disabilities
- Medical conditions
- Retardation
- Mental Illness
- Social Isolation
- Poor support system
- Alcohol and drug abuse

Social isolation and poor parental support can occur together or independent of the risk factors listed above. The adverse impact of social isolation and a poor support system are greater if the special circumstances listed above for children and parents are present.

Social Isolation and Poor Parental Support System Create Risks for Abuse

Social isolation and a poor parental support system can be a factor in child abuse and/or neglect. The risk factors listed above can be overwhelming. These factors, combined with a tendency toward isolation, can create abusive family dynamics.

The following factors are associated with social isolation and can pose varying degrees of risk to the child:

- parental tendency toward isolation;

- family risk factors; and,

- the caregiver's willingness to find and use available community resources.

Assessment of Parental Tendency Towards Isolation

- Intellectual limitations that impair the development of social contacts;

- Poor self-esteem that prevent parents from developing friendships;

- Poor social skills in initiating or developing relationships, or behavior which drives people away;

- Social contacts or friendships are kept at a superficial level;

- Lack of trust for others interferes with developing deep relationships;

- Feeling "different" due to weight problems, disabilities, mental illness, and/or schizoid tendencies;

- Tendency to polarize away from others over perceived slights;

- Inability to find the "middle ground" when there are differences—rigid;

- Extreme immaturity, self-absorption, lack of empathy, impaired judgment, poor impulse control, dependence, or irresponsibility prevent the development of helpful friendships; and,

- Lack of ability to form attachments or restricted or limited ability to show affection.

These situations not only impact parent's relationships with others, but they can adversely impact the parent-child relationship. The parent may demonstrate complete absence of attachment, affection, or acceptance of the child. There may be a tendency to view the child as bad and over-emphasize the child's faults. In cases such as this, parents may administer discipline that is inappropriate, excessive, or harsh in relation to the child's age or level of misconduct. Some parents demonstrate inadequate knowledge of age-appropriate child behavior and do not recognize stages of child devel-

opment. In these cases, unrealistic demands are made of the child. For isolated parents, there are often no alternate role models or assistance and support from others.

Assessment of Family Risk Factors

Character traits described above may limit the ability of the parent to develop or maintain relationships with family members who may be helpful. The parent may be estranged from family members because of their own behavior or due to dysfunction in the family. Some individuals employ the technique of "cut off" to manage anxiety and dysfunction with family members. "Cutting off" may solve the relationship problem, but often leaves the parent further isolated and lonely.

Spouses or live-in partners can pose high risk factors that may contribute to the isolation of the primary parent. Examples include:

- Relationship is characterized by violence;

- Primary parent is purposefully isolated from others due to a dysfunction on the part of the live-in partner or spouse, e.g. domestic violence, intra-familial sexual abuse, alcohol/drug abuse, mental illness, character disordered traits which are offensive; and/or

- Little positive affection, attachment, or good will is expressed between partners and the relationship is characterized by a lack of mutual support.

Extended family members can exacerbate already poor relationships. Examples include:

- Interactions are negative, non-supportive, or unreliable;

- No concrete offers of assistance are made or emotional support is non-existent;

- Family members are critical; or

- Family alienates anyone offering assistance or support due to pride or defensiveness.

Assessment of Parent's Ability to Find and Use Community Resources

The availability of formal and informal supports for parents and children outside of the family are important for the development of healthy relationships. Healthy outlets are especially important if there is dysfunction in the home. Formal support systems such as schools, churches, work settings, neighborhoods, Head Start Programs, home visiting programs, recreational programs such as Boys and Girls

Clubs are positive environments. These programs can supplement a parent's resources for providing adequate care for children and staff can serve as healthy role models for children. Children from dysfunctional families benefit from an alternate experience that is positive.

Children are placed at high risk, however, when the parent denies there is a problem of isolation or refuses to take any level of responsibility for the problem. This is further complicated when the parent is evasive, verbally hostile, physically assaultive, or threatening to outside support systems. Sometimes, in situations such as this, parents refuse to cooperate with service planning or treatment. They actively or passively resist all contacts or involvement; or, the parent actively sabotages efforts by others to assist. On the other hand, it is also imperative that community agencies not produce additional demands and stressors that can make parenting more difficult (e.g. specialized clothing and/or equipment, fees, travel, etc.). Isolated families are less likely to be involved in these activities.

Families and Communities Reaching Out: A Neighborhood Society

It is imperative that professionals working with abused children keep current with familial factors that may cause isolation and increase the risk of child abuse. "Reaching out"

is needed on two levels—the individual parent reaching out for support and neighbors and relatives reaching out to the individual. The isolated individual is better able to reach out if there is understanding of their fears, help with their concerns, e.g. clothing and shoes, and support from social workers or home visiting program caseworkers. "Reaching out" is also needed by neighbors, the community, and the churches. The U.S. Advisory Board on Child Abuse and Neglect called for a "neighborhood society' in which adults "resolve to be good neighbors—to know, watch, and support their neighbors' children and to offer help when needed to their neighbors' families. These resources play an important part in the prevention of child abuse.

Resources

Gaudin, Jr JM. *Child Neglect: A Guide for Intervention.* The User Manual Series by PhD. U.S. Department of Health and Human Services' Administration on Children, Youth and Families, National Center on Child Abuse and Neglect, April, 1993.

A Nation's Shame: Fatal Child Abuse and Neglect in the United States. A report of the U.S. Advisory Board on Child Abuse and Neglect, 1996.

Family Assessment: Risk Variables. Prepared by California State University, Fresno, School of Health and Social work adapted from Illinois Department of Children and Family Services, 1989, Risk Assessment Training Manual. Revised August, 1994.

PART 8

Religious Issues

Religious Issues

Seth Asser, M.D.

Case:

A 12-year-old girl with severe scoliosis is admitted for corrective surgery. The family belongs to the Jehovah's Witnesses and has requested that surgery be performed without blood transfusions. The surgeon has agreed to the family's request. The type and crossmatch that is part of the routine pre-op orders is crossed out. The nurse is concerned and calls the social worker. The social worker has had many previous contacts with the Witnesses so he calls the surgeon to ask if she would like him to prepare the usual court order in case a transfusion should become necessary. The surgeon informs him that there will absolutely be no blood given to this child because this promise has been made to the family. She says that it is probable, but not guaranteed, that the surgery can be performed successfully without transfusion. The social worker and the nurse are very concerned and do not know how to proceed.

Questions

1. Is a 12-year-old able to participate in giving informed consent to perform or withhold medical procedures? If so, can this surgery be allowed to proceed? If not, on what basis can consent be given?

2. What are the risks to the patient, staff, and hospital should the surgery proceed and a bad outcome occur?

3. What can the concerned staff do at this point? What internal and external resources are available to help?

4. What kinds of situations arise in which medical care is refused on the basis of religious belief or practice? What are the responsibilities of mandated reporters and what avenues are available to ensure that dependent children receive adequate, necessary medical treatment?

There are two types of religious organizations that refuse medical care based upon their beliefs. Jehovah's Witnesses do not have a prohibition against medical treatment but do not accept blood transfusion. Christian Scientists and some Pentecostal fundamentalist sects avoid medical treatment for illness, instead relying exclusively upon faith healing. The latter groups raise concern because children of members rarely come to the attention of medical providers. Nevertheless, there are circumstances in which mandated reporters do come into contact with such children and, as child advocates, should be aware of the problems and implications associated with the practice of exclusive reliance on faith healing.

In virtually all cases involving Jehovah's Witnesses in which blood transfusion or component therapy is necessary to prevent disability or to save the life of a child, courts will order the necessary care. In many jurisdictions, judges routinely give such orders over the telephone. In some jurisdictions, juvenile courts have standing policies that allow protective workers to take temporary custody for the purpose of consent to transfuse without immediately notifying the court. The need to avoid all but the most essential transfusions has become generally accepted in the medical community and research efforts are actively pursuing blood substitutes and other therapies. However, situations still arise when blood components are necessary to save the life of a child.

Jehovah's Witnesses do not practice faith healing. They seek and accept medical care and count among their members many nurses and doctors. However, children from families that practice an exclusive reliance on faith healing rarely come into contact with the medical care system, and then usually only after death. In addition to the occasional contacts between emergency services or health care systems with these children, there are other reasons for health care workers to be aware of the problems faced by children from these sects.

First, these children are not given routine immunizations. Almost all states have a religious exemption to mandatory vaccinations. There have been many large and sometimes deadly outbreaks of vaccine preventable illness, which have spread rapidly within such groups, occasionally threatening and infecting vulnerable others. Unimmunized, underimmunized, and immunosupressed individuals who are inside or outside of these immunization refusing communities are placed at unnecessary risk

Second, the number of children who suffer and die from preventable or treatable illnesses is significant. In the past twenty years, there have been more than 200 well-documented instances of young children dying from such easily treatable conditions as pneumonia, appendicitis, or dehydration. Many newborns have succumbed to simple labor and delivery complications.

Almost all states have some form of religious exemptions to the parental duty to provide medical care either in the civil code, the criminal code, or both. In many cases, children who suffered preventable deaths did have contact with mandated reporters. Teachers, social workers, law enforcement personnel and emergency responders failed to take timely action to save the lives of these children. They apparently were under the mistaken impression that the parents' rights to exercise their own freedom of religious beliefs extended to the right to deny their children medical care.

With rare exceptions, when presented with such cases, courts have ordered medical treatment for children of religious objectors based on a long history of case law. Therefore, it should be an important part of the education and outreach functions of child advocacy teams and centers to educate the community in general and mandated reporters in particular about this issue. In order for maximum efficacy of medical care, ill children whose parents are members of faith healing sects must be brought to the attention of authorities promptly. Protective workers and law enforcement should not accept assertions from these parents or their church leaders that the children are under adequate treatment (in their minds, prayer is the only adequate treatment). Court ordered medical care should be sought aggressively through the Juvenile Court.

The American Academy of Pediatrics, the National District Attorney's Association, and other professional groups have strongly condemned religious exemption laws. Many states have conflicting laws in this area, with child abuse codes requiring life preserving medical care for children, but child neglect codes stating that spiritual treatment without medical care should not be considered neglectful. Some states have outright exemptions even in the criminal codes for child abuse and manslaughter. While a few parents have been successfully prosecuted in the past for neglect, child endangerment, and other charges, it has become increasingly difficult to do so because courts have ruled that the conflicts in the various codes deny parents

fair notice of the behavior expected of them. The history, politics, and law of this issue are best reviewed in the paper by Swan found in the reference list. It is imperative that community leaders in the area of child abuse and neglect take a firm stand against religious exemption laws at the state and federal level. Despite court rulings such as "parents may be free to make martyrs of themselves. But it does not follow they are free…to make martyrs of their children…" (U.S. Supreme Court, Prince v. Massachusetts, 1944), pressures from small constituent lobbies such as the Christian Science church have led to many religious exemption statutes, usually at the state level. The presence of these statutes is clearly disrupting the ability of protective service agencies to ensure that children receive timely, appropriate medical care.

The laws in California provide an example of such legal inconsistency. Since 1925, a California law requiring parents to support their children has read, "If a parent of a minor child willfully omits, without lawful excuse, to furnish necessary clothing, food, shelter, or medical attendance, or other remedial care for his or her child, he or she is guilty of a misdemeanor. . . ." Calif. Penal Code Sec. 270

In 1964, a 13-year-old Sacramento girl died from swallowing her own hair. Her mother belonged to the Church of the First Born, which then prohibited women from cutting their hair. The girl disobeyed the rule and then swallowed her own hair, apparently trying to hide her "crime." The church also discourages members from seeking medical care. Her mother was convicted of failure to provide medical care. She argued that the statutory reference to "other remedial care" allowed her to substitute religious rituals for medical care. The court explicitly disagreed. *People v. Arnold* 66 Cal.2d 438, 452 (1967)

In 1976, the Christian Science church lobbied the legislature to add the following to the statute: "If a parent provides a minor with treatment by spiritual means through prayer alone in accordance with the tenets and practices of a recognized church or religious denomination, by a duly accredited practitioner thereof, such treatment shall constitute 'other remedial care,' as used in this section."

In 1984, three Christian Science children died of untreated h-flu meningitis in California. Charges of manslaughter and felony child endangerment were filed against their parents. The parents argued that Section 270 gave them the right to withhold medical care and rely on prayer instead. The California Supreme Court ruled, however, that the religious exemption in Section 270 applied only to a misdemeanor nonsupport charge and not to felonies. *Walker v. Superior Court*, 763 P.2d 852 (1988). The parents were convicted in two of the deaths and acquitted in the third. But one parent filed a writ of habeas corpus in federal court, and a federal district judge overturned her conviction on due process grounds. The court effectively said that the exemption in Section 270 misled the parent. The state did not appeal the ruling. *Walker v. Keldgord*, U.S. Dist. Ct., Eastern Dist. of Calif. #CIV S-93-0616 LKK JFM P.

According to some California prosecutors, the federal ruling applies only to Walker's case and not to any parent who withholds medical care on religious grounds after the California Supreme Court handed down its ruling in 1988. A conviction of a parent who let his baby die of meningitis without medical treatment in 1991 because of Pentecostal beliefs against medical care was upheld. *People v. Northrup*, Calif. 3rd Dist. Ct. of Appeals CO21576 (1997). It is also worth pointing out, however, that in many cases of fatal religion-based medical neglect following the Walker appeal, California prosecutors have not filed charges. For example, two boys from Southern California died of untreated diabetes because their parents relied on Christian Science. Thus, the status quo remains awkward. A federal court has ruled that the religious exemption in Section 270 misled a parent in 1984, but after the California Supreme Court interpreted the laws in 1988, parents no longer have an excuse to be confused. The laws that describe the legal duty of parents to provide reasonable medical care for their children should be clear, compelling and consistent.

The most appropriate response to the scenario is to convene a hospital ethics committee review of the situation. Some of the factors reviewed by such a group would include whether or not the child has reached the statutory age of consent for medical treatment. If not, are the parents acting in their own best interests or that of the child, and if the former, should action be taken in order to secure alternate custody through the court system for the purpose of making medical decisions.

Hospital personnel cannot be compelled to participate in healthcare delivery that they think may not be appropriate. In addition to the nurse noted above, the operating room staff, including the attending anesthesiologist, as well as any other physicians who might participate in the care of the patient would all have to agree to refrain from seeking court ordered transfusion. Advice from hospital attorneys would be essential. In one Northern California case, a university medical center was found liable for breach of promise when surgical consent was obtained with agreement not to transfuse. However, when the 17 year-old patient required blood post-operatively, a court-ordered transfusion was given. Although the transfusion was legal and life saving, it violated the contract that the surgeon had with the patient and family. As a result, a large financial judgment was granted against the hospital. In another case, a minor child was allowed to die following surgery because

the physician felt the need to honor this promise to the family. Such promises cannot be made with the expectation of a rescue of the patient by court ordered transfusion should one be needed.

Reports of "bloodless" surgical techniques appear in the literature and promise good results. However, in the case of some highly complex procedures, such as those requiring cardio-pulmonary bypass, mortality rates remain higher in non-transfused groups. This risk may be acceptable to adults making their own decisions, but it is not clear that children should be put in a situation of higher risk based on parents' religious preferences. Simply, if a court would typically order a life-saving transfusion for a young child in a relative emergency, in most cases that same benefit should be applied to a child undergoing a more elective procedure.

In the case of a 12-year-old, it is possible for a court to grant mature minor status for the purpose of consent to treatment. However, one of the most important tenets of this process is that the decision must be free and not coerced. No matter how mature appearing the thought process and emotions of that child might be, it is not clear that someone that age who is entirely dependent upon parents for food, shelter, clothing, and social support would be able to make a *free* decision.

In addition to hospital resources, consideration should be given to a referral to Child Protective Services. The denial of life sustaining medical care to a dependent child is a form of child neglect that needs to be reported. Currently there is not a legal precedent for prosecution of a health care provider under these types of circumstances. The subtleties and complexities of medical treatment and consent are generally left to be decided by the physician and patient. However, when surrogate decision makers are involved, who may or may not be acting in the best interest of the child, the situation becomes more complex. Presented with the hypothetical scenario of a surgeon who exposes a child to the risk of morbidity or mortality and who does not act to save the child using all available resources because of promises made to the parents, prosecutors have indicated that they would consider an investigation into criminal charges under such circumstances.

The fundamental principles when faced with cases of religious refusal of medical treatment are to be gently persistent, with the emphasis on persistent; and, should that fail, request legal intervention on behalf of the child. When the consequences of either limited medical consent or outright refusal for treatment are threatening to life or limb, the process must be biased in favor of the right of the child to attain the age of consent so that he or she, as an adult, will have the opportunity to make such decisions on his or her own.

Suggested Reading:

Asser, S.M. and Swan, R. Child Fatalities From Religion-motivated Medical Neglect. Pediatrics 1998; 101(4):625-629.

Swan, R. Children, medicine, religion, and the law. Advances in Pediatrics 1997; 44: 491-543

Consent for Medical Services for Children and Adolescents (RE9309). *Pediatrics* 92(2): 290-291. 1993

Sigman, G.S., and O'Connor, C. 1991. Exploration for physicians of the mature minor doctrine. *Pediatrics* 119(4):520-525

Harrison, C., Kenny, N.P., Sidarous, M., and Rowell, M. 1997. Bioethics for clinicians: 9. Involving children in medical decisions. *Can Med Assoc J* 156:825-8

Additional Resource:

Children's Healthcare is a Legal Duty, Inc. PO BOX 2604, Sioux City IA 51106, 712-948-3500

PART 9

When Do You Refer for Mental Health Treatment and Evaluation?

Anthony J. Urquiza, Ph.D., Jean McGrath, Ph.D., Sherri Y. Terao, Jayanthi M. Kasiraj, Ph.D., and Celeste Wiser, M.D.

Case Vignette

Daniel was very aggressive toward his younger brother and the children at school. He was easily frustrated. When things didn't go his way, he would hit, push, and kick his school mates. Daniel would tease, trip, and hit his younger brother when he thought no one was looking.

Shantelle was extremely shy and withdrawn. She hardly spoke and was highly compliant when anyone asked her to do anything. She was extraordinarily quiet and did not resist or flinch when she was given eight immunizations during her foster care medical examination (she had no history of immunizations). Shantelle had a history of physical abuse and severe neglect.

Questions

1. What are indicators of the need for mental health treatment?

2. What are symptoms which warrant a psychological evaluation?

3. What are indicators for psychiatric evaluations?

Statistics

Estimates of the need for mental health services for children and adolescents as indicated by standardized measures range widely for both community and special populations. In community studies, estimates of this need range from 10-22% (Costello et al., 1988, Gould, Wunsch-Hitzig, & Dosrenwend, 1982; Offord et al., 1987; Zahner, Pawelkiewicz, DeFrancesco, & Adnopoz, 1992). Halfon, Mendonca, and Berkowitz (1995) reported that 80% of 213 children entering foster care with a mean age of 3 years were found to have developmental, emotional, or behavioral problems. Landsverk (1999) summarized research studies across several states and found that between one-half to two-thirds of the children entering foster care

exhibit behavior or social competency problems warranting mental health services and called for universal mental health screening of children entering foster care.

Indicators for Mental Health Treatment:

- History of neglect, physical and sexual abuse
- Death of a sibling or a parent
- History of torture
- Child or parent history of alcohol and/or drug abuse
- Depression, sadness, withdrawal and avoidance of others, fearful
- Angry, agitated
- Signs of stress, e.g. unable to go to sleep, wakes during the night, eating problems, quick temper, easily frustrated
- Acting out behavior, e.g. aggressive with peers, caregivers, teachers
- Lack of self-care
- Mistreatment of animals
- Firesetting
- School problems, e.g. poor grades, poor concentration, little participation in activities
- Change or deterioration of behavior
- Suicidal ideation
- Risk of placement disruption due to behavioral difficulties
- Hallucinations or delusions
- Difficulties with self-care not due to developmental disability
- History of receiving psychotropic medication

Clinical or Psychosocial Assessments and Development of Treatment Plans

The first phase of mental health treatment is the clinical or psychosocial assessment.

The primary objectives of the assessment are to:

- Obtain a social, family, and medical history;

- Assess the nature and extent of the presenting problem(s);

- Assess the client's current level of functioning;

- Assess the client's capabilities for improved functioning;

- Assess the client's psychological and behavioral symptoms;

- Identify any existing needs or concerns of the child and family;

- Identify the existing relative strengths and weaknesses of the client(s);

- Determine the capabilities and availability of emotionally supportive resources;

- Target and prioritize symptoms or behaviors;

- Assess the risk of suicide for both the child and the parents;

- Assess the potential revictimization of the child; the potential of the child to act out sexually or physically toward other children; the potential for high risk behavior; and the caregiver's ability to address the child's emotional and behavioral needs and symptoms;

- Assess symptoms across areas of functioning and degree of emotionally supportive resources;

- Assess the client's willingness and motivation to participate in treatment;

- Assess the need for a medical, psychiatric, psychological or educational evaluations;

- Assess the need for community support services;

- Determine the most appropriate form of treatment (e.g. individual treatment, group therapy, family therapy); and,

- Determine treatment goals and strategies.

The second phase of mental health treatment is the development of a treatment plan based upon the outcome of the psychosocial assessment. Treatment planning involves working with the child, the child's parents and caregivers, the social worker, the school, and other significant persons in the child's life to identify individualized, measurable objectives and treatment interventions appropriate for the specific child and family. Progress toward achieving objectives is reviewed routinely and may involve administering standardized behavioral measures or questionnaires to the child, the child's parents or caregivers, and the school.

Purpose and Types of Mental Health Treatment

The purpose of mental health treatment is to alleviate psychological and behavior symptoms and to facilitate the development and maintenance of healthy functioning across an individual's life domains, e.g. home, work, or school.

The primary treatment modalities are:

- Individual therapy (e.g. talk, sand, and play therapy are various treatment modalities)

- Dyadic therapy (e.g. Parent-Child Interaction Therapy)

- Group therapy

- Family therapy

Home-based and family-centered service approaches may also be helpful in supporting children and families. Home visiting programs, family resource centers, family conferencing, and wraparound models are being developed in many communities that enhance existing systems of care.

Indicators for a Psychological Evaluation

Sometimes the clinical or psychosocial assessment indicates a need for a psychological evaluation to obtain more detailed information regarding the child's psychological functioning or when diagnosis is unclear. For a treatment plan to be successful, it is important to know, for example, whether the child is suffering from Post-Traumatic Stress Disorder or has Attention Deficit Hyperactivity Disorder (ADHD) because the symptoms can be similar but the treatment plans are different.

Psychologists are the only mental health professionals accredited to perform psychological testing and evaluation.

Psychologists employ a battery of tests that evaluate:

- Cognitive functioning
  Processing information, learning strengths and weaknesses, memory, verbal and nonverbal abilities, and academic abilities.

- Affective functioning
  Emotions, fantasies, and feelings.

- Adaptive functioning
  How an individual functions in the world in areas such as communication, daily living skills, socialization, and motor.

- Pathological functioning
  Ways in which the individual's internal conflicts and drives distort or overwhelm the ability to deal effectively with the demands of external reality.

- Personality
  Clinical symptoms, personality traits and patterns, and interpersonal functioning.

- Developmental functioning
  Cognitive, communication, social, adaptive, and/or motor development.

Psychological testing can address these questions about an individual:

- What are the client's intellectual strengths and limitations?

- Is there evidence of neurological immaturity or impairment?

- What is the nature of past knowledge and achievements, interests, and aptitudes?

- How adequate is reality testing?

- What is the quality of interpersonal relationships?

- What are the adaptive strengths (application of assets and liabilities to new problems, flexibility of approach, persistence, frustration tolerance, and reaction to novelty)?

- To what degree are impulses maintained under control (under-controlled or over-controlled)?

- How does the person defend psychologically (protect the self from feelings, ideas, and experiences that create anxiety through avoidance, repression, fighting or aggression, etc.) against unacceptable internal needs and demands or

external experiences? How rigid are the client's defenses?

- What are the areas of conflict?

- Does the child have a psychiatric disorder?

- What is the diagnosis?

- What is the child's developmental functioning?

- What treatment strategies and services would be most effective in improving functioning?

- What support services would be helpful to the parents or caregivers?

Indicators for a Psychiatric Evaluation

Psychiatric evaluations are sometimes needed to evaluate complex issues that may need to be resolved with hospitalization or medication support for relief of symptoms.

Psychiatric evaluations are helpful with parents and children in cases involving:

- a previous psychiatric history;

- psychotic symptoms such as hallucinations (e.g. hearing voices), delusional thinking (odd or magical beliefs) or bizarre ideation;

- suicidal ideation or attempts or self-destructive behaviors;

- significant anxiety (fears/worrying) and depression (sadness/withdrawal/anger/passivity);

- episodes of dissociation, i.e. "spacing out";

- inattention, forgetfulness, distractibility, or difficulty concentrating;

- aggressive outbursts (whether toward others or animals) or firesetting;

- hyperactivity or excessive energy;

- changes in sleeping or eating patterns;

- pain or any medical symptom that does not have medical basis;

- regressed behaviors (e.g. bedwetting in a previously "dry" child);

- inappropriate sexualized behaviors; and/or,

- obsessive thoughts or compulsive behaviors.

What is the difference between a forensic evaluation and a clinical evaluation?

Evaluations of Children

Mental health professionals are sometimes called upon to evaluate children for legal purposes. Forensic psychology refers to psychological methods or knowledge applied to the resolution of legal concerns. This is different from a clinical evaluation for mental health treatment. Examples include: a child showing behavioral symptoms of being sexually abused, but will not make any verbal statements; allegations in divorce/child custody disputes which include abuse or neglect; confusion or conflict exists in the case, and an independent professional is needed to sort out the issues.

Forensic evaluations may be helpful in determining whether there is sufficient information to file charges related to child maltreatment and if the child is sufficiently capable of providing valid and reliable information. Typically, this involves determining the child's ability to recall information, acquiring basic information about the complaint, and documenting psychological and behavioral symptoms associated with abuse that support the allegation.

Evaluations of Parents or Caregivers

Evaluations are performed of both abusive and non-offending parents, and other caregivers of children. The purpose of the evaluation of abusive parents is to assess their mental status; the presence of personality disorders, psychiatric problems, or psychopathology, character strengths and weaknesses, the precipitant of the abuse/

neglect and whether the precipitants are chronic or situational; whether the person has a substance abuse problem; whether the parent admits or denies the abuse/neglect and can acknowledge the emotional or physical consequences to the child; whether the parent is amenable to treatment; the type of treatment recommended; and the presence or absence of supportive family and friends.

Evaluation of non-abusive parents include the issues listed above and an assessment of the non-abusive parent's relationship to the abusive parent, e.g. whether the parent is intimidated by or dependent on the abuser and whether the parent is able and willing to protect the child and comply with court orders. Evaluations are also helpful in assessing the capacity of a parent or other caregiver to protect the child and meet the child's physical, developmental, and emotional needs. This may include an evaluation of the nature and quality of the parent's or caregiver's relationship with the child and the types of treatment or support services that would be effective in strengthening parent-child relationships and improving family functioning.

Resources

Peterson, M.S., and Urquiza, A.J. *The Role of Mental Health Professionals in the Prevention and Treatment of Child Abuse and Neglect: The User Manual Series.* U.S. Department of Health and Human Services' National Center on Child Abuse and Neglect, 1993.

The Foster Care Crisis: Translating Research into Policy and Practice. Edited by Patrick A. Curtis, Grady Dale Jr., and Joshua Kendall. Nebraska press in association with the Child Welfare League of America, 1999

Developmental Issues in Abused and Neglected Children

Theresa Witt, Ph.D. and Robin Lee Hansen, M.D.

Case Vignette

Adam is a 6-year-old boy referred for evaluation by his county social worker, due to concerns about a previous diagnosis of Attention Deficit Hyperactivity Disorder and recommendation for medication. Administration of a prescription was postponed pending the results of a developmental evaluation. Concerns raised by both Adam's foster parents and his biological mother report problems with attention and comprehension, risky behavior, deep sadness, being isolated and withdrawn, and inconsistent episodes of hyperactivity. Adam has reportedly been aggressive toward peers in his school classroom and needs a great deal of supervision. Adam also has difficulty understanding why he has "time-out" when he breaks rules or misbehaves. Despite the foster mother's efforts at explaining why Adam has consequences for his behavior, he still seems confused and often becomes upset. The foster mother feels that Adam does not know how to play and have fun, and that he rarely smiles. At night Adam insists on having blankets over him, regardless of the weather, and he becomes upset if she uncovers him. Adam receives no intervention services at this time. Adam was reportedly born via emergency cesarean section due to placenta previa, at approximately 32 weeks gestation (two months premature). He was placed in foster care due to neglect and probable physical abuse. Adam has two siblings, one with a diagnosis of cerebral palsy and another who is struggling in school.

Questions

1. What are developmental disorders?
2. When do you refer a child for a developmental assessment?
3. What impact does abuse and neglect have on child development?
4. How are the results of these evaluations used?

Developmental Disorders

Every year, thousands of children are diagnosed with neurodevelopmental disorders. These disorders, caused by disturbances in the brain's development, can take many forms and are variably expressed. Consideration of the holistic development of the child, including psychosocial aspects of functioning, are important in identifying neurodevelopmental disorders such as autism, learning disorders, mental retardation, cerebral palsy, and the impact of premature birth. Developmental disorders are complex and often co-occurring. Some genetically-based disorders have known incidence rates, such as Fragile X, which has a 1 in 2500 rate of occurrence. Other developmental disorders are more common, such as learning disorders (rates range from 1 in 10 to 1 in 20). Many developmental disorders are the result of biological and environmental risk factors. These risks include: low birth weight, prematurity, exposure to prenatal teratogens (including drugs/alcohol), family history of developmental disorders, poverty, failure to thrive, malnutrition, medical disorders (e.g. lead poisoning, PKU), and child neglect and abuse. For many developmental disorders there are no specific identified causes. To ensure that children receive the best possible care, a specialized multi-disciplinary developmental evaluation is strongly recommended for children with suspected developmental problems.

Indicators for Making a Referral

Early diagnosis gives the child with developmental disorders an important head start. It is especially critical that a treatment plan be determined and implemented before or during the child's early school years. Guidelines for referral for a developmental evaluation include:

- delays in reaching early developmental milestones (such as sitting, crawling, babbling or using words, and learning new social or play skills);

- language delay, cognitive delay, fine and gross motor skill delay;

- hyperactivity or behavior problems;

- regression (loss) of skills;

- school or learning problems;

- atypical behaviors (e.g. inability to interact or play with other children, inattention, daily living skill and self-care deficits);

- history of prenatal drug exposure, low birth weight or prematurity;

- inability to understand or follow directions, or inability to explain ideas or speak clearly; and/or,

- children with histories of child neglect and abuse.

What impact does abuse and neglect have on child development?

Numerous studies have documented the high incidence of developmental disorders in the foster care population. As all aspects of a child's development are closely interwoven, it is not surprising that many children who have suffered negative impact from environmental factors can also demonstrate difficulties in multiple areas of development. In Simms (1989) sample of 113 young foster children in Connecticut, 61% had developmental delays categorized in the following way: language development (52%), fine motor skills (29%), gross motor skills (23%), and cognition (18%). The Blatt (1987) study in New York shows similar data, and also discovered that of the 29 children referred for a neurological screen (sample size of 212) 56% had abnormal examinations. Further, 30% of Halfon's sample was found to have abnormal neurologic findings. In this large sample (n=213) of foster children in California, Halfon (1995) found an 84% incidence of developmental, emotional or behavior problems. This included the following rates of developmental delay: gross motor (33%), fine motor (35%), expressive language (44%), receptive language (35%), cognition (36%), and self–help (37%). The Horwitz (1994) study found that 53% of the 272 children studied showed developmental delays, 92% of whom demonstrated cognitive/language delay, 73% personal/social/adaptive delay, and 56% motor skill delays.

Cicchetti and Toth (1995) and other researchers (Crouch & Miller, 1993; Law & Conway, 1992; Cicchetti & Rogosch, 1994) provide comprehensive reviews of developmental functioning in maltreated and neglected youth. Findings include disturbed attachments, less social competence, and poor adjustment to school across all age ranges. School failure, high grade-retention rates, low achievement

scores particularly in math and reading, and lack of "secure readiness to learn", have been documented. Children with neglect in their history have even greater difficulties in the academic realm, than children who experienced abuse only (Leiter & Johnson, 1994). Several studies have found language and cognitive scores to be significantly lower in abuse and neglect populations, even when socioeconomic status and ethnicity are controlled for in matched subjects (Wright, 1994; Oates et al, 1984; Eckenrode et al, 1993). The impact of neglect and maltreatment on language functioning has been documented even in toddlers (Coster, 1989), as they evidence decreased use of expressive language, less communication about self/needs, and decreased mean length of utterance. Culp et al (1991) found particular vulnerability for language delays in neglected children. The influence of these findings is far reaching, as language functioning is known to effect socio-emotional competence as well (Coster & Cicchetti, 1993). Other areas of development commonly overlooked involve children's play and associated social development. Maltreated preschool children evidence less interactive play, less self-control in social interchanges, and lower peer sociometric rating (Fantuzzo, 1998). Less symbolic play, a greater number of transitions, and higher aggression levels have also been noted (Alessandri, 1991).

The relationship between developmental delays (particularly language delays), and child abuse/neglect continues to be investigated. Famularo (1992) completed an analysis of early developmental risks of abuse/neglect, the most significant of which was behavior problems. A second cluster included low birth-weight, neonatal sleep problems and failure to thrive. Finally, a third factor focused on the parents' perception of their child having a "difficult" temperament during the first year of life. These early developmental issues further underscore the importance of identification and intervention into developmental issues as potential preventive measures against child abuse.

Recent studies have begun to focus on the more immediate impact of these disorders on children's placement status. Horwitz (1994) found that a subset of children with developmental problems remain in foster care for long periods of time. Simms (1989) found higher rates of developmental problems in children approaching school age (in a study assessing children from birth to 6 years), and in children who were older when they were first placed into foster care. It is essential to have knowledge of a child's developmental level (especially language and cognition) in order to obtain a valid interview regarding history of abuse/neglect, and to provide successful psychotherapy goals and interventions.

Since developmental problems can coexist, and many emotional or behavioral symptoms can mimic developmental disorders, special attention must be given to these children with multiple risk factors and frequent changes in their environment and caregiving. Glod & Teicher (1996) found that abused children with post-traumatic stress disorder demonstrate activity levels similar to children with attention deficit hyperactivity disorder. This was found to be particularly true in children experiencing abuse at younger ages. Abused children without PTSD diagnoses were found to have activity levels similar to depressed children. Glod concluded that these findings were due to symptom overlap, not the presence of comorbid disorders. These findings highlight the need for comprehensive understanding of a child's history and development, prior to drawing diagnostic conclusions.

Finally, the Halfon (1995) and Simms (1989) studies have indicated that foster parents or social workers reported concerns regarding only 33 to 40 percent of the children found to have significant developmental, emotional or behavioral problems. These significant problems were found most commonly in children who were first placed into foster care when they were older than two years of age, and those having had multiple changes in placement. Even within the general population, pediatricians have difficulty identifying developmental disorders in children who need intervention and referrals for more comprehensive assessment. Research (Palfrey, 1987) indicates that only 16% of special needs children are identified by their pediatricians, and that screening measures have low sensitivity resulting in an *under*-referral for services.

What is a formal developmental evaluation and how does it differ from psychological and pediatric consultations?

A formal child developmental evaluation requires a multidisciplinary team using an ecological developmental model that recognizes "the complex relationship between the developing person and the environment" (Nuttall et al, 1999). Such a team should minimally include a Social Worker, a Clinical Psychologist with specialized training in child development and developmental disorders, and a Developmental-Behavioral Pediatrician. Assessment requires knowledge of typical and atypical development, cultural and social aspects of behavior, psychometric concepts, multiple diagnostic measures and techniques, ethical/legal issues and an understanding of the child welfare and other intervention service systems.

The Role of the Clinical Psychologist

A Clinical Psychologist helps to assess knowledge and processing abilities through observation and structured methods. Systematic use of specialized techniques and standardized tests are employed to better understand the broad developmental status of a child. This assessment is used as a decision-making tool to assist with diagnosis, designing interventions, monitoring progress, and as a way of finding solutions to problems. Results of such specialized assessments assist in diagnosing mental retardation, learning disorders, ADHD, and in determining the functional outcomes of other neurodevelopmental disorders for treatment planning purposes.

A Developmental Psychological Evaluation can assess the following:

- Cognitive functioning, including how one regards and understands the world, intellectual strengths and limitations;

- Early developmental accomplishment, including developmental milestones in infants and toddlers, language, cognitive, motor, social and adaptive abilities;

- Academic achievement, including approach to learning, preschool or school readiness, and the presence of learning disorders. This area also assesses school problems, the nature of past knowledge and achievements, interests and aptitudes;

- Adaptive functioning, including how one deals with changes, play skills, self-care, communication, daily living skills, coping skills, adaptability and social skills;

- Affective/behavioral functioning, including emotional and behavioral regulation, self-concept/identity, level of impulse control and socio-emotional abilities. The depth and degree of emotional problems (anxiety and depression), or behavioral problems (acting out and aggressive behavior) are assessed;

- Screen psychomotor, language/communication functioning, to determine need for more in-depth assessment by a specialist in those fields;

- Determine personal strengths, resources, risks and vulnerabilities. Factors to consider during the assessment are: strengths and vulnerabilities of the immediate and extended family and friends; local school and community agency resources; family values and culture (race/ethnicity/cultural attitudes and beliefs); and application of assets and liabilities to new problems; flexibility of approach, persistence, frustration tolerance; and,

- Neuropsychological functioning.

What is a neuropsychological evaluation?

- This is a specialized assessment that can assist in understanding complex brain processes and functions. Often this occurs when standard psychological evaluation and educational test batteries have already been administered and answers to problems are still unclear, or intervention strategies are not producing expected results. Examples include: language and auditory processing problems; severe reading deficits; memory difficulties; learning problems; reasoning deficits; visual/motor skill problems; or a discrepancy between abilities and daily functioning. This type of assessment is also used to assess the behavioral/functional impact of acquired brain injury/trauma.

The Role of the Developmental-Behavioral Pediatrician

A Developmental-Behavioral Pediatrician evaluates a child to assess deviations in development and behavior, and to determine specific etiologies of these problems. These include biological insults, such as genetic and chromosomal disorders, perinatal stresses, physical defects and injuries, infections, dietary deficiencies or environmental toxins, as well as psychosocial variables. Specialized neurodevelopmental diagnostic tests, assessments and treatment recommendations are provided for clinical conditions such as mental retardation, autistic disorders, physical disabilities, attention problems, language and learning disabilities, and long-term developmental and behavioral complications of prematurity and prenatal drug exposure.

The Developmental Behavioral Pediatrician evaluates the following:

- Medical or biological risk factors in the medical history;

- Family history relevant to developmental disorders;

- Congenital anomalies and physical findings suggestive of endocrinological, metabolic or genetic disorders;

- Neurological development, including evidence of focal abnormalities, neurological immaturity or impairment, fine and gross motor impairments;

- Physical development, including height, weight, head circumference relative to age;

- Visual and auditory functioning;

- Diagnostic testing, including recommendations for further diagnostic measures and/or interpretation of these measures (such as brain imaging, ophthalmologic and audiometric assessment, metabolic, genetic/chromosomal testing or other diagnostic blood work); and,

- Medication management, including prescriptions to target specific behaviors or medical disorders, and monitoring efficacy of medication and other adjunct interventions.

The Role of the Social Worker

A Social Worker provides a psychosocial assessment of current family functioning and obtains a family history of developmental, educational, social, and psychiatric disorders. The role of the children within the family and community system is identified along with the family's strengths, stressors, and coping strategies. Supportive counseling, case management and resource referrals follow the initial assessment with the intent of assisting the family in becoming effective advocates for their child and developing their ability to provide a nurturing environment in which the child will thrive.

How are the results of these evaluations used?

Early Intervention

Delays left inadequately addressed can become more severe and secondary deficits may develop. The synergistic relationship between a developing child, learning, and environment is vital. Development builds upon itself, and unresolved difficulties in one area can have a detrimental effect on other areas of functioning, and on later development within the same domain.

Treatment Planning

Helping children with developmental disorders grow and thrive in their homes and communities requires a cooperative effort between specialists and therapists, the patient's primary care provider, and the family. The team works together to provide feedback of diagnostic results to caretakers/social workers, to develop individual treatment recommendations and goals, and to refer the child to other appropriate specialists.

Collaborative Relationships

Due to the broad nature of developmental disorders, the clinic may serve as a gateway to other specialized programs/professionals, e.g. genetics, child neurology, speech/language pathology, audiology, physical therapy, pediatric endocrinology. Referrals to community agencies and providers, such as the Regional Centers, Special Education Departments of the school districts, child and family mental health providers, and parent support groups are common.

Follow-up

Patients need to be followed as determined by their individual needs, based on complex and often changing developmental trajectories. Children with moderate to severe or multiple developmental disorders, often require more frequent or long-term monitoring to assist primary providers in preventing and treating problems that accompany disorders, recommend changes in intervention services, monitor the child's general health/development, and help build a support network for the child's family.

Conclusion of Case Vignette

During the comprehensive developmental evaluation, Adam presented as guarded, wary and sad. Adam seemed vigilant of the examiner's facial expressions for feedback, and he did not respond to praise and encouragement in any overt manner. Adam's motor responses tended to be slow and deliberate, and his attention to tasks was generally good. Adam's head circumference was at the 90th percentile, and his height and weight were at the 25th percentile. He has blond hair and blue eyes, with epicanthal folds and large ears. Thickening of the nasal bridge was also present. Dentition was normal, although he had significant crowding, with malocclusion. On neurological examination, he had mild generalized hypotonia with normal reflexes, immature balance and poor gross and fine motor skills. Intellectual assessment indicated deficient cognitive functioning overall (FSIQ = 67). Language screening suggested that his comprehension of connected language is impaired. Adam evidenced adaptive skill deficits in communication, daily living skills, and socialization. Adam's adaptive skills were particularly delayed in the area of socialization. Adam's symptom presentation was not consistent with ADHD, and was better accounted for by developmental delays (both cognitive and language) and emotional difficulties. What appeared to be inattention is likely lack of understanding. Since Adam was functioning at a developmental level much younger than his chronological age, his level of attention, impulse control and activity should be expected to be similar to a younger child as well.

In addition, Adam presented with a number of symptoms reflective of depression and anxiety.

Diagnoses of Childhood Depression with Anxious features and Mild Mental Retardation were made. A DNA probe for Fragile X syndrome was positive for a full mutation, confirming the suspected diagnosis of Fragile X Syndrome as the etiology for Adam's mental retardation. It is suspected that post-traumatic stress disorder may be present as a consequence of his history of child abuse and neglect. Recommendations were made for appropriate special education interventions, an Individualized Educational Plan, referral to the Regional Center, and assessment by a speech-language pathologist to rule out a superimposed language disorder. Participation in individual psychotherapy (play therapy) in a developmentally sensitive manner was recommended to address emotional disturbance. An assessment of the parents' ability to meet Adam's special needs before reunification with them is also warranted. Finally, recommendations were made for developmental enrichment through a stimulating environment, and monitoring of his developmental and emotional functioning through re-evaluation in one year.

Positive Impact

With appropriate evaluation, identification, and intervention, professionals can work collaboratively to offer maltreated children with disabilities a chance to grow; and, to help their caregivers and others who work with them develop a better understanding of their needs and strengths. By providing meaningful solutions to the problems that these children and families face every day, placements can be enhanced to adequately meet children's developmental needs. Through these efforts, children can look toward futures that are stable and positive.

Suggested Readings/References:

Assessing and Screening Preschoolers: Psychological and Educational Dimensions (1999) 2nd edition, Edited by Nuttall, Romero & Kalesnik. Allyn & Bacon

The Classification of Child and Adolescent Mental Diagnoses in Primary Care: DSM-PC (1996) Edited by Wolraich, Felice & Drotar. American Academy of Pediatrics.

Developmental-behavioral Pediatrics (1999) Edited by Levine, Carey and Crocker. WB Saunders Co.

Handbook of Early Childhood Intervention (1990) Edited by Meisels, & Shonkoff. Cambridge University Press.

Interdiscplinary Clinical Assessment of Young Children with Developmental Disabilities (2000) Edited by M. Guralnick, Ph.D. Paul H. Brookes Publishing Co.

Alessandri (1992) Mother-child interactional correlates of maltreated and nonmaltreated children's play behavior. *Development and Psychopathology*, 4, 257-270.

Alessandri (1991) Play and social behavior in maltreated preschoolers. *Development and Psychopathology*, 3, 191-205.

Cicchetti & Rogosch (1994) The toll of child maltreatment on the developing child. *Child and Adolescent Psychiatry Clinics of North America*, 3 (4), 759-776.

Cicchetti and Toth (1995) A developmental psychopathology perspective on child abuse and neglect. *Journal of the American Academy of Child and Adolescent Psychiatry*, 35 (4), 541-565.

Coster and Cicchetti (1993) Research on the communicative development of maltreated children: Clinical Implications. *Topics in Language Disorders*, 13 (4), 25-38.

Coster et al (1989) Communicative functioning in maltreated toddlers. *Developmental Psychology*, 25, 1020-1029.

Crouch & Milner (1993) Effects of child neglect on children. *Criminal Justice and Behavior*, 20(1), 49-65.

Culp et al (1991) Maltreated children's language and speech development. *First Language*, 11, 377-389.

Eckenrode et al (1993) School performance and disciplinary problems among abused and neglected children. *Developmental psychopathology*, 29, 53-62.

Famularo et al (1992) Medical and developmental histories of maltreated children. *Clinical Pediatrics*, Sept., 536-541.

Fantuzzo et al (1998) A contextually relevant assessment of the impact of child maltreatment on the social competencies of low-income urban children. *Journal of the American Academy of Child and Adolescent Psychiatry*, 37 (11), 1201-1208.

Glod & Teicher (1996) Relationship between early abuse, post-traumatic stress disorder and activity levels in prepubertal children. *Journal of the American Academy of Child and Adolescent Psychiatry*, 34(10), 1384-1393.

Halfon et al (1995) Health status of children in foster care. *Archives of Pediatric and Adolescent Medicine*, 149, 386-392.

Horwitz et al (1994) Impact of developmental problems on young children's exits from foster care. *Developmental and Behavioral Pediatrics*, 15 (2), 105-110.

Law & Conway (1992) Effect of abuse and neglect on the development of children's speech and language. *Developmental Medicine and Child Neurology*, 34, 943-948.

Leiter & Johnson (1994) Child maltreatment and school performance. *American Journal of Education*, 102, 155-165.

Oates et al (1984) The development of abused children. *Developmental Medicine and Child Neurology*, 26, 649-656.

Simms (1989) The foster car clinic: A community program to identify treatment needs of children in foster care. *Developmental and Behavioral Pediatrics*, 10(3), 121-128.

Wright (1994) Physical and emotional abuse and neglect of preschool children: A literature review. *Australian Occupational Therapy Journal*, 41, 55-63.

Treatment Programs for Abused Children and Their Families

Marilyn Strachan Peterson, M.S.W., M.P.A.

Comprehensive Sexual Abuse Treatment Program (CSATP)

The first model for treating incestuous families was developed by Henry Giaretto, Ph.D., in the mid-1970s and is now called the "Giaretto Model" or Parents United. In response to an absence of treatment approaches to deal with incestuous families, Giaretto developed the Comprehensive Sexual Abuse Treatment program (CSATP), which consists of:

- individual counseling (child, mother, father);

- mother-daughter or mother-son counseling;

- marital counseling;

- father-daughter or father-son counseling;

- family counseling;

- group counseling for non-offending mothers and fathers, offending mothers and fathers;

- couples, girls, boys, and non-victimized siblings; and,

- a self-help group component (e.g. Parents United, Daughters and Sons United).

Sexual abuse treatment program models have expanded since the original model to include:

- individual and group treatment for adolescent sex offenders

- individual and group treatment for abuse-reactive children (young children who act out sexually towards others as a result of being sexually abused).

Variations of the model have developed over the years; however, the organizing theme of every program is the development of a comprehensive and coordinated approach designed to meet the needs of all of the family members. Local programs' philosophies regarding incarceration and treatment services for the perpetrator are the most frequent reason for the variation in approach. Legislation regarding offender treatment in recent years has facilitated the "deferred entry of judgment approach" whereby select offenders meeting specific criteria can complete mental health treatment in lieu of criminal prosecution.

Child Physical Abuse Treatment

Multiple variables contribute to physical abuse and a successful program must consider how to respond to the multiple stressors that provoke violence. Risk factors for physical abuse include environmental, psychological, and interpersonal stressors:

- environmental stressors such as unemployment, financial problems, poor or inadequate housing, or lack of transportation;

- parental interpersonal stressors such as marital discord, domestic violence, single parenting, imbalanced relationship with marital partner (dominant or noninvolved), past history of abuse, isolation, or inadequate social and familial support;

- interpersonal problems such as low self-esteem, low sense of self-competence, poor self-control, poor interpersonal skills, poor communication skills, poor problem-solving skills, anxiety, depression, or substance abuse;

- poor parenting skills (rigid, authoritarian, or poor limit setting), with little knowledge about child development and current child rearing practices; and,

- child with behavioral problems or special needs that cause stress, such as developmental delay, chronic illness, or physical disability.

Recommended interventions include:

- individual;

- dyad therapy with parent and child;

- group therapy;

- marital counseling; and,

- parenting education groups with a curriculum that includes anger management and impulse control, stress reduction, increasing self-esteem and coping skills, and child management skills.

Neglecting Families: Intensive In-Home Interventions

Intensive, in-home therapeutic counseling and social services have been found to be most effective with neglecting families. The primary goals of these services are to improve parents' abilities to raise their children in a healthy environment, keep families intact through supportive services, and reduce the risk of an out-of-home placement for children. These services are designed to:

- improve family coping skills and functioning;

- provide emotional support to parents;

- model problem solving for coping with everyday problems and parent-child interactions;

- promote positive parenting skills and optimal child development; and

- teach household management skills, including nutrition and financial management.

The programs' "parent the parent" strategy allows initial dependence before encouraging independence. "Do for, do with, cheer on" describes the philosophy and approach of these programs. See Chapter XXII, Prevention, which has a section on Home Visiting Programs.

Resources

These state agencies often fund child abuse treatment programs and have program listings for the State of California. The training organizations listed below provide training to child abuse treatment programs.

Children's Branch
Governor's Office of Criminal Justice Planning
1130 K Street
Sacramento, California 95814
ocjp.ca.gov

Office of Child Abuse Prevention
State Department of Social Services
744 P Street
Sacramento, California 95814
www.dss.cahwnet.gov/getser/cfsocap

CATTA (Child Abuse Training and Technical Assistance Centers)
Northern California Child Abuse Training and Technical Assistance Center
California Institute on Human Services
California State University, Sonoma
1801 East Cotati Avenue
Rohnert Park, CA 94928
www.sonoma.edu/CIHS/html/catta/cattacontact

PCIT Training Center
CAARE Diagnostic and Treatment Center
Department of Pediatrics
University of California, Davis Children's Hospital
3300 Stockton Boulevard
Sacramento, CA 95820
web.ucdmc.ucdavis.edu/medtrng

Parent-Child Interaction Therapy

Anthony J. Urquiza, Ph.D. and Patricia Stock, M.F.T.

Case Vignette

Jake is a three-year old boy who had a history of physical abuse. He resides in a two-parent prospective adoptive home with his 6-year-old sister. Prior to Parent Child Interaction Therapy (PCIT), Jake was kicked out of two day care centers due to aggressive behaviors toward his peers and refusing to follow directions. The prospective adoptive mother was concerned that Jake's behaviors would preclude him from successfully participating in kindergarten when he turned five years old. The prospective adoptive parents were considering terminating Jake's placement with them due to his aggressive behaviors and need for excessive supervision.

Jake and his caregivers were referred to PCIT to address Jake's aggressive behaviors, mood swings, and acts which distanced him away from forming nurturing relationships with others. An additional goal was to avoid the possibility of future multiple placements. Aggressive behaviors included hitting and kicking four or more times per day and biting three to four times per day. He was also defiant ten or more times per day including running away from the caregiver, throwing objects, and refusing to comply with reasonable requests. He would engage in provoking others, refusing to talk, being argumentative, and constantly testing limits placed upon him. This behavior was consistent for more than six months. Jake's expressive speech was also delayed. He would use gestures to indicate what he wanted, or engage in tantrums. He exhibited more than four tantrums per day lasting a minimum of twenty minutes each. The tantrums included striking out, kicking, screaming, and crying. When Jake was initially placed with the current caregivers, he did not want to be touched, talked to, or given much focused attention and nurturing.

The PCIT sessions are near completion with Jake and his prospective adoptive parents. The current results are remarkable. Jake's aggressive acts have decreased significantly. Jake no longer bites or strikes out at others. He accepts affection from his prospective adoptive parents more readily, asks to sit in their laps, cuddles, and accepts hugs. He now enjoys a pat on the back rather than yelling, "Don't touch me!" Jake also seeks to engage in conversation with both caregivers, as well as others. He seldom tells the caregivers to stop talking to him anymore. The focused attention that the caregivers have been giving to Jake has helped increase his speech and ability to listen, considerably. He has learned to be more compliant, requiring less than four timeouts in one week. His willingness to comply with directives given by the caregivers occurs typically eight out of ten times, within a five-second time frame.

Jake prefers to engage with the caregivers with positive interactions rather than experience an absence of engagement when he is misbehaving. He has been able to experience the trustworthiness of his caregivers through their ability to set limits consistently, maintain routine, demonstrate their commitment, and provide a warm, nurturing, fun loving environment. In addition, Jake has been able to attend preschool without any notable behavior problems for over ten weeks, as reported by the preschool staff. As a result, the caregivers have enthusiastically committed themselves to proceeding with the adoption of Jake and his sister.

Questions

1. What is Parent-Child Interaction Therapy (PCIT)?

2. What are the elements of this treatment approach?

3. What training resources are available?

While there are many approaches to treating physically abusive families, Parent-Child Interaction Therapy (PCIT) is an intervention that targets specific deficits found within physically abusive parent-child dyads. PCIT was developed at the Oregon Health and Science University for the treatment of a broad range of childhood externalizing disorders (Eyberg & Robinson, 1983). The foundational model of change is similar to that of a parent training program. The underlying concept is that modifying the way parents interact with their children diminishes child behavior problems which, in turn, reduces the risk that the parents might abuse their children. PCIT, however, is unique in that it incorporates both the parent and child within the treatment session, uses live and individualized therapist coaching, and tailors the process of changing the dysfunctional parent-child relationship to the specific interaction patterns of each parent-child dyad.

PCIT is conducted in two phases: a Relationship Enhancement phase (often described as Child-Directed Interaction) and a Discipline phase (often described as Parent-Directed Interaction). Both phases of treatment are conducted within the context of an initial didactic training, followed by therapist coaching in dyadic play situations. The coaching is conducted from an observation room using a 'bug-in-the-ear' or hearing aide receiving device. Parents are taught and practice specific skills of communication and behavior management with their child. In the Relationship Enhancement phase (typically seven to ten sessions), the primary goal is to create or strengthen a positive and mutually rewarding relationship between parents and their children (see Hembree-Kigin & McNeil, 1996, for a full description of the PCIT program). In the Discipline phase (typically seven to ten sessions, which follow the Relationship Enhancement sessions), the primary goal is to provide specific and effective parenting skills for parents to use in managing their child's behavior.

There have been numerous studies demonstrating the effectiveness of PCIT for reducing child behavior problems. Treatment effects also have been shown to generalize across time, to the home, to school settings, and to untreated siblings. Given the documented effectiveness of PCIT in helping non-abusive parents manage their behavior-problem children, recent research has demonstrated that it is also effective in decreasing child behavioral problems with maltreated children, and enhancing their relationship with their foster parents (Urquiza, Timmer, Zebell, McGrath, & Herschell, 2002).

PCIT is appropriate for children who:

- are between the ages of 2 and 8 years of age;

- are exhibiting chronic behavioral problems at home, school, preschool or daycare;

- are currently living with one or both of their parents (the program is also offered for foster and adoptive parents); and

- may be on medication to manage their behavioral problems.

Although PCIT can be applied to different types of problems, it has been most effectively used with children who are aggressive and/or have behavioral problems (e.g., oppositional behavior, defiance, non-compliance). Since abused children's aggressiveness and behavior problems are widely documented, PCIT is proving to be an effective therapeutic modality for treating abused children who have behavioral problems (Urquiza, Timmer, McGrath, Zebell, & Herschell, 2002).

PCIT Training Program

The CAARE Diagnostic and Treatment Center offers training for agencies to facilitate dissemination and replication of this treatment model. Training is provided in four phases:

Phase One

Phase one is program development which first involves, review and consultation on the training plan and curriculum.

Phase Two

Phase two focuses on the fundamentals of PCIT; providing training on Child-Directed Interaction (CDI) concepts including a description of the theoretical aspects of PCIT and the relationship between PCIT and interventions for high-risk families; Dyadic Parent-Child Interaction Coding System (DPICS) coding; teaching basic PCIT-CDI coaching techniques; and initiating and/or supervising role-plays of parent-child interactions.

Phase Three

Phase three is PCIT Intensive Skill-Building; providing PCIT coaching training; enhancing trainees' CDI skills; providing extensive description and training on Parent-Directed Interaction (PDI); and teaching PDI coaching training to Trainers of Trainers (TOT) staff.

Phase Four

Phase four is the advanced TOT training/consultation/ supervision/training. It is the continued advanced training in PCIT service delivery and includes teaching identified TOT staff all PCIT coaching theoretical concepts, skills, exercises, and procedures; providing supervision to TOT staff regarding specific cases in PCIT assessment and/or PCIT treatment; providing live coaching of TOT staff and clients; conducting written and videotaped training assessments of Advanced PCIT knowledge and coaching to TOT and other staff; and, providing feedback to agency or staff regarding these assessments.

References

Eyberg, S., and Robinson, E.A. (1983). Conduct problem behavior: Standardization of a behavioral rating scale with adolescents. *Journal of Clinical Child Psychology*, 12, 347-354.

Hembree-Kigin, T., and McNeil, C.B. (1995). *Parent-Child Interaction Therapy*. New York: Plenum Publishers.

Urquiza, A.J., Timmer, S., Herschell, A., McGrath, J., Zebell, N., Porter, A., and Vargas, E. (under review). Parent-Child Interaction Therapy: Application of an empirically supported treatment to maltreated children in foster care. *Child Welfare*.

Urquiza, A.J., Timmer, S., McGrath, J., Zebell, N., Herschell, A. (under review). Parent-Child Interaction Therapy: Application to physically abusive and high-risk parent-child dyads. *Child Abuse and Neglect*.

Resources

Parent-Child Interaction Therapy (PCIT) Training Center
CAARE Diagnostic and Treatment Center
Department of Pediatrics
UC Davis Children's Hospital
3300 Stockton Boulevard
Sacramento, CA 95820
(916) 734-6610
http://children.ucdmc.ucdavis.edu

PART 10

Model Health Program for Abused and Neglected Children Placed in Foster Care

Nancy Joye, M.D., Mary Beth Metcalf, M.D., Marcia C. Britton, M.D., Robin Lee Hansen, M.D., Melanie Bobbitt, P.H.N, Agnes Felicano, F.N.P., Nancy Gadsby, P.H.N, and Marilyn Strachan Peterson, M.S.W., M.P.A.

Case Vignette

A family of 13 children, ranging in age from 11 months to 17 years, were taken into custody for general and severe neglect. They presented to the Foster Care Health Program for medical evaluation with a history of essentially no schooling and no immunizations. At the time they were taken into custody, several of the children had respiratory infections with cough that took a few weeks to resolve. One child was treated for pneumonia. No significant home schooling had been done and the oldest child was unable to sign his name although one of the "middle children" had learned a little reading. In addition to the obvious academic deficiencies, evaluation of these children revealed developmental delays in almost all the children, behavior and emotional problems (including severe anxiety) that interfered with adaptation to placement, short stature in five of the children, chronic ear infections in one child leading eventually to tubes and adenoidectomy, significant visual problems in three of the children, severe articulation problems in several of the children including a residual articulation defect in two of the oldest girls, and dental caries in several of the children. Two of the girls later disclosed observation of sexual activity of some of the older children with the father as well as some victimization of the younger children. Consultations with ENT, ophthalmology, pediatric endocrinology and behavior and development were required. Mental health services were also necessary and somewhat difficult to obtain. Several of the children were seen back for immunization updates and other rechecks. Eventually several of the children required sexual abuse examinations.

Questions

1. What medical problems do children have that are placed in foster care?

2. What medical follow-up do foster children need?

3. How many foster children need referrals for dental care?

4. What types of developmental and mental health problems are common in foster children?

Epidemiology/Statistics

There are approximately 6,000 children in foster care in Sacramento County in 1999 and 103,000 in the State of California. Children in foster care suffer high rates of serious physical and psychological problems compared with other children from the same socioeconomic backgrounds. Various studies have been completed on sample populations. About one-third of foster children in all studies suffer from acute and chronic medical conditions.

Foster children are diagnosed with asthma at 3 times the national average. Examples of other medical problems include: anemia (20%); nervous system (30%); respiratory (18%); digestive (15%), and dermatologic problems (23%). Foster children also have multiple health problems. A study completed in Oakland, California (sample size = 213) from which the above statistics were also taken, 30% of the children were diagnosed with one medical problem; 23% with 2 problems; and 29% with 3 or more medical problems. (Halfon, et al, 1995)

Developmental problems have received little attention in the child welfare system, because most caseworkers do not receive training in identifying these problems. Results of the 1995 Halfon study identified the following developmental delays: language development (44%); fine motor skills (33%); gross motor skills (33%); and cognition (36%). Current protocols do not call for mental health screening of foster children upon entry into foster care. The Halfon study identified these mental health problems by functional domain: emotional functioning (60%); relationships (51%); coping (54%); and behavioral problems (29%).

The cause of these conditions are multiple and stem largely from being raised in neglectful homes caused by parental addiction to alcohol and drugs (exacerbated by the crack cocaine epidemic beginning in the 1980s), lack of medical care, domestic violence, uneven school attendance, and unstable living conditions prior to removal from the family. The trauma of family separation, frequent foster placements, and the stress and disruption brought about by lack of permanent placements compound these conditions. Given their overwhelming and complex needs, foster children require and use health services more than other children.

Purpose of a Foster Care Health Program

There is a need for coordinated and consistent medical care and screening for needed dental, developmental, and mental health treatment. The purpose of a Foster Care Health Program is to meet the medical, developmental, mental health, and dental needs of abused and neglected children and adolescents placed in foster care.

Objectives

- Develop a system of health care for children in foster care;

- Screen for developmental, mental health, behavioral, and dental problems;

- Ensure provision of a comprehensive benefit package (Medi-Cal and EPSDT);

- Improve local coordination and delivery of services;

- Employ and integrate foster care public health nurses into the healthcare and children's protective services' system;

- Increase the pool of community medical providers to provide medical homes for these children by reducing barriers to participation;

- Provide standardized training to community medical providers on child abuse and neglect;

- Eliminate access barriers caused by problems in the issuance of Medi-Cal cards;

- Train caseworkers and foster parents on the children's multi-faceted needs;

- Link children to Early Head Start (foster children receive priority for admission); and

- Ensure reliable and accessible history and documentation of the children's health status and future health needs.

Components of a Comprehensive Program

- Initial health screening (clearance exams prior to placement) to identify acute problems;

- Comprehensive health assessment within 30 days of placement to identify acute and chronic medical problems;

- Developmental, mental health, and educational screening and assessment between 30-60 days of placement;

- Routine health care and periodic reassessment of health, development, and mental health status (at least twice during the first year of placement, and annually thereafter);

- Quality Improvement Program; and

- Medical case management and home visiting by public health nurses.

Principal Partners in a Foster Care Health Program Collaborative

- County Child Health and Disability Prevention (CHDP) Program;

- County Children's Protective Services;

- County Mental Health; and a

- Hospital, clinic, or physician group.

Project Services

- Complete "head-to-toe" physical examinations by experienced pediatricians and/or nurse practitioners, preferably with knowledge of child abuse and neglect;

- Protocol for obtaining child sexual abuse consultation with forensic experts;

- Screening for developmental, psychological, and behavioral problems;

- Immunizations and vision/hearing checks;

- Evaluation, treatment and referral to medical subspecialists, dental and mental health experts;

- Development of a health plan which addresses diagnostic, therapeutic, preventive, and rehabilitative care to address the physical and emotional needs of the children;

- Coordinated medical care for all children in a foster family;

- Documentation of children's medical, dental, developmental, and mental health status;

- Coordinated response and follow-up on children's medical and mental health care needs; and

- Referrals to community physicians to be the "medical home."

Program Staffing

- Pediatrician(s) and/or nurse practitioners with training in the needs of foster children;

- RN(s) or LVN(s);

- Patient Care Coordinator (schedules appointments/front and back office work);

- Administrative Assistant;

- Public Health Nurse(s); and

- Data entry personnel to enter health and educational data onto the CWS (Child Welfare Services) State Data System.

Operational Procedures

1. Obtain past medical history.

Biological parents are interviewed by the Foster Care Public Health Nurses after the Juvenile Court Detention hearing to obtain a health history. A standard interview form is used which corresponds to the CWS Health Passport System and is faxed to the medical team.

2. Enroll children in fee-for-service full scope Medi-Cal.

This ensures full medical and dental benefits, and access to EPSDT (Early Periodic Screening, Diagnosis and Treatment) and Supplemental EPSDT. Suggested procedures to expedite issuance of Medi-Cal cards:

- CHDP nurse at Juvenile Court faxes list of children's names to the Medi-Cal Eligibility Unit which issues cards to the foster parents; and

- Children's Protective Services' Dependent Intake Unit faxes the court minute orders regarding dependency to the Medi-Cal Eligibility Unit.

3. Schedule children for medical examinations.

- CHDP Public Health Nurses notify foster parents/caretakers to make medical appointments within 30 days of the child being made a dependent of the court. Foster parents are provided with an explanatory brochure.

- Patient Care Coordinator at the hospital or clinic calls the list of foster parent/caretakers provided by the CHDP Public Health Nurses to schedule appointments.

4. Children are seen for CHDP comprehensive examination and any acute health need.

Foster parents are required to bring the children to the examination to provide a health history and to receive patient education information from the physician. Transporters are not allowed to bring the children to the examination. Typically, children have not had a history of health care, examinations are lengthy and most children need all immunizations. Sexually abused children receive a consult from experts in the evaluation of sexual abuse. Physicians screen for prescription of psychotropic medications due to concerns over inappropriate dosages for children and whether foster children are being inappropriately medicated for behavioral problems. Psychotropic medications cannot be prescribed for foster children without a full mental health evaluation and a court order.

5. Children with health, developmental and behavioral problems are referred to subspecialty clinics, e.g. ophthalmology, dermatology, child development, dental, etc.

Follow up appointments are either made by the Patient Care Coordinator or referral slips are sent to Subspecialty Clinics which schedule their appointments. Public Health Nurses are notified of referrals through the discharge summaries and ensure follow-up appointments are made and kept. Dental referrals are made by calling (in California) 1-800-322-6384.

6. Documentation of Health Care Needs

Three types of documentation can be undertaken depending upon the objectives of the project.

a. Hospital and Clinic Level

At the hospital/clinic level, basic demographic information is recorded, e.g. name of patient, date of birth, date of service, age, gender, type of abuse; health history; examination and laboratory testing results; documentation of dental, developmental and mental health screening; and the types of referrals made to subspecialty clinics for chronic problems, and dental referrals.

b. CWS System Data Base

The CWS system records information on children in which Children's Protective Services has intervened. This is the most effective way of implementing the Health and Education Passport System by having health and educational data entered into this state data system. Collaborate with the local children's protective service agency in your county.

c. Research Data Base

Collaborate with a local university to establish an expanded health database with analysis by statistical experts.

References

Fostering Health: Health Care for Children in Foster Care. Published by The American Academy of Pediatrics, District II, New York State, 2001

Health Status of Children in Foster Care, Neal Halfon, MD, MPH, Ana Mendonca, MPH, Gale Berkowitz, DrPH. *Arch Pediatric and Adolescent Medicine*, Vol. 149, April, 1995.

The Foster Care Clinic: A Community Program to Identify Treatment Needs of Children in Foster Care, Mark D. Simms, MD, MPH., *Developmental Pediatrics*, Vol. 10, No. 3, June, 1989.

A Comprehensive Multidisciplinary Approach to Providing Health Care for Children in Out of Home Care, Steven Blatt, MD, Ronald D. Saletsky, PhD, Victoria Meguid, MB, Catharine Critz Church, PhD, PNP, Maureen T. O'Hara, MS, RN, CNS, Susan M. Haller-Peck, ACSW, June M. Anderson, RN, Child Welfare League of America, 1997.

Impact of Developmental Problems on Young Children's Exits from Foster Care, Sarah McCue Horowitz, PhD, Mark D. Simms, MD, MPH, Raymond Farrington, MSW, *Developmental and Behavioral Pediatrics*, Vol. 15, No. 2, April, 1994.

The Pediatrician and the Child in Foster Care, Moira Szilagyi, M.D., PhD, *Pediatrics in Review*, Vol. 19, No. 2, February, 1998.

Code Blue: Health Services for Children in Foster Care. Published by the Institute for Research on Women and Families, Center for California Studies, California State University, Sacramento. March, 1998.

Resource

Foster Care Health Program
UCDMC CAARE Diagnostic and Treatment Center
UC Davis Children's Hospital
3300 Stockton Boulevard
Sacramento, California 95820
(916) 734-3691

Child Abuse and Juvenile Delinquency: Medical, Developmental and Psychiatric Issues

Diamond Kassam, M.D., M.P.H., Marilyn McCartney, M.D., M.P.H., Rebecca A. Craig, R.N., M.P.A., and Margaret Thompson, R.N., W.H.N.P., M.S.

Case Vignette

Catherine is a 15 year old Caucasian female who appears older than her age. She was referred to the adolescent clinic for school failure and was recently placed on probation for shoplifting as well as fighting with her peers. She has multiple behavior problems including destructive behavior in class and disciplinary action for possession of drugs in school. Catherine has been seen multiple times in the clinic for chest pain and dizziness. She is sexually active and has frequently requested pregnancy testing and STD testing. In terms of personality functioning she has been involved in high-risk taking activities including driving without a license and sexual activity with multiple partners without regard for the consequences of her behavior. She does not use any contraception. She has stolen her stepbrother's Ritalin which he takes for ADHD. She frequently uses marijuana and occasionally cocaine. Catherine's mother accompanies her during the appointment and appears anxious and concerned. She recently separated from her second husband for his drinking problem and spousal abuse. Catherine's recalcitrant behavior preceded the recent separation. Catherine recently accused her step-father of sexually abusing her since age 12. Her mother does not believe this. Catherine has never told the school or clinic staff about this. On today's evaluation, she seems depressed. She has multiple self-inflicted carvings in her skin, some well-healed and some new ones with bright scabs. She has a scar across her left wrist from a suicide attempt one month ago.

Questions

1. What role does neglect, sexual and physical abuse play in the etiology of acting out and high-risk behavior among teenagers?

2. What are the medical, developmental and psychiatric vulnerabilities associated with behaviorally disturbed and antisocial youths?

3. What are their basic health needs and problems related to their lifestyle?

4. What are the responsibilities of the Juvenile Court, Child Protective Services, Probation Department and law enforcement agencies to assure and facilitate adequate diagnosis and treatment of medical and mental health problems?

Abused and Neglected Children's Risk of Arrest as Juveniles and as Adults

Comprehensive and systematically collected data about child abuse and neglect cases and subsequent arrests of children as juveniles and adults is not currently available. Selected studies, however, have been done. Widom (1994) conducted a careful study of arrest outcomes of 908 substantiated cases of physical and sexual abuse and neglect of children who were less than 11 years of age at the time of the abuse incident during the years 1967-1971. Of 908 child victims, 125 experienced sexual abuse only, 28 sexual abuse plus other maltreatment, 70 physical abuse and neglect, 76 physical abuse only, and 609 neglect only. The names of these children and their matched controls were obtained from the files of the juvenile probation department. The results showed that 26% of the abuse/neglect population were arrested for any type of crime as juveniles compared to 17% of the control group, and that 29% were arrested as adults for any type of crime compared to 21% of the control group. These statistics support the conclusion that early childhood victimization places children at increased risk for arrest as juveniles and as adults. Neglect and physical abuse were the highest predictors for arrest as an adult.

- **Arrests for Sex Crimes, Prostitution and Rape**
  Physically abused children were four times more likely to be arrested as an adult for sex crimes of any type especially violent sex crimes (rape/sodomy). Child sexual abuse victims were three times as likely than victims of other types of maltreatment to be arrested as adults (not as juveniles) for prostitution.

- **Runaways**
  Abused and neglected children in general are significantly more likely to be runaways than the control group. The sexual abuse plus group tended to be at increased risk for running away—18% compared to 2.4% for the control group. Of the neglected children, 6.2% ran away and 2.6% of the physically abused children ran away. In this study, there was no direct pathway identified between running away and entry into prostitution as a juvenile as some literature suggests.

What are the health and mental health problems of these high-risk youth?

Health problems of runaway, high risk and delinquent youth include a high incidence of substance abuse, suicide attempts, sexually transmitted disease (STD), high-risk pregnancy with exposure of the fetus to drugs, hepatitis, HIV disease, and serious injuries secondary to firearms and car accidents. Since high risk youth access to health care is limited, their initial contact with nurses and physicians is frequently associated with the criminal justice system, e.g. when they are arrested and taken to the hospital or during health screening at the juvenile hall. A 1998 County study of health status found that in Sacramento, 8% of all females are pregnant at the time of booking and over 35% have chlamydia, gonorrhea or veneral warts. Incidence of bacterial vaginosis, herpes, and other STDs is very high. The females are at particular high risk for HIV disease because of their contact with older, drug-abusing male partners. In addition to lifestyle related health problems, a large number of minors have pre-existing medical problems which have not been addressed in childhood and now have significant complications.

A 1979 Yale University, Child Study Center study of medical histories of 81 incarcerated youth with a socioeconomic and demographic matched non-delinquent sample found that incarcerated youth had:

	DELINQUENT YOUTH	NON-DELINQUENT YOUTH
More hospital visits by age 16	11%	5%
More emergency room visits	6%	2%
More head injuries by age 4	21%	5%
More perinatal difficulties	36.6%	16%
More skull x-rays	33.8%	5.2%
More psychiatric symptoms	44.2%	7.9%
Parents with psychiatric symptoms	22%	3%
History of child abuse	10%	1%

Lewis and Shanok concluded from this study that youth with delinquent behavior were more vulnerable neuropsychiatrically having sustained more perinatal difficulties, accidents, injuries, and abuse. They are also more likely to have psychiatrically disturbed parents than their nondelinquent peers. The combination of psychodynamic and biological factors from medical and psychological trauma result in poor impulse control, learning disabilities, and impaired judgment from central nervous system trauma. This experience coupled with faulty behavioral models in the family and brutality (physical abuse) combine to engender serious delinquent behavior.

Findings by Lewis and Balla (1976) and Lewis and Shanok (1976) found that children referred to a Connecticut juvenile court clinic had unrecognized, undiagnosed, and untreated psychiatric, neurological, and educational disorders which seemed to contribute to their antisocial behavior. This study prompted another follow-up study by Lewis, Shanock, Pincus, and Glaser (1979) to evaluate whether there was any association between the severity of a child's antisocial behavior and his psychiatric, neurological, or psychoeducational status. To answer this question, they compared violent incarcerated juvenile delinquents to less violent incarcerated boys. The findings are summarized on the next page.

	VIOLENT INCARCERATED JUVENILES	LESS VIOLENT INCARCERATED JUVENILES
Paranoid Symptoms	75.5%	0%
Minor Neurological Impairments	98.6%	66.7%
Psychologically	Overall the two groups performed equally on intelligence tests, but both groups were years behind in reading. Severe verbal deficiencies were noted in the more violent group.	
History of Abuse	75%	33%
Witness to Extreme Violence	77%	20%

Significantly, the more violent youth had extraordinary physical (e.g. head injuries, broken bones, burns) abuse histories as children and/or were a witness to extreme violence (e.g. torture, murder, attempted murder).

The authors concluded that the most striking factor between the two groups was the history of physical abuse. Physical abuse often causes central nervous system damage thus contributing to impulsivity, attention disorders, and learning disabilities.

Incarcerated girls began to be a focus of research in the 1990s as more young females were incarcerated than ever before. A recent study (Cauffman, Feldman, Waterman, and Steiner, 1998) found that female juvenile delinquents were nearly 6 times more likely to suffer post-traumatic stress disorder than the general population and 50% more likely to exhibit symptoms than male juvenile delinquents. Half of the incarcerated sample of females reported being victims of sexual or physical abuse.

Steiner, Garcia, and Matthews (1997) looked at post-traumatic stress disorder in 94 incarcerated juvenile delinquents in the California Youth Authority (CYA). PTSD rates were as follows: 48% showed no signs, 20% fulfilled partial criteria, 32% fulfilled all criteria. This compares to a 9.3% lifetime prevalence of PTSD for young adults in the general population. The commonly reported traumatic events were child physical and sexual abuse, domestic violence, sexual assault, murder, grave injury and witnessing community violence (gang violence).

Mason and Evans (1998) studied 396 adolescents (62 females and 334 males) incarcerated in Nevada in 1994. More than half of the juveniles reported physical and sexual abuse. Among many findings, the study showed that significantly more physically and/or sexually abused youth and sexually abused only youth used no methods of contraception when compared to incarcerated nonabused children. Those who did report contraception use favored methods that are considered unreliable or do not offer adequate protection from STDs. Other medical problems found included advanced scoliosis, vision problems, chronic skin diseases (e.g. psoriasis, severe eczema), congenital heart diseases, or malignancies which had not been diagnosed prior to admission.

Some 30% to 40% of minors in the 1998 Sacramento study (referenced perviously) showed significant psychopathology including acute depression, psychotic breakdown, ADHD, anorexia and bulimia, post-traumatic stress disorder (PTSD) and other co-morbidities such as addiction.

Clearly, when a vulnerable youth suffers maltreatment, the result can be health and mental health consequences, drug or alcohol abuse, suicide, delinquency or homicide. To successfully provide healthcare, providers for minors must be non-judgmental, offer compassion, empathy, and assure confidentiality. Medical professionals who provide direct healthcare services should not be involved in collecting forensic evidence (e.g. drug screening) unless medically indicated. Evidentiary examinations for sexually and physically abused youth are best referred to a specialized center. Linkages should be developed to community clinics and healthcare agencies to assist the minors after discharge from the institution.

Recommendations

1. Complete medical evaluations (including a complete history-taking for previous medical conditions, child neglect, physical and sexual abuse, witnessing violence, substance abuse and suicide history); testing for sexually transmitted disease; and evaluating the possibility of pregnancy.

2. Screening for dental problems (although not indicated by these studies, a high rate of dental decay is found among children placed in foster care).

3. Screening for neurological impairments.

4. Screening for developmental delay, learning disabilities, and educational strengths and deficits.

5. Screening for psychiatric and general mental health problems, especially post-traumatic stress disorder, depression, and anxiety.

6. Provision for follow-up medical, psychiatric, and mental health treatment based upon a complete assessment.

7. A trauma oriented approach to juvenile delinquency as well as the traditional behavioral and social support approach is indicated given the significant experience of trauma-related violence.

8. Achieve recognition that undiagnosed medical, neurological, mental health, problems may contribute to the expression of violence.

9. Achieve recognition that child abuse, domestic violence and community violence are contributing factors to juvenile delinquency.

10. Further research is needed on the health, developmental, and mental health problems of abused and neglected children who are arrested for juvenile delinquency. The etiology of their behavior must be addressed to ensure that intervention programs are tailored and responsive to early childhood victimization issues now being played out in delinquent, runaway, and anti-social behavior.

11. Interdisciplinary cooperation and collaboration among agencies and professionals in the justice system, the child protection system, probation, hospitals, schools, and mental health facilities is needed for effective intervention.

12. Comprehensive shelter services (for suicide, pregnancy and sexually transmitted disease prevention, drug abuse treatment, and family reunification, and independent living components) and outreach services (for street youths), and community-based services are needed.

13. School based health and mental health services are critically important to increase access to care.

14. Widespread child abuse and domestic violence prevention programs.

15. Development and implementation of intervention programs for young child physical abuse victims.

Resources

Sexual and Physical Abuse Among Incarcerated Youth: Implications for Sexual Behavior, Contraception Use, and Teenage Pregnancy, W. Alex Mason, Laura Zimmerman, William Evans. *Child Abuse and Neglect*, Vol. 22, No. 10, 987-995, 1998.

Criminal Consequences of Childhood Sexual Victimization. Cathy Spatz Widom, M. Ashley Ames. *Child Abuse and Neglect*, Vol 18, No. 4, 303-318, 1994.

A comparison of the medical histories of incarcerated delinquent children and a matched sample of non-delinquent children. Dorothy Otnow Lewis, MD and Shelley S. Shanok, MPH. *Child Psychiatry and Human Development*, Vol. 9, No. 4, Summer 1979.

Violent juvenile delinquents: Psychiatric, neurological, psychological, and abuse factors. Dorothy Otnow Lewis, Shelley S. Shanock, Jonathan H. Pincus, and Gilbert H. Glaser. *Journal of the American Academy of Child Psychiatry*, No.2, Spring 307-319, 1979.

Medical histories of delinquent and nondelinquent children. D.O. Lewis & S.S. Shanok. Amer. J. Pschiat, 134:1020-1025, 1976.

D.O. Lewis & D.A. Balla. *Delinquency and Psychopathology*. New York; Grune & Stratton, 1976.

Posttraumatic stress disorder among female juvenile offenders. Cauffman, Elizabeth; Feldman, Shirley; Waterman, Jaime; Steiner, Hans. *Journal of the American Academy of Child and Adolescent Psychiatry*, Vol 37, No. 11 (Nov.)1201-1209, 1998.

Posttraumatic stress disorder in incarcerated juvenile delinquents. Steiner, Hans; Garcia, G.; Matthews, Zakee. *Journal of the American Academy of Child and Adolescent Psychiatry*, v36, n3 357-366 (March, 1997).

PART 11

Strategies for Cultural Competency in the Child Abuse and Neglect Field

Strategies for Cultural Competency in the Child Abuse and Neglect Field

Rachel Garcia Guerrero, L.C.S.W.

Case Vignette

The child abuse treatment program staff understand that they need to do a better job to meet the needs of the increasing diverse community. The task feels overwhelming because the benefits of making any real change are not clearly seen by the director. She also believes that color and culture make no difference, that all people are the same, and that her agency is being unbiased in its approach. She believes that the helping approaches traditionally used by the dominant culture are universally applicable. If the system worked as it should, all people—regardless of race or culture—would be served with equal effectiveness. She lacks the will to take a comprehensive view of the changes that need to be made. She approaches this task from the point of view that it is a burden, and too expensive to make these changes. She is looking for a quick fix, something she can add on to the "real work" they do of taking care of children who have been abused. She is looking for ways to add on a few components to make the needed changes. For example, she believes that hiring one Spanish bilingual staff, and one African-American staff, or translating materials fulfills her obligation. She has no plan in place to set goals and objectives to address the needs of the other diverse Asian and new immigrant populations moving to her service area. She does not have a clear understanding of the other diverse communities and the barriers they feel when entering her program. Clients drop out of treatment, compliance with treatment plans is poor, families don't feel understood or welcomed.

Definition

A **"cultural bump"** happens when someone expects a particular behavior and experiences something unexpected when interacting with persons from another culture. This can happen in many informal situations, some of which may not cause any harm, maybe just a little embarrassment. When doing assessment of families and individuals for child abuse investigations, it can become more than just a "cultural bump"; it can be a very serious matter. Cross-cultural assessments in child abuse and neglect cases are critical. Providers must be vigilant in their assessment of families and children to avoid misinterpretations of cultural values, attitudes and behaviors. Lack of cultural and linguistically appropriate services is a barrier to effective assessment, intervention, and positive treatment outcomes.

Questions

1. How can child abuse agencies provide culturally competent services?

2. How do we provide effective culturally competent assessment of children at risk of abuse and neglect?

3. What should professionals know about providing culturally competent care?

4. What are some steps agencies can take toward becoming culturally competent?

Introduction

California demographics are one of the most diverse in the country and will undergo major population changes in coming years. What are child abuse prevention and intervention professionals doing to prepare for an increasingly diverse state? The California Department of Finance (DOF) county population projection by race and ethnic detail project major changes in California population by the year 2040.

Year	White	Hispanic	Asian	African American	American
2000	50.3 %	30.8 %	11.5 %	6.7 %	0.6 %
2010	44.8	34.9	13.3	6.4	0.6
2020	39.9	39.1	14.2	6.2	0.6
2030	35.1	43.5	15.0	5.8	0.6
2040	30.7	47.8	15.5	5.5	0.5

California's diverse population creates many challenges to providers. Agencies must plan for the ever present and expanding changes in the racially, ethnically and culturally diverse population. Many California urban centers are already struggling to keep up.

There are no ethnic/racial groups that condone mistreatment of their children. To say that a particular ethnic, racial or cultural group supports abuse and neglect of their children, signals "cultural incapacity", thereby missing the key to providing culturally competent assessment of children and families.

Cultural Competence is defined as a set of congruent practice skills, behaviors, attitudes, and policies that come together in a system, agency, or among professionals, and enables that system, agency, and professionals to work effectively in cross-cultural situations. Cultural competence may be viewed as a goal towards which agencies and individuals can strive; thus, becoming culturally competent should be viewed as a developmental process.

Child-serving agencies must become culturally competent at all levels of their system to truly move towards providing culturally competent services to the multicultural families in California. It is no longer acceptable to take a piecemeal approach to providing culturally competent care. Cultural competence must be recognized as an intrinsic part of the overall quality of care. This, of course, poses an immense challenge for agencies to adopt necessary changes. Agencies must become culturally competent at the administrative, policy, provider, and direct services levels. Administrators need to understand the critical need to meet objectives to provide culturally competent care to individuals and families who come to their attention. Supervisors must know how to provide culturally appropriate supervision to their staff, including how and when to seek cultural consultation. Direct service providers need to be culturally competent in their assessment, interventions, and services in child abuse intervention. Providers need to have strong overall skills in the field of child abuse and neglect and the ability to determine when it is appropriate to call for a cultural consultant. Optimally, services should be provided in the preferred language of the family, or at least with a qualified interpreter, never a child or another adult from the family. Agencies typically lack needed bilingual, bicultural workers.

Agencies must have the leadership, direction and support to make these moves. Leadership in the area of cultural competency has been seriously lacking in most public and private agencies. Steps to move toward culturally competent care have often been, at worst, nonexistent and at best, fragmented in approach. Success in one area is often misunderstood as being wholly culturally competent. The inclusion of a Spanish speaking person on an assessment team does not mean an agency is culturally competent. For example, a provider of child abuse treatment of a Hmong family needs to be knowledgeable of the culture, history and customs of that family in order to provide competent care.

Cultural-specific traditions, norms or rituals of family structure that are not consistent with the U.S. dominant cultural world view, are at greater risk of being misunderstood and misidentified as abusive. Lack of cultural and linguistically appropriate services is a barrier to effective assessment, intervention, and positive treatment outcomes.

Disincentives to provide culturally and linguistically competent care exist in child-serving systems, many of them cost related. Limited resources are available to hire cultural consultants or to train personnel to create and use strategies to improve cultural competence assessment.

Moving Towards Solutions:

Systems of care need to develop cultural competency strategies to address the diversity of families they now serve and will serve in the future. Cultural competency should be recognized as a developmental process. The five essential elements needed to support development of culturally competent systems and individuals are listed on the next page.

- **Valuing diversity**
  A positive attitude regarding the presence and participation of persons from various racial and ethnic groups, culture, and heritage.

- **Cultural self and system assessment**
  An individual or agency engages in personal and/or system assessment to identify current cultural perceptions.

- **Dynamics of differences**
  Understanding and being conscious of the influence cross-cultural interaction may have. For example, understanding how interpersonal power dynamics are affected by race, culture, language and class.

- **Cultural knowledge**
  Commitment is made to support the expansion of cultural knowledge, thereby accurately interpreting cultural-specific behavior, norms, and values.

- **Adaptation to diversity**
  The system's approach may be adapted to create a better fit between the system and the diverse population it seeks to serve. For example, materials/presentations adapted to the audience at hand, or institutional protocols are assessed for cultural appropriateness.

Cultural competence is viewed as a developmental process. Cross and other leaders in this field describe the cultural competency continuum as beginning in destructiveness and moving toward proficiency:

- Cultural destructiveness
- Cultural incapacity
- Cultural blindness
- Cultural pre-competence
- Cultural proficiency

The following are some organizational components that the mental health field has been moving toward to improve their cultural competency. This list of steps or tasks is a checklist to help move theory into practice. An agency's cultural competency plans should be individualized to the agency because each agency starts at a different continuum point, has unique internal challenges, and different levels of success. Additionally, the communities they serve may vary, requiring different strategies.

Step 1   Seek and obtain organizational leadership commitment for cultural competence.

Step 2   Develop an overall organizational plan to move the agency toward becoming more culturally competent.

Step 3   Identify cultural consultants within the organization and sanction their support in developing a plan for the agency and establishing a multicultural advisory committee. Seek diversity in the committee representation, utilizing individuals that have knowledge and experience with ethnic cultural groups.

Step 4   Establish a clear, *committed vision* for cultural competency. Cultural competency should be integrated into all aspects of the agency, not isolated as a separate component. Agencies must encourage internal dialogue of multicultural issues.

Step 5   Conduct a cultural competency assessment of the organization and the community. Assess the cultural and linguistic competency of the staff. Work with the advisory committee and, if necessary, hire a consultant to assist in the development of the assessment. Examine progress already made by the agency. Be knowledgeable about current resources in the field.

Step 6   Develop specific, short-term and long-term goals and objectives that the agency can realistically accomplish. Incorporate cultural competency planning into existing strategic planning efforts.

Step 7   Take advantage of planned system change. Strengthen cultural competency by including it in any and all system-change strategic planning.

Step 8   Move the agency toward providing culturally competent services. Agency training programs should include cultural competency as an intrinsic component and include cultural-specific training pertinent to the community being served.

Step 9   Work with cultural consultants and community ethnic/cultural organizations in expanding the agency's cultural knowledge. Do not rely on a single consultant; hire a variety of cultural consultants.

Step 10   Make every effort to serve families in their preferred, primary language to avoid misunderstandings.

Step 11   Establish a plan to evaluate efforts and to monitor changes.

This chapter provides the reader with a very brief overview of how agencies and individuals can begin to move toward providing culturally competent care to multicultural populations. Each step listed above requires multiple tasks to operationalize. Cultural competency should be viewed as an overall quality of care issue, not as a component that stands independent of other child abuse assessment and treatment efforts. Cultural blindness in assessment of child abuse cases and the resultant misunderstandings can be very costly to the child, family and agency.

Selected Readings

Towards A Culturally Competent System of Care: Volume I, II, III, The National Technical Assistance Center for Children's Mental Health, Center for Child Health and Mental Health Policy, Georgetown University Child Development Center. Funded by Substance Abuse and Mental Health Services Administration, US Department of Health and Human Services. For copies call (202) 687-8803. http://www.georgetown.edu/research/gucdc/

Cultural Competence Standards in Managed Mental Health Care for Four Underserved, Underrepresented Racial-Ethnic Groups October 1997, Western Interstate Commission on Higher Education (WICHE). http://www.wiche.edu

New York State Cultural and Linguistic Competency Standards: New York State Office of Mental Health. http://www.omh.state.ny.us/

A Practical Guide for the Assessment of Cultural Competence in Children's Mental Health Organizations. The Technical Assistance Center for the Evaluation of Children's Mental Health Systems, Judge Baker Children's Center. http://www.jbcc.harvard.edu/

Cross T., Bazron B., Dennis K., Isaacs M., *Towards a Culturally Competent System of Care Volume I* Washington, D.C.: Georgetown University Child Development Center, CASSP T.A. Center 1989

PART 12

System Review and Evaluation of Present and Previous Injuries in the PICU

Maria Annette Enrione, M.D.

Five Case Vignettes

A 2-month old infant is admitted to the Pediatric Intensive Care Unit (PICU) with the diagnosis of shaken baby syndrome. He was initially seen in a local emergency department with seizures and respiratory failure. Prior to admission to the PICU, a computed tomographic scan of the brain revealed cerebral edema with acute and chronic subarachnoid hematomas consistent with shaken baby syndrome.

An 18-month old toddler is admitted to the PICU with blunt abdominal trauma. A computed tomographic scan of the abdomen revealed a severe laceration of the liver and a duodenal hematoma. The child had no history of trauma and the working diagnosis is non-accidental trauma.

A 13-year old mildly mentally retarded adolescent is admitted to the PICU in septic shock and acute respiratory distress syndrome. The adolescent presented to the emergency department with an acute abdomen and went for surgical exploration. In the operating room, the adolescent was found to have a transected jejunum. Again, no history of trauma and the working diagnosis is non-accidental trauma.

A 3-year old toddler with a neuroblastoma is admitted to the PICU after surgery. The child went to the operating room for placement of a permanent catheter and partial resection of the tumor. He had a Stage I tumor on initial presentation one year previous, but was never returned for follow-up. Now, the child had a Stage IV neuroblastoma.

A 4-year old child is admitted to the burn service with 50% total body surface area burns. The burns, primarily second and third degree, cover most of his lower extremities and buttocks. The child was held under scalding water.

Questions

1. What is the role of the PICU in the identification and evaluation of child abuse?

2. What are the four steps for a comprehensive evaluation?

3. What diagnostic studies may be indicated and why?

4. What are the elements of good documentation in child abuse cases?

All of these cases are examples of children who have suffered from child abuse and require critical care therapies available in a PICU. Only a small percentage of all abused children have injuries or medical needs that require pediatric critical care therapies. These are circumstances where the child has a high risk of dying or being left with significant morbidities. Child abuse in all its forms—physical abuse, sexual abuse, emotional abuse, and neglect—can lead to circumstances where the child is critically ill. Types of abuse that may lead to admission to a PICU admission include head trauma, abdominal trauma, thoracic trauma, asphyxiation, intentional intoxication, i.e. Munchausen by Proxy syndrome, burn injuries, and severe medical neglect. Some of these children can present to a local emergency department with ongoing cardiopulmonary resuscitation and may not be resuscitated.

For the vast majority of children with severe or fatal forms of child abuse, the diagnosis is already made or highly suspected by the time the child is admitted to a PICU. These children often present to community emergency departments and clinics. Because these children need critical care intervention, they are transported to referral centers with pediatric intensive care units. In these pediatric referral centers, there are protocols in place for evaluation, recognition, validation, and reporting of the child abuse. Healthcare providers in these pediatric intensive care units not only care for the medical needs of these children but identify the abuse, find evidence of other abuse, ensure appropriate documentation, and report the abuse to appropriate social service and law enforcement agencies. As part of these protocols, the healthcare team excludes disease processes the can mimic child abuse. Failure of the PICU team to detect and document evidence of abuse may

221

impair ability to prosecute or to intervene for the safety of the child.

Evaluation

Once the child has been admitted to the PICU, the child is medically stabilized and a systematic evaluation of the child is performed. This evaluation includes a complete history, physical examination, diagnostic studies, and consultation.

History is an important part of the evaluation. Once the child has been admitted to the PICU, there is more time to spend gathering information. Various healthcare professionals including resident physicians, attending physicians, subspecialty consultants, nurses, social workers, and law enforcement agents often obtain the history. This history is usually gathered from several people including the primary caretakers, family members, and others involved with the child. This information can then be used to determine whether or not the child has been a victim of child abuse. Often these children have histories of trauma but not of significant force to account for the severity of the injuries. Often there is a history of symptoms for which there has been a delay in seeking treatment. The history may also be inconsistently reported by caretakers to different healthcare professionals and contain significant discrepancies.

A complete physical examination is performed looking for evidence of abuse. This includes close attention to growth parameters. Signs of general neglect include poor skin hygiene and malnutrition. Any injuries sustained by the child are identified and documented. Old healed skin lesions from burns, bruises of varying ages, and abrasions may be evidence of past abuse. These soft tissue injuries are all well documented including the number of injuries, pattern, shape, color, location, and size. A fundiscopic exam is performed looking for evidence of retinal hemorrhages. Genitalia are examined for any signs of sexual abuse.

Diagnostic studies are done to validate the suspicions of abuse and to look for evidence of unsuspected injuries. These studies are also done to exclude disease processes that may mimic child abuse. These diagnostic studies can include laboratory studies and radiographic studies.

- Laboratory studies can include complete blood count, coagulation profile, serum electrolytes, serum glucose, blood urea nitrogen, liver transaminases, amylase, lipase, urinalysis, toxicologic screen, and cultures. The platelet count and coagulation profiles can be helpful if the child has an underlying bleeding diathesis that could account for his/her injuries. A low hematocrit can be helpful to determine the extent of blood loss in a child with suspected or known abdominal trauma. Elevated liver transaminases, amylase, and lipase can direct the physician toward liver or pancreatic injuries, respectively. A urinanalysis showing hematuria may be evidence of renal trauma. A toxicology screen may be obtained if poisoning is suspected. Oral, anal, and genital cultures are obtained for evidence of sexually transmitted diseases if the child is suspected of being sexually abused.

- Radiographic studies are performed looking for confirmation of injuries and evidence of unsuspected injuries. These studies can include skeletal surveys, bone scans, computed tomographic scans of the head and abdomen, and magnetic resonance imaging (MRI).

- Emergently, computed tomographic scans of the head and abdomen are obtained and may be life-saving, if head or abdominal trauma is suspected. If, on a computed tomographic scan of the head there is evidence of brain swelling, subdural and/or subarachnoid blood, intracranial blood, or contusions, the abdomen is subsequently scanned for evidence of abdominal trauma.

- Skeletal surveys are obtained to look for evidence of new and old fractures. A skeletal survey includes radiographs of the posteroanterior and lateral skull, chest, hands, long bones, fingers, and toes. These radiographs can show evidence of posterior rib fractures, subperiosteal hemorrhages, epiphyseal separations, periosteal shearing, metaphyseal fragments, periosteal calcifications, and shearing of the metaphysis.

- Bone scans and MRI studies may be helpful for dating lesions. A MRI of the brain may be helpful for determining the age of the blood. A MRI of the cervical spine may be helpful in hypotonic infants where cervical spine trauma is suspected. These scans are not usually performed emergently.

Consultations obtained from a variety of subspecialists occur once the child is admitted to the PICU. These subspecialists can include child abuse specialists, neurosurgeons, general surgeons, ophthalmologists, medical photographers, and social service professionals.

- Neurosurgeons and general surgeons are consulted to help provide medical and surgical care for children with head trauma and abdominal trauma, respectively. If the child has suffered severe burns, a team of specialists who are experts in burn care provides medical and surgical care.

- Ophthalmologists are consulted to help diagnosis and appropriately document retinal hemorrhages.

- Medical photographers are notified to take pictures of any physical injuries. Color photographs can help document any skin lesions. These pictures can be very helpful in prosecuting the case.

- Child abuse specialists, a team of physicians and other healthcare professionals, skilled in the diagnosis of child abuse are also consulted. This group of specialists can help direct any further diagnostic studies that may be required. They can also help ensure that appropriate documentation and legal notification has occurred.

- Social service professionals are part of the team and help obtain histories, ensure that appropriate legal requirements are met (immediate telephone report to a child protection agency if abuse is suspected and submission of a written report within 72 hours), and provide case management with law enforcement and children's protective services. In addition, they help the families deal with the psychosocial implications of child abuse and its potential implications for the family and the child.

Documentation

Histories obtained from the parents and other caregivers must be accurately documented. Documenting the exact words and using quotations in the medical record can be very helpful to physicians, social workers, law enforcement officers, and prosecutors. As the medical record often becomes a medical-legal document, it is imperative that all evidence of abuse is accurately and appropriately documented. This involves documenting the full extent of the injuries. It may include color photographs or drawings. All appropriate child abuse forms are also filled out. If the abuse is not detected and well documented, the ability to intervene for the safety of the child may be impaired.

Reporting and Diagnosis

All states have laws that require the reporting of child abuse and it is the role of the PICU team to ensure that the suspected abuse have been reported. This may also involve calling child protection agencies in other counties. Many critically ill children are transferred to a PICU from another county, a county other than the one in which the abuse occurred.

Intervention to protect the abused child and siblings who may be at risk for injury requires that the physician be able to say with "reasonable medical certainty" that the child was abused. Consultations with child abuse and other specialists, and specific training in forensic medicine strengthen this ability. Physicians involved in the care of the child are often required to offer evidence of child abuse in court.

Outcomes

As the abused child garners support and sympathy from the healthcare professionals, the family and visitors may be met with conscious or unconscious hostility. It becomes important to remember no one is guilty until so proven and to treat all visitors and family members with respect and professionalism.

Often, the babies with severe head trauma will progress to brain death or persistent vegetative state. Discussions are held with the family about withdrawal of life support and organ donation. Families usually still maintain the right to make these decisions for their child. In some states, in those brain dead children with the diagnosis of fatal child abuse, organ donation is supported by the local coroner's office. The pathologist will often attend the harvesting of organs and complete the autopsy afterward. Consult local policy for obtaining coroner's approval in advance for cases for fatal child abuse.

Summary

When children sustain life-threatening insults from any form of child abuse, they are admitted to a PICU for management. In the PICU, the healthcare team is not only responsible for medically managing the child but ensuring that appropriate evaluation, documentation, and reporting occur. As advocates for these children, our responsibility is to ensure their current and future safety.

References

Chadwick, D.L. and Peterson, B.M. Nonaccidental Injury. In *Pediatric Critical Care, 2nd Edition*. Editors: B.P. Fuhrman, J.J. Zimmerman. Mosby-Year Book, Inc, St. Louis, 1998, pp.43-48.

Monaco, J.E. and Brooks, W.G. The Critical Care Aspects of Child Abuse. *Pediatric Clinics of North America*, 41:1259-1268, 1994.

Protocols with Local Coroners

James Malouf, D-ABMDI

Case Vignette

Daniel, a 15-month-old, died as a result of traumatic injuries. He had been taken to the hospital by his father, where he was pronounced dead on arrival. Law enforcement responded, but when hospital staff indicated there was no evidence of trauma, authorities did not initiate an investigation.

The case came to the coroner's attention with no indication of trauma or foul play. However, the coroner investigator found extensive bruising to Daniel's face, chest, abdomen and hip. Hospital staff suggested that the chest bruising might have been caused by CPR. Based on the external exam, the coroner investigator considered the case a probable homicide and requested that law enforcement attend an autopsy. The autopsy revealed blunt force trauma to the child's torso, compression of flanks and extensive bruising. The mother's live-in boyfriend was arrested and he was convicted of child abuse leading to death. There was no previous documented history of abuse, and no siblings were involved in the incident.

In reviewing this case, the local child death review team discussed the possible ramifications when hospital personnel do not respond to evidence of child abuse. The team also focused on the issues of reliance by law enforcement and social workers on medical opinions. The formation of Suspected Child Abuse and Neglect (SCAN) Teams in all hospitals where children receive treatment was recommended. The team praised the coroner investigator for her actions and advocacy. They discussed the value of increased involvement by investigators from the coroner's office in the review process. As a result, a coroner investigator now regularly participates on the team.

Questions

1. What are the legal mandates for coroners?
2. Why are protocols between local hospitals and the coroner's office important?
3. What are the key elements of a death investigation?
4. What is the role of the coroner on the Child Death Review Team?

Legal Mandates

Coroners have a mandated duty to inquire into and determine the circumstances, manner and cause of death in jurisdictional cases as enumerated by the California Government and Health and Safety Codes. Each of California's fifty-eight counties either have a Coroner, a Sheriff/Coroner, or a Medical Examiner. Regardless of the title of the office of Coroner for an individual county, the legal mandates are the same with regard to the investigation of sudden, unexpected, and traumatic deaths.

Coroner personnel are highly trained in the field of death investigation. It is the role of the Coroner to establish the cause and manner of death of the child. Because of this mandate, the local Coroner's Office plays a pivotal role in the identification, reporting, and management of child abuse and neglect cases which result in the child's death.

Government Code Section 27491 describe the Coroner's mandated responsibility to investigate deaths that are suspicious in nature or the result of trauma. This Government Code Section as well as Health and Safety Code Section 102850 requires that the Coroner be notified immediately by any person having custody and control of a deceased person's body and finding the death to fall within the classifications listed in California Government Code Section 27491.

Cases of SIDS (Sudden Infant Death Syndrome)

With the implementation of SIDS legislation, coroners have several mandated documents that must be completed at the scene and at the time of autopsy. The information obtained is essential for a complete evaluation of the case.

The apparent natural death of an infant may reveal, at the time of the autopsy, to be a death caused by Shaken Baby Syndrome or abusive head trauma or some other type of traumatic death. There may not be any outward evidence of trauma in these cases.

County Coroner and Protocols with Local Hospitals

Hospitals should have written policies and procedures with accompanying checklists to be instituted in the event of a child's death. A protocol between local hospitals and the coroner is recommended.

- Once a patient has been pronounced dead in a hospital and the death falls within the jurisdiction of the Coroner, the body may not further be disturbed by hospital staff.

- The Coroner's Office must be notified immediately to respond to the hospital.

- The attending physician is responsible for accurate and detailed medical record documentation. This documentation should include details of any resuscitation or other treatment conducted before admission to the hospital or in the hospital; notation of the time of death; the child's history and circumstances leading to the death; the physical examination including core body temperature on arrival and findings on the examination of the optic fundi, skin, and genitalia; presumed diagnosis; notation of a skeletal survey, photographs of injuries, forensic sexual assault evaluation, laboratory or any other evaluations performed in the hospital; and, notification of the parents and/or guardians, medical examiner, child's physician, children's protective services, and law enforcement. When possible, documentation should include relative findings from a review of any previous medical records of the patient.

- Hospitals must have procedures in place that prevent the removal of medical appliances, family visitation or any other disturbances that may interfere with the Coroner's investigation.

- The changing of clothing or bathing of the body that falls under the Coroner's jurisdiction, especially infants, is strictly prohibited.

- Any clothing or personal effects either on the decedent or previously removed from the patient must be kept with the body and turned over to the Coroner.

- Personal or referring physicians should be notified of the child's death. Involved and referring physicians should receive a copy of the autopsy report and be responsible for informing the family. For children who do not have a personal physician, postmortem procedures should ensure that the parents receive a written report and explanation of autopsy findings at the appropriate time. The timing of the release of the autopsy report should be coordinated with law enforcement, children's protective services, and the District Attorney's Office, if warranted.

Death Investigations

Deaths that are traumatic, unexpected, obscure, suspicious, or otherwise unexplained in a child younger than 18 years should be investigated. An adequate death investigation includes a scene investigation, complete autopsy, investigation of the circumstances of death, review of the child's medical and family history, interviews with caregivers and first responders, and review of information from relevant agencies and health care professionals.

A complete autopsy consists of an external and internal examination of the body, microscopic examination, and toxicological, microbiologic, and other appropriate studies using a standard infant and child death autopsy protocol.

Review of all relevant records are necessary parts of a death investigation. Relevant records include, but are not limited to, all medical records from birth, social services reports including those from children's protective services, emergency department and paramedic records, law enforcement reports, and child care and school records, if applicable.

Role of the Coroner on the Child Death Review Team

The Coroner is an integral part of the Child Death Review Team by providing critical information obtained during the death investigation and from the autopsy at the child fatality review meeting. The recommended standard of practice for Child Death Review Teams is to use the death certificate signed by the Coroner.

It is important for the Coroner to be actively involved with first responders such as law enforcement and Children's Protective Services (CPS) to ensure the protection of surviving siblings. Collaboration among all agencies enhances the ability to determine accurately the cause and circumstances of death. Information about the death of one child may lead to preventive strategies to protect the life of another.

From the standpoint of the Coroner's Office, the benefits of a Child Death Review Team are:

- Quality assurance of death investigations at the local level;

- Collaboration on difficult or controversial cases;

- Enhanced interagency cooperation;

- Improved allocation of limited resources;

- Better epidemiological data on the causes of death; and,

- Improved accuracy of death certificates.

Coroner's Data

The information that is obtained by the Coroner becomes a matter of public record and can be shared with others openly if the information provided does not hamper or interfere with an on-going criminal investigation. Information can be provided to hospital medical staff to assist on future cases especially if the patient had received extensive medical care prior to the death. The Coroner's Office may also be the source of information for epidemiological and other research.

Organ Donation

On any case that the Coroner has jurisdiction and the family has authorized an organ and/or tissue donation, the Coroner's Office must also approve the donation. Most Coroner's Offices have policies and procedures in place along with special forms in order to authorize this request.

References

Alexander, R.C., ed. *The APSAC Advisor.* Special Issue on Child Fatalities, 7(4), 1994.

Death of a Child in the Emergency Department. *American Academy of Pediatrics Policy Statement*, 93(5), May, 1994.

Granik, L.A., Durfee, M., and Wells, S.J. *Child Death Review Teams: A Manual for Design and Implementation.* American Bar Association, Chicago, 1991.

Investigation and Review of Unexpected Infant and Child Deaths. *American Academy of Pediatrics Policy Statement*, 104(5), November, 1999.

Kaplan, S.R., Granik, L.A., eds. *Child Fatality Investigative Procedure Manual.* American Bar Association, Chicago, 1991.

Resources

California Coroners Association
http://www.coroners.org

State Child Death Review Board, California Department of Justice, Sacramento, California
http://caag.state.ca.us

Physical Rehabilitation for Survivors of Serious Physical Abuse and Neglect

Faye Diskin, O.T.R. and John "Jack" J. Corbett, III, P.T.

Case Vignette

John is a 10-month old who was diagnosed with Shaken Baby Syndrome. His neurological involvement was so extensive that he was in a coma for 2 months. He was unable to move any of his extremities which were rigid from increased muscle tone into an extended posture. John was unable to hold his head up or sit as he once was able to do. He sustained total vision loss.

He received occupational and physical therapy during his extensive hospital stay. Splints were fabricated to position his hands and feet since the increased muscle tone was impacting his range of motion. Passive stretching, tone inhibition positioning and therapeutic handling were used to help decrease his tone, prevent contractures and help make him more comfortable and neurologically more organized. In preparation for discharge, his foster parents were trained on how to stretch his arms and legs, position and lift him comfortably, use his adapted stroller and stimulate his senses with play activities. Therapy continued for John first at an infant stimulation program, then at a handicapped pre-school program, and now at age 5, he is in an adapted school program. John smiles occasionally but not in response to anything in particular and spends most of his day in a wheelchair. He is fed through a tube in his stomach, and requires 24-hour care to meet all of his needs.

Questions

1. What is the role of pediatric physical therapists (PTs) for survivors of serious physical abuse?

2. What is the role of pediatric occupational therapists (OTs) for survivors of serious physical abuse?

3. What are some common child neglect and abuse related outcomes?

4. Why are the child and family dynamics relevant to PTs and OTs?

Types of Abuse

There are multiple devastating injuries that result from child abuse. These insults can permanently and severely damage a child. The most common child abuse and neglect-related injuries that pediatric physical therapists (PTs) and occupational therapists (OTs) contend with include:

- Prenatal drug exposure;

- Shaken Baby Syndrome;

- Orthopedic and neurological injuries from falls, battery, near drowning and suffocation; and,

- Burns.

There is no systematic data collection regarding the numbers of children receiving physical therapy or occupational therapy from physical abuse and neglect.

Pediatric Physical Rehabilitation Therapy

When a child is hospitalized, both occupational and physical therapy can be ordered by the physician. While these two services work together, both disciplines have distinct approaches and areas of expertise. Pediatric therapy techniques differ from adult therapeutic interventions both quantitatively and qualitatively. The child is not seen as a miniature adult. This is true for all aspects of the child: body, mind, spirit, and social ecology. The unique and changing needs of children mandate a distinct philosophy, knowledge of developmental science, and specialized techniques in the provision of therapy. Pediatric physical therapists and occupational therapists work in a variety of environments within the hospital and community. These areas include: pediatric intensive care units, neonatal intensive care units, pediatric acute care floors, inpatient pediatric rehabilitation, outpatient care, clinics, and school therapy programs.

Role of the Physical Therapist (PT)

PTs focus on gross motor skills, functional mobility, balance and patient/primary caregiver education and training. Many components of the patient's neuromusculoskeletal systems must be analyzed to piece together and organize the deficits and strengths. The primary goal of pediatric physical therapy is to expedite and optimize the return of the infant or child's functional motor abilities.

Role of Occupational Therapist (OT)

OTs assess and treat patient's fine motor skills, sensory processing, and their ability to participate in activities of daily living (ADLs). ADLs are those activities performed each day and vary based on a child's age and developmental level. These include self-care, functional mobility, and play/school activities. OTs also assess and provide patients with equipment such as wheelchairs and adaptive equipment that can assist with tasks like self-feeding, bathing, and dressing. Physical and occupational therapists combine their specialized skills and knowledge to maximize their patients' abilities and well being.

Common Child Neglect and Abuse Related Outcomes and Rehabilitation Approaches

- **Prenatal Drug Exposure**
  Children can be impacted developmentally before they are born when their mothers have poor prenatal care and/or have exposed their babies to drugs in utero. Impairments of these children include significant developmental delays, poor state control and feeding difficulties. In the neonatal intensive care units, therapists facilitate oral motor control, positional tolerance, developmental progressions and experiences. Emphasis is placed on primary care giver training and education. Once discharged from the hospital they are often transitioned into infant stimulation and early intervention programs where therapies continue to meet the needs of the developing child.

- **Shaken Baby Syndrome**
  A condition seen after birth usually under one year of age is Shaken Baby Syndrome. This often results in devastating injuries and sometimes death. Injuries include severe neurological damage often causing blindness. Therapeutic intervention involves facilitation of developmental skills including head and trunk control, static/dynamic positional balance, sensory stimulation to help develop other senses to accommodate for lack of vision, therapeutic

handling, splinting, and positioning to normalize muscle tone. These children often need intervention throughout their lives.

- **Orthopedic and Neurological Injuries**
  Head injuries and orthopedic fractures from falls and battery present like non-child abuse sequellae unlike specific areas of pathology such as Shaken Baby Syndrome. PT and OT intervention in these cases is the same as for accidental trauma. These insults vary tremendously and are more difficult to classify as child abuse. Areas of insult depend on what part of the brain was involved during the incident. Severity of involvement depends on the velocity, force, and mechanism of injury. Degree of injury can range from mild memory deficits to complete and sometimes permanent loss of executive functioning and motor abilities.

- **Burns**
  Treatment for child abuse-related burns, just like accidental burns, consists of prevention of contracture and deformity, maintenance of range of motion (ROM) and strength, and the facilitation of daily living skills. ROM is maintained and enhanced through positioning programs and splinting. Active ROM and strengthening activities through structured play reinforce newly acquired ROM. Jobst pressure garments for hypertrophic scar management are worn to maximize function and improve cosmesis.

Coordination with Medical Care

Provision of PT and OT services are coordinated with the child's ongoing medical care. Changes and developments are communicated to the child's physician. As a child becomes more alert and responsive, the therapist's neurological evaluations can reveal deficits that had been previously masked by the child's unresponsive state. These new deficits might reflect injury to a particular region of the brain previously undetected and which is not consistent with the family history given. These findings are communicated to the physician and coordinated with medical care.

Observation of Child-Family Dynamics

Typically the medical team has already contacted Children's Protective Services with suspicions of evidence of child abuse. During the extensive period of follow-up PT and OT care, therapists spend considerable one-to-one time working with the patient and their families. Family dynamics are readily observed. Red flags for child abuse can emerge during treatment. For example, a child may be fearful and flinch when a parent quickly moves an extremity, not mindful of the child's painful state. Poor parenting skills or emotional impulsivity emerge when a parent quickly resorts to harsh punitive measures while attempting to manage a child's behavior during a treatment session. These observations are relevant to how the child may be treated at home and raise a threshold of concern about the child's well-being since he or she requires intensive care due to the changed circumstances of disability.

Case Study of OT and PT Collaboration in the Provision of Care

Steve is a 5-year old who presented to the emergency room unconscious with gross deformation of his right thigh. Noted too were old bruises on the patient's back and along both arms. X-rays revealed left femur and right pelvic fractures. Head CT scan showed a large right subdural hematoma. Emergent craniotomy and subdural evacuation were performed and patient was placed in a right long leg cast. Mother reports that she had been at work at the time. Her live-in boyfriend had been watching her children and said that Steve had jumped off a table (about 2½ feet high) landing awkwardly. Upon investigation, it was found that the boyfriend had a prior history of domestic violence in another state.

Once stable in the pediatric intensive care unit (PICU), therapist's evaluations were conducted. Mom was present at the child's bedside. The boyfriend had restraining orders not allowing him to be with any of the children while investigations continued. Steve's eyes were open, but he only responded visually to light stimulus and grossly withdrew to noxious stimulation on the right side.

Therapy intervention in the PICU included family education and training for passive range of motion and stretching, positioning, and sensory stimulation. A sitting program was also initiated and therapeutic exercises focused on head and trunk control. Low level mobility training, such as rolling, utilized automatic, well-formed motor patterns to encourage purposeful movement.

After a brief stay in acute care, Steve was transferred to the pediatric rehabilitation service. PT focused all functional mobility including rolling, sitting up, transitioning from floor to/from standing, scooting, crawling (with long leg cast), wheelchair mobility, and walking. Treatment incorporated age appropriate play to Steve's cognitive and emotional ability.

The OT introduced activities of daily living (ADLs) including dressing and self feeding using adaptive equipment and one-handed techniques, transfer training, visual-perceptual retraining, facilitation of left upper extremity active movement, and fine motor development. OT also ordered a manual pediatric wheelchair and bath equipment to assist his care while promoting safe independence.

When discharged from pediatric rehabilitation six weeks after his injury, Steve had made great strides in his recovery. However, deficits were still apparent. Still in his long leg cast, Steve had progressed from being unable to stand to walking household distances using a pediatric cane in his right hand with his Mom safely guarding him. He needed his wheelchair for school (plan was to return back to school in a special education program the following year) and community distances. He was able to dress himself using adaptive equipment and techniques. He used his left upper extremity as a stabilizer in bilateral tasks, but had significantly limited hand function. His visual deficits impacted such things as reading due to his inability to scan completely to the left. Steve was transitioned to outpatient OT and PT twice a week to work on his overall motor and cognitive functioning.

Conclusion

Occupational and physical therapists work with abused and neglected children who have suffered preventable devastating injuries. While some of the injuries can completely heal like certain fractures, neurological damage and burns are life long. Although physical healing will improve function and mobility, emotional scars remain forever.

Providing rehabilitation care to survivors of child physical abuse and neglect is part of the role of being a pediatric occupational and physical therapist. PTs and OTs serve an important role in the continuum of care for survivors and in the protection of children.

Resources

American Physical Therapy Association (APTA)
1111 North Fairfax Street
Alexandria, VA 22314-1488
Phone: 703-684-2782'

American Occupational Therapy Association (AOTA)
P.O. Box 31220
Bethesda, MD 20824-1220
Phone: 301-652-2682

Sibling Loss: Grief, Mourning and Recovery

Carol A. Johnson-Schroetlin, Psy.D., Anthony J. Urquiza, Ph.D., Michael Durfee, M.D., and Linda Garcia, M.A., C.C.L.S.

Seven Case Vignettes

Adrian was killed by his mother in the small hotel room where they lived with his brothers and sisters. After the death and placement in foster care, none of the siblings were taken to any type of counseling.

A five-year old girl enters foster care after the natural death of her grandmother, her sole caretaker.

A three-year old boy is the only witness to his mother beating his baby brother to death.

A ten-year old boy is hiding while his father beats his mother into a coma.

An infant loses her mother to suicide.

A five-year old girl suffers permanent scars from scalding burns inflicted by mom's boyfriend.

A six-year old is placed in foster care and his dog is "put to sleep".

Questions

1. What is the impact of non-accidental death upon surviving siblings?

2 Do children of different ages experience death of a sibling differently?

3 Describe common reactions of children to death of a sibling.

4 What type(s) of intervention and support are recommended?

Review of the Literature

There is no literature on the psychological reactions of children who lose a sibling through non-accidental death. There is limited research on children who have had a sibling die during childhood (Fanos, 1996; Hogan & DeSantis, 1994; Hogan & Greenfield, 1991).

Historical literature has questioned if children have the capacity to grieve. Nagy (1948) developed a comprehensive assessment of children's understanding of death, which outlined distinct developmental stages of increased understanding. Krupnick (1984) expanded Nagy's work on the developmental stages in children's understanding of mourning. Krupnick reported that in infancy, there are three stages that characterize the response to loss. These are protest and denial, despair and disorganization and reorganization. Of all age groups, children up to age two adjust most easily. Immediate reactions to the loss may include loss of speech or other recent developmental achievements and/or diffused distress (Krupnick, 1984).

Children between 2 to 5 years of age, do not have a fully developed capacity to put thoughts into words. Because of this, caregivers often erroneously assume children at this age do not grieve. However, it is common at this age for children to experience an unspecific distress that may be masked by denial. Children frequently may reenact the death or funeral activities in their play as a way to master the loss. Children in this age group may repeatedly ask when the deceased person will return, even after they have been told many times that this will not occur and that the person is dead. At times, grief may be expressed through regressive behaviors. Children at this age cannot understand the finality of death, although they can experience grief (Krupnick, 1984).

Children between 5 to 8 years of age, have a more developed cognitive understanding of death. This development period is believed to be the most difficult coping time as these children do not have a fully developed ego capacity. Denial is their chief form of defense. This is also an age of magical thinking and fantasy, and children will often personify death. By age 7 or 8, children have the capacity to begin to understand the finality of death (Krupnick, 1984). By age 10 or 11, causes of death can be understood (Siegel & Gorey, 1994). A death during this development stage may shake their growing sense of automony and invoke feelings of helplessness and loss of control. Denial is the usual means of defense and children may avoid mourning (Krupnick, 1984).

John Bowlby's work on attachment and loss in children emphasizes that grief is a biological function, in which children aim to regain proximity to the attachment figure, from whom separation can cause intense anxiety. Bowlby's research revealed that children as young as 7 to 17 months, who have reached the cognitive developmental milestone of object permanence, and who are separated from their care giver, experience a process of mourning very similar to the mourning of adults (Bowlby, 1980). Additional studies support Bowlby's research and note that children as young as two to three, and increasingly as children attain greater ego strength, are capable of mourning (Barnes, 1964; Bowlby, 1980; Flavell, 1991; Florian, 1985; Anna Freud, 1973; Furman, 1984).

Reactions of children

Studies completed by Hogan & Greenfield (1991), Heiney (1991), Hutton & Bradley (1994) and Fanos' (1996) retrospective study (adults interviewed who experienced a sibling loss during childhood) reported the following reactions to losing a sibling:

Internalized Behaviors
Children who had experienced a sibling loss exhibited higher internalizing behavior problems, such as sadness, depression, anxiety, fear and guilt (Fanos, 1996; Hogan & Greenfield, 1991; Michael & Lansdown, 1986; Heiney, 1991; Hutton & Bradley, 1994).

Confusion and fear
Children described having confused and distorted concepts of illness, death and the relationship between the two. Having thought that only old people die, they struggled with this contradiction in the death of their sibling, and many children believed that they would die at the same age as their brother or sister (Cain et. el., 1964; Fanos, 1996). The disappearance of a family member is simply too blatant to be ignored, yet the circumstances of the death and its consequences can be a source of puzzlement and continuing fear for surviving children. In addition to the unexplained and the inexplicable, children are inundated with feelings that have not been fully experienced nor explored. Especially prominent are the feelings connected with responsibility for the tragedy, the guilt to which these children are susceptible (Krell & Rabkin 1979).

When a child witnessed the death of a sibling, but the circumstances of the event are not clear and are deliberately kept that way, there becomes a conspiracy of silence between the surviving child and the parent(s). The death is not discussed, but the child lives with distrust and a fear of what may be in store of him or her. The parent(s) may conspire with others not to tell the facts to the child so as not to "burden him." In such situations, the living child is haunted by something mysterious and uncertain, knowing and yet not knowing, and afraid to ask for clarification (Krell & Rebkin, 1979). Realities of their parent(s) vulnerability and the all-powerfulness and strength as protectors comes crashing down. Children also described an intense fear of death and a fear that they may die and/or someone else in their family may die. Children reported sleep disturbances and nightmares. (Fanos, 1996; Hogan & Greenfield, 1991).

Guilt
Cain's (1963) historical study and Fanos' (1996) retrospective study both reported that guilt was often present for 5 years or more after a sibling's death. Some children considered themselves responsible for the death and insisted that it was their fault. They felt that they should have died too, or that they should have died instead of their sibling. Guilt feelings were based upon having survived. Studies completed by Krell & Rebkin (1979) reported that guilt feelings were also a result of children's egocentric thinking and in an attempt to find reasons for the death. This egocentric thinking may be linked to an unconscious wish or an actual verbal or physical abuse once inflicted on the deceased child. The shame that is triggered by these thoughts compounds the guilt (Krell & Rabkin, 1970). Anxiety and depressive features often mask this underlying sense of guilt (Hogan & Greenfield, 1991).

Denial
Children and adults (who experienced a death of a sibling during childhood) reported that the ability to avoid feelings and to be stoic was highly valued. Denial and restriction of the self appeared to be the dominant reaction by those interviewed. Personal energy was bound up with warding off unpleasant feelings (Fanos, 1996). Heiney (1991), Rosen (1984; 1986) and Fanos' (1996) work also noted that communication in these families were veiled, discouraged and the surviving children grew up with a family secret. These messages "not to grieve and mourn" came from parents, personal and societal influences. These children attempt to protect their parent(s) or family members from distress by avoiding discussions about the deceased (Rosen, 1984; 1986).

Psychosomatic Complaints
Children reported an increase in illnesses and bodily complaints. Headaches, dizziness and abdominal pains were frequently reported in these children. Enuresis and other regressive behaviors are often seen in young children (Malmquist, 1983).

Re-experiencing Trauma

Research suggests that sibling loss can cause long term distress (Michael & Lansdown, 1986; Rosen, 1984;1986). In addition, Fanos' (1996) study revealed that the death of a sibling was a devastating experience for almost all siblings and often resembled that of a traumatic event in the lives of these individuals. When the death of a sibling is non-accidental and the death is of human design, siblings experienced severe and long lasting affects (Malmquist, 1983).

Adults surviving a sibling loss reported re-experiencing traumatic circumstances. Several theorists have noted the tendency of trauma victims to re-expose themselves voluntarily to situations reminiscent of the trauma. This voluntary exposure may be an attempt to achieve integration through experiencing and re-experiencing the dissociated traumatized self (Fanos, 1996).

Anniversary Reactions

Children also re-experience grief reactions at different times during the life cycle. The anniversary date when their sibling died, graduation, birthdays and other significant events and developmental milestones can re-trigger grief reactions. These anniversary reactions are a normal process of grief and allow children to continue to process their grief.

Emotional Support

Children reported that their caretakers were unavailable to them due to their own grief. Surviving siblings regretted that no one was available to tell them the truth about what happened and to help them process their emotional reactions. Fanos' (1996) study demonstrated a tremendous need for a support person to interact with the siblings and to be honest about the situation. The surviving siblings felt that assistance should have been provided to help them grieve the loss. Research on non-accidental parent death has also revealed that traumatized children who have experienced a non-accidental familial death receive very little psychiatric or psychological attention after such an event (Malmquist, 1983).

Normalization:

Many siblings reported a desire to have contact with other children who have similar experiences. These grieving children reported a need to have their feelings validated and supported, and to know that what they were experiencing was normal in this difficult, traumatic situation. Children reported that it is very helpful to know that there were other individuals who have experienced similar circumstances and they have survived (Black & Urbanowicz, 1987; Fanos, 1996).

Importance of Siblings

The role of the sibling is unique as a sister or brother may function informally as best friend, confident, parental surrogate, and role model into the world. Siblings and parents both contribute to a child's role and identity consolidation (Erikson, 1964 noted in Hogan & Greenfield, 1991), and a drastic change in these relationships resulting from a death has the potential to interfere with the developmental process (Hogan & Greenfield, 1991). The existing literature on this subject and anecdotal experience confirm the following:

- **Children who experience the death of a sibling have a strong need for emotional support and should not be left to resolve the issues by themselves.**

- **Psychic trauma in response to the loss of a siblings must be recognized.**
  Studies have suggested that experiencing a non-accidental familial death often constitutes a psychological trauma for the child. The immediate consequences often include affective intolerance, estrangement, and grief (Pynoos & Eth, 1994). The hallmarks of post traumatic stress disorder are seen in these children, such as amnesia, detachment, restriction of affect, and foreshortening of the future. The warding off of unpleasant affect becomes central and avoidance defenses come into play. Unfortunately, children's families are often struggling with their own avoidance of traumatic anxiety and are not available to assist the child. Therefore, it is essential that the child have the opportunity to explore the traumatic episode in the reassuring presence of an unaffected adult (Eth & Pynoos, 1984). Having a supportive adult to address these traumatic responses as well as the grief the child is experiencing will assist the child through this difficult time.

- **Children's needs are greater when a family member or significant person is the suspect.**
  Confusion follows fatal child abuse or fatal domestic violence. Children also have additional needs if they have witnessed a death. This is aggravated, if the child-witness becomes part of the investigation or court process. Details of violent screams, blood, and being left with a body are very difficult for a child (Eth & Pynoos, 1984). This may also be the type of information that can drive adult support away and be replaced by unreal assurance that "things will be okay". Adult caretakers, including professionals, may be denying reality with the beliefs that the

child is not ready to know, the child is too young to remember, or that children are resilient. Although, at least one-third of children who witness familial violence have behavior or emotional problems (Levine, 1975).

Needs of Children in Placement

There has been no study of grief and mourning issues pertaining to children being removed from their families. Grief and mourning are no doubt part of this experience, especially if children are in placement due to the death of a sibling. They may also be separated from possible support systems, e.g. siblings or extended family at a time of crisis. Children in placement may also miss the funeral of their sibling. The funeral offers children the opportunity to reestablish a repaired image of the deceased, as well as provides opportunities for children to participate in the mourning ritual, which can be beneficial in the grieving process.

Needs of Children with Disfiguring Injury or Disabilities

There has been no study of children with disfiguring injury or disabilities due to non-accidental means or their reactions if this happened to their sibling. Knowledge of the experience is anecdotal.

Hospitalized Siblings

Children with hospitalized sibling(s) or a parent due to violence may miss early hospital visits due to being in placement. Hospital visits can provide helpful reassurance that someone is still alive or less damaged than the child might have imagined. These visits can provide relief for children who have experienced intrusive memories or imagery, which has interfered with their mourning (Pynoos & Eth, 1994).

Criminal and Dependency Investigations

Legal investigations may temper some conversations but children in particular should not be left to their imagination without clear reason. With fatal injuries from violent acts, criminal investigations should not interfere with the need for children and families to say good-bye. Collaborative efforts among professionals and agencies involved in these cases are essential to avoid complex long-term problems in resolving trauma and grief (Eth & Pynoos, 1984).

Funerals

Childhood grief experts note that children should be a part of the funeral and/or memorial service. Worden (1991) notes that by allowing children to participate in the funeral assists children in processing their grief. Participating in the funeral/memorial service makes the loss real for the child, and helps bring home the reality and finality of the death. The funeral service can also provide the opportunity to express thoughts and feelings about the deceased, as well as provides children with the opportunity to reflect and remember the life of the person who is gone. Children can also gain the support of a family member or family friend through participating in the funeral or memorial service (Worden, 1991). Rando (1991) and other clinicians also note the importance of children attending funerals and memorial services. However, some children may not want to attend the funeral, thus, children should be given a choice, after having been told about what will occur at the funeral or memorial service (Webb, 1993).

Responsibilities of Professionals Responding to Children

Adults have an important responsibility when it comes to explaining death to children. The manner in which adults handle the death experience can send a message that may have more effect than the actual content of the message. These messages can be positive or negative and may last a lifetime. Grollman (1990) states, "When you avoid children's reactions, you magnify their fears and replace reality with fantasy and psychological defenses."

Talking about death with children can be difficult. It triggers feelings of loss and vulnerability in the professional or advocate who is serving the child. Adult anxiety may result in withdrawal when the child is trying to tell his version of what happened or is asking for an honest answer to questions about the loss. Children have a basic need to make sense of the world and of themselves in it. When they experience the death of loved one, they become confused and vulnerable. They need comfort, validation and to find a way to extrapolate meaning from the event. Bereaved children need clear, honest information that they can comprehend. They need to have an active role in which they feel involved and important. Children need to be reassured about the grief they are experiencing and witnessing in others. They have a strong need to have their thoughts and feelings accepted by others, and children need to have consistency in their daily lives (Bowlby, 1980).

Bereaved children need a setting in which they can communicate thoughts and feelings openly. Children's adjustment to death is less difficult when families tolerate open expressions of anger, guilt, depression, and shared feelings (Black & Urbanowicz, 1987; Bowlby 1980; Michael & Lansdown, 1986).

Black & Kaplan (1988) in their study of children who have had a parent murdered noted that children who experience non-accidental death in the family should receive professional bereavement counseling, specifically when suffering from a pathological grief reaction, as complicated by post traumatic stress disorder. Post traumatic stress complicates the grief reaction, which inhibits the development of normal mourning. As a result of the bereavement circumstances, e.g., a violent death, these children may be stigmatized and may feel compelled to remain silent. This suppression often results in feelings of sadness, shame, horror and rage, which in turn leads to the likelihood of a pathological grief reaction (Black & Kaplan, 1988).

Guidelines for Working with Bereaved Children

- Ensure that developmentally appropriate interventions are provided;

- Assist children in identifying and expressing their thoughts and feelings about the loss;

- Help children understand concretely the circumstances of the death;

- Give permission for children to grieve;

- Use creative means such as stories, role-play and therapeutic play to facilitate grief work;

- Identify resistant and avoidance behaviors in children; and,

- Identify magical thinking in children which may lead to inappropriate feelings of guilt (Heiney, 1991).

Recommendations for Intervention with Children and Families

- Provide crisis intervention with age-appropriate explanations to minimize any post traumatic stress;

- Demonstrate respect for children's rights for honest, thoughtful support;

- Recognize the importance of hospital visits, attending wakes and funerals, grave visits, creating photograph albums, making drawings, and creating memorials;

- Bereavement counseling which recognizes the child's and the family's need to grieve in their unique way, acknowledges and validates the painful loss, and includes ways of cherishing the positive memories of the loved one through:

  - Individual Therapy (with post traumatic stress and bereavement counseling focus);

  - Family Therapy (with post traumatic stress and bereavement counseling focus); and/or,

  - Group Therapy (with post traumatic stress and bereavement counseling focus).

Recommendations for Protocols and Practice Standards

- Establish standards of practice for helping children who have suffered from a major permanent loss to death or severe injury;

- Develop protocols for interagency collaboration and training for individuals and agencies; and,

- Develop resource directories and a working network around issues of fatal and severe injury.

References

Black. D., & Kaplan, T. (1992). Father kills mother: Post traumatic stress disorder in the children. *Psychotherapy & Psychosomatics* 57, 152-157.

Black, D. & Urbanowicz, M.A. (1987). Family intervention with bereaved children. *Journal of Child Psychology & Psychiatry*, 28 (30), 467-476.

Bowlby J. (1980). *Attachment and Loss*, Vol.3. Basic Books; New York.

Cain, A.C.; Fast, I. & Erickson, M.E. Children's disturbed reactions to the death of a sibling. *American Journal of Orthopsychiatry*, 4, 741-754.

Corr C.A. & Corr D.M. *Handbook of Childhood Death and Bereavement*. Springer Publishing;New York.

Dodka K., et al. (1990). *Children Mourning: Mourning Children*. Hospice Foundation of America; Washington, DC.

Eth, S. & Pynoos, R.S. (1984). The child as witness to homicide. *Journal of Social Issues*, 40 (2), 87-108.

Fanos J. (1996). *Sibling Loss*. Lawrence Erlbaum Associates; Mahwah, New Jersey.

Grollman E. (1990). *Talking about Death: A dialogue between parent and child.* Beacon Press; Boston.

Heiney, S.P. (1991). Sibling grief: A case report. *Archives of Psychiatric Nursing,* 5 (3), 121-127.

Hogan, N.S.& Greenfield, D.B. (1991). Adolescent sibling bereavement symptomatology in a large community sample. *Journal of Adolescent Research,* 6 (1), 97-112.

Hutton, C.J. & Bradley, B.S. (1994). Effects of sudden infant death on bereaved siblings: A comparative study. *Journal of Child Psychology & Psychiatry,* 35, 723-732.

Jewett C. (1992). *Helping Children Cope with Separation and Loss.* Harward Common Press; Boston.

Krupnick, J. (1984). Childhood & Adolescent. In M. Osterweis, F. Solomon & M. Green (eds.) *Bereavement: reactions, consequences and care.* Washington, DC: National Academy Press.

Krell, R. & Rabkin, L. (1979). The effects of sibling death on the surviving child: A family perspective. *Family Process* 18, 471-477.

Levine, M. (1975). Interparental violence and its effects on the children:: A study of 50 families in general practice. *Medical Science Law,* 15, 172-176.

Malmquist, C.P. (1983). Children who witness parental murder: Post traumatic aspects. *Journal of the American Academy of Child Psychiatry* 25 (3), 320-325.

McGoldrick M., Hines P.M., Garcia-Preto N., & Lee E. (1986). Mourning rituals. *The Family Therapy Networker,* Nov-Dec.

Michael, S.A.P. & Landsown, R.G. Adjustment to the death of a sibling. *Archives of Disease in Childhood,* 61, 278-283.

Parkes C.M., Laungani P., & Young B. (1997). *Death and Bereavement Across Cultures.* Routledge; New York.

Pynoos, R.S. & Eth, S. (1994). Children who witness the homicide of a parent. *Psychiatry,* 57, 287-306.

Rando, T.A. (1991). *How to go on Living When Someone you Love Dies.* Bantam; New York, NY.

Rosen, H. (1984, 1986). Prohibitions against mourning in childhood sibling loss. *Omega,* 15 (4), 307-316.

Sims A. *Am I Still A Sister?* Big A Publishing; Albuquerque, NM.

Webb, N.B. (1993). *Helping Bereaved Children: A Handbook for Practitioners.* Gilford Press; New York, NY.

Worden J.W. (1991). *Grief Counseling and Grief Therapy: A Handbook for the Mental Health Practitioner* (2nd Ed.) Springer Publishing; New York.

PART 13

Hospital SCAN Team Models

Nancy C. Hayes, L.C.S.W.

SCAN (Suspected Child Abuse and Neglect) Teams are multidisciplinary teams involved in the identification and treatment of child victimization. While schools and other agencies have created such teams, this chapter will focus on hospital or clinic-based teams. "SCAN" is a name that has a historic familiarity and recognition by most in the field. Other multidisciplinary teams use a number of different acronyms to capture their purpose. Among those are CART (Child Abuse Resource Team), CAST (Child Abuse Services Team), CARE (Child Abuse Resource and Evaluation), and SART (Sexual Assault Response Team). The common mission of these teams is to enhance the identification, reporting, and case management of child abuse and neglect cases through a multidisciplinary approach.

History of SCAN Teams

The first hospital-based child protection teams were established in the late 1950's at Pittsburgh Children's Hospital, the University of Colorado Medical Center, and Children's Hospital in Los Angeles. The three main purposes of these university hospital teams were to: **review cases of child abuse and neglect, provide training and community education to the various disciplines and professions involved in cases, and provide a focus for research** (Krugman, 1988). **Case review** continues to be a primary function of hospital-based SCAN Teams today, with an emphasis on identification, assessment, and treatment planning for child abuse and neglect cases. In the early years, teams were small, mainly consisting of a physician, nurse, and social worker. Now team compositions vary and depend upon the particular setting, its resources, mandates, and interested individuals. Team membership has generally expanded to include nurses and social workers from other areas of the hospital such as the Emergency Department and newborn nurseries, child development specialists, child psychiatry, and mental health providers. Other specialists consult on cases and attend case review meetings as needed (e.g. radiology, ophthalmology, dentistry, chaplaincy, pharmacy, legal counsel, hospital administration, etc.). **Training and community education** is directed toward creating community awareness and understanding of the problem; promoting prevention and early identification; and increasing professionals' knowledge, skills, and abilities for effective intervention. **Research** began with a focus on distinguishing between accidental and non accidental injury, and, over the years, has moved into many other areas of interest to medical and mental health clinicians.

SCAN Teams exist in both public and private hospitals and primary health care settings across the country. According to Besharov (1990) about half the states have statutes that authorize or require the establishment of multidisciplinary teams. California's statutes accommodate a team approach through several provisions. According to the *Child Abuse Prevention Handbook* (Office of the Attorney General, 1993), "As a result of an ongoing team emphasis, significant positive changes have occurred in the identification and reporting of child abuse cases."

Penal code 11166, subd. (e). involves reporting and communication between agencies:

- "When two or more persons required to report are present and jointly have knowledge of a known or suspected instance of child abuse, and when there is agreement among them, the telephone report may be made by a member of the team selected by mutual agreement, and a single report may be made and signed by such selected member of the reporting team. Any member who has knowledge that the member designated to report has failed to do so, shall therefore, make the report."

- Another important provision that facilitates interagency communication and coordination concerns the sharing of information about mandated reports. Penal Code 11167.5 provides that required reports are confidential and may be disclosed as provided by subdivision (b): "Reports of suspected child abuse and information contained therein may be disclosed only to the following........ and hospital SCAN teams. As used in this paragraph, "hospital SCAN team" means a team of three or more persons established by a hospital, or two or more hospitals in the same county, consisting of health care professionals and representatives of law enforcement and child protective services, the members of which are engaged in the identification of child abuse. The disclosure authorized by this section includes disclosure among hospital SCAN teams located in the same county."

Beyond statutory provisions, the *Handbook* encourages and recommends a multidisciplinary approach, coordinated investigations, and collaboration by law enforcement, child protective services, prosecutors, and the medical community.

Tasks of SCAN Teams include, but are not limited to:

- case review of all child abuse and neglect reports;
- review of medical reports for evaluation, follow-up and referrals;
- coordination of treatment planning;
- maintaining a central log of cases and/or a data system;
- preparing an annual summary report; and
- providing training and education.

Primary Care Facility Teams

In the primary care setting, a physician and medical social worker and/or nurse may be designated as resource specialists in the area of child maltreatment. They provide case consultation to other health care providers in their setting. These resource specialists provide guidance regarding the assessment of child maltreatment and development of an adequate information base for diagnosis. They provide guidance on making the required telephone and written reports and developing a treatment plan for follow-up with the family. These specialists may be designated to serve as liaison with area hospitals, law enforcement agencies, child protective services, and other public agencies in all cases of child abuse and neglect seen at the facility. They may also be involved in training and education for the staff at the

facility, developing reporting protocols and procedures for evaluation, and case follow-up.

Secondary Level of Care Teams

Hospital-based multidisciplinary teams typically have a core group of professionals such as physicians, nurses, social workers, child development and mental health specialists, and psychiatry. Team members have specialized training and expertise in the recognition of child maltreatment, assessment and evaluation, the mechanics of reporting and public agency response, and community resources for treatment and follow-up. Other specialists may be called upon as needed for consultation, such as dentists, radiologists, and ophthalmologists. At this level, a representative from the local child protective services and/or law enforcement agency is usually a member.

The hospital-based SCAN Team program may include the availability of 24-hour consultation to hospital staff in order to provide immediate assistance on cases. The consultation service approach does not require the SCAN Team to take over the case from the treatment team, but rather, provide consultation by phone or in person. Referrals typically come from the Emergency Department, newborn nurseries, inpatient pediatric ward, burn unit, and primary care clinics, such as pediatrics, family medicine, and prenatal care. Consultation may also be provided to the psychiatric unit and dental clinics. In many hospitals, consultation with a member of the SCAN Team is mandated. Any faculty or staff, regardless of discipline, is required to seek consultation with the Team whenever there is concern about maltreatment. The consultant provides guidance for interviewing the child and parents, clinical studies needed to assist in making the diagnosis, forensic medical evidence collection, related consent issues, dealing with the family, and making the reports. Many hospital administrations recognize the role SCAN Teams play in reducing and managing risk. Another value-added element is economy of labor—expert consultation results in improved documentation of cases, which in turn, reduces the volume and time spent on communications with investigating agencies and court appearances. If the situation does not warrant a mandated report, the Team may contribute other strategies to use to address the family's problems, or suggest treatment resources.

Another function of SCAN Teams at this level is to provide case reviews at regularly scheduled multidisciplinary meetings. Some teams meet weekly and review every case referred, regardless of whether a report was made. Other Teams review only complex cases in which the diagnosis is more difficult. These case reviews are usually more effective when the treating physician, nurse, social worker, and other relevant staff attend and present their cases, rather than having a "paper review" of the case. Cases where reporting was recommended and completed are reviewed for follow-up. Cases which do not result in reporting are also reviewed to determine other case management alternatives. Multidisciplinary case reviews are particularly helpful in very complex and difficult to sort out cases such as those involving medically fragile/chronically ill children with issues of medical noncompliance, failure-to-thrive, shaken baby syndrome, sexual abuse, medically fragile/chronically ill children where there is noncompliance, and Munchausen by Proxy. The need to consider complex medical, developmental, social, and psychological data may require a separate meeting on a given case. Recommendations made by the SCAN Team are documented.

Follow-up on cases is essential. If no follow-up is done, SCAN Teams do not know what the response of the child protection system is to the case. For example, whether the Team's recommendations were acted upon, and whether the recommended services and treatment plan were put into place. Without follow-up, the team is ineffective and risks being perceived as unrealistic and impractical by child protection and other community agencies.

A centralized log of all referred cases is important. A patient identification code, the child's age, gender, referral source, and type of suspected maltreatment are basic elements of the database. The database allows for identification of major trends such as an increase/decrease in the numbers of reports of abuse and an increase in the overall referrals from the Emergency Department. Depending upon the scope of data collected and recorded, other trends may be identified and lead to further clinical investigation, i.e. an increase in the number of babies delivered exposed to methamphetamines vs. cocaine, more cases from a particular part of the institution's geographic service area, etc. Documenting trends can assist in garnering support for additional community resources or changes in service-delivery.

An annual summary report is useful to document the volume of cases referred, trends, and other activities required of, or undertaken by the SCAN Team. Teaching, research, and quality assurance activities are included in this report. Progress on grants obtained and updates on hospital programs addressing child abuse prevention and treatment issues are also included.

At this level, training and education for mandated reporters for both hospital staff and the community are major functions. A master calendar of annual training programs for medical and hospital staff to provide regular updates on child abuse topics is particularly helpful in teaching institutions where there is continual influx of new faculty and staff. SCAN Teams provide valuable training to child protection social workers, law enforcement, and criminal and dependency court personnel on medical evidentiary exam findings, and updates from the scientific literature. These training programs are opportunities for communication to increase understanding and appreciation of each discipline's role and methodology for assessment/investigation.

SCAN Teams are called upon to provide consultation to community agencies, Child Protective Services (CPS), law enforcement, prosecutors, the courts, schools, etc. CPS may seek consultation from the Team on a case reported by a community person of a child who has never been seen at the hospital. Teams afford access to physicians and other health care providers with expertise in diagnosing child abuse and neglect.

SCAN Teams are also involved in prevention activities such as: sponsoring awareness-raising campaigns in the hospital and community during Child Abuse Prevention Month; sponsoring annual conferences; developing and distributing materials at patient visits and in public areas of the hospital and community on various topics; providing parenting classes and support groups; providing educational materials to parents of newborns; and conducting child safety campaigns.

The activities of SCAN Teams have spawned clinical investigation into a number of areas. As an example, case tracking of prenatally substance-exposed infants in the 1980's at UCLA, led to further research into the developmental effects of this exposure and grant-funded programs to address the problems of the infants and their families. Other important research efforts that have grown out of SCAN Teams are studies on injuries of children who fall from beds and the differentiation of accidental vs. inflicted rib fractures. Other university hospital SCAN Teams are conducting research on injury healing in sexual abuse cases, drug endangered children suffering from exposure to methamphetamines in drug manufacturing homes, and other important research topics. An exciting trend is the potential for multi-site investigations where a number of different hospitals collaborate on research.

Tertiary Level of Care Teams

The element that most distinguishes the tertiary team is the inclusion of public agencies in team membership. Representatives from law enforcement, child protective services, and the public health department are core team members. The challenge for many Teams is that their hospitals serve patients from a large geographic area, requiring them to interface with multiple law enforcement agencies, multiple child protective service offices, public health centers, and courts. The next level of coordinated case investigation involves commitments from agencies to participate in a multidisciplinary, multi-agency approach to investigations and case management.

Spawning new programs

Development of Child Protection Centers

The early SCAN Teams opened up lines of communication between medical facilities and investigative agencies; increased awareness about child abuse and neglect; provided community education; developed cooperative agency partnerships; provided professional training for law enforcement officers, prosecutors, and investigative social workers on how to interpret medical evidentiary exam findings; and, in many instances, established foundational leadership in the community to address the problem of child abuse and neglect. Beginning in the 1980's, Child Protection Centers emerged out of SCAN Teams, and built upon the foundation established by the SCAN Team model. The hospital-based centers began to operate on a much larger multi-disciplinary scale. These programs first developed in response to the need for specialized child sexual abuse medical evidentiary examinations and the higher level of collaboration required with investigative agencies. From this foundation, other services began to be developed and offered such as foster care health programs providing clearance and comprehensive medical exams with screening for medical, developmental, dental, and mental health problems; comprehensive mental health programs including individual, group, and family therapy; research; and more formalized regional and statewide conferences and training programs.

These programs are often extensively involved in addressing larger child protection system policy issues; initiating system change to improve intervention services; developing interagency protocols for case management; and engaging in legislative and public policy advocacy at the State and Federal level.

Multi-Disciplinary Interview Centers (MDICs) or Multi-Disciplinary Interview Teams (MDIT)

Another important development to ensure coordinated case investigations involves commitments from agencies to participate in a multi-disciplinary, multi-agency approach to interview children utilizing child interview specialists.

These programs are often called Multi-Disciplinary Interview Centers (MDICs) or Multi-Disciplinary Interview Teams (MDITs). In some cases, the MDIC/MCIT is located at the hospital. In most instances, the MDIC/MDIT is located at a public agency such as the District Attorney's office or Child Protective Services, and makes referrals to the hospital's child abuse specialists for forensic medical exams. MDICs and MDITs arose from local multi-disciplinary teams and coordinating councils and, in many instances, the original SCAN Team. See the chapter in this manual entitled "Specialized Interview Teams for Children" for further information.

References

Bross, D.C., Krugman, R.D., Lenherr, M.R., Rosenberg, D.A., and Schmitt, B.D. *The New Child Protection Team Handbook.* Garland Publishing, New York, 1988.

Child Abuse Prevention Handbook. Crime Prevention Center, Office of the Attorney General, California Department of Justice, 1993.

Besharov, D.J. *Recognizing Child Abuse: A guide for the concerned.* The Free Press, New York, 1990.

Child Death Review Teams

Michael Durfee, M.D. and Stephen J. Wirtz, Ph.D.

Case vignette: Child Abuse Fatality

Melissa was born into a family whose mother had long-term involvement with children's protective services. The biological father had left the state and was not providing any form of support to the family. The mother had not only chronically neglected the children, but because of her involvement with a series of drug abusing and physically abusive boyfriends had also endangered the children's physical safety. She was allowed to keep her children because she always expressed a willingness to do better and protect her children.

When she moved to another county, CPS made a vague referral that "mother is chronically neglectful and endangers her children". No reference was made to her propensity to enter into abusive relationships or to her being a victim herself. An initial CPS assessment in the new county was satisfactory as the children were clothed, food was available, and housing was marginally adequate. Although a boyfriend was present, no record check was done on him since the new county was not aware of the risk of domestic violence.

One-year old Melissa was killed shortly thereafter by the new boyfriend. The case review by the Child Death Review Team (CDRT) showed that at the time of the initial assessment, the boyfriend was a registered sex offender with prior convictions for child molestation, sales of narcotics, and domestic violence.

As a result of Melissa's death, the county teams identified two needs to prevent future deaths: cross-training on domestic violence identification, referral and intervention for all child services providers; and formal CPS procedures for referrals when transferring cases from one county to another. New CPS procedures were quickly instituted in both counties to assure a thorough sharing of information. Efforts have begun to address the need for domestic violence cross training.

Questions

1. What is a Child Death Review Team (CDRT) and what is its purpose?

2. Who are the members of a child death review team?

3. What criteria do teams use for reviewing child deaths? How do teams conduct their reviews?

4. How long have CDRTs been functioning?

5. What is the role of the State Child Death Review Council?

6. How many children die each year from child abuse or neglect?

7. Can similar teams review fatal domestic domestic/intimate partner violence?

Purposes of Child Death Review Teams (CDRTs)

CDRTs are multi-agency, multidisciplinary state and/or local teams that systematically review child deaths within a specific geographic area. They play a critical role in helping to identify child abuse and neglect fatalities and other preventable child deaths. Local CDRTs are often involved in the case management of child death investigations. State teams primarily serve the local teams or gather data for systems management and policy interventions. Many benefits have accrued from the work of CDRTs, including more accurate identification of child deaths due to child maltreatment, more effective determination of the underlying cause of suspicious deaths, identification of gaps and breakdowns in agencies and systems designed to protect children, and implementation of various prevention interventions.

Depending on their focus, the purposes of CDRTs may include any or all of the following:

- Review and assess whether child deaths are homicides associated with abuse or neglect;

- Review and assess the causes of all child deaths with the intent of identifying circumstances surrounding deaths that could be prevented in the future;

- Improve the criminal investigation and prosecution of child abuse homicides;

- Improve dependency investigations and the protection of surviving siblings;

- Serve as a quality assurance team for death investigations;

- Design and implement cooperative protocols for investigation of child deaths;

- Improve linkages, communication and coordination among law enforcement, social services, the district attorney's office, local health agencies, the coroner and others;

- Provide a forum for agencies to resolve conflicts;

- Collect uniform and accurate statistics on child deaths; and,

- Identify public health issues and make recommendations to county and state policymakers and legislators.

Team Membership

Core members:

- County Medical Examiner or Coroner

- Law Enforcement Officer(s)

- Children's Protective Services

- District Attorney's Office

- Pediatrician (preferably with experience in child abuse evaluations)

Additional members:

- Child Advocate

- Education representative

- Fire Department or Emergency Medical Services' representative

- Mental Health representative

- Liaison with the California Highway Patrol (CHP) (if available)

- Epidemiologist or data person, e.g., Office of Vital Statistics (if available)

- Probation Department officer (if available)

- Injury Control Specialist

Selection Criteria

CDRTs systematically select child deaths for review using predetermined criteria. Usually cases are drawn either from the deaths reported to the coroner or from vital statistics' death certificates. Many counties (e.g., small and mid-sized counties) review all child deaths, whereas larger counties may have more selective review criteria (e.g., only coroner cases). Age criteria usually range from selecting only children under 7 to selecting all children under 20. The most common age criterion is children under 18 years of age.

Examples of review criteria used by various teams:

- All children under age 18

- Coroner's cases of all children's deaths

- "Unexpected", "Unexplained", or "Suspicious" deaths

- Deaths under a certain age

- Deaths of children known to child protective services

- Deaths from certain causes

Recommended minimum criteria:

- All Coroner child death cases

- All children under 18 years of age

Team Functioning

The recommended model program or "Best Practices" involve:

- Systematic intake and review of cases drawn by protocol from the coroner and/or vital statistics records;

- Teams function as a peer review, respecting confidentiality and sharing information across agency lines;

- Authentic peer review with no agency controlling or censuring the information, discussion, or activity of another;

- Multi-disciplinary team membership of investigative agencies with administrative support to collect, analyze, publish, and distribute the data locally for the Board of Supervisors, directors of public agencies and in the newspaper—for the public; and

- Capability for promoting and implementing basic or advanced procedures, policies, and prevention programs through team member agencies (e.g. County Health Department or Child Abuse Prevention Council) or other community resources.

All teams have some level of focus on prevention and typically carry out prevention action plans through the County Health Department. For example, in one California county where it was learned that a disproportionate number of drowning deaths were of Vietnamese children, signs were posted along the popular river beaches in Vietnamese warning of the dangers. Other examples are child passenger safety programs (local hospitals provide car seats to low-income families); swimming pool safety information; fire prevention; and prenatal sobriety radio public service announcements.

History and Focus of Child Death Review Teams

The first teams in California were started in Los Angeles County in 1978 and in San Diego County in 1982. Local teams and the state level team met for years before they were made official by laws in the late 1980's and early 1990's which formally allowed counties to establish interagency child death review teams and to exchange confidential information. Now nearly all of the 58 counties have teams. Other states began developing these teams during the 1980's as well. The Healthy People 2000 Objectives included an objective to establish state teams in at least 45 states by the year 2000. This goal was met and surpassed with at least 48 states reporting some form of local or state teams. The Healthy People 2010 Objectives also includes an objective (15-6) to extend the state-level fatality review process to include all deaths due to external causes of children aged 14 years and under.

Role of the State Child Death Review Council

The California State Child Death Review Council (CSC-DRC) established under the auspices of the Department of Justice (DOJ) was organized to establish leadership at the state level with representatives from key state agencies and associations. According to the legislative mandate, it shall be the duty of the CSCDRC to oversee the statewide coordination and integration of state and local efforts to address

fatal child abuse and neglect, and to create a body of information to prevent child death. Recent goals of the State Council include:

- Create and maintain an integrated, automated statewide data system for all counties and relevant state agencies;

- Promote the use of standardized forms and data collection protocols;

- Foster communication between state and local teams, other states, federal agencies and national associations, including dissemination of data and a statewide directory;

- Address local, state and federal policy legislation issues and guidelines;

- Seek additional resources and funding for county team efforts;

- Support the development of domestic violence death review teams;

- Promote increased awareness of the relationship between domestic violence and child abuse;

- Promote development of a model for small counties, i.e. multi-county teams or cluster groups for counties with populations under 20,000;

- Raise visibility of child deaths and child death review teams through public education programs and the annual state report;

- Promote education and training for child death review team members;

- Develop an evaluation process to assess team effectiveness;

- Encourage continued research efforts at the state and federal level regarding child deaths and related issues; and

- Provide training and technical assistance to local teams.

Epidemiology of Fatal Child Abuse and Neglect

Statistics on the number of child abuse and neglect fatalities in California vary according to which data source is used, e.g., DOJ Homicide Files, Department of Health Services Vital Statistics Death Records, or DOJ Child Abuse Central Index. A description of the three databases is provided at the end of this section. None of the three databases can be considered as the definitive source for identifying child abuse and neglect (CAN) fatalities because each has its own legal mandates, purposes, definitions, and protocols for use. Table 1 displays the numbers reported to each of the state databases from 1996-98. For example, the number of fatal CAN cases is highest in the DOJ Homicide file with 143,110 and 96 recorded in 1996, 1997, and 1998 respectively. In addition to the differences in total numbers reported, the figures do not reflect a one-to-one match of cases between the databases, thus the actual number of CAN fatalities is not known. Because of the potential impact of reporting failures and improper case management, local CDRTs are considered a critical link in the

state's efforts to improve case identification, investigation and management.

Starting with 1996 data, DHS conducts an annual Reconciliation Audit of all child deaths recorded as CAN in the three state data sources by requesting local CDRTs to compare the results of their local case reviews with the state information. This process has produced more accurate estimates for the number of CAN fatalities in California. According to the statewide audit, there were 152 fatal CAN cases in 1996 and 135 in 1997. Under recent state legislation, the Department of Health Services will soon begin to implement a surveillance system for tracking the number of CAN fatalities using local CDRTs as a source of data.

TABLE 1. CHILD ABUSE AND NEGLECT (CAN) AND OTHER HOMICIDES: COMPARISON OF CALIFORNIA'S THREE STATEWIDE DATABASES, 1996-1998

Types of Homicide	DOJ Homicide File			Vital Statistics Death Records			Child Abuse Central Index		
	1996	1997	1998	1996	1997	1998	1996	1997	1998
CAN Homicides	143	110	96	63	33	20	52	47	24
"Other" Homicides	296	272	214	354	359	280	N/A	N/A	N/A
TOTAL HOMICIDES	**439**	**382**	**310**	**417**	**392**	**300**	**52**	**47**	**24**

Source: State Child Death Review Council, 2000

Nationally, child death data from caretaker abuse varies from under 1,000 to over 3,000 cases annually depending upon the sources and methods used to make the estimate. National data sets and local studies consistently show about 40% of these deaths are under age one with 80+% of deaths under the age of five. Anywhere from twenty to fifty per cent have previous child protective agency records. Many, if not most, have some previous medical record, often an emergency room visit. The most common cause or death is blunt force trauma to the head. Other causes of death are trauma to the chest and abdomen, smothering, and forced scalding. The blunt force trauma usually involves use of the hands or feet, in contrast to objects. Medical neglect and severe "supervisorial" neglect are both common causes of fatal CAN.

Elements of neglect are also found in some accidental and natural deaths (not included in the data shown in the chart). This may include intoxicated parents unable to supervise their children, failure to restrain children properly in a vehicle, leaving weapons unsecured, malnutrition, dehydration, leaving children alone locked in a closed car during hot weather, and medical neglect. African American

children, poverty, and families involved in other violence are often over-represented in the statistics. Men kill more than women; however, both genders, all races, all social-economic statues, are represented.

The Sacramento County Child Death Review Team's 1997 analysis of 14 child abuse and neglect deaths, for example, found the following profile of the circumstances surrounding the child deaths :

- the perpetrator was most likely to be male;

- the caretakers were not married to each other; and,

- there was at least one significant risk present (listed in order below):

  - prior history of abuse and neglect;

  - drug and alcohol related and/or a history of drug and alcohol abuse;

  - a history of domestic violence; and/or,

  - perpetrator has a criminal history that includes a violent crime.

Challenges

Developing accurate assessments of child deaths.

Since suspicious child deaths are often not witnessed and young sibling survivors often have limited verbal skills, decisions as to the cause of death rest heavily on the quality of agency investigations. A thorough investigation of the death scene and a complete autopsy are crucial. In addition, review of previous hospital and clinic/private medical records, child protection agency records, law enforcement records and any other available information are usually necessary.

Dealing with disbelief

The shock and horror that children are murdered by their caretakers is hard for most people to believe and thus there is resistance to accepting this possibility.

Resistance to inter-agency cooperation

There is often resistance to open inter-agency cooperation due to past history, internal policies and practices, and efforts to protect each agency . It takes considerable effort to develop a trusting team environment where fault-finding and blame are not the focus, and mistakes can be acknowledged and reviewed. In a supportive team environment, constructive recommendations can be identified and agencies can develop corrective action plans.

Taking action to prevent future child deaths

One of the major goals of the CDRTs is the prevention of future deaths. The in-depth case reviews often uncover agency or broader systems changes that potentially can prevent future deaths. Many teams, however, work at an informal level and do not have a formal procedure or mechanism to translate their insights and recommendations into productive actions or reforms.

Several approaches have been used to increase the impact of CDRTs recommendations. First, many teams produce regular team reports and present them to decision-making bodies and the public. This serves as a powerful tool to gain credibility and public awareness. Second, other teams have developed formal linkages to broader community or children's coalitions that can incorporate the team recommendations into their action agendas. Third, in some cases a member agency (e.g. Health Department or Child Abuse Prevention Council) has accepted responsibility for following up on specific findings and carrying out prevention activities. In addition, many meaningful interventions have occurred through the informal action of individual team members within or across agencies.

Data collection issues

Although some local teams have developed their own data collection tools, there is a compelling need for standard, user-friendly data collection protocols and procedures. Standard definitions for fatal child abuse and neglect and agreed upon core data elements to be collected are needed. Support and training on the use of computer technologies and appropriate software at the local county level will continued to be needed as well. Since the passage of legislation (SB 525, Polanco) in 1999, the California Department of Health Services is implementing a statewide data collection tracking system and providing technical assistance and training.

Increase awareness of grief and mourning issues for surviving siblings and professionals who handle these cases.

It is common for surviving siblings to be overlooked, especially if they are placed in the foster care system, and do not have the opportunity for therapy after the death of a brother or sister.. This issue is addressed in more detail in the chapter on *Sibling Loss: Psychological Treatment for Survivors*. For professionals, critical incident debriefing protocols and/or teams are also helpful for those who have tried to save the child or respond to these tragic child deaths (e.g., hospital personnel, EMTs, law enforcement, and social workers).

Fatal Domestic/Intimate Partner Violence Review Teams

In 1995, California passed a law that allows for the establishment of similar review teams for fatal domestic/intimate partner violence cases. Currently in California at least 15 counties have started such teams. The Attorney General's Office has released in July 2000 a protocol for the development and implementation of inter-agency domestic violence death review teams for use by counties.

Background Information

Causes of Child Deaths in California (1996-1998)

- **Natural Deaths:**
  The leading causes of natural death in 1998 were perinatal conditions, congenital anomalies, malignant neoplasms, and Sudden Infant Death Syndrome (SIDS).

- **Unintentional Injuries:**
  The major causes of injury deaths in California were motor vehicle crashes, drowning, suffocations, and fires and burns.

- **Intentional Injuries**
  The major causes of intentional injuries were homicides by firearms/explosives, suicides, other homicides, and child abuse homicides.

Sources:

- California Department of Health Services, Vital Statistics Death Records. Reported in State Child Death Review Council. *Child Death in California Related to Child Abuse and Neglect, 1996-1998.*

- California Attorney General's Office, July 2000 and prepared by EPIC Branch, State Department of Health Services.

Three Data Systems in California

Through the work of the State Child Death Review Council, efforts are being made at the state and county level to coordinate investigations and information to ensure that cases are recorded properly and consistently in all three systems.

- **Vital Statistics Death Records**
  The data are maintained by the Office of Vital Statistics, Center for Health Statistics, California Department of Health Services and is based upon death certificates filled out by physicians, coroners, or medical examiners.

- **Homicide Files**
  The data are maintained by the California Department of Justice and their source is law enforcement Supplemental Homicide Reports submitted as part of the National Uniform Crime Reporting System. These reports are based upon the law enforcement investigations.

- **Child Abuse Central Index**
  These data are also maintained by the California Department of Justice and are based upon investigated reports of substantiated and inconclusive child abuse or neglect submitted by law enforcement or child protective services. The index includes homicide cases where the suspect was the caretaker.

References

Durfee, MJ, Gellert, GA and Tilton-Durfee, D. Origin and Clinical Significance of Child Death Review Teams. , *JAMA*, Jun 17;267(23):3172-5, 1992.

Durfee M. and Tilton-Durfee, D. Multiagency Child Death Review Teams: Experience in the United States. –, *Child Abuse Review*, Vol. 4: 377-381, 1995.

State Child Death Review Board, California Department of Justice. *Child Death in California 1992-1995.* Attorney General's Office, March, 1997.

State Child Death Review Council. *Child Death in California Related to Child Abuse and Neglect, 1996-1998.* California Attorney General's Office, July, 2000.

US Advisory Board on Child Abuse and Neglect. *A Nation's Shame: Fatal Child Abuse and Neglect in the United States*, USDHHS, ACYF, 1995.

Web sites

ICAN National Center on Child Fatality Review, ICAN/NCFR
http://www.ican-ncfr.org

Prevent Child Abuse – California (California Consortium for Prevention of Child Abuse)
http://www.ccpca.org

Fatal Child Abuse and Neglect Surveillance Program, Epidemiology and Prevention for Injury Control (EPIC) Branch, California Department of Health Services
http://www.dhs.ca.gov/cdic/epic/html/FatalCAN.htm

Web search for "Child Fatality Review" will bring up sites from multiple states.

Specialized Interview Teams for Children

Paula Christian, M.S.W. and Marilyn Strachan Peterson, M.S.W., M.P.A.

Purpose

Multi-Disciplinary Interview Centers (MDICs), sometimes called Multi-Disciplinary Interview Teams (MDITs), have developed in many counties to:

- reduce multiple, repetitive interviews of sexually abused children;

- reduce psychological trauma;

- improve the quality and consistency of child interviews;

- improve and coordinate decision-making regarding the need for medical evidential examinations;

- coordinate the inter-disciplinary response between law enforcement, deputy district attorneys, social workers, and health practitioners; and

- improve coordination and case planning between law enforcement and child protective services (CPS).

Model Approaches

Child interviewing has emerged both as an art and a science. Research published in peer review journals exists on the process of disclosure, and how children understand and answer questions. In addition to technical knowledge, interviewers must have the ability to establish rapport with children, engage them in discussion about sensitive matters, and understand that children under stress are likely to "stonewall" (put up verbal and nonverbal barriers) or deny what happened.

In the drive to reduce repetitive interviews and in the context of high caseloads, an imbalance has occurred in some settings. An over-reliance has developed on the "one-stop" comprehensive interview. Decision-making becomes over-focused on whether the child gave a "good MDIT interview" that day. Research is showing that children tend to disclose events over time as they "test the waters" to see what is safe to say. In general, the model program approach to child interviewing has the following features:

- Developmentally appropriate, forensically defensible questions and methods are used consistent with the age of the child;

- Child interview specialists are specially trained using standard curriculum;

- An interview protocol designed to address law enforcement investigation and child protection needs is followed;

- The interview setting is a warm, child-friendly atmosphere;

- Opportunity exists for follow-up interview(s) by the same interviewer;

- Interviews are videotaped;

- Interviews are observed through a one-way glass by a deputy district attorney from a child abuse prosecution unit, a detective, and a CPS social worker;

- Arrangements are in place for child sexual abuse evidential examinations to be performed by specially trained medical examiners;

- Crisis intervention can be provided;

- Follow-up case management and referrals for mental health counseling are made; and

- Accurate information and support on how to access the State Victims of Crime Program for reimbursement of counseling expenses are given.

Organization and Staffing

Staffing varies between centers according to resources. There are two basic models, and several variations of "organizational home" structures:

- **Site models with specialized staff.**
  The program is located at a specially designed "child friendly" site. Typical staffing includes a program coordinator and child interview specialists. Children are brought to the site which has a specially designed interview room with videotape equipment and a one-way glass. Detectives, CPS social workers, and a deputy district attorney convene to observe the interview and make case planning and management decisions.

- **Joint Response Model**
  In this model, CPS social workers and law enforcement officers coordinate to conduct joint interviews. The interviews take place at various locations, sometimes at a specified site. Interviews are conducted either by CPS social workers or by law enforcement officers who are trained as interview specialists.

- **"Organizational Home" Structures**
  MDICs and MDITs are commonly placed in county district attorneys' offices or child protective services. Sometimes they operate as non-profit organizations or are sponsored by the local child abuse prevention council.

Differences Between Medical Interviews and Specialized Forensic Interviews

1. **Purpose of a medical interview conducted by physicians and nurses:**

   - to determine the likelihood that a child's signs and symptoms are consistent with sexual abuse;

   - to establish the type of physical findings that may be present;

   - to ascertain if a child needs treatment; and

   - to provide information to law enforcement officers, investigative social workers, deputy district attorneys, defense attorneys, and judges about the history and whether it is consistent with case findings

2. **Purpose of a specialized forensic interview:**

   - to establish the child's ability to accurately relate a history;

   - to enhance communication while reducing suggestibility;

   - to obtain a detailed description of the events by asking questions about who, what, when, where, how, how many times; and

   - to avoid unnecessary multiple interviews of the child.

Contact your county department of health and human services, District Attorney's Office, or child abuse prevention council to determine whether an MDIT or MDIC exists in your community.

Resources

Child Abuse Training and Technical Assistance (CATTA) Center, California Institute on Human Services
California State University, Sonoma
1801 E. Cotati Avenue
Rohnert Park, CA 94928-3609
Phone: (707) 664-4394
Fax: (707) 664-2417
Web site: http://www.sonoma.edu/cihs/html/catta/
           textsite/Tcattaabout.html

PART 14

Mandatory Reporting Laws for Health Care Practitioners

Marilyn Strachan Peterson, M.S.W., M.P.A.

According California laws, health practitioners are required by law to report any suspected child abuse and neglect.

Health practitioner is defined as a physician and surgeon; psychiatrist; psychologist; dentist; resident; intern; podiatrist; chiropractor; licensed nurse; dental hygienist; optometrist; marriage, family, and child counselor, trainee or unlicensed intern; licensed clinical social worker; emergency medical technician I and II; paramedic; coroner; state or county public health worker treating a minor for venereal disease; and religious practitioner who diagnoses, examines, or treats children.

There are four types of child abuse that may occur alone or in combination:

- Physical Abuse

- Sexual Abuse

- Emotional/Psychological Abuse

- Child Neglect

These types of abuse usually overlap in the experiences of many children and are linked to short- and long-term psychological sequelae.

Physical abuse is characterized by inflicting physical injury by hitting, punching, beating, kicking, throwing, biting, burning, or otherwise physically harming a child. The injury may be the result of a single episode or of repeated episodes. They physical trauma can range in severity from minor bruising, abrasions, lacerations, burns, eye injuries, and fractures to damage to the brain and internal organs. Head and internal injuries are the leading causes of child abuse-related deaths. This form of abuse includes extreme or bizarre forms of punishment such as torture or confinement of children in dark closets, boxes or rooms for days, months, or even years at a time.

Sexual abuse includes a wide range of conduct: genital exposure; masturbation between adult and child; fondling breasts, genitals, buttocks, and thighs; oral copulation; vaginal or anal penetration by finger, penis, or foreign object; dry intercourse (rubbing penis between child's thighs or anal-genital area); and commercial exploitation through prostitution or the production of pornographic materials.

Emotional/psychological Abuse includes acts or omissions by the parents or other persons responsible for the child's care that have caused, or could cause, serious emotional, behavioral, cognitive, or mental disorders. Emotional/psychological abuse exists on a continuum of habitual behavioral interactions such as belittling through comments, comparisons, and name-calling; scapegoating; humiliating; isolating; screaming and raging; and psychological inaccessibility or rejecting treatment.

Child neglect is characterized by failure to provide for the child's basic needs, whether physical, educational, or emotional.

- **Physical neglect**—refusal or delay in seeking medical or dental care, abandonment, inadequate supervision, passive drug intoxication with illicit drugs, accidental ingestion of illicit drugs, and expulsion from home or refusing to allow a runaway to return home.

- **Educational neglect**—permission of chronic truancy, failure to enroll a child of mandatory school age, and inattention to a special education need.

- **Emotional neglect**—failure to respond to the child's psychological needs for attention, love and emotional security; emotional deprivation and being psychologically inaccessible; exposure to chronic or extreme spousal abuse in the child's presence; and permission for drug or alcohol use by the child.

As a legally mandated reporter, a health practitioner must submit a report as soon as practically possible by phone to child protective services or a law enforcement agency when there is reasonable suspicion of child abuse. The Child Abuse and Neglect Reporting Act specifically provides that neither the physician-patient privilege nor the psychotherapist-patient privilege applies to any information reported pursuant to this law (Penal Code 11171). A person who fails to make a required report is guilty of a misdemeanor or punishable by up to six months in jail and/or up to $1,000 fine, as well as possible civil liable damages.

The mandated reporter must give his or her name when reporting known or suspected child abuse to a child protective agency. However, the name is kept confidential and may be disclosed only in very specific, limited situations such as between child protective agencies, to the district attorney investigating and prosecuting the case, through court orders, or if confidentiality is waived. When making a telephone report of suspected child abuse to the child protective agency, the following information is required:

- Name of the child,

- Present location of the child,

- Nature and extent of the injury, and

- Any other information that led the reporter to suspect child abuse, as requested by the child protective agency.

A written report must be sent within 36 hours to either Children's Protective Services or a local law enforcement agency. The Department of Justice Form SS8572, also referred to as PC11166, is used for this purpose and a copy is attached on the next 2 pages. Upon completion of the investigation or final disposition in the matter, the investigating agency shall inform the mandated reporter about the results of the investigation. The best resource on this topic is the Attorney General's Child Abuse Prevention Handbook.

Resource

Child Abuse Prevention Handbook published by the California Attorney General's Office
http://caag.state.ca.us/search.htm

SUSPECTED CHILD ABUSE REPORT

To Be Completed by **Mandated Child Abuse Reporters**
Pursuant to Penal Code Section 11166
PLEASE PRINT OR TYPE

CASE NAME: _____

CASE NUMBER: _____

A. REPORTING PARTY

NAME OF MANDATED REPORTER	TITLE		MANDATED REPORTER CATEGORY
REPORTER'S BUSINESS/AGENCY NAME AND ADDRESS	Street	City Zip	DID MANDATED REPORTER WITNESS THE INCIDENT? ❐ YES ❐ NO
REPORTER'S TELEPHONE (DAYTIME) ( )	SIGNATURE		TODAY'S DATE

B. REPORT NOTIFICATION

❐ LAW ENFORCEMENT ❐ COUNTY PROBATION ❐ COUNTY WELFARE / CPS (Child Protective Services)	AGENCY		
ADDRESS Street	City	Zip	DATE/TIME OF PHONE CALL
OFFICIAL CONTACTED - TITLE		TELEPHONE ( )	

C. VICTIM
One report per victim

NAME (LAST, FIRST, MIDDLE)	BIRTHDATE OR APPROX. AGE	SEX	ETHNICITY
ADDRESS Street City Zip	TELEPHONE ( )		
PRESENT LOCATION OF VICTIM	SCHOOL	CLASS	GRADE
PHYSICALLY DISABLED? ❐ YES ❐ NO	DEVELOPMENTALLY DISABLED? ❐ YES ❐ NO	OTHER DISABILITY (SPECIFY)	PRIMARY LANGUAGE SPOKEN IN HOME
IN FOSTER CARE? ❐ YES ❐ NO	IF VICTIM WAS IN OUT-OF-HOME CARE AT TIME OF INCIDENT, CHECK TYPE OF CARE: ❐ DAY CARE ❐ CHILD CARE CENTER ❐ FOSTER FAMILY HOME ❐ FAMILY FRIEND ❐ GROUP HOME OR INSTITUTION ❐ RELATIVE'S HOME		TYPE OF ABUSE (CHECK ONE OR MORE) ❐ PHYSICAL ❐ MENTAL ❐ SEXUAL ❐ NEGLECT ❐ OTHER (SPECIFY)
RELATIONSHIP TO SUSPECT	PHOTOS TAKEN? ❐ YES ❐ NO	DID THE INCIDENT RESULT IN THIS VICTIM'S DEATH? ❐ YES ❐ NO ❐ UNK	

D. INVOLVED PARTIES

VICTIM'S SIBLINGS

	NAME	BIRTHDATE	SEX	ETHNICITY		NAME	BIRTHDATE	SEX	ETHNICITY
1.					3.				
2.					4.				

VICTIM'S PARENTS/GUARDIANS

NAME (LAST, FIRST, MIDDLE)	BIRTHDATE OR APPROX. AGE	SEX	ETHNICITY
ADDRESS Street City Zip HOME PHONE ( )	BUSINESS PHONE ( )		
NAME (LAST, FIRST, MIDDLE)	BIRTHDATE OR APPROX. AGE	SEX	ETHNICITY
ADDRESS Street City Zip HOME PHONE ( )	BUSINESS PHONE ( )		

SUSPECT

SUSPECT'S NAME (LAST, FIRST, MIDDLE)	BIRTHDATE OR APPROX. AGE	SEX	ETHNICITY
ADDRESS Street City Zip	TELEPHONE ( )		
OTHER RELEVANT INFORMATION			

E. INCIDENT INFORMATION

IF NECESSARY, ATTACH EXTRA SHEET(S) OR OTHER FORM(S) AND CHECK THIS BOX ❐   IF MULTIPLE VICTIMS, INDICATE NUMBER: _____

DATE / TIME OF INCIDENT	PLACE OF INCIDENT

NARRATIVE DESCRIPTION (What victim(s) said/what the mandated reporter observed/what person accompanying the victim(s) said/similar or past incidents involving the victim(s) or suspect)

SS 8572 (Rev. 12/02)

DEFINITIONS AND INSTRUCTIONS ON REVERSE

DO NOT submit a copy of this form to the Department of Justice (DOJ). The investigating agency is required under Penal Code Section 11169 to submit to DOJ a Child Abuse Investigation Report Form SS 8583 if (1) an active investigation was conducted and (2) the incident was determined not to be unfounded.

WHITE COPY-Police or Sheriff's Department;   BLUE COPY-County Welfare or Probation Department;   GREEN COPY- District Attorney's Office;   YELLOW COPY-Reporting Party

DEFINITIONS AND GENERAL INSTRUCTIONS FOR COMPLETION OF FORM SS 8572

All Penal Code (PC) references are located in Article 2.5 of the PC. This article is known as the Child Abuse and Neglect Reporting Act (CANRA). The provisions of CANRA may be viewed at: http://www.leginfo.ca.gov/calaw.html (specify "Penal Code" and search for Sections 11164-11174.3). A mandated reporter must complete and submit the form SS 8572 even if some of the requested information is not known. (PC Section 11167(a).)

I. MANDATED CHILD ABUSE REPORTERS

- Mandated child abuse reporters include all those individuals and entities listed in PC Section 11165.7.

II. TO WHOM REPORTS ARE TO BE MADE ("DESIGNATED AGENCIES")

- Reports of suspected child abuse or neglect shall be made by mandated reporters to any police department or sheriff's department (not including a school district police or security department), the county probation department (if designated by the county to receive mandated reports), or the county welfare department. (PC Section 11165.9.)

III. REPORTING RESPONSIBILITIES

- Any mandated reporter who has knowledge of or observes a child, in his or her professional capacity or within the scope of his or her employment, whom he or she knows or reasonably suspects has been the victim of child abuse or neglect shall report such suspected incident of abuse or neglect to a designated agency immediately or as soon as practically possible by telephone and shall prepare and send a written report thereof *within 36 hours* of receiving the information concerning the incident. (PC Section 11166(a).)

- No mandated reporter who reports a suspected incident of child abuse or neglect shall be held civilly or criminally liable for any report required or authorized by CANRA. Any other person reporting a known or suspected incident of child abuse or neglect shall not incur civil or criminal liability as a result of any report authorized by CANRA unless it can be proven the report was false and the person knew it was false or made the report with reckless disregard of its truth or falsity. (PC Section 11172(a).)

IV. INSTRUCTIONS

- **SECTION A - REPORTING PARTY:** Enter the mandated reporter's name, title, category (from PC Section 11165.7), business/agency name and address, daytime telephone number, and today's date. Check yes-no whether the mandated reporter witnessed the incident. The signature area is for either the mandated reporter or, if the report is telephoned in by the mandated reporter, the person taking the telephoned report.

IV. INSTRUCTIONS (Continued)

- **SECTION B - REPORT NOTIFICATION:** Complete the name and address of the designated agency notified, the date/time of the phone call, and the name, title, and telephone number of the official contacted.

- **SECTION C - VICTIM (One Report per Victim):** Enter the victim's name, address, telephone number, birth date or approximate age, sex, ethnicity, present location, and, where applicable, enter the school, class (indicate the teacher's name or room number), and grade. List the primary language spoken in the victim's home. Check the appropriate yes-no box to indicate whether the victim may have a developmental disability or physical disability and specify any other apparent disability. Check the appropriate yes-no box to indicate whether the victim is in foster care, and check the appropriate box to indicate the type of care if the victim was in out-of-home care. Check the appropriate box to indicate the type of abuse. List the victim's relationship to the suspect. Check the appropriate yes-no box to indicate whether photos of the injuries were taken. Check the appropriate box to indicate whether the incident resulted in the victim's death.

- **SECTION D - INVOLVED PARTIES:** Enter the requested information for: Victim's Siblings, Victim's Parents/Guardians, and Suspect. Attach extra sheet(s) if needed (provide the requested information for each individual on the attached sheet(s)).

- **SECTION E - INCIDENT INFORMATION:** If multiple victims, indicate the number and submit a form for each victim. Enter date/time and place of the incident. Provide a narrative of the incident. Attach extra sheet(s) if needed.

V. DISTRIBUTION

- **Reporting Party:** After completing Form SS 8572, retain the yellow copy for your records and submit the top three copies to the designated agency.

- **Designated Agency:** *Within 36 hours* of receipt of Form SS 8572, send **white copy** to police or sheriff's department, **blue copy** to county welfare or probation department, and **green copy** to district attorney's office.

ETHNICITY CODES

1 Alaskan Native	6 Caribbean	11 Guamanian	16 Korean	22 Polynesian	27 White-Armenian
2 American Indian	7 Central American	12 Hawaiian	17 Laotian	23 Samoan	28 White-Central American
3 Asian Indian	8 Chinese	13 Hispanic	18 Mexican	24 South American	29 White-European
4 Black	9 Ethiopian	14 Hmong	19 Other Asian	25 Vietnamese	30 White-Middle Eastern
5 Cambodian	10 Filipino	15 Japanese	21 Other Pacific Islander	26 White	31 White-Romania

California Court System: Healthcare Providers as Expert and Percipient Witnesses

Marv Stern, J.D.

Case Vignette

After examining an eight-year-old girl, taken and developed colposcopic photos, and completed the state forensic medical exam report form, the report is turned over to the investigating detective. The case has now moved out of your area of expertise into the legal arena.

Questions

1. How does the court system work?

2. Who is my attorney?

3. What can I do to get ready to testify?

4. What can I expect in court?

5. Do I get paid for this?

The California Court System

California has several different types of courts. Cases are filed in the *Superior* and *Municipal* courts to hold persons accountable for violating the law. *Misdemeanor* offenses (punishable by a year or less in county jail) are prosecuted in Municipal Court, and *felony* offenses (punishable by a commitment to state prison) are prosecuted in Superior Court.

The *Family Court* is a division of the Superior Court, but it is a civil proceeding to decide issues of divorce and child custody. Sometimes during custody battles, an allegation of child abuse or neglect is made against one of the parties. In this case, a referral is made to Children's Protective Services (CPS) to investigate the allegations.

The *Juvenile Court* also includes *Dependency Court*. In the Juvenile Court, offenders are prosecuted who are under the age of 18 at the time they committed their crime. The Dependency Court is charged with protecting children and adolescents from abuse and neglect. It is up to the Dependency Court to determine the appropriate place for a child to live depending upon what has happened to the child.

In the Superior, Municipal, and Juvenile courts, the *District Attorney* is the prosecuting attorney and the defendant is represented by their own lawyer or a court-appointed lawyer and the proceeding is a *criminal prosecution*. In Family Court, each side is represented by their own retained civil lawyer, or they represent themselves. In Dependency Court, in most California counties, the County Counsel represents the interests of the People of the State of California, the child receives a court-appointed lawyer, and the parents receive a court-appointed lawyer or they hire their own. Family Court and Dependency Court are civil proceedings.

Who Is My Attorney?

Expert and percipient witnesses do not have an attorney. In Superior Court, Municipal Court, or Juvenile Court, the People of the State of California are represented by the District Attorney. In Dependency Court, the People are represented by County Counsel.

These attorneys are responsible for filing charges (or in the case of Dependency Court, preparing a *Petition* asking that the minor victim be declared a ward of the court) against the suspect, preparing the case for court, negotiating a possible disposition, and trying the case in court if a trial is necessary. In criminal prosecutions, the trial generally includes a jury. In Dependency Court and Family Court, the judge conducts the trial without a jury.

A criminal prosecution conducted by a Deputy District Attorney can be lengthy, often taking three to nine months. During the investigation/preparation stage, you may be contacted by the Deputy District Attorney and asked to explain the medical findings, and to answer hypothetical questions about what might have caused the conditions that you observed. You may also be contacted by a criminal defense attorney or their criminal defense investigator and asked about your examination. It is your decision as to when and where or if you want to talk to anyone. The only time you have to answer questions is when you are in court.

What Can I Do To Get Ready To Testify?

Most cases are resolved without the need for medical testimony in court. The vast majority of criminal prosecutions are resolved by way of *plea bargain*, in which the prosecution and defense agree on a punishment for the offender without the need for a trial. Most Dependency and Family Court cases are resolved in a similar fashion, where the parties agree on a plan for the children in question without the need for a trial.

Some cases do require a trial. You will eventually receive a *subpoena*, almost always from the Deputy District Attorney. There are instances when a defense attorney finds that the report favors the defense, in which case, the defense attorney will issue a subpoena instead. Sometimes, both attorneys subpoena you. A subpoena is an order from the court to appear at a certain date and time at the courthouse. A careful examination of the subpoena will tell you the name of the suspect, which attorney subpoenaed you, and when you are to appear in court. Subpoenas generally do not have the name of the child examined on them. Keep in mind that the date on the subpoena is generally a guess as to when you will be needed. Rarely will you ever be needed on the exact date and time as listed on the subpoena.

After receiving a subpoena, call the attorney who subpoenaed you. Ask them for the name of the patient so that you can obtain your records and start to prepare. Ask to be placed *"on call"*, which means that you maintain your normal schedule and the attorney promises to call you at least the day before he or she needs you in court. Provide your pager number so that you can be reached easily. Be sure to tell the attorney about any planned trips out of the area, even if they are several weeks away.

Sometimes, you will be given a *subpoena duces tecum* (sub dt). This is a subpoena that requires you to bring or mail something to court. This generally will be for the medical records or pictures. The subpoena duces tecum will have directions on it as to where, when, and how you provide these records. If you receive a subpoena duces tecum from a defense attorney, it is usually a good idea to call the Deputy District Attorney and let him or her know that you received the sub dt.

If you do not appear in court on the date for which you were subpoenaed without contacting the attorney who subpoenaed you, received a waiver, or were placed on call, the court can issue a bench warrant for your arrest. If you discover that a warrant has been issued for you, call the Deputy District Attorney immediately. Remember that if you have been subpoenaed by more than one attorney, you need to speak to each. The Deputy District Attorney cannot release you from a defense subpoena.

When you speak to the prosecutor who subpoenaed you, discuss your preparation for trial. You will do a much better job as a witness if you know what you are going to be asked. Schedule a pretrial meeting with the prosecutor to go over the questions he or she expects to ask you. It also gives you a chance to educate the prosecutor about your findings, and to suggest areas of questioning the prosecutor might not have considered that you believe would be helpful to explain findings to the jury or judge.

In your meeting with the prosecutor, discuss the need for any visual aids that you feel might enhance the presentation of your testimony. Blown up photos can be very effective in demonstrating to a jury what your examination revealed. Preparation well in advance of the trial date is the best way to do the best job on the witness stand.

Your meeting with the prosecutor will also include anticipated areas of cross-examination by the defense attorney. While no one can be certain what another lawyer will ask, it probably will not be too difficult to anticipate what the defense attorney will want to ask you about. Again, research and preparation of these potential issues will make you much more effective under cross-examination, and greatly alleviate any stress you might feel about going to court.

What Can I Expect In Court?

The trial may take several days before it gets to your testimony. Initially, the attorneys and the judge will meet to go over pretrial motions, which generally set the ground rules for what evidence will be deemed admissible, and how it will be presented. Then, jury selection begins which can often take a few days. Once a jury is seated, opening statements by each attorney are given and the first witness is called.

Once a trial has started, the judge will expect each attorney to proceed promptly with witnesses so that the jury is always kept busy and there is no waiting time for a witness to appear. This forces the attorneys to keep witnesses waiting out in the hallway to testify, since it is impossible to predict how long each witness will take on the witness stand.

Generally, the attorney who is calling you as a witness will attempt to bring you to court at a time that least inconveniences your schedule and keeps you waiting to testify for as short a period of time as possible. Sometimes, that is not possible. You may even find that you are waiting for an hour or two at the end of the day and never get called into the courtroom to testify. Then, you will have to return the next day. As frustrating as this might be, the careful administration of justice is as important a function in which you will ever participate, and your patience and understanding will be greatly appreciated.

Once you are called in to testify, you will be sworn as a witness and seated on the witness stand. The attorney who brought you to court will question you first, utilizing *direct examination*, which is a form of questioning without suggesting an answer. Occasionally, the opposing attorney may *object* to the question or your answer. If the judge *sustains* the objection, wait for the next question. If the judge *overrules* the objection, go ahead and give your answer. If you do not remember the question, ask that it to be repeated.

After the first attorney has finished his or her questioning, the other attorney will begin *cross-examination*, which is a form of questioning that implies the answer that the attorney expects you to give.

It is often a tactic of cross-examination for the attorney to suggest something in his question that is not correct, in the hope that you will validate that impression or fact by failing to correct him. Do not hesitate to point out to the attorney that his or her assumption is incorrect.

It also is often a tactic to attempt to tire you out or anger you through lengthy and repetitive questioning. If the attorney can irritate you and provoke you to show frustration or anger, your credibility with the jury will be effected and render your testimony less valuable. No matter how lengthy, repetitive, and stupid the questioning may be, answer these questions politely, and do not argue with the attorney. If you have been on the stand a long time and need a break, it is appropriate to ask for one.

After the opposing attorney questions you, the first attorney gets a chance to follow-up with questions. This can go on several times. Then, you will be excused by the judge. Generally, you will still be on call after you have testified, in case something of importance comes up in the trial that requires your testimony again.

Do I Get Paid For This?

If you or your employer have a contract to provide forensic medical examinations, the contract may provide for a pre-set court appearance fee. Otherwise, forensic medical examiners negotiate their own fee.

If you come into contact with the case because the victim came to you for medical treatment, you will be considered a *percipient* witness, one who directly witnessed something that is an issue in the trial. Generally, these witnesses are not paid for their time and testimony. Certainly, you can ask the attorney who subpoenaed you if his office is willing to pay you for your time away from your normal employment.

Sometimes, you will be contacted by an attorney and retained as an *expert* witness, asked to review medical records or photographs and, based on your expertise in the field, asked to render an opinion as to what these records mean. You and the attorney who wants to retain you will negotiate your fee for your preparation and courtroom time.

Resources

California District Attorney's Association
http://www.cdaa.org

California Public Defender's Association
http://www.cpda.org

California Trial Lawyer's Association
http://www.caoc.org

California SART Manual, Chapter 11, SART: Prosecution Component, published by California Coalition Against Sexual Assault (CALCASA)
http://www.calcasa.org

Testifying in Court: The Health Professional on the Witness Stand

John McCann, M.D. and Ruth Marie Young, J.D.

Case Vignette

As a physician, nurse practitioner, registered nurse, you are new to the child abuse team. You have examined about 20 children referred over the past three months by law enforcement agencies and Children's Protective Services. A subpoena has been placed on your desk to testify in Superior Court.

Questions

1. What is the role of the expert witness?

2. What are helpful procedures to follow in pretrial or prehearing preparation?

3. List helpful hints for testifying in court.

4. What are appropriate responses to some tactics used in cross-examination?

The Role of the Expert Witness in Child Maltreatment Hearings

The role of the health professional in performing medical examinations is a fact finder, not a victim advocate. Professionals in this field must accept the difficult challenge of simultaneously being forensically and medically objective while being a concerned caregiver.

The expert's opinion must be objective regardless of the source of the request. The ultimate test for accuracy and impartiality is a willingness to prepare testimony that can be used unchanged for either the plaintiff or the defendant. In addition to subject expertise, the expert is often expected to provide the judicial system with the standards of practice applicable to the given case. Credible experts do not take narrow personal views and condemn those practices which clearly fall within generally accepted practice standards nor do the experts condone performance which clearly falls outside of practice standards. (American Academy of Pediatrics, 1989).

The role of the physician requested to testify always needs to be clarified. In some locales, testimony by a physician qualifies as "expert testimony" (Kunin, 1984). It is important for the physician to clarify with the attorney whether the role expected is expert witness with special training and experience in child maltreatment; or, a physician trained within a clinical field and familiar with the particular case in question. In some cases, these roles overlap. If the attorney does not clarify which role is expected, it is appropriate for the clinician to specify what type of information can be provided regarding the case and whether the clinician feels qualified to be considered an expert in child maltreatment. When the clinician is presented in court as an expert witness, the opposing attorney is expected to inquire about the clinician's qualifications as an expert. General qualifications include background, education, degrees, publications, and the extent and length of practice. Specific qualifications may include the number of similar cases the clinician has evaluated or treated, and the number of times the clinician has testified on such cases (Kunin, 1984). Before agreeing to serve as an expert witness, review the following issues with the attorney:

- your views about the case;

- your biases or potential biases in the case;

- the nature of the special expertise required in testifying on this case; and

- your expected role.

This review will help the attorney choose the best witness to assist in the case. This also prevents the clinician from having the experience of being removed from a case by an attorney requesting an expert opinion when that expert opinion does not support that attorney's position.

Remember, although you may qualify as an expert witness, your opinion is one of many that is weighed by the judge in child maltreatment hearings or by the jury in criminal trials. The final judgment is not made by the expert but by the judge or jury.

Tips for the Clinician as a Courtroom Witness in a Child Maltreatment Trial

The bearing that the expert's testimony has on a case is determined both by the thoroughness of preparation and by the manner in which the testimony is presented.

Prehearing Preparation

1. Obtain a signed consent of the court order prior to discussion or release of medical records.

2. Gather pertinent materials (e.g., records, photographs, x-rays, lab reports).

3. Review the medical record. Note medical findings and other pertinent information. Examples include parent-child interaction, the child's and parents' behaviors, conflicting stories, and any follow-up observations. Parent-child interactions and their respective behaviors are frequently described in nursing notes.

4. Confer with counsel to discuss factors relevant to the case and the expectations of you. Review your testimony for flaws, apparent omissions, inconsistencies, bias or prejudice. Clarify what is fact, hearsay, or opinion. Develop responses to possible cross-examination. Discuss with counsel the physical arrangements, seating, and local methods of procedure.

5. Ask whether you are expected to provide a written report including findings, recommended treatment, and any other suggestions. This report may serve as a baseline for future hearings if the case is stipulated before the trial (mutual agreement by all parties to the facts as stated in the filing).

6. Discuss fees with the attorney before court. Fees are common, particularly for expert testimony. Fees can include preparation time, expenses, work time lost, court time, etc. Fees are "customary" for such services and are not contingent upon the outcome of the litigation (American Academy of Pediatrics, 1989). In certain cases, the professional's time is considered *pro bono republico* and the clinician will not be reimbursed.

7. Work with the attorney to minimize lost time at work. You have a right to schedule your time for court. Almost all courts will defer to the busy schedules of clinical professionals, particularly experienced forensic medical examiners. If asked, most attorneys will attempt to schedule your testimony at a time most convenient for you.

8. Be prepared to support your opinion with knowledge of current scientific literature, not merely anecdotal experience. Review scientific journals, articles and studies that effect areas of proposed testimony. Be aware of significant controversies in the field and be able to articulate and refute the contrary point of view. Be sure your literature review includes both sides of the debate.

9. Thoroughly review all files related to the case. Organize the file so that if you take it with you to the witness stand, you can refer to specific sections quickly. You will appear more competent and well-organized. (Attorneys vary in their position about experts having files on the stand.)

10. Insist on meeting with the attorney to thoroughly discuss your proposed testimony. Review the questions the attorney will be asking and the points you and she believe should be made, as well as how best to make them. (A poor performance by the expert will reflect badly upon the poorly prepared attorney and the witness, too!)

11. Discuss with the attorney likely areas of cross examination and strategize on how they can best be answered.

12. Observe the testimony of an experienced colleague to decrease anxiety about the process.

General Attitude and Demeanor

1. Be honest. Avoid exaggeration or speculation, both of which may be easily exposed and damage your credibility.

2. Listen carefully to the question. If you don't understand the question, request that it be repeated, rephrased, or explained. Don't anticipate the question.

3. Take your time answering questions.

4. Maintain eye contact with the person asking the question.

5. Speak slowly, audibly, and clearly. Do not memorize or read your testimony.

6. You may refer to the medical record or to any exhibit, letter or document available. If you have some doubt, ask to review the document before answering. Although you may bring notes regarding the case, be aware that these may be subpoenaed.

7. Maintain your composure regardless of what happens in the courtroom or how you are seemingly

discredited or vilified by an attorney. Keep your temper—don't argue with the examiner, respond with "cute" or "witty" comments, or give "tricky" answers to questions. Your credibility will suffer if you do.

8. Testify with conviction without prefacing each answer by saying "It seems to me…" or "I believe…" Such responses will elicit objections from the opposing attorney and make you appear uncertain about your testimony.

9. You should appear respectful, sincere, dignified, interested, attentive, and courteous at all times. Do not be smug or project a "know-it-all" attitude.

10. Avoid sounding partisan, being an advocate, or moralizing.

11. Do not be surprised if the judge asks you a question. Answer it unless your attorney directs you otherwise.

12. Do not manifest relief, triumph, or defeat when leaving the witness stand. Walk with confidence at a normal pace.

13. Be aware of your body language:

    • Use good posture; slouching may convey sloppy practice or lack of confidence.

    • Place your hands on your lap; avoid placing your hands over your mouth when you speak.

    • Keep your arms in a natural, comfortable position; folded arms may be considered a defensive or judgmental gesture.

14. Be aware of nonverbal communication or distracting habits which may send inaccurate messages to the jury, e.g. scowling, fidgeting, tugging at your ear, twisting or running your hands through your hair, wringing your hands, biting your nails, or chewing gum.

15. Dress appropriately and professionally.

16. Request to have water available.

Responses to Questions

1. Avoid overly technical and scientific terms. Communicate and educate the judge or jury in layman's terms as you would a patient. When doing so, look at the judge or jury when responding. When testifying on sexual abuse, explain and spell labels used by the child for body parts and functions. You may use these terms when testifying about your interview with the child.

2. Be responsive to the specific question asked, and answer it directly. If the question contains several parts, answer it in several parts. If the question cannot be answered without explanation, say so.

3. If you do not know or have forgotten the answer to the question, say so. Do not guess.

4. Don't hesitate to say, "I don't know"!

5. Answer the question asked. Do not volunteer information—unless the information will explain the answer more completely. Do not try to sneak answers in on the opposing attorney.

6. Stop speaking immediately if an objection is made by one of the attorneys during the course of your testimony. Wait until the judge rules. Your are permitted to answer if the objection is overruled. Ask to have the question repeated if necessary. If the objection is sustained, a new question must be submitted for you to answer.

7. You must know the basis of your opinion. When asked, it is preferable to refer to the basis or rationale for your treatment decision or opinion as "my education, training, clinical experience and judgment" rather than a specific medical text. If you cite a text as authoritative, it can be used against you in cross-examination.

8. If you give a wrong answer, do not hesitate to correct it immediately.

9. If two of your responses are inconsistent, don't panic—your attorney may give you an opportunity to explain and clear up your answer. If you strongly feel that you need assistance, you can request counsel with the attorney.

10. If asked, admit to having talked to the attorney concerning your preparation for this case. Jurors realize that an efficient and thorough attorney discusses the case with the witnesses.

11. If asked if you are being compensated for testifying in court, simply say, "yes."

12. Do not accept the opposing counsel's summary of your testimony unless it is correct.

13. In your testimony, appear reasonable and knowledgeable and do not overstate facts or opinions. The fact that you considered alternative explanations or theories makes you appear unbiased and thorough.

14. Do not change your demeanor in responding to opposing counsel's questions just because that attorney is the opponent. Remain attentive and respectful and do not argue with counsel.

15. Concede points that should be conceded.

16. Do not get caught in yes or no answers if you cannot legitimately answer yes or no. Indicate you cannot accurately or completely answer yes or no without misleading the trier of fact.

17. Be aware that on cross examination some questions may be asked that assume false information. If you do not know whether information given to you hypothetically is true, repeatedly emphasize that your opinion is based on the assumption that the attorney is accurately representing the facts.

Common Tactics of Cross Examination

Always remember that questions on cross-examination may have no basis in reality. The defense attorney's purpose is to plant seeds of doubt in the jurors' minds.

TACTIC: Mispronouncing your name or misidentifying your title

Example: Addressing a physician as Mr. Johnson

Purpose: To distract or disturb the witness drawing the witness' attention to the error thereby disrupting concentration and making the witness more subject to inadvertent error.

Response: Ignore the error, concentrate on the question counsel is asking. Do not try to retaliate by addressing defense counsel in a similar manner.

TACTIC: Suggestive question (tends to be a leading question, allowable on cross-examination)

Example: "Wouldn't you say that…" "Isn't it true that…"

Purpose: To suggest an answer to the question in an attempt to confuse or to lead the witness.

Response: Do not agree with the question unless it is completely accurate. Concentrate carefully on the facts, disregard the suggestion. Answer the question.

TACTIC: Friendly counsel

Example: Very courteous, polite; questions tend to take witness into his/her confidence. "Now you and I are professionals, we both want what is best for this family, and we both know it is best keep families together. Isn't that right, Dr. Jones?"

Purpose: To lull the witness into a false sense of security in hopes that answers will be given in favor of the opposing attorney.

Response: Stay alert; bear in mind that the purpose of the defense is to discredit or diminish the effect of your testimony.

TACTIC: Condescending counsel

Example: Benevolent in approach, over-sympathetic in manner to the point of ridicule. "These types of injuries are understandably upsetting, especially to physicians who have been lucky enough not to have seen a lot of them. Any compassionate human being would be angry upon seeing a child hurt in this manner. Now Dr. Brown, having had a chance to distance yourself from the emotional impact of first seeing Sara's injuries, wouldn't you say it is at least possible that these injuries occurred when she fell off the couch?"

Purpose: To give the impression that the witness is inept, lacks confidence or may not be a reliable witness.

Response: Give firm decisive answers. Ask to have the question repeated if improperly phrased. "Yes, it is possible, but in my best medical opinion, it is extremely unlikely."

TACTIC: Badgering, belligerent

Example: Counsel staring you right in the face, shouting, "That is so, isn't it?"

Purpose: To anger or to intimidate and to disturb the witness' sense of logic and calmness. Generally accompanied by rapid fire questions.

Response: Stay calm and speak in a deliberate voice, allowing the prosecutor time to make appropriate objections. Do not allow yourself to be badgered into expressing an opinion you do not hold.

TACTIC: Demanding a "yes" or "no" answer to questions that need an explanation

Example: "Then from what you observed, no sexual abuse occurred, correct?"

Purpose: To prevent all pertinent and mitigating details from being considered by the jury.

Response: Explain the answer to the question, "I found no physical indicators of sexual abuse, but that does not mean sexual abuse did not occur." If stopped by the counsel's demands for a "yes" or "no" answer, pause until the court instructs you to answer in your own words.

TACTIC: Reversing witness' words

Example: Witness answers, "The neighbor was inside the house. Mrs. Smith and the child were outside." Counsel says, " Now you say that the neighbor was outside and Mrs. Smith and her child were inside."

Purpose: To confuse the witness and to demonstrate a lack of confidence in the witness.

Response: Listen intently whenever counsel repeats back something you have said.

TACTIC: Conflicting answers

Example: But Dr. Jones, Dr. Smith just said, etc…

Purpose: To show inconsistency in procedure, standards, observation, examinations, or clinical judgment. Additionally, it is used to unnerve the witness by implying that the clinician is less adequate than another clinician. This tactic is often used regarding diagnosis, treatment approaches, measurements, and times.

Response: Remain calm. Conflicting statements tend to make a witness nervous and defensive. Communicate confidence in your opinion while acknowledging that different professionals may have different opinions. Do not get drawn into making statements about your competency relative to that of another witness. Be guarded in your answers on measurements, times, etc… Unless you have exact knowledge, use the term "approximately." Refer to the record.

TACTIC: Staring with an extended pause

Example: After the witness has answered, counsel just stares as though there were more to come.

Purpose: To provoke the witness into offering more than the question asked. A long pause normally causes one to feel compelled to say more than is necessary.

Response: Wait for the next question.

TACTIC: Nonverbal disapproval

Example: Staring as if in disbelief. Rolling of eyes. Shaking of head in a disapproving manner.

Purpose: To belittle the witness by implying disbelief, exasperation, or contempt. Such attacks tend to shake your confidence and cause you to question your own competence.

Response: Remain calm, confident, and pleasant. Do not respond in kind.

TACTIC: This is all guesswork

Example: You can't tell whether findings are consistent with sexual abuse or other types of injury?

Example: The findings themselves tell you nothing about how they occurred?

Purpose: Defense attorneys will use this approach to show the jury there are many other situations which may have caused these injuries. Sometimes the situations proposed will seem ridiculous, e.g. falling off a bicycle, falling onto a tree branch, playing doctor with other kids, self-exploration by child, and self-insertion of small toys or objects etc.

Don't assume the explanations proposed by the defense are obviously ridiculous to the jury. Typically, the more significant the findings, the higher the likelihood that jurors with any medical experience will have been kicked off the jury panel.

Response: Simply state and explain your opinion.

TACTIC: You will find what you are looking for

Example: Isn't it true that your job is to look for signs of sexual abuse?

Example: You only examine children who are brought in after allegations of abuse have already been made?

Purpose: The defense attorney will attempt to demonstrate to the jury that your findings are not objective.

Response: My job as a pediatrician is to examine children referred to me, and to provide an assessment and interpretation of findings.

TACTIC: Opinion is based on reliable information

Example: Did you interview the child? Were you told of the allegations? Did you use that information in forming your opinion?

Example: Did you know the child had a history of emotional problems before you took the information? Were you aware the child had made previous allegations? Did you know the child has been in trouble at school? History of lying?

Purpose: These questions have nothing to do with your exam. That is the point...these questions permit the defense attorney to give the jury a preview of the closing argument at the same time he points out the unreliability of the information on which you based your opinion.

Response: Don't let them rattle you. Remember be prepared to state, explain, and justify your opinion.

TACTIC: You don't know your job, i.e. incompetence

If the defense has done a decent job with any of the previous tactics or they have been able to get you flustered on the stand...they will then proceed to attack your competence.

Example: Set Up—Isn't the photo review determination made with several doctors or nurses. So you're just mimicking someone else's opinion. So your work is monitored and reviewed to determine its accuracy.

Purpose: To reduce your credibility.

Response: Remember, these questions may seem offensive to you but they may be real issues to a jury.

Anticipate how you might handle questions of this type. Remember: You're the expert!

References

Berliner, Lisa, and Rebecca J. Roe. "Tips for Experts when Testifying." *NRCCSA News*, Vol.4, No. 5. Sep/Oct 1995

"Brief Review of Common Tactics of cross-examination." *Child Protective Services Inservice Training for Supervisors and Workers* (U.S. Dept. HHS, no publication date listed).

PART 15

Role of Law Enforcement, Crime Laboratories, the District Attorney, and the Public Defender

Captain R.P. "Toby" Tyler, Theresa F. Spear, and Marv Stern, J.D.

Law Enforcement

Law enforcement's mission is to protect children, investigate crimes and prepare investigative reports. The investigative reports are reviewed by the district attorney's office to determine whether criminal charges should be filed. In California, there are over 400 city police departments, 58 county sheriff's departments, and 58 county district attorney's offices. Many have specialized child abuse units.

Law enforcement officers evaluate child abuse cases in the context of criminal laws, which are contained in the penal code. Their objective is to obtain a factual history, collect and preserve evidence, and to prove the truth. The investigative objectives are to:

- determine if child abuse or neglect occurred;
- determine who is responsible;
- collect and preserve evidence;
- identify a suspect;
- provide support to Child Protective Services in removing a child from the home;
- assist the District Attorney in the prosecution of cases; and,
- provide testimony and evidence in Superior Court for criminal cases and Juvenile or Family Court for dependency cases.

For child abuse cases within the family, there is a concurrent investigation with county Children's Protective Services (CPS). To improve investigative outcomes, a collaborative team approach between CPS and law enforcement is important. Professional law enforcement associations include the California Peace Officers Association, California Police Chiefs Association, California State Sheriffs Association, and California Sexual Assault Investigators Association. POST (Peace Officers Standards and Training), part of the Department of Justice, is a major training organization for law enforcement officers.

Criminalistic Laboratories or Forensic Labs

There are 31 public crime laboratories in California: 19 city and county laboratories and 12 California Department of Justice Laboratories. There are also a number of privately operated crime laboratories. The crime laboratory analyzes and interprets evidence collected by medical and law enforcement personnel. Its objective is to provide information useful for identifying or eliminating persons suspected of committing the crime. Forensic scientists evaluate biological evidence, hair, foreign materials such as fiber, grass, dirt, clothing and other evidence from the scene of the crime, and photographs. The crime laboratory communicates its results to law enforcement through written reports and to the courts through testimony. Because the recipients of the results are often not scientifically trained, the laboratory bears a special responsibility to provide complete, technically accurate information which is understandable to a lay audience. Criminalists are also involved in training law enforcement and medical personnel. The professional association is the California Association of Criminalistics.

DNA typing has revolutionized the analysis of biological evidence. It is now possible to obtain very discriminating information from a wide variety of biological evidence. This information allows evidence collected from the patient, suspect, or crime scene to be linked. In addition, DNA testing is now sufficiently sensitive that valuable genetic information can be routinely obtained from very small or old evidence samples. A much higher success rate is now possible for typing small evidence samples such as fingernail scrapings, blood, and saliva samples due to DNA typing.

The other major advancement is the ability to use DNA typing results as an investigative tool to identify potential assailants in sexual assault investigations. The California

Department of Justice DNA Laboratory maintains a data-bank of DNA profiles from convicted offenders. It is now possible to search a DNA profile from an evidence sample (collected from a patient or crime scene) against a databank to help identify the perpetrator of a crime. This means that DNA results can be used much like fingerprints to help solve serious, violent crimes in California.

District Attorney

The role of the district attorney is to prosecute felony and misdemeanor violations of law in the courts of the county they are assigned to. Each county in California has its own District Attorney's Office. Cases are referred by the law enforcement agency in whose jurisdiction the crime occurred. Detectives investigate the case and present it to a district attorney who reviews the case and decides whether or not to file criminal charges. If a felony is charged, a preliminary hearing will precede a jury trial. The defendant can plead guilty at any stage, even during the middle of trial. If the case does go to trial, it will be heard by a jury of twelve persons, who must decide guilt or innocence unanimously. The professional association for district attorneys and their deputies is the California District Attorney's Association.

Public Defender and the Defense Bar

Persons charged with a crime are entitled to a legal defense and protection of their constitutional rights. If they can afford their own lawyer, they can hire one. If they cannot, the county will appoint and pay for a lawyer for them. This lawyer usually is an assistant public defender, but in some counties a private attorney is hired by the county. The professional association for defense attorneys are the California Public Defender's Association and the California Trial Lawyer's Association.

Resources

POST. *Guidelines for the Investigation of Child Abuse, Child Neglect, Sexual Abuse, and Sexual Exploitation.* Published by POST (Peace Officers Standards and Training), Department of Justice, Sacramento, CA.

California District Attorneys Association
http://www.cdaa.org

California Public Defender's Association
http://www.cpda.org

California Trial Lawyer's Association
http://www.caoc.org

Role of Child Protective Services (CPS)

Laura Coulthard, M.S.W.

Child Protective Services (CPS) is at the cornerstone of every community's child protection efforts. CPS has several purposes:

- to receive reports of suspected child abuse and neglect and, from those reports, identify and protect children who have been abused or neglected or who are at risk of abuse and neglect;

- to provide or arrange for services to help families meet their children's developmental (health, mental health, dental, educational, housing, clothing, nutritional) needs;

- to reduce the likelihood of maltreatment occurring in the future by changing conditions and/or facilitating and requiring behavioral change to prevent maltreatment;

- to collaborate with law enforcement agencies, the juvenile or family court (depending on the jurisdiction), the district attorney's office, medical facilities, and community service agencies to ensure coordination of effort on behalf of abused and neglected children;

- to work with community agencies providing a broad range of services (e.g. home visiting programs, Head Start, mental health and drug/alcohol treatment programs) to ensure access by families to needed services;

- to identify gaps in community services and support or facilitate initiatives to increase capabilities or new initiatives to serve children and families.

The CPS process consists of six essential stages:

- Intake

- Initial Assessment/Investigation

- Child and Family Assessment

- Case Planning for the Child and Family

- Service Provision

- Evaluation of Child and Family Progress

- Case Closure or Continuous Monitoring

- Permanency Planning and Adoptions

Resource

Child Protective Services: A Guide for Caseworkers, National Center on Child Abuse and Neglect, The User Manual Series, U.S. Department of Health and Human Services, Administration for Children and Families.

Role of the Medical Social Worker in Child Abuse Prevention

Sandra J. Guine, L.C.S.W., A.C.S.W., Carol Wildes Adolph, L.C.S.W., and Jonaas Walton, L.C.S.W.

Case Vignette

Yolanda, a 16 year-old mother, brought her 6 month infant girl to the Emergency Room with a severe diaper rash. The mother and the daughter were already involved with the child protection system due to inadequate family support for the young mother. The mother and daughter reside in separate foster homes. The mother was granted weekend custody of the infant. She was afraid to take the baby to see a doctor and delayed in taking the child for medical care. She believed that the child protective worker would accuse her of harming the infant. The mother did not try any over-the-counter products because she was unaware of this form of medication. Yolanda experienced abuse as a younger child. Her mother's boyfriend sexually abused her at 9 years of age. Her mother is an alcoholic and all of her siblings are in different placements. Yolanda's boyfriend (father of the infant) is now in jail for domestic abuse of her. Yolanda feels conflict about missing out on her adolescence. She feels incapable and does not understand the type of care and nurturing a 6-month-old baby needs. There are no adults in her life to provide role modeling as a parent.

Role of the Medical Social Worker

The medical social worker works in various departments in a hospital setting attending to the psychosocial needs of patients receiving medical care. In various hospital units, most often in the Emergency Department, Pediatric Ward or Intensive Care Unit, Burn Unit, or an outpatient Urgent Care Clinic, the medical social worker will encounter signs and symptoms of child abuse and neglect. The responsibilities of the medical social worker are to:

- identify, assess, and coordinate intervention with Children's Protective Services (CPS) and law enforcement agencies;

- ensure interdisciplinary collaboration and cooperation with allied health staff;

- document the psychosocial interview with children and parents in the medical record;

- ensure compliance with child abuse and neglect mandatory reporting laws;

- make referrals to community resources;

- provide crisis intervention; and

- ensure follow-up case management.

Purpose

The psychosocial assessment is the initial step in determining the child and family's biological, psychosocial, emotional, and economic needs. The assessment should include baseline questions designed to identify issues that may impact the health of the child. Interventions provided for the child and family during this assessment are critical, and should be supportive, preventive, educational, and curative.

Presenting Problems to Consider During Assessment

- Injuries inconsistent with the account of how they occurred

- Time delay between time of injury and seeking treatment

- Multiple injuries to different anatomical sites in various stages of healing

- Bilateral or patterned injuries

- Repeated chronic injury

- Missing patches of hair

- Circular bruise punches

- Intentional burns

- Human bites

- Possibility of sexual abuse

- Possibility of child neglect

- Chronic headaches

- Severe anxiety or panic attacks

- Sleep or eating disturbance

Assessment/Interview Issues Raising Red Flags for the Child and Family

- Signs of physical, medical, or educational neglect

- Mental health history

- Troubled and/or stressful family history

- Lack of emotional or social support, social isolation

- Environmental, housing, income, transportation and financial issues

- Substance abuse history

- Spousal abuse

- History of incarceration

- History of domestic violence

- Medical and/or mental disabilities

- Social problems

- History of parental physical and sexual abuse

- Prior or present child protective services history

- Family bereavement history

- A gun in the home

- Threats of homicide/suicide by the parent(s)

- Suicide attempts by the child

Issues raising concerns for further inquiry

- Overly inappropriate protective parents (e.g. Munchousen by Proxy)

- Non-compliance with medical recommendations

- Frequent emergency room visits

- Extremely fearful of medical procedures or extremely overly compliant child

- Non responsiveness of the parents to the child's emotional needs

- Physical and/or emotional impairments of the parents(s)

- Limited problem solving ability of the parent(s)

Referral and Collaboration Resources

- County Department of Children and Family Services

- Local law enforcement agencies

- Hospital resources and programs

- Community social service agencies and mental health treatment programs

- Domestic Violence Counseling Programs

- Foster Youth Mentoring Programs

Case Resolution

Several counseling sessions were conducted with the teen mother at the hospital. The teen mother was assessed with very low self esteem; history of sexual, physical, and emotional abuse; learning difficulties; interpersonal conflict with family members and boyfriend; poor nurturing skills; unrealistic expectations of the baby and herself; and depression. The Child Protective Social Worker (CPSW) was informed regarding the condition of the baby and the sessions with the teen mother. The CPSW provided consent for several community referrals. Efforts were also made to include both foster mothers and the birth mother in the case plan. Both of the foster mothers agreed to share and incorporate child development and care of the baby information with the teen mother. The teen mother accepted a referral to a parenting class for new teen moms. Weekly counseling sessions were arranged for the teen mother which also provided transportation, babysitting services, baby and mother exercise classes, and a tutor for the mother.

Selected Readings

The Role of Mental Health Professionals in the Prevention and Treatment of Child Abuse and Neglect, Kempe Children's Center, 1825 Marion Street, Denver, Colorado, 80218, 1993

Psychosocial Evaluation of Suspected Sexual Abuse in Children, Second Edition, The American Professional Society on the Abuse of Children, June, 1997

Psychosocial Evaluation of Suspected Psychological Maltreatment in Children and Adolescents, National Psychological Maltreatment Consortium and The American Professional Society on the Abuse of Children, June, 1997

Diagnostic Imaging of Child Abuse, American Academy of Pediatrics, Volume 87, Number 2, pp.262-264

Screening for Childhood Physical Abuse & Sexual Abuse among Outpatient Substance Abusers, Simpson, T. L ; Westerberg, V.S., Little, L. M., & Trujillo, M. Journal of Substance Abuse Treatment, 11, (1994)

Role of Nurses in the Detection, Evaluation, and Prevention of Child Abuse

*Cathy Boyle, P.N.P., Barbara Bradstock, M.A., R.N., Dianna Costa, R.N., F.N.P.,
Agnes Felicano, F.N.P., and Fleurette Kersey, P.H.N.*

School Nurse

The major focus of school nursing services is the prevention of illness, the promotion of wellness, early detection and management of physical, mental, and social health problems, and the prevention and control of communicable disease. Another important area of responsibility is the management of children with special health care needs in the school setting.

The demands on school nursing services have grown more complex in recent years. Today's school nurse must be equipped to assess health problems related to a multitude of causes. Examples include: infectious diseases; pregnancy; drug and alcohol abuse; child neglect, child physical and sexual abuse; chronically disorganized families; mental illness, depression and suicide; eating disorders; physical and learning disabilities; athletic injuries; poor nutrition; and chronic disease. The school nurse must be able to recognize and manage minor illness, offer skilled health counseling and guidance, detect potential health problems, make appropriate medical referrals, and act as the personal physician's extension into the school setting to meet the health needs of the child patient during the school day. School nurses are registered nurses and are required to have a bachelors degree and a health services credential.

Children with varying degrees of disabilities are now in the regular school setting. Many of these students require specialized caretaking procedures such as tracheostomy suctioning, catheterization, ostomy care, nasogastric tube feeding, or maintenance of orthopedic devices. Some children require administration of medications with varying side effects, in varying amounts, and at varying times during the school day. It is often important for a school nurse to assess the problem, consult with the child's physician or school medical consultant, and administer and/or supervise paraprofessionals administering the physician-prescribed services.

The school nurse works with the parents, the child's regular physician, the school medical consultant, and/or a local health officer to provide services regarding prevention of infectious disease; supervision of handwashing, basic body safety, diapering, and custodial concerns; and, to monitor methods of food handling, and other health and mental health issues of students.

Public Health Nurse

The public health nurse is a registered nurse with special training and interest in community health issues. The concept of public health nursing began in the United States. The term "public health nurse" originated in 1893 and emphasizes the community responsibility of the nurse. The role of the public health nurse is to teach preventive health measures and to administer public health programs directed towards:

- the promotion of positive health and vitality;

- the prevention of infectious and noninfectious disease as well as injury;

- the organization and provision of services for diagnosis and treatment of illness; and,

- rehabilitation of sick and disabled persons to their highest possible level of function.

Public Health Nurses (PHN) assess both the medical and the psycho-social needs of children and their families. The PHN provides assistance and education to help parents meet the needs or their children. Nurses tailor their assistance on the basis of in-home assessments that are specific to each client family and take into account both the developmental needs of the children and the abilities of their parents or caregivers. Individualized programs may include nutritional counseling and basic home economics such as how to maximize limited food resources. In many cases, nurses will evaluate parental skills and provide specific advice or information towards developing more effective parenting styles. The goal in all cases is to help families be healthy and self-sufficient in providing for the needs of their children.

Examples of public health programs include:

Maternal Child Health Programs

- Perinatal Outreach Services and Educational Programs
- Low Cost Infant/Child Car Seat Program and Seat Belt Safety Program
- Bicycle Safety Program
- Child Abuse and Domestic Violence Prevention Programs

Children's Medical and Dental Services

- Child Health and Disability Prevention Program (CHDP)
- California Children Services (CCS)
- Genetically Handicapped Person Program (GHPP)
- Children's HIV Program

Prevention of Communicable and Chronic Disease

- Immunization Program
- HIV/AIDS Program
- Tobacco Education

Children in Foster Care

Public Heath Nurses have a key role in collaboration with Children's Protective Services. They make home visits and assess the health status of children and families. By obtaining a health history on the children and by interviewing biological parents, the PHN can collaborate with physicians to provide medical case management and meet the special needs of these children. PHNs have become essential to ensure that all foster children receive a medical examination within 30 days of placement in foster care and that all indicated follow-up medical, dental, and mental health care are received by the children.

Clinical Forensic Nursing: Nurse Practitioners and Nurses

Clinical forensic nursing is defined as the application of clinical and scientific knowledge to questions involving the civil and criminal investigations of sexual assault, child

sexual and physical abuse, and traumatic injury (particularly domestic violence and elder abuse). As first responders in a medical setting, forensic nurses and nurse practitioners must be prepared to meet the complex examination and documentation requirements of the investigative process. Forensic examiners through the proper collection and documentation of forensic evidence are an essential component of clinical forensic medicine. In California, forensic nurse practitioners and nurses are integrally involved in the implementation of the California Medical Protocol for the Examination of Sexual Assault and Child Sexual Abuse Victims. They are performing forensic examinations and documenting findings on standard state forensic medical examination forms. Efforts are underway to expand this role in California to include domestic violence, elder abuse, and child physical abuse and neglect forensic medical examination forms. Refer to the Office of Criminal Justice Planning (OCJP) website for further information.

Hospital, Clinic or Private Physician Practice Nurse

Registered nurses (RNs) and Licensed Vocational Nurses (LVNs) come into contact with abused and neglected children in various ways. They may be working in an emergency room, urgent care clinic, general pediatric clinic, or a private practice. It is important for nurses to receive training in the identification, reporting, and case management of child abuse, neglect, sexual assault, domestic violence and elder abuse victims. Nurses must be aware of their responsibilities as mandated reporters and know how to contact Children's Protective Services (CPS) and Adult Protective Services (APS). New foster care health programs are developing in which RNs and LVNs are participating in specialized clinics to provide quality health care for foster children.

Nurse Practitioners

A nurse practitioner is a registered nurse (RN) with advanced education and clinical training in a health care specialty area. Nurse practitioners work with people of all ages and their families, providing information patients need to make informed decisions about their health care and lifestyle choices. Nurse Practitioners practice under the rules and regulations of the Nurse Practice Act of the state in which they work. Most nurse practitioners are also nationally certified in their specialty area (e.g. pediatric, cardiology, nephrology, neonatology, obstetrics and gynecology). They are recognized as expert health care providers.

Nurse practitioners serve as the regular health care provider for children and adults during health and illness.

In order to provide complete health care, Nurse Practitioners:

- obtain medical histories and perform physical examinations;

- diagnose and treat acute health problems such as infections and injuries;

- diagnose, treat, and monitor chronic diseases such as diabetes and high blood pressure;

- order, perform, and interpret diagnostic studies such as lab work and x-rays;

- prescribe medications and other treatments;

- provide prenatal care and family planning services;

- provide well-child care, including screening and immunizations;

- provide health maintenance care for adults, including annual physicals;

- promote positive health behaviors and self-care skills through education and counseling; and

- collaborate with physicians and other health professionals as needed.

Many nurse practitioners are also actively involved in education, research, and legislative activities to promote quality health care for all people in the United States.

Resources

American Nursing Association
http;//www.nursingworld.org

California Nursing Association
www.calnurse.org

National Association of School Nurses
www.nasn.org

American Academy of Nurse Practitioners
www.aanp.org

International Association of Forensic Nurses
www.forensicnurse.org

SAFE, SANE, CARE and SART Nurse and Nurse Practitioner Examination Teams

Marilyn Strachan Peterson, M.S.W., William Green, M.D., Cathy Boyle, P.N.P.

History

An eight-year old girl is brought to the Emergency Room by patrol officers. She had told her best friend that her stepfather was touching her private parts. The child had told her mother, but the mother did not believe that the stepfather could do such a thing. The girl's best friend told her mother and this mother called the local police department. Patrol officers responded to the child's school and the girl confirmed that her stepfather was sexually abusing her, and her older sisters ages 10 and 15. After a records check, law enforcement officers learned that there had been a reported incident with a 17-year old neighbor girl who previously babysat for the family.

Questions

1. What is the best approach for performing quality medical-evidentiary examinations?

2. What team models exist for urban and rural areas?

3. What knowledge and skills should these medical professionals have?

4. What procedures should be followed?

5. What about quality assurance?

Epidemiology

In 1999, there were 9,443 forcible rape cases reported to the State Department of Justice by California law enforcement agencies. This number does not include other types of sexual assault. During the same period, there were 28,503 sexual assaults reported to California rape crisis centers.

Annual statistics are available from the California Department of Justice on the number of investigations by type of crime conducted by law enforcement agencies. Statistics on all forms of child physical and sexual abuse and neglect reported to local child protective services agencies can be obtained from the State Department of Social Services.

Clinical Presentation

Victims of sexual assault and acute child sexual abuse present with varied affect depending upon the patient's coping style. Some present visibly upset and distressed, while others present with very outward controlled calm. The underlying emotions are often fear and anxiety. These feelings may be driven by multiple factors: the incident itself, concerns about the reactions of others, the impact of disclosure upon the family, or apprehension about the medical procedures.

The *California Medical Protocol for Examination of Sexual Assault and Child Sexual Abuse Victims*, which can be obtained from the State Office of Criminal Justice Planning, contains detailed information on the approach to patient care, interview methods for obtaining patient history, forensic medical examination procedures, evaluating the possibility of pregnancy and sexually transmitted disease, and post traumatic stress disorder.

Specialized Medical Examination Teams: A Coordinated Approach to Patient Care

Many communities are developing specially trained nurse examiner programs using mid-level practitioners (nurse practitioners and physician assistants) or nurses both with a physician medical director. There are various acronyms for these teams: SAFE (Sexual Assault Forensic Examiners), SANE (Sexual Assault Nurse Examiners), SART (Sexual Assault Response Team), CARE (Child Abuse Response Examiners), and CAST (Child Abuse Services Team). The SART acronym has now been broadened as a concept to describe a coordinated response between patrol officers, detectives, rape crisis advocates, crime laboratories, the District attorney's office, and the medical examination team.

Some examination teams are hospital based and some are free standing. They are dedicated to timely, comprehensive attention to the medical and emotional needs of the patient and to the forensic needs of the criminal and juvenile justice system. To function optimally, regular meetings between representatives of the various disciplines are recommended

Two Types of Medical Evidentiary Examinations

The California crime laboratories determined the 72-hour criteria for collecting evidence by conducting sexual assault and acute child sexual abuse forensic medical examinations. The colposcope (magnification equipment) was introduced in the early 1980's by pediatricians as a means to detect subtle signs of child sexual abuse thereby establishing the concept of the non acute sexual abuse examination for children. The colposcope established a new standard of practice by enabling examiners to detect subtle injury and/or changes in the genital or rectal area caused by sexual abuse and is now the standard of practice for all types of sexual assault examinations. Colposcopes have magnifying lens ranging from 4 to 30x power and can have 35mm camera or video camera attachments.

- **Acute Medical Forensic Examinations**
  Less than 72 hours have passed since the incident

- **Nonacute Medical Forensic Examinations**
  More than 72 hours have passed since the incident

Importance of Successful Multi-Disciplinary Collaborations

Collaboration strengthens the response of individual agencies and unites them into a coordinated team approach. No one agency can successfully handle all aspects of a sexual assault or child sexual abuse. Each agency is important and has its strengths and limitations. Effective multi-disciplinary teams generate a stronger response and produce more effective outcomes for the victim and the criminal justice system. There are five stakeholders to successful team collaborations and intervention:

- the victim or survivor;
- the family;
- the neighborhood;
- the community; and
- the People of California.

SART: A Community Interagency Team Intervention Model

Sexual Assault Response Team (SART) is a multi-disciplinary, interagency, sexual assault intervention model. It is a team approach to implementing a comprehensive, sensitive, coordinated system of intervention and care for sexual assault victims. SART organizes the process of intervention and the community response to sexual assault. The partners of the SART model are public and private agencies. The SART model recognizes that the victim of sexual assault and the criminal justice system have distinctive sets of needs. Sometimes there are inherent conflicts between these two sets of needs and goals. Through professional collaboration between agencies, both sets of needs can be accommodated.

The needs of the sexual assault victim are:

- coordinated response;
- sensitive intervention;
- cultural competency;
- early emotional support and advocacy;
- information about investigative, forensic medical exam, and criminal justice procedures;
- accessible, prompt, high quality forensic medical examination;
- prophylaxis against sexually transmitted disease;
- assessment of possible pregnancy risk and emergency contraception, if requested;
- follow-up medical care;
- counseling;
- counseling for family members;
- justice; and
- closure.

The needs and goals of the criminal justice system are:

- protection of the victim and the community;
- participation by the victim in the investigative and judicial process;
- accessible, prompt, high quality forensic medical examinations;
- forensic medical follow-up evaluation, if indicated;

- optimum recognition, collection and handling of potential evidence;

- accurate documentation of medical findings and evidence based interpretations;

- prompt exams to reduce patrol officer waiting time at local hospitals;

- identification and apprehension of a suspect;

- competent case investigation;

- reliable analysis of evidence;

- credible expert testimony;

- effective prosecution; and

- competent representation for the defendant by defense counsel.

What does SART do?

- **It organizes the process of intervention.**

- **It organizes the community response to sexual assault.**

Key features of specialized sexual assault forensic medical examiner teams are:

- coordinated team notification and assembly;

- prompt forensic medical examinations for acute cases;

- uninterrupted forensic medical examinations;

- specially trained sexual assault forensic medical examiners;

- defined areas of expertise in sexual assault, child sexual abuse, or both;

- pre-authorization for reimbursement based upon negotiated contracts;

- joint interviews, whenever possible, and/or coordinated interviews;

- dedicated exam space and equipment;

- sexual assault forensic medical exam peer review;

- continuous quality improvement;

- collaboration and cooperation with community resources; and

- standards of practice.

Knowledge and Skills Needed by Medical Personnel in the Performance of Sexual Assault Evidential Examinations

Standard curriculum has been developed by the California Medical Training Center at the University of California, Davis for training sexual assault forensic examiners. Advanced and specialized courses are under development. Knowledge and skills needed to perform these examinations are presented on the following pages.

A. Knowledge

Medical personnel performing evidential examinations must be knowledgeable about:

- the broad spectrum of potential evidence and physical findings present in these cases;

- the importance of the sexual assault history;

- the dynamics and outcomes of victimization related to sexual assault;

- preventing loss, degradation, deterioration, and contamination of evidence;

- proper evidence collection and preservation procedures;

- samples needed for toxicological analysis;

- collection of reference samples;

- indications for both medical and forensic follow-up;

- state laws regarding the performance of sexual assault forensic medical examinations, the state protocol, and the standard forms used to document findings;

- the roles of law enforcement and child protective services, rape crisis centers, deputy district attorneys, and crime laboratories;

- how to obtain both crisis intervention and longer term mental health counseling;

- how to effectively testify as an expert witness; and

- how to identify a consultative network for on-going peer review of medical evaluations and interpretation of findings.

B. Skills

Medical personnel must be able to:

- Perform a medical screening examination to assess the patient's clinical condition and to make appropriate and timely triage, consultation, and referral decisions;

- sensitively interview patients to obtain a complete sexual assault history;

- utilize patient history to perform a complete forensic medical examination;

- explain to the patient what items need to be collected and for what purpose;

- identify and describe pertinent female and male genital and anorectal anatomical structures;

- use enhancement techniques for detection and documentation of findings, e.g., colposcopy and forensic photography;

- collect, label, document, and preserve all types of evidence for analysis by the crime laboratory;

- maintain and document the chain of custody for evidence;

- maintain the integrity of the evidence to ensure that optimal results are obtained from any subsequent laboratory examination;

- evaluate the possibility of pregnancy and discuss treatment options;

- evaluate the possibility of sexually transmitted disease, collect appropriate specimens, and provide prophylactic treatment according to the age of the patient;

- identify and document injuries;

- interpret physical findings;

- collect toxicology and reference samples;

- recognize conclusions and limitations in the analysis of findings;

- complete the standard state forms for documenting the forensic medical results of the exams;

- implement a quality assurance program;

- inform law enforcement about items connected with the assault which may be at the crime scene, e.g. wipes, lubricants, towels, condoms, etc.; and

- discuss findings and assessments with law enforcement and social service investigators and attorneys.

Additional Knowledge and Skills Needed by Medical Personnel in the Performance of Child Sexual Abuse Evidential Examinations

Standard curriculum has been developed by the California Medical Training Center at the University of California, Davis for training pediatric sexual assault forensic examiners. Advanced and specialized courses are under development.

A. Knowledge

Medical personnel performing evidentiary examinations must be knowledgeable about:

- common interpersonal dynamics involved in the sexual abuse of children and adolescents, and potential outcomes related to victimization;

- how sexual abuse may effect children's and adolescents' behavior at different developmental stages;

- how a child's or adolescent's reaction to sexual abuse may effect their response to the medical evaluation, the most common fears and concerns they have regarding their own body following sexual abuse;

- psychological approaches that may be used in preparing a child or adolescent for the medical evaluation;

- common fears a family member may have regarding the medical evaluation;

- psychological approaches that may be used in preparing a family member for the child's or adolescent's medical evaluation;

- health professionals' responsibilities as "mandated reporters";

- the roles of law enforcement, child protective services, rape crisis centers, deputy district attorneys, and crime laboratories; and

- how to identify a consultative network for on-going peer review of medical evaluations and interpretation of findings.

B. Skills

Medical personnel must be able to:

- conduct a developmentally appropriate forensically defensible interview of the child or adolescent;

- perform a general physical examination for the detection of physical findings;

- use enhancement techniques for detection and documentation of findings, e.g., colposcopy and forensic photography;

- perform a comprehensive, sensitive, multi-method examination of the ano-genital regions of the child or adolescent;

- utilize ancillary examination techniques such as saline, vital dyes, and Foley catheters when indicated;

- recognize the physiologic changes, including the Tanner Stages of secondary sexual development that occur as a result of hormonal influences in both males and females;

- identify the more common variations of normal and abnormal ano-genital physical findings of a child or adolescent;

- recognize the current state of tissue changes that occur as a result of the healing process of any ano-genital injuries encountered;

- use appropriate terminology in recording findings and interpretations on forensic medical report forms;

- how to obtain both crisis intervention and longer term mental health counseling;

- how to appropriately debrief the child or adolescent and family members and address their concerns following the medical evaluation; and

- how to testify effectively as an expert witness.

Urban and Rural Team Models

Large urban hospitals may specialize and have one team for adolescent and adult victims of sexual assault, and one team for child sexual abuse. Rural teams may serve adults, adolescents and children. Some rural teams in proximity to urban centers may perform the acute child sexual abuse examination and refer the non acute sexual abuse examinations to specialized programs which see a high volume of cases and have a higher level of expertise. Telemedicine connections to urban centers can help rural teams build expertise with case consultation. Monthly case consultation meetings are held between urban and rural programs in California.

Selected Readings

California Medical Protocol for Examination of Sexual Assault and Child Sexual Abuse Victims and required Standard Forensic Medical Sexual Assault and Child Sexual Abuse Forms. Published by the Governor's Office of Criminal Justice Planning
www.ocjp.ca.gov

California SART (Sexual Assault Response Team) Manual Published by CALCASA (California Coalition Against Sexual Assault)
www.calcasa.org

Resources

California Medical Training Center at UC Davis provides training throughout the State on how to perform sexual assault, child sexual abuse, domestic violence, and elder abuse medical forensic examinations.
http://web.ucdmc.ucdavis.edu/medtrng

Role of the First Responder in Child Abuse: Emergency Medical Technicians (EMTs) or Paramedics

Captain Michael F. Balash

Firefighters and Emergency Medical Technicians (EMTs) see first hand that not all children grow up in a safe environment. Many times the firefighter and EMT are the first step toward identification and intervention in child abuse and neglect cases. Vulnerable children benefit, and the family can then receive the assistance they need to stop abuse and neglect.

First responders must be alert and informed about the signs of child abuse. A few common signs include: multiple bruises; injuries inconsistent with reported mechanism of injury; burns; severe head injuries; repeated calls to the same address; and, conditions consistent with neglect, such as signs of malnourishment, untreated illness, or unsafe living conditions. It is also important to focus on the parent or caregiver, noting alcohol or drug use, conflicting statements or an unconcerned parent.

Emergency care is always the first priority. As always, assess the ABCs, attend to the injuries and attempt to transport all cases of suspected abuse. Abused children may have injuries in different stages of healing. The parent or caregiver who called 911 may be reluctant to provide a history of injury or refuse transport. If this occurs, call law enforcement for on-scene assistance.

Remember, child abuse is a crime, protect the scene until law enforcement arrives. Accurate documentation is essential. In writing the report, do not make assumptions, be objective, and avoid unprofessional comments. Good documentation of findings and observations is essential to assist law enforcement officers to conduct complete investigations, and it protects you and your department from legal liability.

When child abuse is suspected, firefighters and EMTS have a legal obligation to call Children's Protective Services (CPS) as soon as possible to make a verbal report. A written report on Department of Justice Form SS 8572 must be submitted within 36 hours of the verbal report to Emergency Medical Services (EMS) Division (depending on local policy). The original will be sent to Children's Protective Services and a copy will be filed at the EMS Division.

Resources

California Professional Firefighters
1780 Creekside Oaks, Suite 200
Sacramento, CA 95833
Phone: 916-921-9111
Fax: 916-921-1106
Web site: www.cpf.org

National Association of Emergency Medical Technicians
408 Monroe Street
Clinton, MS 39056-4210
Phone: 1-800-34-NAEMT
Fax: 601-924-7325
Web site: www.naemt.org

California State Firefighters' Association, Inc.
2701 K Street, Suite 201
Sacramento, CA. 95816-5113
Phone: 800-451-2732
Fax: 916-446-9889
Web site: www.csfa.firedept.net

Role of Dentistry in the Identification and Prevention of Child Abuse and Neglect

Kathleen A. Shanel-Hogan, D.D.S., M.A.

Dentists, dental hygienists and registered dental assistants are required by law to report suspected cases of child abuse and neglect, elder abuse and domestic violence. Dental professionals serve an important role in the detection of abuse because 65% of physical abuse to children involved injuries to the head, face, neck, or mouth. Increased awareness of dental/facial injuries as potential indicators of child abuse/neglect enhances the recognition ability of all mandated reporters.

The signs and symptoms of dentofacial trauma may include:

- avulsed teeth;
- lip lacerations;
- tongue injuries;
- frenum injuries; and/or,
- jaw and facial fractures.

The signs and symptoms of dental neglect include the following:

- untreated, rampant caries;
- untreated, pain, infection, bleeding, or trauma; and/or
- lack of continuity of care once informed that the above conditions exist.

What can dental professionals do?

- establish office procedures and participate in training to improve identification of abuse and/or neglect;
- discuss child abuse and neglect at staff meetings;

- provide clinical articles to staff members;
- encourage staff to discuss concerns within the office; and,
- invite local medical experts to dental meetings to present information and discuss examples of case findings.

In approaching the parent or care provider:

- decide whether to discuss your suspicions with the parent/caregiver;
- refer to your legal obligation to report suspected cases of abuse; and,
- use a supportive approach; do not accuse anyone or be judgmental.

Legal and liability issues pertaining to reporting child abuse and neglect:

- mandated reporters have immunity from civil and criminal liability when making a child abuse report;
- penalties are established in state law for not reporting;
- healthcare provider/patient privilege is not applicable in these cases; and,
- confidentiality of a reporter's identify is assured.

Summary of why dental professionals must report suspected abuse:

- early intervention can prevent further abuse;
- state law requires it; and,
- there is civil liability for not reporting.

Resources

P.A.N.D.A. (Prevent Child Abuse and neglect through
Dental Awareness) Program
California Dental Association
www.cda.org

California Dental Association's Council on Community
Health
P.A.N.D.A. Coalition of California
http://www.deltadentalca.org/news/panda.html

Role of Veterinarians in the Detection of Animal Abuse and by Extension, Potential Child Abuse

Compiled by Michelle Kim, B.S.

Veterinary Medicine is a branch of medical science that deals with the prevention, cure, or alleviation of disease and injuries of animals. About 60 per cent of the veterinarians in the U.S. are in private practice. Many treat all animals, but in recent years and in the densely populated areas of the country, many have limited their practice to pets or the treatment of certain populations such as horses, cattle, poultry, or zoo animals. Others deal with certain animal medical problems such as veterinary ophthalmologists, dermatologists, radiologists, and pathologist.

In the course of practice, veterinarians may encounter suspicious injuries or neglectful living conditions for animals. Examples include:

- Inadequately explained injuries;

- Injuries inconsistent with history given;

- Wariness of physical contact;

- Inadequate food, water, and shelter;

- Keeping the animal in unsanitary conditions, e.g. animal excrement, and/or

- Failure to seek prompt veterinary care for injuries or debilitating conditions requiring care.

The presence of animal abuse or neglect may indicate the potential of child abuse, domestic violence, or elder/dependent adult abuse. Persons intervening on the behalf of animals need to consider whether the assaultive behavior extends toward the children in the family. Coordination is needed between County Children's Protective Services, Adult Protective Services, and law enforcement agencies (if criminal acts toward others are suspected).

Resources

American Veterinary Medical Association
1931 North Meacham Road – Suite 100
Schaumburg, IL 60173
Phone: 847-925-8070
Fax: 847-925-1329
Web site: http://www.avma.org

California Veterinary Medical Association
5231 Madison Avenue
Sacramento, CA 95841
Phone: 916.344.4985
Fax: 916.344.6147
Web site: http://www.cvma.org

American Humane Association
63 Inverness Drive East
Englewood, CO 80112-5117
Phone (toll free): 800-227-4645
Phone: 303-792-9900
Fax: 303-792-5333
Web site: http://www.americanhumane.org

Rape Crisis Centers

Kay Buck, Mary Beth Carter, Linda Bowen, and Marilyn Strachan Peterson, M.S.W., M.P.A.

The Meaning of Sexual Assault

Sexual assault is experienced as a physical and psychological traumatic intrusion to the body and spirit of a person. Sometimes survivors are exposed to a near death experience both in reality and in perception. Sexual assault survivors experience a complete loss of control over their life and this experience causes profound and enduring trauma. The philosophy of rape crisis centers is that sexual assault does not have to be a life-defining event. Victims can become survivors. They can regain control over their life, and the dignity of their humanity can be restored.

Roles and Responsibilities of Rape Crisis Centers

Rape crisis center advocates provide continuity of care from the first contact to case closure. Wrap-around counseling, supportive accompaniment services, information and clarification about investigative and medical forensic exam procedures, and community resources are provided on a 24 hour 7 day per week basis (24/7). Advocates also support the survivor after the investigative and forensic medical exam procedures are completed, whether or not a suspect is apprehended, whether or not charges are filed, whether or not the case goes to trial, whether or not there is a conviction, and whether or not the defendant is sentenced to state prison, county jail, or is released. After a sexual assault, Post-Traumatic Stress Disorder (PTSD) (also known as Rape Trauma Syndrome) may persist for months and years. For this reason, crisis intervention, supportive services, and follow-up counseling are essential to every sexual assault survivor. Intensity and duration of services are key elements of crisis resolution. Rape crisis center advocates also provide counseling and supportive assistance to survivors who never report the crime. These services are invaluable community resources and are essential to address the aftermath of sexual assault and to facilitate the recovery and well-being of the survivor. They are also an aide to the success of the criminal justice process because the advocacy provided by the rape crisis center ensures continuous emotional support to the survivor.

Standard Services

- 24-hour crisis intervention;
- follow-up counseling by telephone and in-person;
- individual and group counseling sessions;
- advocacy and accompaniment services during medical examinations, law enforcement processes, and court procedures;
- information and referral services for victims and the general public;
- community and school education;
- sexual assault prevention and education programs and self-defense classes; and,
- training for other agency professionals who interact with sexual assault victims.

Origins of Rape Crisis Centers

The early stages of the women's movement began in 1848 and culminated in 1923 when Federal legislation was enacted giving women the right to vote. The catalyst for the movement was an abolitionist (anti-slavery) congress in London where American women, including Elizabeth Cady Stanton, were forced to sit in the balcony behind curtains. This and similar experiences galvanized women to seek voting rights and the right to own property in their own name. The Great Depression and World War II marked the following two decades. A burgeoning union labor movement began in the 1940s and it was noted then that women received half the pay that men did for equal work. The labor movement created fertile ground for the evolution of the women's movement.

In the 19th and 20th centuries, rape was used as a tool to express racism. As early as the 1870s, African American women began to organize anti-lynching campaigns. The Black Women's Club movement emerged in the late 1890s from this organizing effort. This movement was responsible for the inception of several national groups that organized against rape and the response to it in the culture of the United States.

The second stage of the women's movement was sparked by the civil rights movement in the 1960s with the enactment of the Civil Rights Act of 1964. Title VII of the Act banned race and sex discrimination. In October 1966, the National Organization for Women (NOW) was formed to champion and ensure the rights of women guaranteed by Title VII and to advocate for other issues and laws on behalf of women. The women's movement, in turn, spawned two major social movements on behalf of women in the 1970s—the anti-rape movement and the social movement on behalf of battered women. The anti-rape movement developed out of "Speak Outs" in which women gathered and recounted stories of victimization by perpetrators and by individuals and systems responsible for helping them. The first "Speak Out" was held in New York City in 1969. BAWAR (Bay Area Women Against Rape), one of the first rape crisis centers, was established in 1971 in Berkeley, California. This center remains strong today.

Resources Published by CALCASA

- California Sexual Assault Response Team (SART) Manual
- Strategic Forum Report: A Vision to End Sexual Assault
- Support for Survivors: A Training Manual for Sexual Assault Counselors
- Counseling Tools for the Prevention and Reduction of Post Traumatic Stress Reactions

Major Advocacy Associations

CALCASA (California Coalition Against Sexual Assault)
1215 K Street, Suite 1100
Sacramento, CA 95814
Voice: 916-446-2520
Website: www.calcasa.org

NCASA (National Coalition Against Sexual Assault)
125 N. Enola Drive
Enola, Pennsylvania 17025
Voice: 717-728-9764
Fax: 717-728-9781
Website:
http://www.dreamingdesigns.com/other/indexncasa.html

Shelter and Counseling for Battered Women

Linda Berger

Origin of the Movement

The modern day women's movement emerged out of the civil rights movement in the late 1960's which spawned major social progress on behalf of women in the 1970's — the anti-rape movement and the social movement on behalf of battered women. The second major social change began with battered women calling the rape crisis hotlines established in the early 1970's. Hotlines and shelters were then established to provide women with support and protection from domestic violence. Some programs retain their roots with rape crisis centers and are part of the same organization. Other communities established separate counseling and shelter programs for battered women and their children.

Advocates for battered women moved quickly to obtain funding for shelters, to change laws, and to provide training for law enforcement officers and medical personnel. Early institutionalization of this movement may have been aided by statistics which showed that more law enforcement officers were killed in responding to domestic violence calls than any other type of crime. The second wave of public policy and funding support for this cause came with major news stories of movie, television, and sports celebrities involved in domestic violence. Today, this movement has established mandatory screening and reporting laws for medical personnel in California among many other important legislative efforts.

Health Consequences for Women Experiencing Domestic Violence

- Lifetime prevalence rate of 31% for domestic violence is greater than prevalence rates for breast or cervical cancer;

- Physical assault causes severe and disabling injuries;

- Physical assault is also linked to chronic health problems such as chronic pelvic pain, stomach ulcers, spastic colon, frequent indigestion, diarrhea or constipation, respiratory problems, arthritis, chronic neck or back pain, migraine and other frequent headaches, stammering, hearing and vision problems, sexually transmitted infections, and aggravation of other medical conditions;

- Mental health problems can be caused by intimate partner violence. Forty-six percent of victims report symptoms of anxiety disorder, 45% experience post-traumatic stress disorder; 37% report symptoms of depression, and 29% of all women who attempt suicide were battered;

- 240,000 pregnant women are reported to be abused annually—10.7% of abused women deliver low birth weight babies; and

- Average cost of low birth weight delivery is $50,300 compared to the average cost for term deliveries—$3,355.

Health Consequences for Children Experiencing Domestic Violence

- Children who witness domestic violence are more likely to exhibit behavioral and physical health problems including depression, anxiety, aggression, oppositional/defiant behavior and violence towards peers. They are also more likely to attempt suicide, abuse drugs and alcohol, run away from home, engage in teenage prostitution, and commit sexual assault crimes.

- Young children exposed to violence are at increased risk for developmental problems such as speech and language delay which impact school readiness and academic performance; and

- Fifty percent of men who assault their wives frequently assault their children. The U.S. Advisory Board on Child Abuse and Neglect suggests that domestic violence may be the single major precursor to child abuse and neglect fatalities in this country.

Standard Services Offered by Domestic Violence Shelters

- 24-hour crisis intervention and shelter;

- professional and peer counseling;

- assistance with legal and social services;

- accompaniment and advocacy with medical facilities, law enforcement and social service agencies;

- support, accompaniment, and advocacy with court processes and procedures;

- assistance in establishing new abuse-free households;

- services and programs for children who experience abuse or witness domestic violence;

- training for professionals responding to domestic violence; and,

- public awareness, prevention and educational programs.

Resources

Major Advocacy Associations
Statewide California Coalition for Battered Women
P.O. Box 19005
Long Beach, California 90807-9005
1-888-SCCBW-52
http://www.sccbw.org

California Alliance Against Domestic Violence
926 J Street, Suite 1000
Sacramento, California 95814
http://www.caadv.org

Family Violence Prevention Fund
383 Rhode Island Street, Suite 304
San Francisco, California 94103
http://www.fvpf.org

References

Coker, A., Smith, P., Bethea, L., King, M., McKeown, R., Physical Health Consequences of Physical and Psychological Intimate Partner Violence, Archives of Family Medicine, Vol. 9, May 2000.

Danielson, K., Moffit, T., Caspi, A., and Silva, P., Comorbidity Between Abuse of an Adult and DSM-III-R Mental Disorders: Evidence From an Epidemiological Study, American Journal of Psychiatry, Vol. 155(1), January 1998.

Gelles, R.J. and Harrop, J.W., Violence, Battering, and Psychological Distress Among Women, Journal of Interpersonal Violence, Vol. 4(1), 1989.

Housekamp, B.M. and Foy, D., The Assessment of Posttraumatic Stress Disorder in Battered Women, Journal of Interpersonal Violence, Vol. 6(3), 1991.

Jaffe, P. and Sudermann, M., Child Witness of Women Abuse: Research and Community Responses, in Stith, S. and Straus, M., Understanding Partner Violence: Prevalence, Cause, Consequences, and Solutions. Families in Focus Services, Vol. II. Minneapolis, MN: National Council on Family Relations, 1995.

Parker, B. McFarlane, J., Soeken, K., Abuse During Pregnancy : Effects on Maternal Complication and Birth Weight in Adult and Teenage Women, Obstetrics and Gynecology, Vol. 844, No. 3, September 1994.

Stark, E., and Flitcraft, A., Killing the Beast Within: Woman Battering and Female Suicidality, International Journal of Health Sciences, Vol. 25 (1), 1995.

Straus, M., Gelles, R., and Smith, C., Physical Violence in American Families: Risk Factors and Adaptations to Violence in 8,145 Families. New Brunswick: Transaction Publishers, 1990.

Supplementary Homicide Reports, 1976-96.

March 2002 Certification Domestic Violence Manual published by WEAVE, Sacramento, CA.

Wolfe, D.A., Wekerle, C., Reitzel, D. and Gough, R., Strategies to Address Violence in the Lives of High Risk Youth. In Peled, E., Jaffe, P.G. and Edleson, J.L. (eds.), Ending the Cycle of Violence Community Responses to Children of Battered Women. New York: Sage Publications, 1995.

Agency for Health Care Policy and Research, Center for Organization and Delivery Studies, Healthcare Cost and Utilization Project. Hospital Inpatient Statistics, 1996.

Center for Disease Control and Prevention, The Atlanta Journal and Constitution, 1994.

Family Violence Prevention Fund, Fact Sheet: Health Care Response to Domestic Violence, 2001.

http://endabuse.org/

U.S. Advisory Board on Child Abuse and Neglect, 1995. A Nation's Shame: Fatal Child Abuse and Neglect in the United States: Fifth Report. Washington D.C: Department of Health and Human Services, Administration for Children and Families.

Role of the Therapist

Cynthia Anne Winn, L.C.S.W.

Role of the Therapist

The therapist has an important role in helping a child recover from the effects of abuse and neglect. The therapist serves a number of functions, including:

- Helping the child address issues related to abuse and neglect,

- Serving as a model for appropriate adult–child relationships,

- Working to improve family relationships, and

- Supporting positive and productive peer relationships and support systems.

The therapist's initial function is to establish rapport and develop a trusting relationship that will help the child address the thoughts, feelings, and behaviors that are generated by abuse and neglect. The therapist promotes the child's awareness and understanding of abuse dynamics, encourages growth and development beyond the role of victim or the inappropriate identification with the offender, and supports the child's individuality and personal integrity. The therapist teaches the child to care for him/himself, think about his/her behavior, and make choices that maximize his/her safety. The therapist also needs to help the child regain trust, faith, and investment in meaningful relationships.

As an adult, the therapist models appropriate behavior including nurturing, affection, and the expression of feelings. The therapist gives the child the opportunity to explore issues of trust, acceptance, affiliation, and emotional intimacy. The child can integrate the therapist as a role model for safe and nurturing relationships. The therapist also shares the child's hopes, excitement, and curiosity about life in order to help his/her client reinvest in his/her future.

The therapist models and maintains good clinical boundaries. He/she understands the vital bond between child and parent and does not attempt to take the place of the parent. Instead, the therapist helps the child and parent and does not attempt to take the place of the parent. The therapist helps the child and parent interact appropriately and offers alternative problem-solving models for parent-child relationships. The therapist also helps the child to be as realistic and practical as possible when relating to parents with problems. It is a difficult task to help a child to be realistic, while not taking away his/her hope for change and improvement in his/her parents.

Although clinical interventions and psychotherapy with parents is beyond the scope of this manual, it is vital that every effort be made to improve and maintain the child's relationship with family members. Children need to express a full range of feelings regarding their family members. The therapist can be more helpful by remaining neutral and empathetic to the child's situation than by taking angry and punitive stances toward parents and unavailable family members. Conjoint therapy with a parent and child, family therapy, or role-playing family interactions when no parent is available can help the child attain a realistic and pragmatic approach to his/her parents and family. Formal training in the processes and dynamics of these various treatment modalities is encouraged prior to their use.

One of the most important functions of the therapist is to facilitate the child's investment in a positive and protective support system that continues to be available to the child when therapy ends. Children who have been abused or neglected may not know how to interact appropriately with people who could be supportive, helpful, and appropriate for social interaction. Children need to learn social interaction and interpersonal skills that will facilitate their interaction with peers and adults. Individual therapy can begin this process by offering a supportive environment in which to address the child's experience, needs, and abilities and by allowing the child to learn to interact appropriately with an adult. Therapy offers the child an opportunity to verbalize and explore many of the issues or concerns typical of victims of abuse and neglect. It also offers the child an opportunity to practice expressing feelings and to learn behaviors that can generate appropriate responses from adults and peers. Group therapy can further this process by allowing a child to participate in a group in a group of his/her peers who have had similar experiences. This group experience can help the child realize that many of his/her behaviors or reactions are typical for children who have been abused or neglected. Group therapy allows the child to practice and modify many of the skills he/she has learned in individual therapy. These skills include listening, sharing, responding with interest and empathy, and demonstrating age-appropriate concern and affection. It is much easier to insert corrective information or action when a therapist witnesses a problematic interaction than when he/she learns about that problem later. Many of these skills that can be utilized in a neighborhood or school setting increase the child's likelihood of finding appropriate and responsive friends.

Participation on team activities can increase cooperation and appropriate social interactions and can offer esteem-building experiences for the child. Participation in social and school groups allow the child an opportunity to apply and practice his/her acquired social skills and relate to other children as peer rather than as a victim of abuse and neglect.

Types of Therapy

Play Therapy

Play therapy is an effective modality that helps the child express feelings, act out behaviors, and gain mastery and control over memories and feelings generated by the abusive or neglectful experience. A child uses play to manage his/her fears and anxieties about the abuse, express his/her feelings about what happened to him/her, and demonstrate their knowledge and understanding about relationships. Play therapy allows the child to represent symbolically those events that generate fear and anxiety and helps the child move toward resolution and integration of the frightening experience.

Play therapy is especially effective with children who do not have the verbal or cognitive skills necessary to participate in a more direct approach to discussing their feelings. A child who is developmentally or emotionally unable to express him/herself verbally can benefit from an experience that allows him/herself to demonstrate his/her feelings, fears, and attempts at mastery.

Themes that are repeated during play therapy should be studied. Interventions need to be developed to help the child gain a sense of mastery and control over an overwhelming experience. It is incumbent upon the therapist to interpret this play material in a manner that adds insight and meaning to the child's experience and facilitates resolution or closure of the traumatic event.

Individual Therapy

Usually, individual therapy is the child's first introduction to treatment. It is an opportunity for the child to interact with a supportive and knowledgeable adult and develop a relationship that models appropriate adult–child relationships. Individual therapy also allows the therapist time to assess and evaluate the child's interpersonal skills and help the child learn age-appropriate and engaging behaviors to interact with peers.

The goal of individual therapy is understanding, integration, and resolution of those experiences that affect development, interaction, and safety. Individual therapy is most beneficial in helping children address developmental issues of trust, mastery and control, and identity. Individual therapy generally is helpful in supporting disclosure of abuse and neglect, helping the child identify issues related to their experience, and in resolving intrapersonal issues.

A child who will testify during a criminal proceeding can benefit from individual therapy. It can help the child address his/her fear and anxiety related to confronting the perpetrator and testifying in front of strangers. Most children are also less likely to be affected by or incorporate other victims' circumstances than are children who have participated in group therapy before having to testify.

Group Therapy

Group therapy is especially helpful for decreasing isolation, improving social skills, and monitoring and intervening in problematic interactional patterns of behavior. Group therapy also allows the child to identify and learn from peers and group leaders and helps the child learn new and possibly more effective ways of interacting and communicating about his/her circumstances. Group therapy can facilitate participation with a supportive and understanding peer group and allow the child to practice many of the skills that will improve his/her ability and evaluate relationships. Additional benefits provided by group therapy include normalization of the experience by hearing similarities in victims' feelings and responses to abuse and neglect, corrective capitulation of the primary family group, development of socializing techniques, acquisition of the sense of belonging, and catharsis.

Group therapy is not warranted for a child who is unable to manage his/her impulsive behavior. This child would be disruptive in group or unable to gain acceptance. A child with limited social skills often needs individual therapy to prepare him/her for the social experience of group therapy.

Family Therapy

Family therapy is most helpful when the family is willing and able to view the abuse and neglect as an issue that needs to be addressed by all the members in the family. Family therapy is an opportunity to explore roles and relationships, help family members recognize the impact that their behavior has on each other, and increase family cohesion and belonging. Family therapy can facilitate problem solving and improve communication between members. Family therapy seems most helpful after the individual family members have addressed their intrapersonal and developmental issues in individual or group therapy.

Family therapy is often an effective tool to help family members address feelings related to reunification (when the child or offending parent has been removed from the family) and develop new behaviors that help each family member feel capable of contributing and benefiting from living together.

Family therapy is not warranted when adults, especially if they are perpetrators of abuse, are unwilling to take responsibility for their behavior. Issues of blame, anger, and violence can be addressed in a family therapy format, but each individual participant must feel safe and capable of eliciting protection, if necessary.

Resources

Winn, C. A., *Treatment for Abused and Neglected Children: Infancy to Age 18*, The User Manual Series. Published by the U.S. Department of Health and Human Services, Administration for Children and Families, Washington, D.C., 1987.

Peterson, M. S. and Urquiza, A. J., *The Role of Mental Health Professionals in the Prevention and Treatment of Child Abuse and Neglect*, The User Manual Series. Published by the U.S. Department of Health and Human Services, Administration for Children and Families, Washington, D.C., 1987.

Role of the Child and Adolescent Psychiatrist in Child Abuse

Emily Harris, M.D.

Risk for psychiatric disorders

Approximately 500,000 children live in foster care nationwide. Current research estimates that about 85% of them have an emotional or substance abuse problem or both. Despite these high rates, most affected children do not receive psychiatric services until there is a crisis situation and even then, many may remain without access to services. Due to the urgency of these needs, the American Academy of Child and Adolescent Psychiatry in partnership with the Child Welfare League of America produced a policy statement urging mental health and substance abuse screening for all children in foster care to better identify and meet the needs of this vulnerable population.

Abused and neglected children also become involved in the juvenile justice system at a higher rate compared to their peers. Similarly, among incarcerated youth, rates of reported sexual and physical abuse are high. Although this subgroup hasn't been studied independently, the high rates of unrecognized, undiagnosed and untreated child and adolescent psychiatric disorders in juvenile justice settings are reminiscent of the findings in foster care. Victims of physical abuse may be especially vulnerable due to injury or damage to the central nervous system which may contribute to the development of learning disabilities, attention and impulse disorders.

Role of the child psychiatrist

Child and adolescent psychiatrists are physicians who specialize in the diagnosis and treatment of disorders of thinking, feeling and/or behavior affecting children, adolescents and their families. Child psychiatrists receive medical education and training, and have the knowledge and experience necessary to integrate the biological and psychosocial aspects of children's problems and needs. All child psychiatrists complete four years of medical school, training in adult psychiatry, and specialized training focused on normal child and family development as well as the diagnosis and treatment of childhood disorders.

A comprehensive assessment by a child psychiatrist evaluates the current concerns of the infant, child or adolescent in the context of individual, family and environmental factors including physical, genetic, developmental, emotional, cognitive, educational, family, peer, and social domains. The evaluation usually includes direct observation or interview of the child and collateral information from the caregiver, teacher, and other adults involved with the child. Child psychiatrists often work in collaboration with or provide consultation to other mental health professionals, other physicians and professionals in schools, social agencies, and juvenile justice agencies.

Disorders that appear in childhood are diverse such as pervasive developmental disorders, attention-deficit hyperactivity disorder (ADHD), learning disabilities, mental retardation, and conduct disorders. Children also experience serious mood and anxiety disorders that are often the precursors of adult disorders. Research suggests that most adult disorders have their onset in childhood or adolescence even though the disorder is often not diagnosed or treated until adulthood.

Most psychoactive medications prescribed for children have not received the rigorous testing utilized in adult clinical trials. Currently, the research lags behind the clinical use of psychoactive medications in children and adolescents. Nonetheless, children often benefit from multi-modal treatment approaches and, in many cases, psychotropic medication plays a key role. The most effective treatment approaches involve the combination of psychosocial interventions and medication. Appropriate use of psychoactive medication can provide relief from disabling and distressing symptoms and enable the child to grow, develop and succeed in his/her efforts in the family, with peers, and at school.

In summary, child psychiatrists have the knowledge and experience to address the biological and psychosocial aspects of an abused child's problems and needs. Child psychiatry addresses multiple aspects in the comprehensive mental health care of abused children through consultation to mental health clinicians and the provision of direct clinical services. Equally important is the child psychiatrist's role in primary and secondary prevention through early recognition and intervention. Child psychiatrists also collaborate with and consult to the many and diverse agencies involved in the care and concerns of abused children.

Resources

American Psychiatric Association
http://www.psych.org

California Psychiatric Association
http://www.calpsych.org

American Academy of Child and Adolescent Psychiatry
http://www.aacap.org

Role of the Psychologist

Anthony J. Urquiza, Ph.D.

Clinical psychologists typically engage in three areas of practice: psychological assessments and evaluations, psychotherapy, and clinical research. Many clinical psychologists focus their career on a specific area of practice, such as child psychology, child development, developmental disabilities, or family violence.

To become a clinical psychologist, an individual must complete a doctorate degree (a Ph.D. or Psy.D. which usually involves 5-6 years of graduate level clinical and academic training). This graduate level training usually emphasizes both clinical training in psychology and training in scientific research. Psychologists may also complete postdoctoral training programs to acquire more advanced clinical training and/or training in research. Once the doctorate degree is acquired, psychologists usually practice in the areas described below.

Psychological Assessment/Evaluations

Most clinical psychologists provide mental health evaluation and treatment of children, adults, and families. They are the only mental health professionals accredited to perform most psychological testing and evaluation. Psychologists often employ a battery of tests that evaluate a variety of mental health abilities, including: **cognitive functioning** (intellectual and perceptual abilities, and how one understands the world); **affective functioning** (emotions and traumatic responses); **adaptive functioning** (how feelings and skills are employed to deal with the challenges and tasks life presents to an individual); and, **psychopathology** (the ways in

an individual may have difficulty functioning due to mental health problems, and/or maladaptive responses to traumatic or painful life experiences). In general, psychological tests and assessments can address the following types of questions about an individual:

- What are the client's intellectual strengths and limitations?

- Are there difficulties in processing visual and/or auditory information (which may reflect neuropsychological immaturity or impairment)?

- How adequate is reality testing?

- What are the qualities, strengths, and challenges of interpersonal relationships?

- What are the adaptive strengths of the client (coping resources, application of assets and liabilities to new problems, flexibility of approach, persistence, frustration tolerance, and reaction to novelty)?

- To what degree are impulses maintained under control (undercontrolled, overcontrolled)?

- How does the person defend psychologically (protect the self from feelings, ideas, and experiences that create anxiety through avoidance, repression, etc.) against unacceptable internal needs and demands, or external experiences? How rigid are the client's defenses?

- What are the areas of interpersonal conflict?

Psychological Treatment

In clinical psychology, the process of conducting psychological treatment primarily focuses on the alleviation of unpleasant or distressing mental health symptoms. The symptoms may be relatively minor (e.g., decreased academic performance) or may significantly impair the client's functioning (e.g., sleep disturbance, panic attacks). Depending on the type and severity of the presenting problem, a psychologist may see the client individually, in a group (with other clients who may have similar concerns), with one or two other people (who may be involved in treatment), and/or with the client's family. Examples for involvement in psychological treatment include:

- Alleviation of depressive symptoms (e.g., sleep disturbance, decreased appetite, low mood);

- Acquisition of specific skills (e.g., social skills, problem-solving skills);

- Decrease family conflict (e.g., arguing, parent-child problems, aggression);

- Enhance specific relationships (e.g., parent-child, sibling, or marital relationship); and

- Decrease traumatic symptoms (e.g., nightmares, fears, anxiety, intrusive imagery).

Clinical Research

An important aspect of being a clinical psychologist may involve conducting clinical research. Research usually involves extensive knowledge and understanding of a specific aspect of psychology (e.g., child development, post-traumatic stress disorder, child maltreatment, domestic violence) and the process by which scientific methods are used to further this knowledge. Quantitative research methodology involves developing a hypothesis, identifying dependent and independent variables, studying a statistically relevant sample of subjects to acquire aggregate information about members of a specific population, analyzing and interpreting the data, describing the study outcomes, and submitting an article for publication in a scientifically based peer review journal. Qualitative research methodology seeks to understand the response of a large number of people by in-depth understanding of a few individuals within their environmental context.

Resources

American Psychological Association
http://www.apa.org

California Psychological Association
http://www.calpsychlink.org

PART 16

Home Visiting Programs: At-Risk Families with Newborns

Linda Kimura, M.A.

Case Vignette

A young mother arrives at the hospital in labor with her 14-month old toddler in tow. She fled from another state, seeking shelter from her abusive boyfriend. Now nine months pregnant, her father, who took her in temporarily, has kicked her out. As her toddler tugs and whines, the young mother breaks down while talking to a hospital social worker summoned by the admissions clerk. As they talk, psycho-social concerns are unearthed, including lack of resources, anxiety and a general feeling of being overwhelmed by the prospect of single parenting two small children. The young mother feels abandoned, alone and fearful. As she wipes her eyes, her toddler pulls on her hospital gown. The young mother cries out, "Behave, just behave, if you know what's good for you—grow up and stop acting like a baby! You need to help me!"

Questions

1. Why focus on prevention, especially during the neonatal period?

2. What presenting issues or problems leading to child abuse and neglect are commonly seen in overburdened families?

3. What program practices have been shown to support families and reduce the risk of abuse and neglect to newborns and young children?

4. What outcomes have been demonstrated across the United States by child abuse and neglect prevention programs that offer intensive in-home visitation?

According to the 1995 U.S. Advisory Board on Child Abuse and Neglect report, approximately 2,000 children (5 children per day) die from child abuse and neglect annually in the United States. Nationwide, about 79% of severe abuse and neglect, and most deaths, occur among children under age five with the median age of death being 2.6 years.

Parents, who lack basic resources and information about parenting, and have limited educational and work experiences, are at greatest risk for using inappropriate and/or dangerous child rearing methods. As their children grow up, they are at increased risk for truancy, drug abuse, delinquency, and mental illness.

Prevention is the key to eliminating child maltreatment before it ever starts. The consensus in the field is clear—there is no one single model or approach that will solve all problems; but it is possible to create a unique and appropriate constellation of prevention services in each community. A critical part of the constellation is in-home visitation around the time of birth and during the first years of life. Family focused, child centered programs, aimed at assisting parents in providing safe, healthy, nurturing homes for their children, can significantly reduce the potential for child abuse and neglect. Studies show that such services also increase family social support, optimize child health and development outcomes, promote positive parent-child attachment, increase children's resiliency, and improve family problem solving.

In 1991, the U.S. Advisory Board on Child Abuse and Neglect cited home visiting programs at the time of birth as its major recommendation to prevent child abuse and neglect, and singled out the state of Hawaii's Healthy Start model as outstanding. The Advisory Board called upon the Federal Government to implement universal voluntary neonatal home visitation programs for new parents. Many programs already exist, however, they are not universally implemented throughout the U.S. For example, more than one-fourth of all Public Health Departments have been visiting new families for over 100 years. There are also a variety of community-based models ranging such as Parent Aide Programs, Parents as Teachers, Head Start, and Early Head Start. Healthy Families America, based on the Hawaii Healthy Start model, operates in over 400 sites in most states, the District of Columbia, and Canada.

Research demonstrates the success of these programs. Early work by Dr. Henry Kempe showed that after two years of home visiting services, there was no abuse in families receiving home visitation services and a 20% rate of severe abuse requiring hospitalization in the control group. In the Hawaii Healthy Start program, between 1987 and 1991, there were no reports of abuse in 99.3% of families and no reports of neglect in 98.5% of families receiving services.

In-home visitation around the time of birth to prevent child abuse and neglect is important for these reasons:

- Research on brain development in very young children indicates that positive reciprocal interactions and other environmental factors are critical in the development of neural pathways that lay the foundation for future learning and emotional regulation.

- The birth of a child provides a window of opportunity for parents who are eager to support their new infant.

- Working with new parents before negative parenting patterns are established provides the greatest chance for parents to be successful.

- Working with new parents facilitates supportive family intervention before the time when most abuse and neglect occurs.

- A variety of longitudinal studies indicate that the risk of child abuse and neglect can be significantly reduced if support and education services are provided around the time of birth.

Common presenting problems upon enrollment in neonatal home visitation programs to prevent child abuse and neglect include:

- Lack of positive social support, marital or family problems;

- Late or no prenatal care, poor prenatal compliance, and other health problems;

- Unstable housing, income or transportation;

- History of substance abuse, interpersonal violence or incarceration;

- History of or current depression or psychiatric care;

- Childhood history of abuse and neglect;

- Unintended and unwanted pregnancy;

- Abortion or relinquishment sought at a late date;

- Unrealistic or rigid expectations for the infant;

- Single parent, no spousal support, or young parent with older companion;

- Acculturation difficulties (unable to communicate or locate resources in dominant culture);

- Less than 12 years education or illiterate in primary language; and

- Significant lack of information about child development.

Generally accepted program best practices include:

- Prevention oriented, voluntary services beginning prenatally or around the time of birth;

- Systematic standardized assessment to determine the need for and intensity of a variety of services;

- Long term and intensive services (at least one home visit per week) with structured criteria for increasing or decreasing the level of intensity over a period of years;

- Culturally relevant services that reflect the idea that beliefs, practices and concerns vary widely from culture to culture, family to family and individual to individual;

- Interventions and techniques that are strength-based and solution-focused;

- Home visitors selected for education, experience and personality characteristics shown to be supportive for at-risk parents (e.g. ability to build trust, non-judgmental, accepting of small steps, ability to function as a member of a team, and personal issues successfully resolved);

- Intensive, specific on-going training for staff and regular reflective, relationship-based supervision of direct service workers;

- Commitment to low caseloads in order to provide quality services;

- Outcome and process-based evaluations of program goals and objectives; and

- Links to a variety of other resources, services and natural supports in the community.

TWO NATIONAL MODELS DEMONSTRATING BEST PRACTICES IN NEONATAL HOME VISITATION:

	Healthy Families America	Early Head Start Home Based Option
Focus	Prevent child abuse and neglect through systematic screening and assessment of children and family needs; positive parent-child attachment and bonding; healthy child growth and development; and building family strengths.	Provide safe and developmentally enriching caregiving environments for young children. Support families in their roles. Mobilize communities. Ensure highly trained staff.
Home Visitor Caseload	1:15 weekly	Maximum 1:12; Average 1:10
Supervisor Caseload	1:5	varies
Reflective Supervision	weekly	usually weekly
Multi-disciplinary	yes	yes
Acceptance age	prenatal—2 weeks	prenatal—3 years
Length of program	5 years	3 years
Intensity of visits	Once per week with criteria for increasing or decreasing intensity depending on needs	Once per week plus 2 parent-child groups per month
Income	all	90% low income 10% reserved for children with disabilities, regardless of income.
Multi-cultural focus for training	yes	yes

Long-term, intensive neonatal home visitation requires initial on-going training in a variety of areas including:

- indicators, prevention and treatment of child abuse and neglect;

- anticipatory infant and child development;

- constructs of attachment theory and techniques for promoting parent-child relationships;

- family centered services, family dynamics and solution-focused problem solving skills;

- indicators, prevention, treatment options and community resources for domestic violence and substance abuse;

- communication skills and techniques for promoting parental empowerment and self-efficacy;

- basic infant/toddler and parental and postnatal health and access issues; and

- collaboration, teamwork, safety and prevention of burnout.

Sample Outcomes

Parent and Family

- Increases in parent's sense of efficacy in meeting child and family's needs;

- Increased knowledge of and pride in parenting and child development;

- Increased ability to respond to children's needs sensitively, including reduction in corporal punishment; and

- Increased intervals between pregnancies.

Child

- Reduction in infant mortality rates;

- Higher immunization and health care user rates;

- Increased developmental gains; and

- Increased social functioning, including conflict negotiation and problem solving.

Community

- Increased collaborations between service partners;
- Increased parent participation in community systems;
- Decreased rates of child abuse and neglect; and
- Decreased costs for treatment services for older children.

Case Resolution

The hospital social worker referred the young mother to the local Healthy Families America in-home visiting program. Early contact by a trained and nurturing home visitor resulted in the mother finding stable, inexpensive housing in a well-respected housing group, where mutual support was readily available from other young parents. Weekly home visits focused on concrete needs, enhancing parent-child relationships and learning positive parenting practices, including age-appropriate expectations and perceptions to reduce the potential for abusive punishment. As her situation improved, visits focused on planning for a stable, secure future. With the encouragement from her home visitor, she attended a support group for survivors of abuse and play-based developmental activities at the Healthy Families America Center.

Selected Readings:

The David and Lucille Packard Foundation. Center for the Future of Children, *Home Visiting*, Vol.3, Num.

3, Los Altos, CA, Winter 1993.

Daro, D., Jones, E., and McCurdy, K. Preventing *Child Abuse: An evaluation of services to high-risk families*. William Penn Foundation, Philadelphia, 1993.

Egeland, B., Carleson, E., and Sroufe, M. Resilience as a Process. *Development and Psychology*, 5:517-528, 1993.

Fuddy, L.J. *Outcomes for the Hawaii Healthy Start Program*. State of Hawaii, Dept. of Health, Family Health Services Division, Maternal and Child Health Branch, 1994.

Resources:

Healthy Families America
www.preventchildabuse.org

Early Head Start
www.ehsnrc.org

Parent Support Lines: Support for Parents to Prevent Abuse

Sue Bonk and Marilyn Strachan Peterson, M.S.W., M.P.A.

Case Vignette

Caller is a single mother of a three-year old daughter who is negative, defiant, cries, screams, and "everything's a struggle." Mother is very distraught, gets frustrated, yells, and doesn't know what to do. She feels isolated, lonely, and depressed. Volunteer acknowledged that a three-year old can be challenging and shared information with her from the child development resource book that addressed the "typical behavior" of a three-year old. Mother shared how she responds to daughter when she exhibits these behaviors. Volunteer allowed mother to vent her frustration and, when appropriate, began to engage her in brainstorming options for responding to the child's negative behavior. The following examples were among those discussed: be consistent, redirect child when her behavior seems to escalate; have natural consequences for inappropriate behavior; or give a short time out (one minute per age of child). Advised mother that children go in and out of development stages and that this behavior will not last forever. Volunteer made referrals to parenting classes, a hospital advice nurse, and continued dialogue with her daughter's pediatrician. Caller was encouraged to call again if needed. (Length of call was 35 minutes)

Questions

1. What is a parent support stress line?
2. How does it help parents?
3. How is it organized?

Epidemiology/Statistics

Over 600,000 reports of child abuse and neglect are made every year in California to Children's Protective Services. Not every instance of child abuse and neglect is reported to authorities. There is a strong need for supportive services for parents in stress, to help them meet the challenges of raising young children, to help them cope with major life stressors and cumulative frustrating circumstances. Data from established 24-hour parent support stress lines in California metropolitan areas shows that 8,000 to 15,000 calls are received every year.

Purpose of a Parent Support Stress Line

To prevent child abuse and neglect by providing child rearing information, crisis intervention, emotional support and referrals to parents in stress.

To provide a non-threatening resource for parents or caretakers who need someone who will listen, offer reassurance and support and refer the caller to important community resources available to them.

Program Models

- Parent support stress line which operates 12 to 24 hours per day with trained volunteers supervised by a volunteer coordinator or case manager. Calls are typically "patched through" by an answering service to volunteers who work defined shifts and provide information and support over the telephone.

- Parent support stress line and respite care programs (often called crisis nurseries) which provide supervised 24-hour respite care for children for a specified number of days and for specified age groups. These programs employ staff and are actively involved in counseling parents, connecting them to community resources, and providing case management.

Basic Elements of a
Parent Support Stress Line

- Trained volunteers (approximately 40 to cover 24 hours per day, weekends, and holidays).

- Volunteer Coordinator who recruits and trains volunteers, provides quality assurance, and represents the program in the community.

- Public awareness plan which includes radio and television public service announcements, posters and brochures for distribution in public areas, presentations to community, social and civic groups.

- Established linkages with key referral agencies, e.g. suicide prevention lines, drug and alcohol treatment programs, emergency housing programs, food banks, financial assistance, rape crisis centers and battered women counseling and shelter programs, parenting education and parent support groups.

- Defined volunteer training program which covers topics such as dynamics of child abuse and neglect, crisis intervention, parent needs, family violence, family dynamics, child and adolescent developmental stages, talking to youth, parent development, mental health issues, developmental disabilities, grief and mourning, family diversity awareness, basic protocols and procedures, and intervention philosophy.

- Volunteer procedures which include a structured interview and reference check, and policies and procedures regarding commitment to the program and performance expectations, e.g. calling the Volunteer Coordinator if they cannot make their shift or arranging for coverage.

- Data collection system for recording the number of calls per day, time of calls, length of calls, the presenting issue of the caller, type of intervention, e.g. crisis intervention and referral, information only, and referrals made.

Basic Elements of a
Parent Support Stress Line and a
Crisis Nursery or Respite Care Program

Refer to next chapter on Crisis Nurseries: Respite Care for Overwhelmed Parents

Additional Resources

Sacramento Parent Support Line and Crisis Nursery, Sacramento, California

Parent TALK Line, San Francisco, California

Crisis Nurseries: Respite Care for Overwhelmed Parents

Sue Bonk and Marilyn Strachan Peterson, M.S.W., M.P.A.

Three Case Vignettes

Monique is a single mother of four young girls, ages 7, 6, 1 and four months. She was not working and on welfare. Monique called the Crisis Nursery when she was evicted from her apartment. All of the homeless shelters were full and she had nowhere to go with her four children. The three oldest girls stayed at the Crisis Nursery, and Monique was able to keep the baby with her at a friend's house until she could find another place to stay. Monique was referred to a transitional housing program. She was accepted and can live there for two years. She calls the Sacramento Crisis Nursery a "blessing" and is grateful for the assistance in helping her find housing while her children were safe and well-cared for.

Dana is a single mother of two sons who had just escaped a violent living situation with the boys' father. Dana was determined to remove herself and her children from the violent environment, but was having painful physical symptoms, possibly related to past domestic violence injuries. She had no place for her children to stay while she sought medical help. She called the crisis nursery for help. The boys stayed at the Nursery while Dana took care of both her medical problems and legal issues to protect herself and her children from future harm.

Karen and Al came to the SCN when their Down's Syndrome infant was ten days old. They were both distraught about their baby's diagnosis, to the point of questioning whether they would keep the boy or relinquish him for adoption. While the baby stayed at the Crisis Nursery, the parents were connected with resources from Sacramento County Adoptions, Alta California Regional Center, and the Down's Syndrome Parent Support Program. At the end of thirty days, it was recommended that the baby go to a voluntary foster home while the parents continued to struggle with their decision on the future of their child. The parents ultimately decided to keep their

baby. They brought their four-year old daughter to the Nursery while they adjusted to having the baby home with them. The parents have continued to keep in touch with the Nursery staff and are doing well, receiving support from the Parent Support Program.

Questions

1. What is a crisis nursery?

2. How does it help parents?

3. Why do parents use it?

Epidemiology/Statistics

Lack of financial resources, depression, overwhelming life events, cumulative frustrations, and the challenges of raising young children combine to create the potential of episodic or chronic abuse of children. Over 600,000 reports of child abuse and neglect are made every year in California to Children's Protective Services. Crisis nurseries offer respite care to parents and caretakers who need temporary assistance in raising their children and dealing with life stressors.

Purpose of a Crisis Nursery

- To prevent child abuse and neglect by providing a temporary, loving and safe, home-like environment for children and to offer counseling and support to their families;

- To provide a voluntary alternative of counseling and support for parents in a time of crisis, and to prevent a family crisis from escalating and having an adverse impact on the children; and

- To develop parents' capabilities.

305

Program Services for Children

- Six Bed Program Model

- Ten Bed Program Model

- Respite Residential Care for Children

  - Short Term (24 hours to 4 days depending upon the needs of the family)

  - Long Term (up to 30 days);

- Health screening and immunizations, if indicated;

- Nutritious meals; and

- Developmentally appropriate play activities for the children, attention, and nurturing.

Services for Parents/Caretakers

- Intake assessment of the crisis and development of a case plan;

- Family Counseling;

- In-home family support;

- Parent education groups;

- Referrals to community resources, e.g. drug/alcohol treatment, housing programs, etc.;

- Information and education about healthy lifestyles;

- Case Management;

- Client Advocacy; and

- Follow up.

How do Parents Hear About these Programs?

- Referral from another organization;

- Children's Protective Services;

- Friend(s); and

- Television, radio, brochure, newspaper, relative, physician, church, school, support group.

REASONS IDENTIFIED BY PARENTS AT INTAKE FOR BRINGING CHILDREN TO THE CRISIS NURSERY	
Respite	50.5%
Look for housing	34.3%
Attend counseling	22.2%
Get medical help or hospitalization for self or family	20.2%
Recommended by other	19.2%
Look for job	11.1%
Deal with legal issues	10.6%
Recover from an illness	10.6%
Get child away from domestic violence	9.6%

STRESSORS MARKED BY PARENTS AT INTAKE	
Money concerns	61.6%
Depression (33% reported use of antidepressant)	53.0%
Overwhelmed by responsibilities	44.9%
Problems with transportation	37.9%
Often feel alone	33.3%
Don't trust many people	30.8%
Hyperactive child	29.8%
Problems with partner	28.8%
Lack of close friends	22.2%
Drug addiction	12.6%

At an exit interview of parents after receiving services, all of these reported stressors declined by an average of 40%. These statistics are from the evaluation study of the Sacramento Crisis Nursery cited below.

Presenting medical conditions of the children

Significant medical conditions included asthma, developmental disabilities, developmental delays, histories of serious infections, and positive for drugs at birth.

Suggested Staffing of a Crisis Nursery

24-hour "awake" staff
Senior childcare and childcare worker on each shift
Case Manager/Counselor
Secretary/Receptionist
Director

Financial Support for Crisis Nursery Programs

United Way
Foundation grants
Federal and state grants
Community support

Additional Resources

The Evaluation of the Sacramento Crisis Nursery 1997-1999, Rose and Associates, 1999.

Bay Area Crisis Nursery
Concord, California

First Step Crisis Nursery
San Joaquin Child Abuse Prevention Council
Stockton, California

Para Los Ninos
Los Angeles, California

Sacramento Crisis Nursery
Sacramento, California

Family Resource Centers

Brooke Allison, M.A.

Case Vignette

Rebecca called the Family Resource Center upset, enraged, sobbing hysterically and feeling as though her life was out of control. At the time she called, she was involved in a domestic violence relationship. She also had an unaddressed, unresolved history of childhood sexual abuse (multiple perpetrators including a male relative who she had told her mother about and was not believed). She said her husband had assaulted her at least twice (she later admitted it was much more). Her mother-in-law was actively trying to get her declared an unfit mother and to take her two youngest children away from her. Her first child had died—a stillbirth. Her six-year-old daughter, Stephanie, was showing signs of an eating disorder (anorexia). Stephanie often did not eat, especially when the family was under extreme stress, or after a domestic violence episode. There was only one vehicle in the family, and it was being used as a control issue. Her youngest child who is three had been hospitalized with pneumonia. There was on open case with CPS, and the parents had gone to court fighting over child custody, domestic violence, child support, visitation and divorce issues. Dad had tried to commit suicide at least twice, and both Mom and Dad had been arrested. The family was in utter chaos and breakdown.

Six weeks later, with the help of the Family Resource Center (FRC), Rebecca's life is on track. Rebecca is in counseling on a weekly basis at the center and is receiving domestic violence prevention assistance. Through referrals from the resource worker, she has developed a family plan with her FRC case manager. She now has acquired her own car and has re-enrolled in a LVN (Licensed Vocational Nurse) training program. Rebecca has enrolled her daughter in elementary school and she has moved in with a roommate, cutting her overhead expenses in half.

The two youngest children have been placed voluntarily with relatives on a temporary basis. This has afforded Rebecca a much needed rest and an opportunity to examine her life without the daily stress of caring for two children under age 2. She is no longer living with her abusive boyfriend, and says "I will not let anything stand in the way of continuing the changes in my life." With the ongoing assistance of the FRC, Rebecca is looking for employment. Before her children come home, she will have completed a parenting class and will be enrolled in the FRC home visiting program.

Questions

1. What is a Family Resource Center?
2. Why are Family Resource Centers important?
3. What are the guiding principles?
4. What services do they offer?

Family Resource Centers (FRCs) are "one stop shops" located in the heart of the communities they serve, offering under one roof a variety of social services essential to enhanced family and child functioning. FRCs represent one important way to avoid the fragmentation of services that plagues many families in need, providing, instead, comprehensive, coordinated services for the entire family close to home.

Guiding Principles

The Family as Target Population

The family, rather than the individual child or parent, is the primary target population for family resource centers. An attempt is made to influence and change the context within which individuals live and support (or hurt) one another. Thus, while services are offered for the individual (e.g., employment readiness, counseling), equal emphasis is placed on reducing a family's social isolation, improving its self-sufficiency and income, and connecting families to a network of pro-social support.

Family Support Continuum of Care

Family Resource Centers share a commitment to families by providing continuum of care from prevention, early intervention, rehabilitation and treatment to aftercare support. While a typical FRC emphasizes prevention, early intervention, and aftercare, it also assists a family to access in-depth, long-term services.

Comprehensive, Collaborative, Integrated Service Delivery System

Inherent in comprehensive, collaborative, integrated service delivery is the knowledge that:

- the families have multi-faceted needs;

- the causes of family dysfunction are many and interrelated; and

- solutions and services must attend to a family's needs comprehensively.

Fundamental to this principle is that while virtually all services may be needed, no one agency can provide them all. To be successful, essential public and private agencies should co-locate or link together through universal intake and referral to ensure that services are integrated, non-redundant, easily accessible, and cost-effective.

Comprehensive Services

While not all FRCs provide all of the services listed below, the following is the optimal set of offerings which provide families with the most comprehensive opportunity to change their lives, and to positively effect their destiny:

- Parent education such as classes, support groups, peer-to-peer interaction, Parent-Child Interaction Therapy (PCIT);

- Child development activities such as Play and Grow, Mommy and Me;

- Resource and referral links to community resources and services;

- Drop-in availability with a comfortable place for confidential conversations, and neighbor-to-neighbor meetings;

- Peer-to-Peer Supports such as support groups, and mentoring programs;

- Life skills and advocacy such as anger management classes, communication skills, budgeting, cooking classes, etc;

- Case management using an integrated multi-disciplinary team approach;

- Child abuse/neglect treatment services such as family support home visiting, emergency resources, counseling, individual, group, and family treatment;

- Access to health, dental and mental health services with onsite referral and advocacy for public health insurance programs such as Medi-Cal, Health Families Insurance, Denti-Cal, and EPSDT funded mental health services, etc;

- Family economics and self sufficiency trainings through CalWorks, job preparation and search, and community employment resources;

- Family literacy and education support such as ESL (English as a Second Language) and GED educational programs, tutoring, and vocational technology centers;

- Counseling for mental health, substance abuse, interpersonal violence issues;

- Youth development through mentoring programs, after school activities, community service, and community family fun events; and

- Community development activities such as advocacy, housing, employment, capacity building, and community celebrations.

Ensuring Program Quality, Success, and Sustainability

Program Evaluation

To ensure program success, staff must be committed to an ongoing assessment of the quantity, quality and outcome of program services. Are we doing what we said we would do? What difference does our services make in the lives of our target population? Collecting and analyziing the data to answer these questions must be part of an FRC's daily operations, and utilized routinely by administrative and program staff for the purposes of ongoing "course correction" to improve program effectiveness.

Effective Management

FRCs must be committed to creating and maintaining a good management system. Good management requires hiring the right staff; then training, supervising, and motivating them to excel as part of the FRC Team. This is complex work that requires serious, ongoing attention to detail and insistence on staff accountability up and down the line. One of the most important tools of effective management is ongoing internal program evaluation and staff accountability for quality services to children and families.

Funding Diversity and Sustainability

To ensure sustainability, a FRC must have a diverse funding base. Over-reliance on one or two sources can be fatal when, as is inevitable, a major funding source is withdrawn. Many successful FRCs combine funds from dozens of sources—including state, federal, local, and private grants—to support their work. FRCs must also be careful not to become overly dependent on grant funds. Rather FRCs should diversify their funding base to include client fees, contracts with referring agency or fees-for-service, and state and Federal funds such as Medi-Cal, CalWorks, Crime Victim Compensation Fund, and EPSDT (Early Periodic, Screening, Diagnosis Evaluation and Treatment).

Resources

Family Resource Centers, Vehicles for Change. Office of Child Abuse Prevention, California Department of Social Services, 2000.
http://www.dss.cahwnet.gov/cdssweb/ChildAbuse_188.htm

Parent Training Programs

Kerby T. Alvy, Ph.D.

Five Case Vignettes

A 17-year old mother has brought her 3-month old infant to an emergency room with signs of "shaken baby syndrome".

The parents of a 4-year old African American child have been reported by the staff of a Head Start agency to child protective services for using excessive corporal punishment to control their very active son.

A Latino farm worker family of newly-immigrated and non-English speaking parents has been observed beating all four of their children.

The school nurse at an upper middle class school continues to have the same angry teenager referred to her for falling asleep in class and suspects troubles at home.

An alcohol and cocaine addicted women with three children is being treated for her drug problems and she is also frequently reported for being abusive and neglectful with her children.

Questions

1. What are the most appropriate parent training programs for families who abuse and neglect their children or for families who are at high risk for abuse and neglect?

2. Who are the most appropriate instructors of parent training programs for abusive and neglectful families?

3. Which types of organizations are the most appropriate sponsors of parent training programs for abusive and neglectful families?

4. How can child maltreatment professionals contribute to insuring that the best programs for these populations are available in their local communities?

History of Parent Training

The idea of educating parents to promote their children's welfare and development has a long history in the United States, dating back to the 1800's when the first groups for mothers were formed to discuss how best to raise children (Brim, 1965; Harman and Brim, 1980). In the 20th century, a rich array of professional groups, including educators, psychiatrists, and psychologists, began developing classes and programs for educating parents, drawing on new research findings about child development and child rearing and upon their clinical experiences. Prior to the 1970's the majority of parenting classes available to the general public were offered through school-based parent education classes, child guidance clinics, and mental health clinics. These classes mainly focused on child development, not positive discipline for effective behavior management.

Beginning in the 1970's, a new approach for training parents emerged: parenting skill-building programs. These programs were designed to improve parenting effectiveness by providing a clear parenting philosophy and a set of skills and strategies that could be used immediately to deal with a variety of child rearing challenges and problems. The programs were carefully constructed with very specific strategies and skills to be taught in a regular sequence of training sessions, one session a week for eight to ten weeks. Teaching techniques included role playing, experiential exercises and assignments for parents to complete at home with their children. Curricula were available in trainers' manuals, and the programs had guidebooks for parents to read and use as they proceeded through training sessions. The programs were designed for use with relatively small groups of parents (8 to 15 parents) rather than with the individual families or large groups.

These brief and well-constructed programs began to be used in communities outside of where they had been originally created and field-tested. As a result, they became known as standard parent-training interventions, although, they never reached more than a small percentage of parents. These programs had originally emerged out of the mental health and child guidance fields, and they represented a systematic attempt to share with parents the skills, attitudes, and strategies that mental health professionals had found helpful with children. The most widely known and used of these innovative skill-training programs included the Rogerian psychology-oriented Parent Effectiveness Training program (PET) created by Dr. Thomas Gordon (1970, 1976), the Adlerian psychology-oriented Systematic Training Effective Parenting program (STEP) by Drs. Don Dinkmeyer and Gary McKay (1976), and a variety of behaviorally-based programs including the Confident Parenting: Survival Skills Training Program (Eimers and Aitchison, 1977; Center for the Improvement of Child Caring, 1999).

Numerous studies were undertaken to assess the effectiveness of these programs. A study of 24 of these studies (a meta analytic study) showed that when these programs are used with parents of normal children they produce very positive improvements in parenting attitudes and behavior, and in child attitudes and behavior (Medway, 1991), with the behaviorally-based programs producing the largest behavioral changes.

These three types of programs became the models for all subsequent parenting skill-building programs and many of the skills and strategies that they teach have since been incorporated into other programs (Alvy, 1994).

There now exists culturally-adapted versions for some of these programs, including the Effective Black Parenting Program for African American Parents (Center for the Improvement of Child Caring, 1997) and the Los Ninos Bien Educados Program (Center for the Improvement of Child Caring, 1989) for Latino Americans, both of which are adaptations of the Confident Parenting Program. These programs include child-rearing issues that are specific to the cultural groups and they teach parenting skills in culturally sensitive ways.

In addition, there now exists different versions of the standard programs that are focused on parents of different aged children, rather than the original versions that were for parents-in-general. For example, there is now a version of the STEP program for parents of infants and toddlers, Early Childhood STEP, and a version for parents of teens, STEP Teen (Dinkmeyer and McKay, 1989, 1990).

Many programs now use video technology as they teach skills, including the Active Parenting Program (Popkin, 1983, 1990) which is grounded in Adlerian parenting ideas.

Of the programs mentioned thus far, only the behaviorally-based programs like Confident Parenting, Effective Black Parenting, and Los Ninos Bien Educados were originally designed for use with parents who are at high risk for child abuse and neglect (such as poverty-level parents and parents whose children present major management problems).

There are now several other excellent skill-building programs for high-risk populations. The Nurturing Program by Dr. Stephen Bavolek and his colleagues, which has versions for parents of children 0-5, 5-12, 13-18 and for teenage, foster, and adoptive parents, was designed specifically for use with child abusing and neglecting parents. It includes a training component for parents and a parallel training component for the children (Bavolek, Comstock, and McLaughlin, 1983). The Strengthening Families Program by Dr. Karol Kumpfer and her colleagues was originally created for use with substance abusing families, most of whom are also child abusing families. This program has three training components: parent training, child training, and family training components (Kumpfer, DeMarsh, and Child, 1989).

The Nurturing and Strengthening Families programs include additional training components which recognizes that abusive and neglectful families need more than parent training in order to become more humane in their child rearing. They not only need these more multi-faceted programs but usually also need individual and/or family therapy, as well as other remedial or rehabilitative help.

Important Considerations about Parenting Programs

- The effectiveness of any of these programs depend upon how faithfully they are replicated in local communities, hospitals, agencies, and schools. In the research studies that confirmed their effectiveness, the programs were conducted in the exact manner that they were designed to be delivered. That is, all of the parenting ideas, skills, and homework assignments were used, the full number and length of training sessions were used; all program components were used; and, the programs were taught by instructors who were carefully trained to deliver them. The extent to which a local agency replicates or implements the program in this thorough and faithful manner is the extent to which it will produce similar positive results. Effectiveness depends upon fidelity of replication.

- Instructor qualifications and background are particularly important in providing these programs with abusive, court-referred families. Not only do these instructors need to be professionally trained to deliver the programs, but they need to be educated and familiar with the legal requirements and implications of working with these families, as well as with the experience of having one's child rearing practices supervised, monitored, and scrutinized. These are often atypical, multi-problem families with deep resentment and anger. Teaching parenting programs with these families is very demanding work.

- Ideally, parenting programs should be delivered within an agency where other needed services for the parents and the children are readily available. Or, they should be delivered as part of a community collaborative or network of services.

- Utilize parenting programs specifically designed for families' particular socioeconomic, cultural, and personal characteristics. These include the behaviorally-based programs like Confident Parenting, the culturally-specific behaviorally-based programs like Effective Black Parenting and Los Ninos Bien Educados, the Nurturing Program, the Family Strengthening Program and some of the other programs that are described on the family strengthening web sites mentioned later.

- If these programs do not currently exist in your community, efforts should be made to bring them there by having local personnel trained to deliver them. The Center for the Improvement of Child Caring (www.ciccparenting.org or 800-325-CICC) conducts professionally-led instructor training workshops annually in different cities in California, and also maintains a clearinghouse and catalog on parenting programs. CICC can also put local service providers into contact with other instructor training groups nationwide. The California State Office of Child Abuse Prevention is also a good source of information in this area (http://caag.state.ca.us/cvpc/fa_child_abuse.html).

Selected Reading and References

Alvy, K.T. *Parent Training Today: A social necessity.* Center for the Improvement of Child Caring, Studio City, CA, 1994.

Bavolek, S.J., Comstock, C.M., and McLaughlin, J.A. *The Nurturing Program: A validated approach to reducing dysfunctional family interactions.* National Institute of Mental Health, Final Report, Grant No. 1R01MH34862, Rockville, MD.

CICC's Confident Parenting Program: Instructor's Manual. Center for the Improvement of Child Caring, Studio City, CA, 1999.

CICC's Los Ninos Bien Educados Program: Instructor's Kit. Center for the Improvement of Child Caring, Studio City, CA, 1989.

CICC's Effective Black Parenting Program: Instructor's Kit. Center for the Improvement of Child Caring, Studio City, CA, 1997.

Dinkmeyer, D. and McKay, G.D. *Systematic Training for Effective Parenting: Leader's Manual.* American Guidance Service, Inc., Circle Pines, MN, 1976.

Dinkmeyer, D. and McKay, G.D. *Leader's guide, STEP/Teen: Systematic Training for Effective Parenting of Teens.* American Guidance Service, Inc., Circle Pines, MN, 1990.

Dinkmeyer, D., McKay, G.D., and Dinkmeyer, J.S. *Early Childhood STEP: Leader's Manual.* American Guidance Service, Circle Pines, MN, 1989.

Eimers, R. and Aitchison, R. *Effective Parents – Responsible Children: A Guide to Confident Parenting.* McGraw-Hill, New York, 1977.

Gordon, T. *Parent Effectiveness Training.* Wyden, New York, 1970.

Gordon, T. *PET in Action.* Perigee Books, New York, 1976.

Harmon, D. and Brim, Jr. O.C. *Learning to be Parents: Principles, Programs and Methods.* Sage Publications, Beverly Hills, 1980.

Kumpfer, K.L. and Alvarado, R. Effective Family Strengthening Interventions. *Juvenile Justice Bulletin*, November 1998. U.S. Department of Justice, Office of Juvenile Justice and Delinquency Prevention.

Kumpfer, K.L., DeMarsh, J.D., and Child, W. *The Strengthening Families Program: Parent Training Manual.* Department of Health Education, University of Utah and Alta Institute, Salt Lake City, UT, 1989.

Medway, F.J. Measuring the Effectiveness of Parent Education. In Fine MKJ (ed.), *The Second Handbook on Parent Education.* Academic Press, New York, 1991.

Popkin, M. *Active Parenting: Handbook.* Active Parenting, Inc. Atlanta, GA, 1983.

Popkin, M. Active *Parenting of Teens: Leader's Guide.* Active Parenting Publishers, Marietta, GA, 1990.

TABLE 1. STEP: SYSTEMATIC TRAINING FOR EFFECTIVE PARENTING PROGRAMS

Early Childhood STEP

Session 1: Understanding Young Children
Session 2: Understanding Young Children's Behavior
Session 3: Building Self-esteem in the Early Years
Session 4: Listening and Talking to Young Children
Session 5: Helping Young Children Learn to Cooperate
Session 6: Discipline for Young Children
Session 7: Young Children's Social and Emotional Development

STEP: Elementary School Age Children

Session 1: Understanding Yourself and Your Child
Session 2: Understanding Beliefs and Feelings
Session 3: Encouraging Your Child and Yourself
Session 4: Listening and Talking to Your Child
Session 5: Helping Children to Cooperate
Session 6: Discipline That Makes Sense
Session 7: Choosing Your Approach

STEP: Teen

Session 1: Understanding Yourself and Your Teenager
Session 2: Changing Your Response to Your Teen
Session 3: Communicating Respect and Encouragement
Session 4: Encouraging Cooperation and Problem Solving
Session 5: Using Consequences to Build Responsibility
Session 6: Deciding What to Do: Part 1
Session 7: Deciding What to Do: Part 2

TABLE 2. CENTER FOR THE IMPROVEMENT OF CHILD CARING: CONFIDENT PARENTING PROGRAM

Session 1

- Basic Behavioral Concept: Behavior is Shaped by Its Consequences
- General Descriptions of Behavior vs. Specific Descriptions
- Pinpointing Behaviors
- Charting Behavior

Session 2

- Learning and Behavior Change
- The Effective Praise Method
- Individual Consultations

Session 3

- Ways of Decreasing Behavior
- The Mild Social Disapproval Method
- The Time Out Method
- The Ignoring Method
- Data Review and Case Consultation

TABLE 2. CENTER FOR THE IMPROVEMENT OF CHILD CARING: CONFIDENT PARENTING PROGRAM, continued

Session 4

- Special Incentive Systems
- Data Review and Case Consultation

Session 5

- Individual Consultations on Behavior Change Projects
- Role Playing Practice on Skills

Session 6-10

- Individual Consultations on Behavior Change Projects
- Role Playing Practice of Skills
- Graduation at 10th Session

TABLE 3. CENTER FOR THE IMPROVEMENT OF CHILD CARING: LOS NINOS BIEN EDUCADOS PROGRAM

Session 1

- What Parents do for Children: Parental Functions and Responsibilities
- The Meaning of Bien and Mal Educado: Parental Definitions and Home Assignment

Session 2

- Role Expectations: Family Roles, Sex Roles, Age-related Roles
- Expectations are like a Coin: They have a "Do" and a "Don't" Side
- Describing and Counting "Do" and "Don't" Side Behaviors Home Assignment

Session 3

- The Context of Raising Children in the United States
- Types of Adjustments Made by Spanish-speaking Families to the U.S. Context: Assimilation, Isolation, Multi-Cultural

Session 4

- Child Abuse: Proper and Improper Parenting in the United States
- The Mild Social Disapproval Method and Related Home Application Project

Session 5

- Considering the Causes of Disrespectful Child Behaviors
- Child Development Information
- The Family Platica Approach
- The Show and Tell Method

TABLE 3. CENTER FOR THE IMPROVEMENT OF CHILD CARING: LOS NINOS BIEN EDUCADOS PROGRAM, continued

Session 6
- The Ignoring Method
- The Time Out Method
- People, Places, Things, and Activities Your Child Likes Questionnaire

Session 7
- Extensive Skill Review
- The First/Then Special Prizes (Premios Especiales) Method

Session 8
- The Questionnaire and the Cosas Buenas List
- The Point System Special Incentives (Premios Especiales) Method

Session 9
- Review and Application of the Special Incentives Method
- Individual Consultations

Session 10
- Review and Practice of All Program Skills
- Individual Consultations

Session 11
- Review and Practice of Program Skills and Concepts
- Individual Consultations

Session 12
- Further Reviews
- Graduation Ceremony with Certificates

TABLE 4. CENTER FOR THE IMPROVEMENT OF CHILD CARING: EFFECTIVE BLACK PARENTING PROGRAM

Session 1
- The Path to the Pyramid of Success for Black Children

Session 2
- The Social Learning Theory Ideas
- Charting Behavior

Session 3
- The Effective Praise Method
- The Street to Destruction
- The Extended Black Family

Session 4
- Disciplining: Traditional Black Discipline and Modern Black Self-Discipline

Session 5
- Family Rules
- Young Children and Drugs
- Specific Drugs and Their Effects

TABLE 4. CENTER FOR THE IMPROVEMENT OF CHILD CARING: EFFECTIVE BLACK PARENTING PROGRAM, continued

Session 6
- Children's Developing Abilities
- Thinking Stages and Family Rules

Session 7
- Changing the Home Environment
- The Thinking Parent's Approach

Session 8
- Reasons for Not Using Corporal Punishment
- Mild Social Disapproval

Session 9
- The Ignoring Method
- Single Parenting
- Relaxation Technique

Session 10
- The Time Out Method
- The Good Stuff Questionnaire

Session 11
- The Point System Method

Session 12
- Further Focus on Drugs

Session 13
- Chit-Chat Times
- Black Put Downs

Session 14
- Definitions of Racism
- Staying on the Path

Session 15
- What to Say at Graduation
- Proverbs and Sayings

TABLE 5. NURTURING PROGRAM FOR TEENAGE PARENTS AND THEIR FAMILIES: TRAINING COMPONENT FOR TEENAGE PARENTS

Session 1
- Assessing Parenting Strengths
- Program Overview and Home Practice

Session 2
- About Me
- Being a Teenage Parent in My Family

Session 3
- Basic Skills
- Baby Proofing: Home Practice

Session 4
- Recognizing and Understanding Feelings
- Praise for Being and Doing: Home Practice

Session 5
- Needs, Behavior, and Self-esteem
- My Needs, My Self-esteem, and Me

TABLE 5. NURTURING PROGRAM FOR TEENAGE PARENTS AND THEIR FAMILIES: TRAINING COMPONENT FOR TEENAGE PARENTS, continued

Session 6
- I Statements and You Messages
- Know Me, Know How I Feel

Session 7
- Personal Power
- Spoiling Your Children

Session 8
- Handling Stress and Anger
- Myths about Spanking

Session 9
- Discipline, Rewards, and Punishment
- Redirection

Session 10
- Rules and Rewards
- Bodies, Conception, and Pregnancy

Session 11
- Punishing Behavior
- Dating, Love, and Rejection

Session 12
- Helping Children Manage Their Behavior
- Love, Sex, and AIDS

Session 13
- Ignoring
- Touch, Personal Space, and Saying No

Session 14
- Stimulating and Communicating
- Body Map
- Vacation Visualization

Session 15
- Nurturing Routines
- Diapering and Dressing Nurturing Routines

Session 16
- Nurturing Feeding Routines
- Using Drugs

Session 17
- Establishing a Nurturing Bath Time Routine
- Peer Pressure

Session 18
- Establishing a Nurturing Bedtime Routine
- Make-up, Skin, and Hair Care

Session 19
- Toilet Training
- Self and Family Growth

Session 20
- Hopes and Fears
- Assessing Parenting Strengths
- Certificate Awards
- People Power

TABLE 6. STRENGTHENING FAMILIES PROGRAM: PARENT TRAINING COMPONENT

Session 1: Introduction
- Group Building

Session 2: Decentering
- Perceptual Role Taking
- Affective Empathy

Session 3: Reinforcements
- Attending

Session 4: Goal Statements
- Child Development
- Behavioral Goals

Session 5: Differential Attention/Charts and Spinners
- Using Rewards

Session 6: Communication I
- Relationship Enhancement

Session 7: Communication II
- Speaker
- Listener
- Coach
- Mode Switching

Session 8: Communication III
- Relationship Enhancement Practice

Session 9: Alcohol and Drug Education
- Use/Abuse
- Discussion

Session 10: Problem Solving
- Negotiation
- Making Requests
- Compliance Cues

Session 11: Limit Setting I
- Differential Attention
- Overcorrection
- Time-Out
- Punishment

Session 12: Limit Setting II
- Video
- Practice: Dyads Exercise

Session 13: Generalization and Maintenance
- Schedules of Reinforcement
- Fading
- Troubleshooting

Session 14: Implementation
- Program Development
- Review

Head Start and Early Head Start Programs

Marilyn Strachan Peterson, M.S.W, M.P.A.

Head Start

Head Start is a national program which provides comprehensive developmental services for America's low-income, pre-school children ages three to five and social services for their families. Specific services for children focus on education, socio-emotional development, physical and mental health, and nutrition.

Since its development in 1965 by the Office of Economic Opportunity, Head Start has served over 15.3 million children and their families. Head Start plays a major role in focusing attention on the importance of early childhood development. The program has an impact on: child development and day care services; the expansion of state and local activities for children; the range and quality of services offered to young children and their families; and the design of training programs for those who staff such programs. Outreach and training activities also assist parents in increasing their parenting skills and knowledge of child development.

The cornerstone of the program is parent and community involvement—which has made it one of the most successful pre-school programs in the country. Approximately 1,400 community-based non-profit organizations and school systems develop unique and innovative programs to meet specific needs.

Major Components of Head Start

Head Start provides diverse services to meet the goals of the following four components:

- **Education**
  Head Start's educational program is designed to meet the needs of each child, the community served, and its ethnic and cultural characteristics. Every child receives a variety of learning experiences to foster intellectual, social, and emotional growth.

- **Health**
  Head Start emphasizes the importance of the early identification of health problems. Every child is involved in a comprehensive health program, which includes immunizations, medical, dental, mental health, and nutritional services.

- **Parent Involvement**
  An essential part of Head Start is the involvement of parents in parent education, program planning, and operating activities. Many parents serve as members of policy councils and committees and have a voice in administrative and managerial decisions. Participation in classes and workshops on child development and staff visits to the home allow parents to learn about the needs of their children and about educational activities that can take place at home.

- **Social Services**
  Specific services are geared to each family after its needs are determined. They include: community outreach, referrals, family need assessments, recruitment and enrollment of children, and emergency assistance and/or crisis intervention.

Early Head Start

Early Head Start (EHS) is a federally funded community-based program for low-income families with infants and toddlers and pregnant women. Its mission is to promote healthy prenatal outcomes for pregnant women, enhance the development of very young children, and promote healthy family functioning. EHS evolved out of Head Start's long history of providing services to infants and toddlers through Parent Child Centers, Comprehensive Child Development Centers (CCDPs) and Migrant Head Start programs.

To help design this initiative, the Secretary of Health and Human Services formed an Advisory Committee on Services for Families with Infants and Toddlers in 1994. The committee set forth the vision and goals for Early Head Start that had been shaped by lessons learned from the Comprehensive Child Development Programs, Parent and Child Centers, Migrant Head Start Programs, locally designed Head Start programs, and other early child development and family support efforts serving families with very young children.

Principles

The community-based Early Head Start programs are based on a foundation of nine principles:

- **High Quality**
  Programs are founded in the knowledge, skills, and professional ethics embraced by the fields of child development, family development, and community building. Of particular importance is an understanding of the unique nature of infant and toddler development. Program practices spring from an awareness of both the opportunities for intervention and the fact that young children are particularly vulnerable to the effects of a negative caregiving environment. The commitment on the part of the Federal government to ensure program quality includes a training and technical assistance network, program performance standards, and research and evaluation activities.

- **Prevention and Promotion**
  The proactive promotion of healthy child development and family functioning begins before conception, and continues prenatally, upon birth, and through the early years. With an emphasis on promoting healthy child development, the prevention and detection of developmental concerns is an important focus of this program.

- **Positive Relationships and Continuity**
  Strong positive relationships between the child, family, and staff that continue over time are key elements in a high quality program. These relationships recognize the parent-child bond as the child's most significant relationship. Infant and toddler caregiving practices must support child attachment by minimizing the number of different caregivers and supporting long-term caregiving relationships. The relationship between staff and family is based on respect for the child and family's home culture.

- **Parent Involvement**
  The Early Head Start initiative supports the highest level of parent involvement and partnership. Programs make a special effort to support the role of fathers in parenting activities. Programs recognize the parents as the child's primary nurturers and advocates. Parents are also active participants in policy and decision-making roles.

- **Inclusion**
  Programs are welcome and fully include children with disabilities. The individual needs of each child are evaluated and responded to in a way that builds upon individual strengths. Programs also support the child and family's full participation in community activities.

- **Culture**
  The home culture and language of each family are supported as an important aspect of early identity formation. Programs also explore the role of culture and language in child and family development, and community values and attitudes.

- **Comprehensiveness, Flexibility, Responsiveness, and Intensity**
  Program services are grounded in the belief that all families can identify their own needs and strengths, set their own goals, and are capable of growth. Programs must maintain the flexibility to respond with varying levels of intensity based on families' needs and resources.

- **Transitions**
  Programs are responsible for facilitating a smooth transition from Early Head Start into Head Start or other high quality programs and support services. A smooth transition is important to ensure each child continues to receive enriching early child development services and each family continues to receive the support services necessary to healthy family development.

- **Collaboration**
  Collaboration with local community agencies and service providers maximize the resources available to families with young children in a cost-efficient and comprehensive manner. Early Head Start programs, with the recognition that no one program can meet all of a child and family's needs, seek to build strong alliances within the communities in which they operate.

Eligibility Criteria

Early Head Start (EHS) is a child development program for low-income families. Each Early Head Start program is responsible for determining its' own eligibility criteria. Family income is one key factor in determining eligibility. The federal poverty guidelines are used to evaluate family income. Early Head Start programs may elect to target their services to a particular population to best meet the unique needs of families and children in their community. Contact the EHS program in your area for specific information about how to enroll or refer a child and family to local Early Head Start.

Resources

Administration for Children and Families, United States Department of Health and Human Services, "Head Start", http://www2.acf.dhhs.gov/programs/hsb/html/head_start_fs.html, October 5, 1999.

Administration for Children and Families, United States Department of Health and Human Services, "The Early Head Start National Resource Center", http://207.153.212.104/ehs.htm, September 24, 1999.

School-Based Services for the Prevention of Child Abuse and Neglect and Services for Children in Foster Care

Barbara J. Bradstock, M.A., R.N. and Marilyn Strachan Peterson, M.S.W., M.P.A.

The Position of Schools

Schools are in a unique position to address the problem of abuse and neglect by virtue of the school's position in the community, the staff's training and expertise, the availability of physical facilities, and the presence of nearly all children 5-17 years of age at school. The list below illustrates schools' potential involvement in prevention and services:

- school-based educational programs;
- joint school-community programs;
- individual action on the part of staff;
- services for children in foster care;
- staff training for reporting and for detecting the signs of abuse and neglect;
- addressing the issue of teachers and school personnel as perpetrators;
- detection and intervention in multi-generational abuse cycles.

School Based Educational/Prevention Programs for Children and Adolescents

Several areas of prevention can be addressed with children and adolescents:

Awareness of family violence and sexual assault (including date rape)

To break the cycle of violence, a building block curriculum is important to educate children and adolescents at appropriate age levels using developmentally and culturally appropriate teaching methods about the existence of these problems. For many years in California, there was a $10 million annual appropriation for K-12 education on child abuse and neglect. This was discontinued during the long economic recession in the 1980's. Some of this information is now disseminated through family life courses or after school programs, but not systematically through the grades or with a standard curriculum.

Life skills training

Life skills training is learned by participating in activities during the school day and in after-school activities. Children learn to interact with peers and teachers in ways that are essential for personal development. Many children, especially those from troubled families, need to learn basic skills for becoming adequately socialized, productive adults such as:

- how to share feelings;
- how to get their needs met appropriately;
- how to ask when they need help;
- how to delay gratification;
- how to separate feelings from actions;
- how to take responsibility for their own actions;
- how to make appropriate choices and decisions;
- how to trust;
- importance of dependability, reliability, and responsibility; and
- importance of treating others with respect and consideration.

Preparation for adulthood and parenthood

Older children and adolescents need basic knowledge in these areas:

- normal sexuality;
- child development;

- parenting skills; and
- life management skills.

Self-Protection Training

Children and adolescents need to know how to identify risks and take protective steps in these circumstances:

- what to do if there is abuse, neglect or family violence in their family;
- what to do if there is alcohol or drug abuse in their family;
- how to handle being offered alcohol or drugs;
- how to handle their sexuality and pressure for sexual relations; and,
- how to identify risk-posing individuals.

After School Programs

These programs provide positive socialization experiences, appropriate role models, and a place to belong through:

- sports and organized activities;
- peer socialization activities;
- healthy relationships with adults; and
- academic mentoring.

Support for Adolescent Parents and Children

Young parents need support in order to finish school such as:

- inclusion of adolescent parents in mainstream education;
- parenting skills education;
- child care for young children of adolescent parents;
- referrals for assistance if they feel they are at risk as abusers;
- health and mental health assessments for parent(s) and children; and
- assistance with accessing health, mental health, and social services.

Referral Sources for Teens

Resource and referral information should also be available to teens regarding:

- sexual assault (including date rape);
- domestic violence (including dating violence); and
- parental stress and support lines (for teen parents).

Joint School–Community Programs

Joint school community programs may include:

- school-based health, mental health, community agencies and organizations;
- staff training regarding Children's Protective Services and community resources; and,
- joint school-community parent education programs on discipline, early childhood growth and development, adolescent problems, alcohol and drug addiction, and family violence.

Individual Action

Individual teachers and school personnel should:

- know how to identify and report child abuse and neglect;
- know how to recognize that low grades, cheating, behavior problems, withdrawal and other behaviors may signify problems in the home, and receive training on how to deal with these students;
- network with Foster Youth Services in their school district to obtain information and assistance on issues regarding identified Foster Youth enrolled within that district school site;
- encourage and invite the social worker assigned to an identified foster youth to attend conferences, back-to-school night and meetings when necessary; and
- obtain information on the resilience literature and understand the significance of being a mentor and role model for children to enable them to develop resilience in the face of troubled circumstances.

Services for Children in Foster Care

The following types of coordination and services are needed to ensure consistent education for children in foster care:

- computerized data system to record the child's school grade and course completion status, immunization records, and health history easily retrievable and transferable to all schools;
- school counseling to provide support and educational planning; and,
- access to funds to assist foster high school youth to submit applications to colleges or vocational schools.

Staff Training for Reporting and for Detecting Signs of Abuse and Neglect

School personnel play a critical role in the early detection of child abuse and neglect. School personnel should not hesitate to report suspicious injuries or behavior. Investigation of suspected abuse by child protective agencies may save a child from repeated injuries. The duty of school personnel is to report, not investigate. Several categories of school personnel are mandated reporters:

- teachers;
- teachers aides;
- instructional aides;
- teachers assistants;
- school administrators;
- custodians;
- child care workers; and
- all nurses are mandated including school nurses.

All school personnel must attend training on how to identify child abuse and neglect and how to make verbal and written child abuse and neglect reports. Regular updates and reminders about mandatory reporting should also be provided. Instructors providing this training should receive ongoing professional development.

Teachers and School Personnel as Perpetrators

Sadly, teachers and school personnel have also been identified as perpetrators of sexual abuse, physical assault, or verbally threatening behavior. In these circumstances, perpetrators must be reported to the local law enforcement agency. Protocols should be established and training provided to facilitate appropriate handling of these cases to ensure that the rights of all parties (victims and alleged perpetrators) are protected.

Resources

The Role of Educators in the Prevention and Treatment of Child Abuse and Neglect, The User Manual Series. Published by the U.S. Department of Health and Human Services, Administration for Children and Families, Washington, D.C., 1987

Child Abuse Prevention Handbook, Crime and Violence Prevention Center, Office of the Attorney General, California Department of Justice

Media Campaigns

Marilyn Strachan Peterson, M.S.W., M.P.A.

A well-planned public education campaign is an important tool for shaping public values in order to change social norms, individual attitudes, behaviors, and public policy. The best examples in recent years are the social reform movements against drunk driving—MADD (Mothers Against Drunk Driving); the anti-smoking campaign; teen pregnancy prevention; and, the well-known "cracked egg" commercial educating the public on the hazards of drug abuse.

Successful Approaches

The MADD organization employs three key strategies—public education through a media campaign, public speaking to community groups, and increasing criminal and civil penalties, including revocation of drivers' licenses. The media campaign includes public service announcements on television and radio, and large ads in newspapers and magazines. Public speaking focuses on social and civic groups, and high schools.

The anti-smoking campaign relies largely on various media strategies, including television and radio public service announcements, and newspapers ads visualizing the harmful effects of smoking on lungs; billboards publishing research findings on the effects of tobacco; articles in popular magazines; lawsuits against cigarette manufacturers; printed warnings on cigarette packages; and, increasing taxes on cigarettes to make the habit more expensive.

The anti-drug abuse media campaign features the well-done "cracked egg" commercial broadcast on television. At the local level, law enforcement officers implement the Drug Abuse Resistance Education (DARE) campaign in the public schools by sending officers to give presentations to school children.

The teen pregnancy prevention campaign has largely focused on television and radio public service announcements on targeted radio stations and television programming periods of heavy viewing.

Campaign Goals

A media campaign typically has five major goals: inform, change attitudes or behaviors, influence public opinion, gain acceptance of ideas, and encourage the target audience to act in support of a position.

Because a well-informed public is a more supportive public, the first goal of public education is to make people aware of a concern and why changes need to be made. Citizens must understand "why" before they can change their attitudes or behavior. Information and a consistent message can help achieve this goal.

According to public relations experts, the key to changing public opinion is to develop a hard-hitting message from the core of the information you wish to communicate (Cutlip, Center & Boom, 1985). The message must be communicated consistently. Most successful political campaigns operate on the philosophy that the public will come to believe a message as truth if repeated over and over again.

Information campaigns can also change public attitudes and opinion. For example, in 1989 the Public Agenda Foundation conducted focus groups of 400 citizens in Alabama. Prior to being given information on the benefits of probation and intermediate sanctions, these citizens were given 23 cases and asked to sentence offenders to probation or prison. In the pretest, 18 of the 23 cases were sentenced to a prison term. After they watched a video highlighting how community corrections programs work, these same citizens gave only four of the 23 cases prison sentences.

For lasting change to occur, the message must motivate the target audience to act. The information must be designed to create this "call for action." For example, after every public presentation, it is important to explain what action(s) the audience can take.

Public opinion will also change if the message is received and endorsed by a community's "opinion leaders." The National Opinion Research Center, located at the University of Chicago, indicates that since 1930, public policy has been altered on a particular issue when approximately 10 to

14 percent of the general public changed their opinion. Often, the majority will not act on information unless selected groups or individuals—acting as role models—have already endorsed it. Media education planners must learn who the community's opinion leaders are and aim their public education campaign at these individuals and groups.

Campaign Strategies

Typical public education media campaigns involve three basic strategies—information, advocacy and community relations.

Informational strategies

- Educational materials, e.g. handouts, brochures, fact sheets;
- Posters in laundromats and common public areas;
- Press releases sent to newspapers, radio and television stations;
- Public Service Announcements (PSAs) on television and radio;
- Speakers bureau comprised of volunteers and staff to provide information and build partnerships with community groups and opinion leaders;
- Large one-page newspaper ads promoting informational or behavioral change messages;
- Articles published in trade and consumer publications, Op-Ed articles in local newspapers, or articles in popular magazines and distribution of the reprints;
- Bus signs, bus stop signs, billboards, bumper stickers are messengers moving throughout a community. "Break the Silence on Domestic Violence" is a 1999 slogan moving throughout California communities on city buses sending a message of change.

Advocacy Strategies

Advocacy means organized action to achieve the establishment of new laws or regulations; adoption, modification or elimination of a policy; or, establishing new funding streams to support programs and services.

Advocacy involves four basic strategies:

- Develop a position paper describing the problem or need to be addressed, the proposed action or program to solve the problem, the costs involved and a list of potential supporters or opponents.

- Take the position paper to key stakeholders, associations, and interest groups for discussion and a requests for support.
- Meet with newspaper editorial boards requesting that an editorial be written in support of the issue.
- Collaborate with state and local agencies to develop a "state agency colleague" to help shape public policy at both the state and local, sometimes national levels.

Community Relations Strategies

"Never doubt that a small group of thoughtful citizens can change the world: indeed it is the only thing that ever has."—*Margaret Meade, sociologist*

Community relations are important to establish communication and coordination between groups, to build support or break down barriers between an organization and the community, to build community partnerships and to advocate for a particular issue.

Some of the ways that positive community relations can be developed include the following:

- Meet with agency executive staff or organization boards;
- Offer and provide training;
- Join the organization—an action that communicates a powerful message of support for the organization's work;
- Participate in local events, such as civic meetings and agency fairs;
- Hold open houses to showcase the organization; and,
- Sponsor community education classes for special groups.

All of these actions help build powerful links and partnerships between organizations and individuals in the community.

Successful Elements of a Media Campaign

The media can be a powerful ally for any organization, however, it is important to understand how the media works. According to DeJong and Winsten's (1998) research, a successful public service campaign embodies the following principles:

- a long-term commitment;
- clear objectives and methods designed to meet the objectives;

- knowing the audience—message testing helps ensure that the right messages are reaching the right audiences at the right time and in the right way;

- careful selection of the media outlets to be used in the campaign;

- evaluation to monitor the progress of the campaign and to assess its impact; and,

- approaching the media with newsworthy events.

Homework and practice are needed to understand which events local media consider newsworthy; and, what is newsworthy in a small town may not interest a large city newspaper or television station. Typically, the media is interested in individual case histories (rather than generalities), ways of saving taxpayers money and protecting public safety.

Responding to Media Calls During the Campaign

Program administrators must take responsibility to ensure that reporters have all the information they need to write an accurate story. General guidelines are to:

- Learn the reporter's name and identify the purpose of the story;

- Inquire about the audience—the type of people who will read or listen to the program—and direct your message at them;

- Anticipate issues likely to be asked about ahead of time and practice your response so the reporter's questions won't catch you off guard;

- Be articulate and concise about how the issue either has an adverse impact upon people or will have a positive impact upon people's lives;

- Be up-to-date on statistics, current events and news which relate to the subject and would be interesting to the reporter;

- Let the reporter know how to reach you if additional information is needed;

- Do not ask to read the reporter's copy or request changes before publication;

- If the story seriously misrepresents the facts, contact the publication's editor and ask for a correction;

- Disregard minor slips in an otherwise accurate story;

- Respond promptly to reporters because, like you, they have deadlines; and

- Develop an ongoing media relations program; when a crisis occurs, it may be too late to try to educate the media.

Systematic Approach, Organization and Commitment

No organization will achieve their goals through an occasional speaking engagement or by distributing a brochure. It takes an organized effort using proven strategies. Public education needs to be given a high priority in order to convince the public and policymakers of the benefits of any program, service or community need.

References

Cutlip, Scott M., Allen H. Center, and Glenn M. Boom. 1985. *Effective Public Relations.* Englewood Cliffs, New Jersey: Prentice Hall.

DeJong, William and Winsten, Jay A. 1998. *The Media and the Message: Lessons Learned From Past Public Service Campaigns.* Washington, D.C: National Campaign to Prevent Teen Pregnancy.

Hill and Knowlton. 1975. *Critical Issues in Public, Relations.* Englewood Cliffs, New Jersey: Prentice Hall.

Huskey, Bobbie, February 1987. *Public Relations: Beyond Marketing.* Englewood Cliffs, New Jersey: Prentice Hall.

Huskey, Bobbie, and Roy Wiley. 1992. *Media Relations Manual.* Chicago: International Association of Residential and Community Alternatives.

PART 17

Reimbursement for Services

Marilyn Strachan Peterson, M.S.W., M.P.A., Kathleen A. Shanel-Hogan, D.D.S., M.A., and Michael Siegel, J.D.

Medical and psychological services for abused and neglected children have sources for reimbursement. Local and state funding streams can be identified and accessed for the development of specialized services and teams.

Contracts for Services

Medical Evidentiary Examinations

Penal Code 13823.95 states that costs for sexual assault and child sexual abuse evidentiary examinations are the responsibility of law enforcement agencies. This section of the penal code states that no costs incurred by a qualified health care professional, hospital, or other emergency medical facility for the examination of the victim of a sexual assault, as described in the protocol developed pursuant to Section 13823.5, when the examination is performed, pursuant to Sections 13823.5 and 13823.7, for the purposes of gathering evidence for possible prosecution, shall be charged directly or indirectly to the victim of the assault. These costs shall be treated as local costs and charged to the local governmental agency in whose jurisdiction the alleged offense was committed. Bills for these costs shall be submitted to the law enforcement agency in the jurisdiction in which the alleged offense was committed which requests the examination. The law enforcement agency in the jurisdiction in which the alleged offense was committed which requests the examination has the option of determining whether or not the examination will be performed in the office of a physician or surgeon. If the patient does not consent to evidence collection, the cost of the examination is the responsibility of the patient.

Several California hospitals contract with local law enforcement agencies or, in some cases, the District Attorney's Office to pay for the cost of medical evidentiary examinations. The underlying concept is that the criminal justice system is paying for the collection of evidence and interpretation of forensic medical findings. In addition to law enforcement agencies, some county departments of social services (child protective services' division) contract to pay for evidentiary examinations. They are willing to contract for services because not all cases meet the criteria for law enforcement investigation and authorization for examinations. The cases can still meet the criteria for child protective services' investigation and supporting forensic medical information may be needed for the Juvenile Court in order to sustain a petition for a child to be made a dependent of the Court.

Evidentiary Examinations Versus Medical Treatment

Law enforcement and child protective service agencies are not responsible for the costs of medical treatment. To make this distinction clear, some hospitals are developing profiles for evidentiary examinations for neglect, failure-to-thrive, sexual and physical abuse examinations to distinguish between the forensic medical aspects of the examination for documentation of abuse or neglect, and medical treatment.

The profile for a child sexual abuse examination is relatively simple to establish because the procedures are not diagnostic of medical conditions with the exception of testing for pregnancy and sexually transmitted disease. Since these conditions are diagnostic of sexual abuse in children, the testing costs are part of the evidentiary examination. Prophylaxis for sexually transmitted disease is factored into the examination charge at some hospitals for public health reasons and because of poor follow-up on the part of patients. (For adults and sexually active adolescents, testing for pregnancy and sexually transmitted disease is not part of the required state protocol for evidentiary examinations because the results are not considered diagnostic of sexual assault).

Diagnostic examinations for child physical abuse including Shaken Baby Syndrome and neglect (especially failure-to-thrive) are more extensive and costly. Some hospitals are moving toward distinguishing the medical evaluation of the child and a separate fee for the forensic evaluation of the diagnostic findings. Under this model, the medical diagnostic testing and treatment would be charged to the patient's natural sponsor code (private or public insurance) and the forensic evaluation fee would be charged to criminal and juvenile justice investigative agencies.

Sources for Fee for Service Reimbursements

Crime Victim Compensation

Victims of child physical and sexual abuse are eligible for $70,000 for out-of-pocket expenses for treatment of injuries resulting from the crime, rehabilitation and counseling expenses. The crime must be reported to law enforcement or child protective services. The source of funding for the Victim Compensation Fund is fines and penalties levied against convicted offenders, e.g. felonies and misdemeanors and includes financial crimes.

Applications for victims under 18 years of age at the time of the crime should be filed with the State Victims of Crime Program before their 19th birthday if possible. If filed prior to age 18, applications should be signed by the minor's parent, legal guardian or county social worker. Applications filed beyond one year of the crime or beyond the victim's 19th birthday may be accepted in certain circumstances for good cause.

To obtain reimbursement, an application must be submitted to the State Victims of Crime Program ("VOC") which is under the State Victim Compensation and Government Claims Board. Applications can be filed directly with the Program (call 1-800-777-9229) or through either a local county victim/witness assistance program or a private attorney. (Call 1-800-VICTIMS at the Crime Victims Resource Center for the telephone number of your local victim/witness assistance office.) Attorney representatives are paid by the Victims of Crime Program a fee equal to 10% of the approved award up to a maximum of $500, and these fees are not deducted from the claimant's award. Gov. Code Sec. 13965(d) and (e).

Documentation that a crime occurred is needed to support the application. Only one of the following items is required: a police report, a child protective services report, a medical report, or documentation of prosecution of the case. Prosecution is not required to obtain reimbursement for expenses related to the crime because many variables affect whether or not prosecution occurs.

In addition to medical expenses, the Victims of Crime Program pays for crime-related mental health benefits for the victim, siblings, and non-offending parents as shown below:

Child Victim	$10,000	
Child Victim's Siblings/ Grand Parents	$3,000	(each)
Primary Caregiver	$10,000	(non offending parent)
Primary Caregiver and Step-parent	$10,000	(split)
Foster and Adoptive Parents	$3,000	

The Victims of Crime Program is the "payer of last resort"; and, other sources of reimbursement such as health or disability insurance must be used first. Medi-Cal would be considered the primary payer for medical costs for those patients eligible for Medi-Cal benefits at a facility or program which accepts Medi-Cal. Further discussions are being held to distinguish the "payer of last resort" with some advocates asserting that 'perpetrator dollars" should be used before "taxpayer dollars".

Child Health, Disability and Prevention (CHDP) for Foster Children

The CHDP Program provides medical and dental health check-ups for infants, children and youth through age 20 who have full scope Medi-Cal. Infants and toddlers receive well-baby care and immunizations; school-age children (ages 4-12) receive health check-ups and immunizations; and teenagers and young adults (ages 13-20) receive health check-ups.

CHDP provides growth and development checks; all immunizations needed; dental, vision, and hearing screening; nutrition check-up; health and tobacco education; and tests for anemia, blood lead, urine, TB, and others as needed. WIC referrals are made for children to age 5.

Children removed from their homes and made dependents of the court are eligible to receive a CHDP examination after their initial removal and after each change in placement. Model programs are developing in which physicians are being paired with public health nurses to ensure provision of the initial comprehensive examination and all indicated follow-up medical care.

Early Periodic Screening, Diagnosis and Treatment (EPSDT): Mental Health Treatment

The purpose of EPSDT funding is to:

- provide screening services to identify defects, conditions, and illnesses; and

- provide diagnostic and treatment services "to correct or ameliorate" defects and physical and mental illnesses and conditions discovered by the screening services, whether or not such services are covered under the State plan.

Case management services which assist EPSDT-eligible individual to gain access to needed medical, social, educational, and other services are also covered. Fee-for-service EPSDT case management services may be provided by a child protection agency, other agency or entity serving children, or by an individual provider whom the Department finds qualified by education, training, or experience to provide EPSDT case management services.

Full service Medi-Cal eligible (also called non-restricted Medi-Cal) children and youth ages 0-21 and their families are entitled by federal mandate receive EPSDT benefits. Services provided under EPSDT that are not available to all Medi-Cal beneficiaries are called "EPSDT Supplemental Services". Any individual under the age 21 with a non-restricted Medi-Cal card may receive EPSDT Supplemental Services which are defined as any medical/dental service requested for a person under 21 years of age which exceeds the scope of benefits available for the general Medi-Cal population. These are services which correct or ameliorate defects or physical and mental illnesses or conditions discovered by the screening services.

Examples of covered services include case management evaluation and services, home nursing services, mental health evaluation and services, occupational therapy evaluation and services, pharmacy, physical therapy evaluation and services, and speech therapy evaluation and services.

These funds are administered locally by county departments of mental health in California. Model programs for children placed in foster care are pursuing this funding stream as a source of mental health treatment of psychological, developmental, and behavioral problems.

Healthy Families Insurance

Healthy Families Program provides comprehensive health, dental, and vision services for children ages 1 through 18 and their families whose family income is too high for no-cost Medi-cal. There is a low monthly family contribution for the plan under $10 per month. Children made dependents of the court placed with relatives or children placed in foster care may be eligible for this plan. A caretaker relative or foster parent applying for the child(ren) use the child's income and the child must live in the same household. One of many reasons to examine this plan, if the family is eligible, is the mental health benefits. Eligibility criteria for mental health benefits include having been a victim of child abuse and neglect, witnessing domestic violence, and family dysfunction caused by alcohol and substance abuse. This program is administered by the State of California at 1-800-880-5305.

Medi-Cal

Medi-Cal provides comprehensive health, dental, and vision benefits for children up to age 19. It also covers pregnancy related services for women, which include: family planning, prenatal care, labor and delivery and post-partum care. Questions about Medi-Cal can be answered by calling 1-888-747-1222.

California Medi-Cal Dental Program (Denti-Cal)

Children removed from their homes for reasons of abuse and neglect are often found to have moderate to severe dental problems. Once made dependents of the court, they are made Medi-Cal fee-for-service and this applies equally to Denti-Cal. If the child has a previous dentist of record, consider contacting the dental office to determine if they participate in the Denti-Cal fee-for-service program. County departments of social services and foster parents, acting as the beneficiary's representative, can identify participating dentists in the fee-for-service Denti-Cal program and receive referrals by calling the Beneficiary Services toll-free number (800) 322-6384. The toll-free lines are available from 8:00 a.m. to 5:00 p.m. Monday through Friday. When calling, the beneficiary representative must have the recipient's name and social security number.

Additional information that can be requested from the Beneficiary toll-free telephone operators include: assistance with scheduling and rescheduling Regional Screening appointments, information about share-of-cost and copayment requirements of Denti-Cal, general inquiries, complaints and grievances, and information about denied, modified or deferred treatment authorization requests (TARs).

Examples of covered dental services for children include: examinations, emergency palliative treatment, dental sealants, prophy and scaling cleanings, x-rays, oral surgery (extractions, biopsies, infection drainage, tumor removal, fractures, dislocations), nitrous oxide, general anesthesia, root canals, pulpotomies, silver amalgam and composite restorations, stainless steel and laboratory processed crowns, space maintainers, orthodontics for handicapping malocclusion and cleft palate services.

Resources

Governor's Office of Criminal Justice Planning
Sacramento, California
http://www.ocjp.ca.gov

State Victims of Crime Program
Sacramento, California
http://www.boc.cahwnet.gov/Victims.htm

State Department of Health Services
Sacramento, California
http://www.dhs.ca.gov

State Department of Mental Health
Sacramento, California
http://www.dmh.cahwnet.gov

Training and Technology Resources for Physicians and Nurses

Marilyn Strachan Peterson, M.S.W., M.P.A.

State Funded Medical Training Centers

California Medical Training Center

The California Training Center has been established by state law (Penal Code Section 13823.93) to provide training for physicians and nurses on how to perform evidential examinations for child abuse and neglect, domestic violence, sexual assault, and elder and dependent adult abuse. Training is also provided to criminal justice and investigative social services personnel on the interpretation of medical findings for use in case investigations, prosecution, and for others involved in the evaluation of forensic evidence. The Center is funded by the Governor's Office of Criminal Justice Planning.

The purpose of the training centers is to improve California's health care system response to victims by:

- increasing the knowledge and skills of physicians and nurses;

- increasing the quality of medical-legal examinations through protocols and training;

- improving the responsiveness of health care providers and quality of intervention;

- improving the interface with law enforcement and social service agencies; and,

- increasing victim access to qualified medical personnel.

The legislative mandate is to:

- develop and implement standardized medical curriculum and training programs;

- develop a telecommunication system for training and consultation;

- develop guidelines for reporting and management of child abuse, domestic violence, and elder abuse;

- provide training for criminal justice and social service investigative personnel on medical examination findings;

- promote the interdisciplinary approach in the assessment and management of cases; and,

- provide training in the dynamics of victimization.

Telemedicine and Teleconferencing for All Disciplines

Telemedicine enables healthcare providers to obtain timely consultations with leading experts. The purpose of telemedicine is to improve the quality of healthcare and eliminate access barriers such as geography, travel time, and cost of specialists. This technology can fill the gaps in access to care and provide support to physicians and nurses in rural communities. Telemedicine and telecourses are evolving rapidly with technology. Various types and resources are listed below:

- **POTS (Plain Old Telephone System) and POMS (Plain Old Mail System)**
  Telemedicine began with POTS and POMS. Case consultation began through telephone consultation and using the mail system to send photographs of injuries to experts at other locations for assistance in interpretation and case management.

- **Videoconsultation: Real Time and Store and Forward**
  With the advent of technology, e.g. computers, audio-visual equipment, high-speed telephone lines and fiberoptics, videoconsultation has emerged in localities where individuals have an interest in technology and there is adequate technical support.

- **Real Time Consultation**

  The term "real time" refers to live, clinician to clinician consultation most often between a tertiary hospital and an outlying clinic in a rural area. The rural clinician may need back-up in a particular subspecialty, for example, obstetrics or dermatology. A clinic is scheduled for certain times and days of the week and the tertiary hospital physician is scheduled to consult with the rural physician at that time. Videocameras are permanently set up and the tertiary clinician monitors the examination and observes the findings at the same time as the rural physician.

- **Store and Forward Consultation**

  The term "Store and Forward" means to photograph or videotape the examination; to save or "store" the videotape or photograph; and, to forward it to a specialist or expert at a tertiary center for consultation. Software exists to transmit photographic and videotaped images over telephone lines. Hardware requirements include a computer and monitor at both sites. Confidentiality and the transmission of medical records have been addressed in the development of this software.

Store and Forward has been found to be most practical in the field of forensic medicine to evaluate child abuse and sexual assault cases. First, the timing of forensic exams is often unpredictable and given the low volume of cases in rural areas the "scheduled clinic" approach is more difficult to implement. Second, the time demands are high upon the few forensic medical experts in child abuse and sexual assault. A Store and Forward system makes it easier to view transmitted photographs and videotapes on a time schedule that works for the forensic expert.

Second Opinion is a telemedicine software which allows practitioners to capture and store images and then transmit them from one site to another within a secure environment. The software is used on a standard computer and runs over telephone lines for direct modem connection or via email. Images may be input via scanned photographs or slides, video frames, clips, or digital camera and are organized in patient folders keeping all images associated with a particular patient together. Practitioners have the ability to measure, draw, annotate, document, and exchange this information with other users of the software. With this software, practitioners have the ability to store images and transmit them to a colleague for an assessment of the findings. It can also be used as a vehicle for periodic peer review sessions.

Second Opinion Software and Colposcopes for Assistance in Interpreting Findings

Two California physicians (Astrid Heger, M.D. and Bruce Woodling, M.D.) pioneered the concept of using a colposcope (typically found in gynecologic and primary care clinics) to assist in the evaluation of child sexual abuse cases. The colposcope began to be used in the early 1980s as a means to detect subtle signs of child sexual abuse. The introduction of the colposcope established the concept of a nonacute sexual abuse examination. This was an important development for children because they are more likely to delay disclosure of sexual abuse than to report it immediately.

The colposcope established a new standard of practice by enabling pediatric examiners to detect subtle injury and/or changes in the genital or rectal area. Its use facilitated the development of standards for evaluating normal and abnormal findings caused by sexual abuse. It is used for both acute and nonacute child sexual abuse forensic examinations. Beginning in the late 1990s, the colposcope began to be used for adult/adolescent sexual assault forensic medical examinations.

The colposcope has magnification capabilities that can magnify images from 4 to 30x power. A 35mm camera was first added followed by video cameras to capture and preserve the images of findings through photographs and videotape.

This innovation was followed by linking the colposcope's 35mm camera or video camera to the Second Opinion software program. This software program was developed in consultation with Dr. Heger and a software development company to link health practitioners in rural areas to experts in urban areas who see a high volume of cases. The colposcope enables the examiners to focus on an area of a body, magnify the view, and press one of two buttons to capture an image. One button actives a video camera link that creates a still image from live video of the physician's view through the colposcope. The other button activates a 35mm camera that takes a picture of the physician's view through the colposcope. The video images are transferred into the Second Opinion system through a capture board, a personal computer "card" that captures the video and transforms it into a computer-based image file. The 35mm pictures are turned into digital images using a scanner.

Interactive Video Consultation

Video consultation is generally focused on one or more case studies and is handled through point-to-point computer transmissions. This type of consultation is held around a computer monitor and 4-6 professionals (or more depending upon the size of the monitor or screen) can be accommodated at each site. Point-to-point refers to a connection between a tertiary hospital and one or more outlying areas. A simultaneous telephone connection on a speaker phone is set up and visual images are transmitted on the computer monitor.

Telecourses or Distance Learning through Satellite Transmissions

These terms are used to refer to courses transmitted simultaneously to different sites to a live audience. A tertiary center broadcasts the course to pre-determined sites. Large broadcast centers in California include the California State University system which can broadcast to 100 state university and community colleges; POST (Peace Officer Standards and Training) which can broadcast to all law enforcement agencies and district attorney's offices in California; and, Kaiser Permanente which can broadcast to its network of hospitals.

CD ROM Courses

Reference materials and courses are now being developed on CD ROMs. For example, child sexual abuse medical findings and their interpretation can be obtained on a CD ROM.

Internet

Courses and reference materials are offered through various internet sites and links. Use the various search engines.

Telemedicine Resources

American Telemedicine Association
http://www.atmeda.org

Telemedicine and TeleHealth Networks
http://www.med.umich.edu/telemedicine/Symposium/suleiman

Telemedicine Information Exchange
http://tie.telemed.org

Telemedicine Today
http://www.telemedtoday.com

Resources

California Medical Protocol for Examination of Sexual Assault and Child Sexual Abuse Victims. Published by the Governor's Office of Criminal Justice Planning, 1130 K Street, Sacramento, CA 95814.
http://www.ocjp.ca.gov

California Medical Training Center at UC Davis
http://web.ucdmc.ucdavis.edu/medtrng

California Medical Training Center (CMTC): Developing Forensic Medical Examiner Programs, June 2002 issue. Published by the California District Attorneys Association.
http://www.cdaa.org

Data Resources

Geoffrey M. Hash, J.D.

Data is a necessary tool in planning the implementation, expansion, or improvement of any program. In the past, data systems have often been isolated and difficult to access. When it was accessible, it was often difficult to interpret. The development of the Internet and the World Wide Web has made dramatic changes in our ability to access information. Today, there is a rich supply of data, reports and articles surrounding nearly any topic. This availability does not necessarily make the task of tracking down relevant data any easier. Countless hours can be spent sorting through search engines and clearinghouses for data needed to finish research projects or grant proposals. Information about the following data information systems has been provided to facilitate and simplify these searches.

A brief description of each agency is provided along with the web site address and any other contact information that is available. There are seven groupings of sources that should help pinpoint your search. These groupings are: *Social Services Data, Health Services Data, Criminal Justice Data, Population/Demographic Data, Legal Sites, General Sites, and Clearinghouse Sites*. While all of the web sites listed are fairly user-friendly, some are more concise than others. It should be noted that there are thousands of web sites dealing with child abuse and neglect issues. This list is not an exhaustive listing of this type of site. Rather, it is a listing of what seems to be the most complete, concise, and user-friendly sites available at the time of this writing.

Social Services Data

California Department of Social Services: Data Analysis and Publications Branch

The California Department of Social Services has assigned the Data Analysis and Publications Branch with the responsibility of providing program information that ensures funding and supports management decision making. On the Data Analysis and Publication Branch's web site, a variety of raw data as well as final reports on issues including foster care, public assistance, elder and dependent adult abuse, child abuse, and adoptions can be found. The quickest way to conduct a search is by using the on-line Product Catalog.

- http://www.dss.cahwnet.gov/isb/

- California Department of Social Services
  744 P Street
  Sacramento, California
  95814
  (916) 657-3667

Health Services Data

California Department of Health Services: Center for Health Statistics

The California Department of Health Services has an extensive collection of data and reports available via several web-sites. One of the most comprehensive sites, Office of Health Information and Research, has direct links to Vital Statistics Data Tables for the state as well as individual counties. In addition, statewide and county population data figures broken down by ethnicity, age, and sex can be found.

- http://www.dhs.ca.gov/hisp/chs/OHIR/ohirindex.htm (Office of Health Information and Research)

- http://www.dhs.ca.gov/hisp/index.htm (Health Information and Strategic Planning Home Page)

- **General Information** (916) 445-4171 /
  Vital Statistics (916) 445-6355

California Department of Health Services: Division of Communicable Disease Control

Working in cooperation with local, national, and international health officials, healthcare providers and the public, the Division of Communicable Disease Control is responsible for performing a variety of research, programming and educational functions. Several different branches and sections make up the DCDC. These include the Sexually Transmitted Disease Control Branch, Immunization Branch, Office of Health Communication and Education, Tuberculosis Control Branch, and the Refugee Health Section. From the Division of Communicable Disease Control home page, information, reports, and data specific to the above-mentioned areas can be found. The home page shows Disease Tables broken down by year and type of disease.

- http://www.dhs.ca.gov/ps/dcdc/dcdcindex.htm

- California Department of Health Services
  Division of Communicable Disease Control
  PO Box 942732 MS-486
  Sacramento, CA 94234-7320
  Voice (916) 327-6989
  Fax (916) 324-0050

California Department of Health Services: Sexually Transmitted Disease Control Branch

In an effort to define high-risk populations, assess STD trends, monitor prevalence of select STDs, and measure health impact and cost, the STD Control Branch provides and maintains a statewide surveillance system. On this website, STD reports containing detailed statistical analysis covering many geographic and demographic areas can be found.

- http://www.dhs.ca.gov/ps/dcdc/html/stdindex.htm

- California Department of Health Services
  Division of Communicable Disease Control
  PO Box 942732 MS-486
  Sacramento, CA 94234-7320
  (916) 322-2087 (STD Surveillance and Data Unit–General Inquiries)
  (916) 323-1458
  (916) 324-3187

California Department of Health Services: Office of AIDS

The Office of Aids Home Page contains many valuable resources including AIDS Case Statistics, AIDS Death Statistics, information on current legislation, and forms. In addition, annual reports detailing how AIDS has impacted specific racial/ethnic groups in California can be found. Within these reports, an extensive range of data including modes of exposure, rates of exposure specific to ethnicity/racial group, and rates of exposure by racial/ethnic groups and age is shown.

- http://www.dhs.ca.gov/ps/ooa/ooaindex.htm

- Office of AIDS
  611 North 7th Street
  PO Box 942732
  Sacramento, CA 94234-7320
  (916) 445-0553

Centers for Disease Control: National Center for Health Statistics

This site has direct links to the following Surveys and Data Collection Systems: The Research Data Center, National Vital Statistics System, National Health and Nutrition Examination Survey, National Health Care Survey, National Health Interview Survey, National Immunization Survey, National Survey of Family Growth, The State and Local Area Integrated Telephone Survey, and the Data Warehouse (an on-line data archival system).

- http://www.cdc.gov/nchs

- National Center for Health Statistics
  Division of Data Services
  Hyattsville, MD
  20782-2003
  (301) 458-4636

Centers for Disease Control: Data Services

The Centers for Disease Control Data and Statistics web site is primarily a clearinghouse for other sites containing data and statistics on a wide range of health issues. However, there are also links to several reports on this site.

- http://www.cdc.gov/scientific.htm

- Centers for Disease Control
  Division of Data Services
  Hyattsville, MD
  20782-2003
  (301) 458-4636

Criminal Justice Data

California Department of Justice: Criminal Justice Statistics Center

The California Attorney General has the responsibility of collecting, analyzing, and reporting data, which provide valid measures of crime and the criminal justice process. As a result, this site contains more than 3,400 statistical tables, 59 reports, 26 publications, links to federal, state, and local agency statistics, links to other criminal statistic services, and links to Incident Based Reporting databases. On this site, Uniform Crime Reports for homicide, forcible rape, juvenile felony crime arrests, violent crimes committed against senior citizens, domestic violence, crime and delinquency, and hate crimes can be found. In addition, the CJSC maintains 15 databases covering many areas of criminal justice. A brief description of each database, along with a link to the corresponding reports, is available at this site. Finally, non-published information can be accessed through the Special Request Office.

- http://caag.state.ca.us/cjsc/index.htm
  (Criminal Justice Statistics Center)

- http://caag.state.ca.us/
  (California Attorney General's Home Page)

- California Department of Justice
  Criminal Justice Statistics Center
  Attn: **Special Requests Unit**
  P. O. Box 903427
  Sacramento, CA 94203-4270
  Telephone: (916) 227-3509
  Fax: (916) 227-0427

California Department of Justice: Crime and Violence Prevention Center

The Crime and Violence Prevention Center provides a wide range of prevention information, technical assistance, and resources in the areas of child abuse, family violence, domestic violence, elder abuse, sexual assault, and battered women.

- http://caag.state.ca.us/cvpc/index.html

- California Attorney General's Office
  Crime and Violence Prevention Center
  P.O. Box 944255
  Sacramento, CA 94244-2550
  (916) 445-9555

Governor's Office of Criminal Justice Planning

While there is not a large collection of data available for public use at the OCJP web site, there are several reports available listing various programs administered by the Office of Criminal Justice Planning. There are many programs in the areas of child abuse, sexual assault, and elder abuse. In addition, there are reports listing community resources that are available. The Domestic Violence Resource Exchange Agency List is one such report and is located at http://www.ocjp.ca.gov/brochures.htm.

- http://www.ocjp.ca.gov/

- Governor's Office of Criminal Justice Planning
  1130 K Street
  Sacramento, California 95814
  (916) 324-9100

U.S. Department of Justice: Bureau of Justice Statistics

The Bureau of Justice Statistics website contains a very large amount of information in several forms including abstracts, statistical reports, and other publications. From the home page, an extremely wide range of information including reports on homicide trends (by age, circumstance, weapon, region, etc...), crime, drug, and justice facts at a glance, expenditures, and demographic trends in correctional populations can be found. While there is a large amount of information here, there is also a very efficient search engine to help expedite your search. In order to help familiarize yourself with the site, it is recommended to take the tour, which is located at http://www.ojp.usdoj.gov/bjs/tour/intro.htm.

- http://www.ojp.usdoj.gov/bjs/

- U.S. Department of Justice
  Office of Justice Programs
  Bureau of Justice Statistics
  Washington, DC 20331

National Center for Victims of Crime (NCVC)

This site has a limited number of statistical analyses. Links to information on federal legislation and public policy affecting all areas of crime are provided.

- http://www.ncvc.org/index.html

- National Center for Victims of Crime
  2111 Wilson Boulevard, Suite 300
  Arlington, VA 22201
  (703)276-2880 / telephone
  (703)276-2889 / fax

Population/Demographic Data

California Department of Health Services

See full description in Social Service Data section.

- http://www.dhs.ca.gov/hisp/chs/OHIR/populationindex.htm

- **General Information** (916) 445-4171 /
  Vital Statistics (916) 445-6355

California Dept. of Finance: Demographic Research Unit

The Demographic Research Unit of the California Department of Finance is designated as the single official source of demographic data for state planning and budgeting. This site contains detailed demographic information.

338

- http://www.dof.ca.gov/html/Demograp/druhpar.htm

- Department of Finance
  915 L Street
  Sacramento, CA 95814
  (916) 445-3878
  FICALPOP@dof.ca.gov

Government Information Sharing Project

This is a very useful web site providing demographic and economic information in an easy-to-understand interface that nearly anyone can use to access state and federal government information. This web site utilizes an interactive, graphical format that is both concise and consistent. The user will find numerous links to other government web sites. The information provided by this site is gathered from Bureau of Census, Bureau of Economic Analysis, National Center for Education Statistics, and The MESA Group.

- http://govinfo.kerr.orst.edu

Southern California Association of Governments (SCAG)

A list of web sites providing information on population, demographics, and other statistical information. This site includes links to: Association of Bay Area Governments, Bureau of the Census, California Department of Finance (official demographic data), California regional, county, and city information Government Information Sharing Project (demographic, economic, and governmental information organized by county) Guide to Statistical Computing Resources on the Internet (lists resources relevant to statistical computing, including resources pertaining to SAS and SPSS statistical packages)

- http://www.scag.ca.gov/weblink/link18.htm

- http://www.scag.ca.gov

- Southern California Association of Governments
  818 West Seventh Street, 12th Floor
  Los Angeles, CA 90017-3435
  Phone: (213) 236-1800
  Fax: (213) 236-1964

Legal Sites

ABA Center on Children and the Law

The ABA Center on Children and the Law is an excellent resource for child welfare law updates and summaries. It contains information on court improvement, child protection, foster care, adoption, and many useful links to other related sites.

- http://www.abanet.org/child

- 740 15th Street, NW
  Washington, DC 20005-1022

General Sites

The Children's Defense Fund

The Children's Defense Fund web-site provides some very general statistical reporting on child abuse. There is also a very large amount of information available on child welfare issues including current legislation updates, health insurance concerns, childcare, teen tobacco/drug use, and education.

- http://www.childrensdefense.org/index.html

- National Headquarters: Children's Defense Fund
  25 E Street NW
  Washington, DC 20001
  202-628-8787
  cdfinfo@childrensdefense.org

- California Headquarters: Children's Defense Fund
  101 Broadway, Second Floor
  Oakland, CA 94607
  Tel: 510-663-3224

US Department of Health and Human Services: The Administration for Children and Families

This web-site provides a variety of reports and links to other sites that contain information on all issues concerning children and families.

- http://www.acf.dhhs.gov

- Administration for Children and Families
  370 L'Enfant Promenade S.W.
  Washington, DC 20447

US Department of Health and Human Services: The Administration for Children and Families– Children's Bureau

This web site contains direct links to many reports and a large amount of statistical information compiled by the oldest federal agency for children. The most recent federal child maltreatment report, titled *Child Maltreatment 1997: Reports from the States to the National Child Abuse and Neglect Data System* can be found here. In addition, there is information on current legislation, grant/funding availability, and foster care programs.

- http://www.acf.dhhs.gov/programs/cb

Clearinghouses

The American Professional Society on the Abuse of Children (APSAC)

- http://www.apsac.org

The California Welfare Information Clearinghouse

- http://www.c-wic.org

The Child Abuse and Neglect Database Instrument System (CANDIS)

- http://www.musc.edu/cvc/candis.htm

The Child Welfare League of America

- http://www.cwla.org

The Federal Interagency Forum on Child and Family Statistics

- http://childstats.gov/index.htm
- Childstats@ed.gov

The National Black Child Development Institute (NBCDI)

- http://www.nbcdi.org

The National Clearinghouse for Alcohol and Drug Information (NCADI)

- http://www.health.org

The National Clearinghouse on Child Abuse and Neglect Information

- http://www.calib.com/nccanch/index.htm
- National Clearinghouse on Child Abuse and
  Neglect Information
  330 C Street, SW
  Washington, DC 20447
  Phone: (800) 394-3366 / (703) 385-7565
  Fax: (703) 385-3206

The National Criminal Justice Reference Service (NCJRS)

- http://www.ncjrs.org

The National Data Archive on Child Abuse and Neglect

- http://www.ndacan.cornell.edu/#top

The National Indian Child Welfare Association

- http://www.nicwa.org

The National Resource Center on Child Maltreatment

- http://www.gocwi.org/nrccm

The National Resource Center for Community Based Family Resource and Support Programs (FRIENDS)

- http://www.frca.org/friends.htm

The National Resource Center for Foster Care and Permanency Planning

- http://www.guthrie.hunter.cuny

Prevent Child Abuse America

- http://www.preventchildabuse.org

The Welfare Information Network

- http://www.welfareinfo.org
- The Welfare Information Network
  1000 Vermont Avenue, NW, Suite 600
  Washington, DC 20005
  Phone: 202/628-5790
  Fax: 202/628-4206

Importance of Data Collection Systems

Michael Durfee, M.D., Sheila Anderson, M.A. and Brooke Allison, M.A.

The historic focus of professionals working in the field of health and human services is the client. Client assessment, case planning, treatment and services coordination are the consumers of time and attention. Yet, sound planning, decision-making, internal management, and allocation of resources are dependent on generating reliable data. Decisions made by common sense, anecdotal information, experience or protocol can only take the decision-maker to a certain point. These information sources do not compare to the level of confidence that sound data can provide.

Uses of Data

The primary uses for health and human service data are:

- problem identification and description;
- performance or program management;
- program evaluation; and
- cost-effectiveness and/or cost-benefit analysis.

Problem Identification

This means to identify and describe the nature and scope of a problem, to describe it in statistically meaningful ways and to show whether the problem is increasing or decreasing. This can include forecasting whether the problem will increase or decrease due to the presence or absence of certain factors.

Performance or Program Management

Performance management focuses on the organization, departments, processes (e.g. investigations/dispositions), programs, products or services, projects, teams, groups, or individuals. The emphasis is on producing results which are typically measured by a data unit or multiple indices (e.g. number of child abuse reports, number of cases opened for investigation, number of children placed in foster care, number of children returned to their parents).

Typical questions answered include:

- How many clients received services?
- What is the demographic and geographic profile of clients receiving services?
- What services were provided?
- What services are used and needed?
- Who benefits from the services?
- What are the medical, developmental, mental health and dental needs of these children?
- To what extent were these needs met?

Increasingly, funding entities and policy leaders are asking questions about program and service outcomes, effectiveness and efficiency. Above all, the fundamental questions agencies must be able to answer are: Who has benefited and how? What outcomes have been achieved? What are the costs of the program?

Program Evaluation

Program evaluation is designed to assess the performance of a program or impact of a service. Typical questions answered include:

- Did the services and activities have the intended impact;
- Did the services and programs reach the intended target population;
- How can service outcomes be improved;
- What adjustments and refinements to services, training, staffing and other variables are needed to improve the services; and,

- Is the service or program cost-effective (e.g. serves the intended number of clients).

Program evaluations can be conducted internally if on a small scale and intended for a limited audience. Often they are conducted by independent evaluators working in collaboration with the program being evaluated. To be effective, the program staff must commit to the process to ensure sound and reliable data collection. Evaluations conducted by independent evaluators are usually on a higher, more complex scale and involve both descriptive and outcome data. It is important that both providers and evaluators understand that the purpose of evaluation is to ensure sound program development and to assist the provision of quality client services. In the ideal situation, evaluation is the friend of the provider, not its adversary. Evaluation feedback allows for crucial course correction along the program development path. A good working relationship between evaluator and provider requires collaboration and input from the beginning of the process followed by mutual sensitivity to provider and evaluator issues, training and technical assistance.

Cost-Benefit Analysis

The purpose of cost benefit analysis is to determine whether the benefits of the program are equal to or are greater than the costs involved. If the benefits do not measure up to the costs, decisions are often made to either reduce operating costs or to discontinue the program.

Types of Data

- **Descriptive Data**
  At a minimum, data needs to describe the program components and count the clients and services. Data should describe the population served numerically as a whole and by categories such as demographic, geographic, and other classifications. The next gradient of data collection includes counting the number and length of services delivered. For example, the total length of services per family can be obtained if both the number of service units and the average duration of service are known. First estimate or determine statistically, the average duration of a service (e.g. for a home visit, the average stay is 2 hours). Multiply the average duration by the number of visits to determine the hours of service provided for each family. Descriptive data are also employed to detail the

process by which services are delivered and the program administered (e.g. number of planning committee meetings, attendance, and number and type of staff employed for the program).

- **Outcome or Performance Data**
  Outcome data addresses the impact of the services or intervention. Outcome measures can vary from simple to complex. Simple outcome measures include counting the number of children whose immunization records are up-to-date before and after participation in a preventive home visiting program, reduction of the high school drop out rate for students receiving tutoring, and pre-, post-testing of a training program. Examples of complex outcome measures include measuring changes in human behavior or mental health status before and after an intervention or assessing improved performance by staff following training. Complex measures typically require multiple tools or testing instruments in order to capture the range of data necessary to draw conclusions.

- **Surveillance Data**
  There are various types of surveillance data (e.g. health, social services, criminal justice, vital statistics). Surveillance data is used to track various trends either relevant to or affecting the general population.

- **Collaborative Trend Analysis**
  Collaborative trend analysis involves the collection, aggregation, and analysis of the same data from a variety of sources in order to identify trends and patterns.

- **Non-traditional Data**
  There is a trend to include non-traditional data collection to document broader systems change. This evaluation may include broad indicators of changes in communities or target groups such as increased participation in community and school events. The reasons for collecting nontraditional data include the lack of availability of other types of data and the length of time required to obtain relevant data. For example, improved school readiness by children may be a goal of a preventive home visitation program. If, however, the home visitation services are initiated at birth, the necessary data will be unavailable for at least six years. For the short-term, other indicators must be measured in order to assess program performance.

- **Collaborative and Aggregate Data**
  Collaborative and aggregate data collection is used to identify trends. Examples of collaborative data collection include local jurisdictions (e.g. law enforcement, health, social service agencies) reporting to a central registry at the State level to count or measure trends. This type of data collection also occurs at the local level. For example, Los Angeles County Department of Health Services' Child Abuse Prevention Program data system counts, among other things, the number of child abuse reports or evaluations along with basic demographic data from public and private health practitioners countywide. Healthy Start sites in schools report statistical data to both local school districts and the State Department of Education for compilation and analysis.

- **Integrated Data Systems and Trend Analysis**
  Integration of data collection across various systems allows multiple providers to share information regarding the same case. This method can reduce service redundancy and enhance coordinated service delivery. To the extent that data are aggregated within and across systems or combined into a comprehensive system of diverse data from various providers, trend analysis is facilitated. Trend analysis involves presenting client, program, or social variable data over time, optimally over a several years period of time. The longer the span of the data collected, the more reliable the data analysis.

Considerations in Developing Data Systems

Developing a sound data collection system requires careful planning and ongoing monitoring. Considerations for program managers planning a data collection system include:

- **Database Application (software program)**
  Select the appropriate software program. Currently there are two database creation tools used by non-profit and governmental organizations. There are database kits that give the user tools to create database applications. For a discussion of database applications and tips on database design use, refer to the Nonprofit Genie at http://www.genie.org.

- **Type of Data**
  Determine what information is needed for program planners and decision-makers.

- **Quality of Data**
  Devote time and attention to ensure consistent and reliable data collection and data entry. Otherwise, data analysis will be incomplete and inaccurate. Clear definitions and procedures and staff training is critical.

- **Flexibility**
  Adopt a flexible data system that can accommodate changes. A rigid and difficult to modify data collection process may not suit long-term program needs. Over time, and sometimes in response to data and evaluation, programs revise services or targeted clients. As programs change, data systems must be flexible to respond.

- **Access**
  Data must be accessible and easily retrievable. Systems designed to produce only periodic reports may not be sufficient for ongoing feedback and internal management.

- **User Friendly**
  Keep data collection simple and easy. Otherwise it will not be used. Excessive time requirements and a complex data collection system may outweigh its value. It is important to balance the magnitude of data with the ability to manage the system. One pitfall is the "camel syndrome", e.g., a form devised by a committee whose members think they need every piece of data imaginable but will never use it.

- **Staff Training**
  A data collection system is only as reliable as the quality of data entered into it. Training for staff who will collect, enter and manage the data is essential for sound data. Likewise, they must have sufficient time to properly and thoroughly complete data requirements.

Pitfalls to Avoid in Data Collection

- Complex forms with easily misunderstood phrases and requirements, including forms designed to collect information that will never be used;

- Insufficient training or time for program staff to complete data collection requirements, resulting in inaccurate, incomplete, or falsified data; and,

- Inadequate training for staff as to how and why data should be collected, resulting in a lack of commitment to data collection and program evaluation.

Positive Results of Data Collection and Analysis

- Knowledge base upon which to make informed client, program, and policy decisions;

- Information with which to create protocols and set standards for the field;

- Understanding of whether or not a program or strategy "works," and should therefore be replicated, abandoned, or revised;

- Support for making informed funding decisions, or for encouraging funders to support the program;

- Ability to hold a program accountable for accomplishing what it promises; and

- Information with which to evaluate program effectiveness, and analyze a program's cost versus its benefit.

Data collection is costly for health and human service agencies in terms of financial resources for internal staffing costs and/or an outside evaluator. These costs are likely outweighed by the benefits to the program. Solid data leads to increased accountability, identification of trends, funding to solve a problem, and answering the fundamental question "but does it work?"

Resources

Information Management
Informational Resources Management Association
http://www.irma-international.org

Role of the County Health Department

Elliott Schulman, M.D.

The role of the county health department is to ensure public and environmental health. Some health departments operate primary health care clinics. Services and programs are listed below:

Primary Health Care Services

The goal of primary health care services is to provide and implement:

- Primary health care services for medically indigent adults and eligible adults and children;
- Contracts to fund alcohol and drug abuse treatment programs;
- Pharmaceutical and medical supplies to support health and mental health programs;
- Child Health Disability and Prevention (CHDP) Program which funds provision of health assessments and immunizations; and
- Women, Infants, and Children (WIC) Program which provides supplemental food and nutrition education to low income pregnant and breast feeding women, and to parents of children under five years of age.

Environmental Health

The mission of environmental health is to improve, protect, and promote public health and environment to:

- prevent disease and injury;
- prevent air and water pollution;
- reduce environmental harm; and
- ensure proper disposal of hazardous waste.

Maternal and Child Health (MCH)

The goal of the MCH Program is to:

- improve pregnancy outcomes;
- enhance child health and development;
- prevent unintentional injury;
- reduce child abuse and neglect;
- promote positive parenting; and
- reduce infant mortality.

Preventive Health Services

The mission of preventive health services is to provide:

- screening and treatment for STD, TB, Hep B, HIV/AIDS, immunization, preventable disease, and other communicable disease;
- refugee screening; and
- family planning.

Injury Prevention Program

This program is designed to provide education on:

- bicycle safety;
- infant and child car seat program; and
- swimming pool safety.

Communicable Disease Prevention and Control

The role of the county health department is to:

- investigate acute disease reports and outbreaks;

- summarize disease surveillance results;

- coordinate disease prevention and control efforts; and

- respond to disease control concerns of community health care professionals.

Public Health Promotion & Education

The goal of the Public Health Promotion and Education Unit is to assure the optimum health and well being of the community through the provision of epidemiology and disease control services and vital records. Examples include:

- AIDS Education & Prevention Program

- Childhood Lead Poisoning Prevention Program

- Dental Health Program

- Epidemiology & Disease Control

- Integrated Children & Family Services

- Immunization Education Program

- Maternal, Child & Adolescent Health Programs

- Public Health Laboratory

- Public Health Nursing Services

- Public Health Veterinarian

- Senior Health Education Program

- Tobacco Education Program

- Ryan White CARE Act

- Violent Injury Prevention

- Vital Records

Resources

County Health Departments Association
http://www.csac.counties.org

American Public Health Association
http://www.apha.org

California Conference of Local Health Officers (CCHLO)
http://www.medepi.org/cclho/about-us.html

Role of the County Department of Human Assistance

Cheryl Davis

The County Department of Human Assistance (DHA) serves people in need through various programs and services. Working together with local churches, schools, non-profit groups, businesses and other governmental agencies, DHA helps low-income families and individuals move from welfare to work by connecting them to a variety of skill-building, employment and job-support opportunities. Guided by the specific needs of the community, DHA's primary goal is to create and carry out programs and activities that help families and individuals reach their highest potential.

DHA's programs are specifically designed to help low-income families and individuals find workable solutions to daily-living problems as they make the transition from welfare to the workplace. These programs include:

- **CalWORKs** (California Work Opportunity and Responsibility to Kids)
  The blueprint for what is sometimes referred to as "welfare reform", this program helps families find and keep jobs through numerous employment services and activities. It also provides short-term cash assistance to those who qualify, including children being cared for by relatives.

- **Employment Assistance**
  Helps community members find and keep jobs through practical, hands-on activities such as pre-employment training workshops, resume assistance, job referrals, on-the-job training, job fairs and "dress-for-success" seminars, among others.

- **General Assistance**
  Provides short-term cash aid and social services designed to help single people either find work or, if disabled, obtain aid from other sources. Disability Case Management helps disabled recipients apply for Social Security Disability and SSI/SSP benefits.

- **Homeless Programs**
  The Homeless Continuum of Care is made up of programs operated by diverse community-based organizations and the County. Services assist clients with short-term shelter needs, transitional/permanent housing, and counseling that addresses the core issues of unemployment, physical/mental health, substance abuse and domestic violence.

- **JobLink**
  Connects qualified job seekers to employers.

- **MediCal**
  Provides medical and dental coverage to those who meet certain federal/state qualifying criteria.

- **County Medically Indigent Services**
  Helps county residents without other medical coverage obtain health services at area clinics.

- **Food Stamps**
  Enables low-income households to buy more food and stretch their monthly food budgets.

- **Foster Care**
  Provides financial and medical help for children who are placed in foster homes.

Other services include:

- **Senior Corps**
  Provides local service opportunities for people 55 and older and includes Foster Grandparents, Senior Companions, Retired and Senior Volunteer Programs.

- **Senior Nutrition Services**
  Delivers hot meals to the homebound frail elderly and serves noon meals at various sites throughout the county.

- **Volunteer Services**
  Connects volunteers with DHA programs. Students can earn course credit through internships.

- **Veterans Services**
  Counsels veterans, their dependents and survivors, and determines eligibility for benefits.

Resource

California Health and Human Services
http://www.chhs.ca.gov

Role of County Mental Health Department

Lisa Bertaccini, L.C.S.W.

The role of a county Mental Health Department is to ensure the treatment of adults and children with severe and persistent mental health problems so as to enhance their quality of life. This is accomplished by developing systems of care that articulate a vision and guiding principles; identify target populations; clarify goals, and establish client and system outcomes.

Mental health programming includes:

- A single point of entry and authorization for planned mental health services to ensure the coordination of care and enhance efficiency and effectiveness.

- Acute or crisis intervention and stabilization for individuals experiencing a psychiatric emergency.

- An array of outpatient mental health services of varying intensity depending on clinical need. This may include day treatment and intensive home visitation programs, as well as clinics on school sites and in family resource centers and other community settings. These programs treat victims of child abuse and neglect and individuals at risk for child abuse and neglect, homelessness, juvenile justice involvement, and truancy. Specific services include individual and family therapy, social rehabilitation counseling, case management, medication support, and crisis intervention.

- Mental health consumer and family advocacy and programming by users of the public mental health system, including self-help centers and peer support networks.

- Psychiatric inpatient hospitalization for individuals in need of longer term psychiatric stabilization.

- Augmented mental health treatment for children and adults in need of additional supports in residential settings.

- Crisis residential programs.

- Locked residential settings for individuals on conservatorship or who are determined appropriate for them.

- An office of patients rights or ombudsmen services.

- A quality improvement oversight component system wide that ensures quality of care and tracks performance outcomes.

There are also coordinating and policy-making bodies in place for addressing needs of children and youth. For example, interagency placement committees meet to address the placement needs of children in the child protective, probation, developmentally disabled, special education or mental health systems. Executive level policy boards develop policies that address sytem gaps and prioritize the development of needed services.

Resources

California Mental Health Director's Association
http://www.cmhda.org

Role of State Agencies

Compiled by Michelle Kim, B.S.

California Department of Health Services

The mission of the California Department of Health Services (DHS) is to protect and improve the health of all Californians. With the support of dedicated and skilled employees and the application of public health sciences, the Department is committed to:

- reducing the occurrence of preventable disease, disability, and premature death among all Californians;

- closing the gaps in health status and access to care among the State's diverse population subgroups;

- providing leadership and setting the standard in reforming health care into a coordinated, accountable, and affordable health care system, which emphasizes access to appropriate preventive measures and high-quality services;

- building and fostering strong partnerships for health with local health agencies, public and private agencies, community-based organizations, providers, consumers, educational and academic institutions, and other interested groups; and,

- improving the quality and cultural competence of the Department's operations, services, and programs.

DHS is organized into seven programs and six support areas. Some of the programs are:

- Health Information and Strategic Planning;

- Licensing and Certification;

- Medical Care Services;

- Office of Multicultural Health;

- Office of Women's Health;

- Prevention Services; and,

- Primary Care and Family Health.

Contact Information:
California Department of Health Services
714 P Street
Sacramento, CA 95814
(916) 445-4717 (general line)
(916) 654-0499 (Children Services Program)

Website:
www.dhs.cahwnet.gov

California Department of Social Services

The mission of the California Department of Social Services (DSS) is to serve, aid, and protect needy and vulnerable children and adults in ways that strengthen and preserve families, encourage personal responsibility, and foster independence. DSS is responsible for administering four major program areas:

- Welfare

- Social Services

- Community Care Licensing

- Disability Evaluation

The larger role of DSS involves protecting the interests of all Californians by fairly and equitably administering all laws affecting public welfare, including directing the work of local agencies through the formulation and implementation of statewide regulations and policies.

Contact Information:
California Department of Social Services
744 P Street
Sacramento, CA 95814
Phone: (916) 657-3667

Website:
http://www.dss.cahwnet.gov

350

Community Care Licensing (CCL)

Community care was originally envisioned as a normalizing and least restrictive environment for persons needing basic care and supervision that would assist them in performance of the activities of daily living. The children and adults placed in such settings were envisioned as requiring little more than a healthful safe and supportive environment.

Enacted in 1973 to be administered by the Department of Health, CCL was established to form a statewide system of community care (separate from health care) for persons with mental and developmental disabilities, and socially dependent children. The CCL was designed to establish new regulations for licensing non-medical out-of-home care facilities. In the late 1970's, CCL was transferred to DSS.

Today the CCL Program also deals with the care for persons whose needs require the management of severe behavior adjustment problems, serious mental disorders, and significant medical needs.

Contact Information:
NORTHERN REGIONAL OFFICE
8745 Folsom Blvd., Suite 130
Sacramento, CA 95826
Phone: (916) 229-4500
Fax: (916) 229-4508

COASTAL REGIONAL OFFICE
801 Traeger Ave., Suite 105
San Bruno, CA 94066
Phone: (650) 266-8860
Fax: (650) 266-8877

SOUTHERN REGIONAL OFFICE
5900 Pasteur Court, Suite 125
Carlsbad, CA 92008
Phone: (760) 929-2121
Fax: (760) 929-2133

LOS ANGELES REGIONAL OFFICE
100 Corporate Pointe, Suite 350
Culver City, CA 90230
Phone: (310) 665-1940
Fax: (310) 665-1979

Website:
http://www.dss.cahwnet.gov/CCLD/default.htm

Governor's Office of Criminal Justice Planning

The mission of the Office of Criminal Justice Planning (OCJP) is to formulate and implement statewide criminal justice policy through comprehensive planning and program funding. This agency provides grants for:

- criminal suppression, law enforcement, and prosecution;
- victim services; and,
- crime prevention.

OCJP was established in 1968 in fulfillment of a federal requirement from the Law Enforcement Assistance Administration (LEAA) that each state have an office to plan and coordinate the implementation of LEAA block grant funds, and incorporate a broad range of criminal justice programs. The Office serves as the lead agency to address crime prevention, crime suppression, criminal justice issue planning, and victim services in California.

The Victim Services Division is comprised of the following branches:

Domestic Violence Branch
Funds projects designed to increase the availability of services to battered women and their children.

Sexual Assault Branch
Funds projects which address violence against women, including rape crisis centers, sexual assault response team victim advocates, prosecutors and probation officer training, medical evidentiary training centers, and specialized programs addressing the needs of underserved ethnic populations.

Victim/Witness Branch
Funds projects for local government and private nonprofit agencies that support a range of services to reduce the trauma of criminal acts, e.g. victim/witness counseling, submitting applications to the Victim Restitution Fund, assistance with domestic violence restraining orders, etc.

Violence Against Children Branch
Funds projects to increase the availability of treatment and prevention services to victims of child abuse and their families, to enhance prosecution efforts, and to provide training for professionals working in the field of child abuse.

Contact Information:
Governor's Office of Criminal Justice Planning
1130 K Street, Suite LL60
Sacramento, California 95814
Phone: (916) 324-9100

Website:
www.ocjp.ca.gov

Office of the Attorney General California Department of Justice: Crime and Violence Prevention Center

The Attorney General's Crime Prevention Center was established in 1952 to provide leadership in crime prevention policy, program, and resource development. In April 1994, the Center was renamed the Crime and Violence Prevention Center (CVPC) to emphasize a commitment to long-term solutions to violence. The mission is to initiate and promote policies and programs that improve the quality of life in California through the prevention and reduction of crime and violence.

To accomplish this mission, the CVPC provides training, technical assistance, multimedia resource development, legislative and research support services to law enforcement and other government agencies, schools, health and social service organizations, community groups, and the general public. The Center's goal is to foster cooperative efforts at the community level; mobilize local, state, and national resources; and develop and promote programs that effect change. CVPC's major program areas include:

- Community Oriented Policing and Problem Solving (COPPS)

- Drug and Alcohol Abuse Prevention

- Family Violence Prevention, including Child Abuse, Elder Abuse, and Domestic Violence

- General Crime Prevention

- Safe Schools—School/Law Enforcement Partnership

- Violence Prevention

- Youth Gang Prevention

- Multimedia Resource Development

- Research and Legislation

The Crime and Violence Prevention Center:

- Administers the Statewide Child Death Review Program that is responsible for:

  - overseeing the coordination and integration of state and local efforts to address fatal child abuse and neglect;

  - produces and distributes the *Child Death in California* report, an annual publication containing state and local data and other relevant information on preventing child deaths;

  - maintains and distributes the *Child Death Review Team Directory* which lists each county's child death review team member by name, address, telephone, and fax number;

  - produces and distributes the *Child Abuse Prevention Handbook*, an overview of the prevention, detection, reporting, treatment, investigation, and prosecution of child abuse;

  - produces and distributes *Shadows to Light... A Guide to Child Abuse Reporting*, an information and motivational video for mandated reporters on the Child Abuse Reporting Law; and,

  - produces and distributes *We're gonna be OK!*, an energetic music video designed for children from families involved with domestic violence. These videos can be purchased for $19.95 a copy from Cal Image Associates, (916) 638-8383 or (800) 982-1420 when calling outside of California.

- Produces state-of-the-art publications, videos, and public awareness materials. The CVPC has its own graphic design and desktop publishing capabilities and directs and produces its own videos, recognized for their outstanding quality and usefulness;

- Works closely with local, state, and national organizations and agencies and is committed to collaboration and sharing of resources. The Center supports the work of statewide professional associations involved in crime and violence prevention and maintains membership in state and national professional prevention organizations; and,

- Supports the Family Violence Prevention Program which influences public policy and increases public awareness in the field of family violence prevention. The Center offers technical assistance and resources on the prevention of violence toward children, women, and the elderly, and promotes efforts that build on family strengths.

Contact Information:
Crime and Violence Prevention Center
California Department of Justice
1300 I Street, Suite 1150
Sacramento, CA 95814
Phone: (916) 324-7863

Website:
http://caag.state.ca.us/cvpc

Child Protection Program

The Child Abuse Unit in the Department of Justice is responsible for maintaining a statewide, multi-jurisdictional, centralized index of completed child abuse investigation reports. The Child Abuse Central Index (CACI) contains reports from child protective agencies, i.e., police, sheriff, county welfare and probation departments. These reports pertain to alleged incidents of physical abuse, sexual abuse, mental/emotional abuse, and/or severe neglect. Each child protection agency is required by law to forward to the DOJ a report of every child abuse incident it investigates, unless an incident is determined to be unfounded or is a report of general neglect.

Services provided by the unit are:

- notification to CPA's of any prior child abuse investigation involving the same suspects and/or victims;

- information to CPA's to assist in the investigation of suspected child abuse; and,

- name search of potential child care providers and adoptive parents to identify prior reports of child abuse that might result in disqualification from licensing, adoption or Trustline Registry.

The Child Abuse Unit is within the Department's Bureau of Criminal Information and Analysis and can be reached by telephone at (916) 227-3285.

Role of State Boards

Compiled by Michelle Kim, B.S.

California Medical Board

The Medical Board of California is a state governmental agency which licenses and disciplines medical doctors. The Board provides two principal types of services to consumers: license information and investigation of complaints against physicians. The Board is not a physician referral service and does not regulate health plans or insurance companies.

The mission of the California Medical Board is to protect consumers through proper licensing of physicians and surgeons and certain affiliated healing arts professions by vigorous, objective enforcement of the Medical Practice Art. Besides regulating physicians, the Medical Board also governs the activities of physical therapists, physician's assistants, dispensing opticians, accupuncturists, podiatrists, and speech pathologists.

Physician license renewals occur every two years. For license renewal requirements, the physician is to submit certification of taking 25 Continuing Medical Education (CME) credit hours per year for a total of 100 CME credit hours every four years. The Board recommends that the certificates of completion be maintained for at least six years.

Contact information:
Medical Board of California
1426 Howe Avenue, Suite 54
Sacramento, CA 95825-3236
(916) 269-2466

Website:
www.medbd.ca.gov

California Board of Registered Nursing

The Board of Registered Nursing (BRN) is a state governmental agency established by law to protect the public by regulating the practice of registered nurses. The BRN is responsible for implementation and enforcement of the Nursing Practice Act which covers the laws related to nursing education, licensure, practice, and discipline. The Nursing Practice Act created a nine-member Board which serves as the BRN decision-making body.

The mission of the BRN is to protect the health and safety of consumers and promote quality registered nursing in the State of California. To accomplish this mission, the Board will:

- establish and uphold competency standards, provide guidance and interpretation, prevent patient harm, and intervene with discipline and rehabilitation;

- serve the public in a customer-oriented, well-managed, and respectful manner; and,

- provide employees with the opportunity for satisfying work in an atmosphere of shared commitment.

The BRN performs a variety of activities in its mission to protect consumers, including:

- setting educational standards for nursing programs which prepare individuals to become licensed as registered nurses;

- approving California nursing programs;

- evaluating licensure applications;

- issuing and renewing licenses;

- issuing certificates;

- taking disciplinary action if a nurse violates the Nursing Practice Act; and,

- managing a confidential diversion program for rehabilitation which is an alternative to the discipline process for nurses who are chemically dependent or have mental illness.

To become licensed applicants must:

- complete the educational requirements;

- pass a national licensing examination; and,

- be cleared through a background check for conviction of any crime which might make the applicant ineligible for licensure.

License renewal requirements are as follows:

- Your first California RN license is issued for two birthdays—NOT two years—and expires the last day of the month following your birth date. From that date on, it will expire every two years, if renewed in a timely manner.

- If you obtained your initial RN license by passing the national licensing examination (NCLEX-RN) within the past two years and this is your first renewal, you are exempt from the Continuing Education (CE) requirement.

- After your first renewal, your license will expire every two years if renewed on a timely basis. Proof of completing thirty (30) hours of continuing education is mandatory for every renewal for an active license after the first time.

Contact information:
Board of Registered Nursing
400 R Street, Suite 4030
Sacramento, CA 95814-6200
916-322-3350

Website:
www.medbd.ca.gov

California Board of Psychology

The Board of Psychology is one of 30 regulatory entities which falls under the organizational structure of the Department of Consumer Affairs. It solely exists to serve the public by:

- protecting the health, safety, and welfare of consumers of psychological services with integrity, honesty, and efficiency;

- advocating the highest principles of professional psychological practice; and,

- empowering the consumer through education on licensee/registrant disciplinary actions; and,

- providing the best available information on current trends in psychological service options.

This mission is accomplished by ensuring that psychologists provide consumers with appropriate and ethical psychological services and do not exploit consumers by abusing the power advantage inherent in any psychotherapeutic relationship.

The Board also works to ensure that all psychology license applicants possess minimal competency to practice psychology independently and safely by:

- requiring candidates to obtain an appropriate doctorate from an approved or accredited university;

- requiring the completion of a minimum of 3,000 hours of supervised professional experience; and,

- passing a national written examination and a California oral examination.

To renew a license, a psychologist must complete 36 hours of approved continuing education every two years, which includes lectures, conferences, seminars, workshops, grand rounds, video conferencing, and distant learning technologies. Correspondence courses, independent study, and home study programs are not acceptable, except for qualified individuals with a disability who apply to the Board and receive approval.

Contact information:
California Board of Psychology
1422 Howe Avenue, Suite 22
Sacramento, CA 95825-3200
(916) 263-2699

Website:
www.dca.ca.gov/psych

Board of Behavioral Sciences

The mission of the Board of Behavioral Sciences (BBS) is to protect the consumer by establishing and maintaining standards for competent and ethical behavior by the professionals under the jurisdiction of the BBS. The BBS licenses Clinical Social Workers, Educational Psychologists, and Marriage, Family and Child Counselors, by developing and administering written and oral examinations for its licensing programs, developing regulatory standards and conducting an enforcement program which investigates consumer complaints.

Licenses for MFCC and LCSW are required to be renewed every two years. After January 1, 2000, 36 hours of continuing education are required to renew licenses.

Contact information:
Board of Behavioral Sciences
400 R Street, Suite 3150
Sacramento, CA 95814
(916) 445–4933

Website:
www.bbs.ca.gov

Role of Federal Agencies

Compiled by Michelle Kim, B.S.

Department of Health and Human Services

The mission of the Department of Health and Human Services (DHHS) is to protect health and give a special assistance to those who need aid. It is the principal agency for protecting the health of all Americans and providing essential human services. Because this agency is responsible for the public health, DHHS supports the world's largest medical research effort, assures the safety of foods and health care products, and combats against the havoc of drug and alcohol abuse. DHHS is also the largest grant-making agency in the federal government, providing some 60,000 grants per year.

DHHS includes more than 300 programs, which cover some of these major areas:

- medical and social science research;
- preventing outbreak of infectious disease, including immunization services;
- medicare (health insurance for elderly and disabled Americans) and Medicaid (health insurance for low-income people);
- child support enforcement;
- improving maternal and infant health;
- funding Head Start and Early Head Start Programs;
- preventing child abuse and domestic violence;
- substance abuse treatment and prevention; and,
- services for older Americans, including home-delivered meals.

Contact information:
The U.S. Department of Health and Human Services
200 Independence Avenue, S.W.
Washington, D.C. 20201
(202) 619-0257
Toll Free: 1-877-696-6775

Website:
www.hhs.gov

Department of Justice

The mission of the United States Department of Justice (DOJ) is to enforce the law and defend the interests of the U.S. according to the law, provide Federal leadership in preventing and controlling crime, seek just punishment for those guilty of unlawful behavior, administer and enforce the Nation's immigration laws fairly and effectively and ensure fair and impartial administration of justice for all Americans.

In carrying out this mission, the Attorney General, as the Nation's chief law enforcement officer, directs and oversees the activities of the more than 110,000 attorneys, investigators, correctional personnel and other employees of the United States Department of Justice.

Although the office of the Attorney General dates from 1789, the Department of Justice was not established until 1870. Today, its responsibilities are diverse and wide ranging. These responsibilities are carried out through the Department's component organizations: the Federal Bureau of Investigation (FBI) and the Drug Enforcement Administration (DEA) investigate Federal crimes; the United States Marshals Service (USMS) protects the Federal judiciary, apprehends fugitives, detains prisoners and supports the Federal courts; the United States Attorneys and the litigating divisions prosecute offenders and represent the U.S. government in Federal court; the Immigration and Naturalization Service (INS) controls the borders and carries out the Nation's immigration statutes; and the Federal Bureau of Prisons (BOP) incarcerates sentenced offenders. The Office of Justice Programs (OJP) and the Office of Community Oriented Policing Services (COPS) assist State and local governments. OJP's National Institute of Justice (NIJ) develops and disseminates knowledge about crime and justice issues; its Bureau of Justice Statistics (BJS) collects, analyzes, publishes and disseminates information on crime, criminal offenders, victims of crime and the operation of the justice systems at all levels of government. Other components also help administer our system of justice and further the Department's mission (the

United States Trustees, the Community Relations Service, the Justice Management Division, the Executive Office for Immigration Review, the Office of the Inspector General, among others).

The DOJ is organized around the seven functional areas through which the Department carries out its mission. These are:

- investigation and prosecution of criminal offenses;
- assistance to state and local governments;
- legal representation, enforcement of federal laws, and defense of federal government interests;
- immigration;
- detention and Incarceration;
- protection of the Federal Judiciary, improvement of the justice system; and,
- management.

Contact information:
U.S. Department of Justice
950 Pennsylvania Avenue, NW
Washington, D.C. 20530

Website:
http://www.usdoj.gov

Office of the Surgeon General

The responsibilities of the Surgeon General are to:

- administer the Public Health Service (PHS) Commissioned Corps, which is a uniquely expert, diverse, flexible, and committed career force of public health professionals who can respond to both current and long-term health needs of the Nation;
- provide leadership and management oversight for PHS Commissioned Corps involvement in Departmental emergency preparedness and response activities;
- protect and advance the health of the Nation by educating the public, advocating for effective disease prevention and health promotion programs and activities, and, by providing a highly recognized symbol of national commitment to protecting and improving the public's health;
- articulate scientifically-based health policy analysis and advice to the President and the Secretary of HHS on the full range of critical public health, medical, and health system issues facing the Nation;

- provide leadership in promoting special Departmental health initiatives, e.g., tobacco and HIV prevention efforts, with other governmental and non-governmental entities, both domestically and internationally;

v elevate the quality of public health practice in the professional disciplines through the advancement of appropriate standards and research priorities; and

- fulfill statutory and customary Departmental representational functions on a wide variety of Federal boards and governing bodies of non-Federal health organizations, including the Board of Regents of the Uniformed Services University of the Health Sciences, the National Library of Medicine, the Armed Forces Institute of Pathology, the Association of Military Surgeons of the United States, and the American Medical Association.

The mission of the PHS Commissioned Corps is to provide highly-trained and mobile health professionals who carry out programs to promote the health of the Nation, understand and prevent disease and injury, assure safe and effective drugs and medical devices, deliver health service to Federal beneficiaries, and furnish health expertise in time of war or other national or international emergencies.

As one of the seven Uniformed Services of the United States, the commissioned corps is a specialized career system designed to attract, retain, and develop health professionals who may be assigned to Federal, State, or local agencies or international organizations to accomplish its mission.

Contact information:
U.S. Surgeon General
200 Independence Ave. SW
Hubert H. Humphrey Building Rm 716G
Washington, DC 20201
Phone: (202)690-7694
Fax: (202)690-6960

Website:
www.surgeongeneral.gov

Centers for Disease Control

The Centers for Disease Control (CDC), located in Atlanta, Georgia, is an agency under the Department of Health and Human Services (DHHS). Its mission is to promote health and the quality of life by preventing and controlling disease, injury, and disability. The CDC's pledge is to preserve public health by:

- being a diligent steward of the funds entrusted to it;

- providing an environment for intellectual and personal growth and integrity;

- basing all public health decisions on the highest quality scientific data, openly and objectively derived;

- placing the benefits to society above the benefits to the institution; and,

- treating all persons with dignity, honesty, and respect.

Offices institutes, and agencies within the CDC include:

- Associate Director for Minority Health

- Associate Director for Science

- Freedom of Information Act Office

- National Vaccine Program Office

- Office of Health and Safety (OHASIS)

- Office of Women's Health

- Epidemiology Program Office

- National Center for Chronic Disease Prevention and Health Promotion

- National Center for Health Statistics

- National Center for HIV, STD, and TB Prevention

- National Center for Infectious Diseases

- National Center for Injury Prevention and Control

- National Immunization Program

- Office of Global Health

- Public Health Practice Program Office

Contact information:
Centers for Disease Control and Prevention
1600 Clifton Rd., NE
Atlanta, GA 30333, USA
(404) 639-3311 (CDC Operator)
(800) 311-3435 (CDC Public Inquiries)

Website:
www.cdc.gov

Role of State Associations

Compiled by Michelle Kim, B.S.

California Medical Association

The California Medical Association's mission is to promote the science and art of medicine, the care and well-being of patients, the protection of the public health, and the betterment of the medical profession; to promote similar interests in its component societies; and to unite with similar organizations in other states and territories of the United States to form the American Medical Association.

The CMA was founded in 1856 by 76 physicians to set medical standards and create a forum for exchanging medical information and experience, as California was growing rapidly from the wake of the Gold Rush and entering statehood. At that time, it was often impossible to distinguish the trained physician from the self-styled healer, so the CMA arose from the need of doctors to professionalize.

Currently there are more then 30,000 members in the CMA. It is the largest state medical association in the United States and has become the leader in the socio-economics of medicine. Today, the CMA has emerged as a leading advocate for improving the quality of health care, as well as being a leader in legal advocacy on behalf of physicians and patients.

Contact information:
California Medical Association
1201 K Street, Suite 1050
Sacramento, CA 95814-3906
Phone: (916) 444-5532
Fax: (916) 444-5689

Website:
www.cmanet.org

California Nurses Association

The purpose of the California Nurses Association (CNA) is to foster high standards of nursing practice, promote the professional and educational advancement of nurses, and promote the welfare of nurses so that all people may have better health care services, regardless of race, age, gender, disability, lifestyle, religion, or health status.

Some of the objectives of the CNA are to:

- establish and promote implementation of standards of nursing practice, nursing education, and nursing services;

- encourage members to adhere to the ethical obligations of nurses as patient advocates;

- continually review and clarify the role of the nurse in the delivery of health-care services;

- interpret the aims of the various educational programs and career opportunities in nursing to nurses, prospective nurses, and the public;

- identify the educational needs of practitioners and to work with appropriate groups to provide programs to ensure currency of practice; and,

- initiate legislation and proposals for governmental regulations and take stands supporting or opposing those which affect the public health, nursing, or nurses.

Contact information:
The California Nurses Association
2000 Franklin St.
Oakland, CA 94612

CNA Regional Offices:		
	Fresno	209-261-9571
	Los Angeles	310-664-6369
	Oakland	510-273-2200
	Sacramento	916-446-5021
	San Diego	619-299-3731
	Santa Clara	408-920-0290

Website:
www.califnurses.org

California Healthcare Association

California Healthcare Association's (CHA) vision is "an optimally healthy society." Through effective leadership and member participation, CHA seeks to develop consensus, establish public policy priorities, and represent and serve hospitals, health systems, physician organizations and other health care providers. In concert with its member organizations, CHA is committed to establishing and maintaining a financial and regulatory environment within which hospitals, health systems, physician groups and other health care providers can continue to provide high-quality patient care.

CHA provides members with state and federal representation and advocacy in the legislative and regulatory areas through an agenda designed to improve health care quality, access and coverage; promote health care reform and integration; achieve adequate health care funding; improve and update laws and regulations; and restore public trust in health care.

Contact information:
California Healthcare Association
1215 K Street, Suite 800
P.O. Box 1100
Sacramento, CA 95812-1100
Phone: (916) 443-7401
Fax: (916) 552-7596

Website:
www.calhealth.org

California Dental Association

The California Dental Association (CDA) is dedicated to improving the oral health of the public, to promoting the art and science of dentistry, and to serving the needs of its members in the pursuit of these goals. As an organization, the CDA is committed to refining the processes of continuous learning and communication to anticipate, influence, and effect change on dental information and dental care advocacy.

The CDA has formulated some specific goals to promote its vision and mission in the field of dentistry:

- to educate and inform the public of the benefits of oral health and quality dental care, including support of model practices that incorporate quality assurance, reasonable reimbursement, and patient responsibility;

- to support models for licensure by credential;

- to develop and implement a voluntary quality assurance program to evaluate quality of dental care delivery systems for members;

- to strengthen its relationships with the Legislature and the Board of Dental Examiners to enhance communication relative to dental practice regulations; and,

- to find ways to further increase accessible dental care for all Californians concentrating on those segments of the population which are now underserved.

Contact information:
California Dental Association
1201 K Street
Sacramento, CA 95814
(916) 443-0505

Website:
www.cda.org/cda

California Conference of Local Health Officers (CCHLO)

The mission of the California Conference of Local Health Officers (CCLHO) is to prevent disease and promote the health of the public. The Conference was established in statute in 1947 to advise the Department Health Services, other departments, boards, commissions, and officials of federal, state and local agencies, the Legislature and other organizations on all matters affecting health. The legal authorization for CCLHO is found in the California Health and Safety Code Sections 100290, 100295, 100925, and 100950.

The membership of the Conference includes the 61 legally appointed physician Health Officers in California, one from each of the 58 counties and the three cities of Berkeley, Long Beach, and Pasadena.

The Conference provides a state/local forum for the discussion of significant health issues in order to develop recommendations for appropriate health policy. This includes legislative and regulatory review. The CCLHO meets semi-annually and its Board of Directors meets monthly. Its various program committees consider technical and policy issues in communicable disease control and prevention; health promotion and chronic disease prevention; environmental health; binational health; maternal, child and adolescent health; disaster preparedness; health surveillance and data analysis, and public health practice.

Priority Action Areas:

- Improve the infrastructure of public health in California at both the state and local levels;

- Investigate and control communicable diseases, both epidemic and endemic;

- Monitor the health of the population; and,

- Prepare for and responding to disasters.

Contact Information:
CCLHO
Prevention Services
California Department of Health Services
714 P Street, Room 1492
Sacramento, CA 95814
Phone: (916) 654-0023
Fax: (916) 657-3095

Website:
http://www.medepi.org/cclho/about-us.html

California District Attorney's Association

Originally composed of county counsels and district attorneys, the California District Attorney's Association has been in existence for over 50 years. As the interests of the group became increasingly diverse, the members decided to form an organization comprised exclusively of prosecutors. In 1974, the California District Attorney's Association (CDAA) was incorporated with the mission to serve the needs and promote the interests of California's prosecutors.

Today, CDAA has over 2,300 members, operating with a full-time staff headquartered in Sacramento. The CDAA serves as a source of continuing legal education and legislative advocacy for its membership and provides a forum for the exchange of information and innovation in the criminal justice field.

Contact information:
California District Attorney's Association
731 K Street, Third Floor
Sacramento, CA 95814-3402
Phone: (916) 443-2017
Fax: (916) 443-0540

Website:
www.cdaa.org

Role of National Associations

Compiled by Michelle Kim, B.S.

American Medical Association

The mission of the American Medical Association (AMA) is to establish and promote ethical, educational, and clinical standards for the medical profession and to advocate for the highest integrity of the physician/patient relationship.

Founded in 1847 by a group of physicians, the AMA's core purpose is to promote the art and science of medicine and the betterment of public health. This involves the development and promotion of standards in medical practice, research, and education; strong advocacy agenda on behalf of patients and physicians; and the commitment to providing accurate, timely information and discourse on matters important to the health of Americans.

The AMA has two national offices:

Headquarters:
515 North State Street
Chicago, IL 60610
(312) 464-5000

Washington Office:
1101 Vermont Avenue NW
Washington, D.C. 20005
(202) 789-7400

Website:
http://www.ama-assn.org

American Humane Association

The American Humane Association (AHA) is one of the nation's oldest agencies dedicated to the protection of children from abuse and neglect. Since 1878, AHA has provided national leadership in the development of programs, policies, and services on behalf of children who are abused and neglected.

AHA's main objectives are to:

- increase the abilities, knowledge, and effectiveness of child protection professionals and child protective service agencies;

- enhance the community's capacity to respond effectively to the needs of vulnerable children and families;

- improve the information and capacities available to public and private child welfare agencies that help them to respond effectively to child abuse and neglect; and

- facilitate a concerted national response to the problem of child maltreatment.

As a national association of child protection programs, agencies and individuals, AHA's membership includes state and local social service agencies, courts, hospitals, schools, mental health professionals, professional social workers, child advocates, and concerned individuals in every state. AHA provides professionals and concerned citizens with the facts, resources, and referrals they need to make informed decisions to help children and families in crisis. AHA is guided by a national program advisory committee and by a national Board of Directors.

Contact information:
American Humane Association
63 Inverness Drive East
Englewood, Colorado 80112-5117
Phone: (800) 227-4645
Fax: (303) 792-5333

Website:
http://www.americanhumane.org

National Association of Children's Hospitals and Related Institutions

The National Association of Children's Hospitals and Related Institutions (NACHRI) is a non-profit membership organization of children's hospitals, large pediatric units of medical centers and related health systems, including those that specialize in the rehabilitation of children with serious chronic or congenital illnesses.

The mission of NACHRI is to promote the health and well-being of children and their families by supporting children's hospitals and health systems that are committed to providing excellent health care to children through education, research, health promotion and advocacy. NACHRI's vision is a society in which all children and their families have access to the full continuum of pediatric health care services required to allow each child to achieve optimum health status. To achieve this vision, NACHRI and its members are advocates for high quality, cost effective clinical care, education, research, and advocacy for children and their families.

Goals:

- Strengthen and promote children's hospitals and health systems as cost effective, high quality, accountable, community oriented, technologically advanced and discovery oriented organizations;

- Strengthen children's hospitals and health systems to be effective advocates for the health of children and to further the mission of children's hospitals;

- Strengthen the ability of children's hospitals and health systems to seize new opportunities and face new challenges; and

- Strengthen the ability of children's hospitals and health systems to organize, finance, deliver and be accountable for health care to children and their families

Contact information:
National Association of Children's Hospital and Related Institutions
401 Wythe Street
Alexandria, VA 22314
Phone: (703) 684-1355
Fax: (703) 684-1589

Website:
www.nachri.org

American Professional Society on the Abuse of Children (APSAC)

APSAC is an interdisciplinary professional organization whose mission is to ensure that everyone affected by child maltreatment receives the best possible professional response. This mission is carried out by:

- professional education which promotes effective, culturally sensitive, and interdisciplinary approaches to the identification, intervention, treatment, and prevention of child abuse and neglect;

- promoting research and guidelines to inform professional practice;

- educating the public about child abuse and neglect; and

- ensuring that America's public policy concerning child maltreatment is well-informed and constructive.

"Children are the underlying focus and concern of all of APSAC's activities. Among the APSAC member's highest priorities are to nurture and support the development of children."

Contact information:
Michael Hertica
Torrance Police Department
3300 Civic Center Drive
Torrance, CA 90503
Phone: (310) 375-0613

Website:
www.apsac.org

American Academy of Pediatrics

The American Academy of Pediatrics (AAP) believes that children deserve optimum health and require the highest degree of health care because of the inherent worth of all children. The mission of the AAP is to attain optimal physical, mental and social health and well-being for all infants, children, adolescents, and young adults by purposing its members to dedicate their efforts and resources to their patients health, safety, and well-being. Members include pediatricians, pediatric medical subspecialists, and pediatric surgical specialists.

The AAP was founded in June 1930 by 35 pediatricians who met in Detroit in response to the need for an independent pediatric forum to address children's needs. When the AAP was established, the idea that children have special developmental and health needs was a new one. Preventive health practices now associated with child care—such as immunizations and regular health exams—were only just beginning to change the custom of treating children as "miniature adults."

Activities of the AAP focus on furthering the professional education of its members through continuing education courses, biannual scientific meetings, seminars, publications and statements from committees and sections. The AAP also publishes *Pediatrics*, its monthly scientific journal; *Pediatrics in Review*, its continuing education journal; and *Healthy Kids* magazine.

The AAP executes original research in social, economic and behavioral areas and promotes funding of research. It maintains a Washington, D.C. office to ensure that chil-dren's health needs are taken into consideration as legislation and public policy are developed. The AAP's state advocacy staff provides assistance to chapters, promoting issues such as child safety legislation and Medicaid policies that increase access to care for low-income children.

Contact information:
National Headquarters
The American Academy of Pediatrics
141 Northwest Point Boulevard
Elk Grove Village, IL 60007-1098 USA
Phone: (842) 228-5005
Fax: (847) 228-5097

Website:
www.aap.org

PART 18

Future Directions and Developments

Future Directions and Developments

Marilyn Strachan Peterson, M.S.W., M.P.A. and Michael Durfee, M.D.

1. Child Abuse is a Public Health Problem

Significant medical, mental health, developmental and dental problems are experienced by victims of child abuse and neglect. Research studies show that criminal justice, domestic violence, mental health, and juvenile justice problems can be traced to childhood histories of abuse and neglect.

2. Early Childhood Intervention Programs Will Gain Momentum

Increased knowledge about infant and toddler development has uncovered the need for pre-natal, infant, toddler and pre-school early intervention and support programs. As a culture, we are beginning to look at the experience of being a young child. In response, health systems are starting to focus on early identification of high-risk families.

3. Media Campaigns Provide Primary Prevention Opportunities

Media campaigns with behavioral change messages are needed. The public has seen the positive outcomes from the MADD (Mother's Against Drunk Driving) campaign which combined public education programs with sanctions such as high fines, loss of driver's license, and time in jail to reduce drunk driving. Sustained media campaigns are needed to establish a broad-based cultural value against child abuse and neglect and in support of children.

4. Child Neglect Will No Longer Seem as a Benign Condition

Historically, physical and sexual abuse have been viewed as the most devastating conditions. Child neglect is beginning to be viewed as a pernicious condition reducing the effectiveness of a human being. Research shows that neglect is more likely to cause mental health conditions, school dropout, teen pregnancy, and adult incompetency than other forms of abuse.

5. Recognition of Emotional Abuse is Emerging

Emotional abuse is now being recognized. While many citizens avoid the topic of child abuse and neglect, the topic of emotional abuse resonates. This may be due to several factors, e.g. the large number of families adversely effected by alcoholism, drug abuse, other addictions, family dysfunction, and parental mental illness.

6. Connections are Being Recognized between Domestic Violence, Alcohol/Drug Abuse, Child and Animal Abuse

Historically, these fields of interest have operated on parallel tracks. Through experience, the interconnectedness of these problems is now being linked.

7. Drug Endangered Children have Become Visible

The most recent frontier crossed in problem identification is the drug-endangered child. Drug enforcement agents found children living in squalor and serious neglect when they raided drug-manufacturing homes. They began to pair up with children's protective service social workers to intervene on behalf of children. Model programs are developing which include medical testing of children to detect accidental and non-accidental drug ingestion. There is a burgeoning awareness about the hazards of illegal drug use upon children.

8. Child Abuse Forensic Examinations are Evolving as a Medical Subspecialty

Child abuse medical experts have worked diligently throughout the years to scientifically document how to distinguish between accidental and non-accidental injury; to distinguish signs of sexual abuse and normal deviations; and, to identify psychosocial failure-to-thrive conditions in infants. A new professional drive is underway to achieve recognition of child abuse evaluations as a medical subspecialty. This development is supported by primary care physicians who need the expertise of these subspecialists.

9. **Links with Regional Centers and a Clearer View of the Connection Between Disabilities and Child Abuse is Developing**
The relationship between physical abuse and neglect and disabilities has historically been ignored. Child abuse intervention professionals, especially medical and mental health professionals will develop closer links with Regional Centers, related professions, and advocates to document the connection between disabilities and abuse.

10. **Technology: Computers and Telemedicine will Expand Knowledge**
Computers, the Internet, interactive web based courses, list servers, CD Roms, and telemedicine will revolutionize knowledge about child abuse and neglect. Computers and telemedicine will bring the experts to rural areas and increase access of rural hospitals and physicians to current knowledge and research.

11. **Foster Children Need Attention**
Over 100,000 children are currently in foster care in California. Program development and coordination are needed to address the medical, dental, educational, mental health, and developmental needs of these vulnerable children.

12. **Child Abuse and Neglect Adversely Impact Child Development**
Largely unknown as a field of expertise, child development evaluations need to be recognized as a necessary component in the evaluation of young children. Most professionals intervening in cases are untrained on the adverse effects of child abuse and neglect upon child development and behavior. Recognition of this problem, training professionals, and training more child development experts to work in the field of child abuse and neglect are needed.

13. **Improper Medication of Children's Behavior Problems (Bad Boy Cocktails) is Being Recognized**
Concern has emerged over improper medical management of behavioral problems by primary care physicians. Instead of properly managing behavioral problems, children are being medicated with various combinations of psychotropic drugs, tranquilizers, and improper dosages. Training on child behavior management for primary care physicians, parents, foster parents, social workers

and others who intervene with families; clear and effective policies; and, monitoring improper administration of psychotropic drugs is needed. Over-diagnosis of ADHD (Attention Deficit Hyperactivity Disorder) and the use of major tranquilizers and anti-depressants have replaced knowledge of child behavioral management. Psychotropic drugs have become the "silver bullet" for intervention.

14. **Quality Assurance Procedures for Child Protective Service Social Workers is Gaining Ground**
Quality Assurance (QA) or Quality Improvement (QI) have a long history in medicine with origins in controlling infectious disease in hospitals. Quality Assurance is emerging in the social work profession as a means of monitoring and evaluating decision making. Few models exist and are not widely implemented. This will change due to emerging liability issues and lawsuits over improper decision making.

15. **Collaboration between County Mental Health and Children's Protective Services is Needed**
These two cultures must find a way of interacting for the benefit of the community's children. The interaction between these two entities vary from adversarial, to mutual distrust, to benign neglect. Few models exist showing a positive and productive cooperation and planning. Lawmakers and state and county policy makers may need to intervene to achieve productive collaborations.

16. **Funding for Mental Health Services is Increasing**
Funding for mental health services is expected to increase because mental health problems are not perceived as shameful any longer and occur in the best of families; riverbanks and prisons are not seen as the best places for the mentally ill; and outbursts from the mentally ill such as school and work-site shootings are causing ordinary people to feel vulnerable.

17. **Victim Restitution Benefits Exist for Abused Children**
Largely misunderstood, the State Victims of Crime Fund is a source of funding for psychological counseling for victims. This fund is based on fines and penalties levied upon convicted offenders, which range from DUI (Driving Under the Influence), to large bank fines and, in California, tops $100,000 million per year. Child physical and sexual abuse and some child neglect victims are eligible.

18. **Multi-disciplinary Interview Teams and "One Stop Shopping" Concepts**
These teams emerged in the early 1990's as a means to reduce the multiple repetitive interviews of sexually abused children. The concept is excellent, but has led the way to the expectation that a child will give a "comprehensive interview" on a particular day and time. This led to the idea of a "good MDIT interview" on which a case went forward. Research documents that children disclose over time and may not reveal all information on a particular day despite the "child friendly environment", crackers and juice, and interviewers trained in forensically sound, developmentally appropriate interviews. The "one stop comprehensive interview" also assumes connections between professionals that may not exist.

19. **Abused Dependent Children Now Receive Legal Representation**
Sometimes there is a "conflict of interest" between the priorities of the departments of social services entrusted with the care of abused children and the needs of the abused child. State law now requires that dependent children have legal representation. Counties have now established non-profit law firms or contracted with for-profit law firms to ensure that the legal rights of the abused child and needs for medical, mental health, dental, educational and developmental services are met.

20. **Home Visiting is a Effective Primary and Secondary Prevention Model**
The states of Hawaii and Vermont have implemented universal home visiting programs for new parents. The key to effectiveness is "intensity and duration". Home visitors carry small caseloads, visit extensively to provide support, and stay with the family for three years. The danger is the implementation of less expensive variations of the model which may not be effective and the concept is scrapped because "it doesn't work."

21. **Alcohol and Drug Abuse Treatment are Key Components for Child Abuse Prevention**
There is a lack of resources for alcohol and drug abuse treatment and abundant information showing the cost effectiveness of out-patient treatment. County, State and Federal government need to combine efforts to plan how to expand resources to address these problems. Alcohol and drug abuse are the source of many social problems. In addition, information on dual diagnosis of substance abuse and mental health problems, and planning for intervention

and treatment is sorely needed for this complex aspect of the problem.

22. **Parents With Problems Adversely Affect Children**
The tendency of alcohol and drug programs and mental health programs serving adults with problems is that little focus is given to the children in these situations. Minor improvements in adult behavior are applauded while children sometimes endure disastrous living conditions.

23. **Training for Social Workers Needs to be Skilled Based, Up-to-Date and Relevant**
Skill based training is needed. Training must be based on proven intervention strategies and grounded in current literature and research. Social workers in particular need basic academy training comparable to the law enforcement and medical model before serving in the field of child protective services. Bachelor and Masters level social work education tends to be eclectic instead of a systematic range of basic to advanced training. Skills and abilities needed by employers (largely county and state government) need to be taken into consideration.

24. **Program Directors Need Funding Expertise**
Grants expire and program directors need to continue services beyond the life of a grant. More training and expertise is needed on federal and state funding streams to institutionalize programs and services. Successful programs more and more need 'funding wizards'.

25. **What Constitutes Family for Children Today...and Mentors**
Friends and family now comes in all shapes and sizes with many relationship variations. The important factor is whether or not these variations support healthy child development. The resilience literature shows that a mentor whether it was a teacher, a neighbor, a family member or a family friend was consistently cited as the importance difference in a child's emotional survival out of adverse circumstances.

26. **Parent Training Needs Expansion**
With the loss of the extended family, new parents have few role models and sources of support. Systematic parent training programs are needed from the prenatal through the teenage years. Parents need information on child development, good parenting practices, help on understanding their limitations and where to go for help.

27. **Cultural Competency Needs to be Adopted as a Value**

Cultural competence means understanding how to relate to persons from all cultures at all levels of an organization, e.g. front-line, supervising, management, and administration. Organizations must demonstrate cultural competency at all levels.

28. **Communities Must Initiate a Triad Approach to Prevention and Intervention...**

To be effective, a community's approach must include primary and secondary prevention and tertiary intervention. Primary prevention means to prevent child abuse from ever happening through public education and by establishing cultural norms and values regarding the proper treatment of children; secondary prevention means to target at-risk populations to prevent child abuse; and tertiary intervention means to intervene after it happens and to try to prevent it from happening again.

"Never doubt that a small group of thoughtful citizens can change the world; Indeed it is the only thing that ever has."

Margaret Mead, Sociologist

NOTES

NOTES

Other Books by Volcano Press

UNIQUITY
P.O. BOX 10
GALT, CA 95632-0010
(800) 521-7771

UNIQUITY
P.O. BOX 10
GALT, CA 95632-0010
(800) 521-7771

Learning to Live Without Violence
by Dr. Daniel Sonkin and Dr. Michael Durphy

Aprender a Vivir Sin Violencia (*Learning to Live Without Violence, Spanish Edition*)
Adaptation by Dr. Jorge Corsi

Counselor's Guide to Learning to Live Without Violence
by Dr. Daniel Sonkin

Family and Friends' Guide to Domestic Violence
by Elaine Weiss

Physician's Guide to Domestic Violence
by Ellen Taliaferro, M.D. and Patricia Salber, M.D.

Walking on Eggshells
by Dr. Brian Ogawa

Sourcebook for Working With Battered Women
by Nancy Kilgore

Testifying Under Oath: How to be an Effective Witness
by James Vukelic, Esq.

Family Violence and Religion: An Interfaith Resource Guide
Complied by the Staff of Volcano Press

Are you interested in making a tax-deductible contribution of Volcano Press books to your local women's shelter, school, social services agency or other organization?

If so, find out about the gift certificate program offered by Women and Children's Support Resources, a (501(c) 3) at www.wcsr.org

VOLCANO
· PRESS ·